CW00346795

LYLE PRICE GUIDE

PRINTED Collectables

The publishers wish to express their sincere thanks to the following for their involvement and assistance in the production of this volume:

Editor	TONY CURTIS
Text By	EELIN McIVOR
Editorial	ANNETTE CURTIS
	DONNA RUTHERFORD
	CLAIRE COSSAR
Art Production	CATRIONA DAY
	DONNA CRUICKSHANK
	NICKY FAIRBURN
Graphics	JAMES BROWN
	MALCOLM GLASS
	DOROTHY GLASS

British Library Cataloguing-in-Publication Data.
A catalogue record for this book is available from the British Library.

I.S.B.N. 86248 - 156 - 2

Typeset by Word Power, Berwickshire
Printed and bound in Great Britain by
Butler & Tanner Ltd, Frome and London

LYLE PRICE GUIDE

PRINTED Collectables

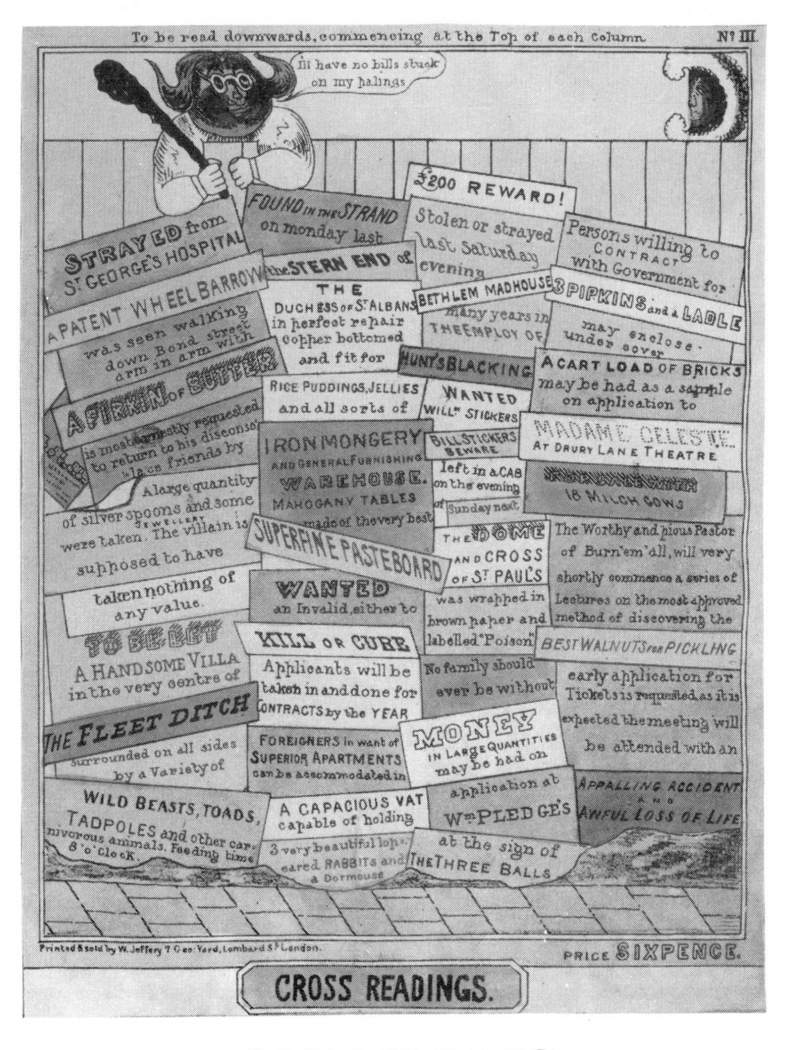

TONY CURTIS

CONTENTS

ACKNOWLEDGEMENTS

J.F. Bradshaw, 33 Shaw Crescent, Sanderstead, Surrey, CR2 9JB
Border Bygones, The Vallets, Forge Crossing, Lyonshall, Kington, HR5 3JQ
Butterfield & Butterfield, 220 San Bruno Avenue, San Francisco CA 94103, USA
Butterfield & Butterfield, 7601 Sunset Boulevard, Los Angeles CA 90046, USA
Christie's (International) SA, 8 place de la Taconnerie, 1204 Genève, Switzerland
Christie's Monaco, S.A.M, Park Palace 98000 Monte Carlo, Monaco
Christie's Scotland, 164–166 Bath Street, Glasgow G2 4TG
Christie's South Kensington Ltd., 85 Old Brompton Road, London SW7 3LD
Christie's, 8 King Street,London SW1Y 6QT
Christie's East, 219 East 67th Street, New York, NY 10021, USA
Christie's, 502 Park Avenue, New York, NY 10022, USA
Christie's, Cornelis Schuytstraat 57, 1071 JG Amsterdam, Netherlands
Christie's SA Roma, 114 Piazza Navona, 00186 Rome, Italy
Christie's Swire, 2804–6 Alexandra House, 16–20 Chater Road, Hong Kong
Christie's Australia Pty Ltd., 1 Darling Street, South Yarra, Victoria 3141, Australia
Colin & Janet Davis, 86 Canford Drive, Addlestone, Surrey, KT15 2EY
Eldred's, Box 796, E. Dennis, MA 02641, USA
Finarte, 20121 Milano, Piazzetta Bossi 4, Italy
Denis Gifford
Hilary Humphries, The Cigarette Packet Collectors Club, 15 Dullingham Road, Newmarket, Suffolk, CB8 9JT
Michael Johnston, 18 Barking Road, Needham Market, Ipswich, IP6 8ET
Michael Jones, 5 Blunts Hall Drive, Witham, Essex, CM8 1LZ
Dave Lewis Art Studio, 20 The Avenue, Starbeck, Harrogate, North Yorkshire, HG1 4QD
Duncan McAlpine, Flat 4, 55 Lordship Road, Stoke Newington, London, N16 0QJ
Michael Moon, 41, 42 & 43 Roper Street, Whitehaven, Cumbria, CA28 7BS
Douglas Morgan, 'Homeport', 22 Summerfields Avenue, Hailsham, East Sussex, BN27 3BP
R. Moy, Spread Eagle Antiques, 8 Nevada Street, Greenwich, SE10
Onslow's, Metrostrore, Townmead Road, London SW6 2RZ
Phillips Manchester, Trinity House, 114 Northenden Road, Sale, Manchester M33 3HD
Phillips Son & Neale SA, 10 rue des Chaudronniers, 1204 Genève, Switzerland
Phillips West Two, 10 Salem Road, London W2 4BL
Phillips, 11 Bayle Parade, Folkestone, Kent CT20 1SQ
Phillips, 49 London Road, Sevenoaks, Kent TN13 1UU
Phillips, 65 George Street, Edinburgh EH2 2 JL
Phillips, Blenstock House, 7 Blenheim Street, New Bond Street, London W1Y 0AS
Phillips Marylebone, Hayes Place, Lisson Grove, London NW1 6UA
Phillips, New House, 150 Christleton Road, Chester CH3 5TD
Paul Sheppard, The Vallets, Forge Crossing, Lyonshall, Kington, Herefordshire
Skinner Inc., Bolton Gallery, Route 117, Bolton MA, USA
Mr Solly, 13 Greenways, Beckenham, Kent BR3 3NG
Sotheby's, 34–35 New Bond Street, London W1A 2AA
Sotheby's, 1334 York Avenue, New York NY 10021
Sotheby's, 112 George Street, Edinburgh EH2 2LH
Sotheby's, Summers Place, Billingshurst, West Sussex RH14 9AD
Sotheby's Monaco, BP 45, 98001 Monte Carlo
Tim J. Stannard, Lombard House, 145 Charles Street, Birmingham B3 3LP
Paul Surridge, Saplings, Kent Loke, Aldborough, Norfolk NR11 7AA
Ute Twite, Togford, Stogumber, Taunton, Somerset TA4 3TN
T. Vennett Smith, 11 Nottingham Road, Gotham, Nottingham NG11 0HE
M. Veissid & Co., Hobsley House, Trodesley, Shrewsbury SY5 7ND
Bryon Whitworth, 17 Hill Street, Colne, Lancs BB8 0DH
Danny Widuch, 14 Ewhurst Avenue, Sanderstead, South Croydon, Surrey CR0 0DG
John Wilson, 50 Acre End Street, Eynsham, Oxford OX8 1PD
Mr C.A. Winder, 22 Mayfield Grove, Harrogate, N. Yorks
Yesterday's News, 43 Dundonald Road, Colwyn Bay, Clwyd LL29 7RD
Yesterday's Paper, Ivybank House, 122 Upgate, Louth, Lincolnshire LN11 9HG

PRINTED Collectables

How many of us, in the course of our everyday lives, come into contact each morning with a Ming brushwasher or an 18th century ormolu and satinwood commode? Printed collectables, on the other hand, are things which surround every single one of us every hour of our waking day. You get up in the morning, remove, perhaps, your razor blade from its wrapper, tip cereal out of a cereal packet, pack your lunch box with a soft drink bottle (complete with label), buy your bus or train ticket to work, and your newspaper to read on the way. That's quite a few already – all of which you will find in this book – and it's not yet 9am!

It's all a question of looking at things with new eyes, for just about everything that's printed is now, potentially, highly collectable. But it's also a question of looking at everything with a highly discerning eye if you're not to disappear under an avalanche of paper! One of the best aspects of collecting printed ephemera is that you don't require vasts amount of space, showcases or whatever, in which to house them. One of the more insidious aspects is, however, that they do have a way of taking over the house nonetheless!

Another plus point is that large and attractive collections can be built up for very little outlay, since many items, in whatever branch of the field, from children's books to calendars, from matchbox labels to membership cards, can still be picked up for a few pounds or even less. On the other hand, at the top end of the range the rewards can be enormous. There can be few adults today who did not as a child take some kind of illustrated comic. First editions are the ones to look out for here, with a first edition of the US Action Comic No. 1 holding the record at £60,000. British comics such as the Eagle, featuring that cult hero Dan Dare, and the Beano, are equally sought after, and first editions will fetch sums comfortably into four figures.

Printed collectables are also known as ephemera, and the term is significant when it comes to determining value, for few were ever designed for more than an ephemeral existence. They are, by their very nature, fragile, and condition is all important to the value of the survivors.

The other main criterion is rarity. Many people have, for example, kept copies of newspapers with memorable headlines such as the Munich crisis, the Coronation, or Kennedy's assassination, and these will not fetch a great deal. On the other hand, a Lifeboat Saturday postcard, delivered by air from Manchester to Haslingden in 1902, will sell for £1,675. Bubble gum wrappers, which must rank as the most ephemeral of all ephemera, also reflect this fact in the money which they attract. A Mars Attacks wrapper from 1962 will sell for at least £100 among the cognoscenti.

Then again, your average bus or train ticket, even those dating from decades ago, will usually only fetch a few pence. If it commemorates a special journey, however, the price rockets, culminating perhaps in the £12,100 paid for Neville Chamberlain's air ticket for his fateful visit to Munich in 1938. So hang on to your Concorde Tickets or any for last, pre-Beeching rail journeys, or those issued at stations now closed. And coffin tickets do seem to attract a ghoulish premium!

To dedicated collectors of printed ephemera of whatever kind, however, the nostalgia value often far outweighs the monetary value of their collections. For these provide a vivid and fascinating glimpse of the life of a bygone age, much more effective than any account in a history book could be. How about a business card for A W Walker, Castrator of Horses, Calves, Lambs, Pigs, etc (Etc???!!!) or a label for the soft drink 'Rosey Rapture', to set the imagination running?

So printed ephemera is something we all, but all, possess, even if it's the newspaper used to line a drawer or laid under a carpet. Chances are, we've all stored a menu, a programme or a greetings card or whatever in a drawer as a cherished memento. Maybe it's time to get it out and see whether, apart from the sentimental value to you, it might form the basis of a fascinating collection. Be warned, however, it's a bug that bites deep, and once bitten, life may never be quite the same again!

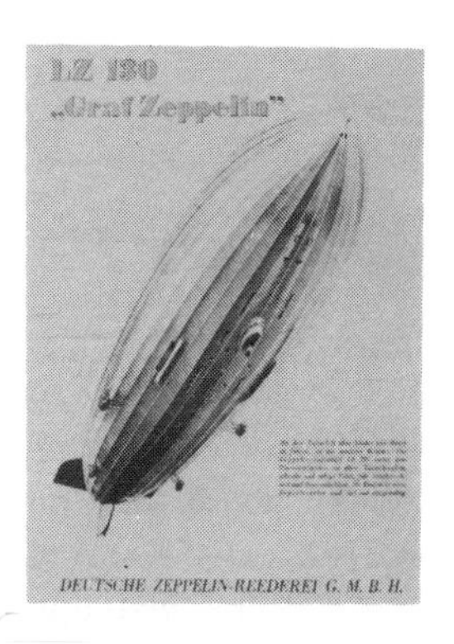

A rare LZ 130 'Graf Zeppelin', folding broadsheet with detailed cut-away and publicity information for this, the last Zeppelin built, dated *5/39*.
(Christie's) £165

A 1931 Schneider Trophy Contest Official Souvenir Programme. (Christie's S. Ken) £187

R.A.F. Display, Hendon, seventeen programmes, 1921 to 1937.
(Christie's) £242

W. G. Barrett – The Schneider Trophy, published by Pools Advertising Service Ltd., 30 x 20in. (Onslow's) £50

Moth Minor sales literature with price list and specification, 1939.
(Onslow's) £60

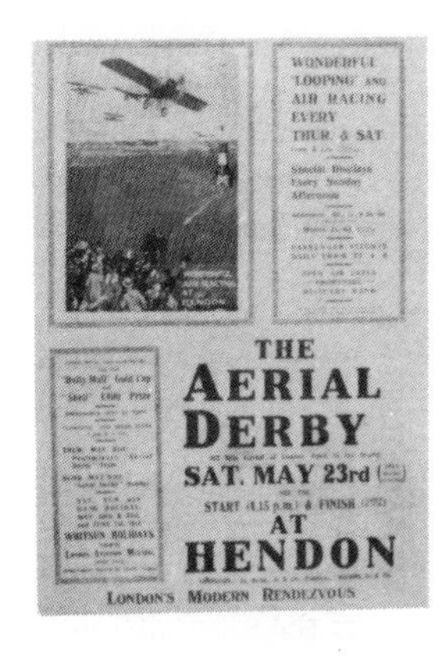

The Aerial Derby, published by The Dangerfield Printing Co., London, '15, on linen, 29¾ x 20in.
(Onslow's) £180

Harold McCready, 'Imperial Airways City of Wellington', double crown, April 1929.
(Onslow's) £600

Lecornu (J): La Navigation Aérienne, 6 edn., Paris, 1913, original cloth, gilt.
(Christie's) £104

Bristol 'Bulldog' Mk IV, original publicity booklet, colour cover, photos, text, 16 pages, 1st Edition, 1930.
(Christie's) £132

Nationale Luchtvaart School, lithograph in colours, by Kees Van den Haan, backed on linen, 31 x 23in.
(Christie's) £1,320

Bristol 'Blenheim' I, original manufacturer's publicity brochure, colour cover, photos, text, 24 pages.
(Christie's) £187

Air France poster, Amerique du Sud, lithograph in colours, printed by Perceval, Paris, backed on linen 39 x 24in.
(Christie's) £275

'Imperial Airways The British Airline Weekly Service Between Africa India Egypt and England', double royal.
(Onslow's) £500

A commemorative paper napkin printed *A Souvenir in Commemorative of the FIRST FLYING WEEK IN ENGLAND held on Doncaster Racecourse from Friday Oct. 15 to 23, 1909*, 14 x 14¾in.
(Christie's) £121

Geoffrey Watson – Women's Royal Air Force, published by Employment Exchange, 30 x 20in. (Onslow's)
£330

Anonymous, Imperial Airways, lithograph in colours, circa 1936, backed on linen, 38 x 25in.
(Christie's) £715

Aero Club du Rhone et du Sud-Est 13eme. Grand Prix, 1924, lithograph in colours, backed on linen, 63 x 47in.
(Christie's) £1,430

A menu card, The Graf Zeppelin over New York from the first Europe Pan-American flight, issued by the Louis Sherry Hotel N.Y., 1929.
(Christie's) £242

Sizaire-Berwick Automobiles, 1919. £12

Royal Mail Line, 1927. £7

Perrier, The Champagne of Table Waters, circa 1900. £4

Nestle's, Here's My Milk Chocolate, 1956. £4

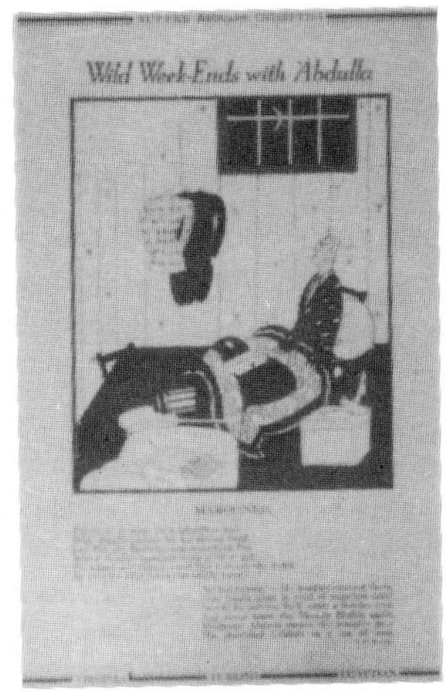

Abdulla, Wild Week-Ends, 1930's. £5

Electrolux, The New Cleanness, 1920's. £8

Broadwood Pianofortes, circa 1900. £5

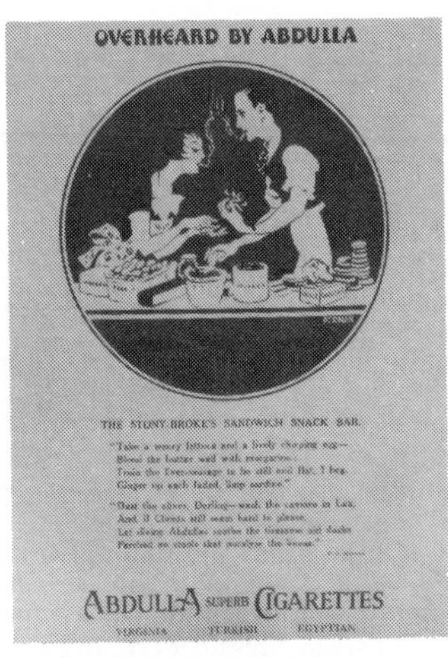

Abdulla, The Stony-Broke's Sandwich Snack Bar, 1930. £5

(Yesterdays Paper)

Mackintosh's Quality Street, 1954. £4

Pratts High Test Petrol, 1929. £10

BUCHANAN'S
"BLACK & WHITE"
The Highest Standard of Quality
JAMES BUCHANAN & CO. LTD. 26 Holborn, London E.C.1

Buchanan's 'Black and White', 1927. £8

Hovis Bread and Biscuits, 1896. £8

Mullard, Master Radio, 1928. £4

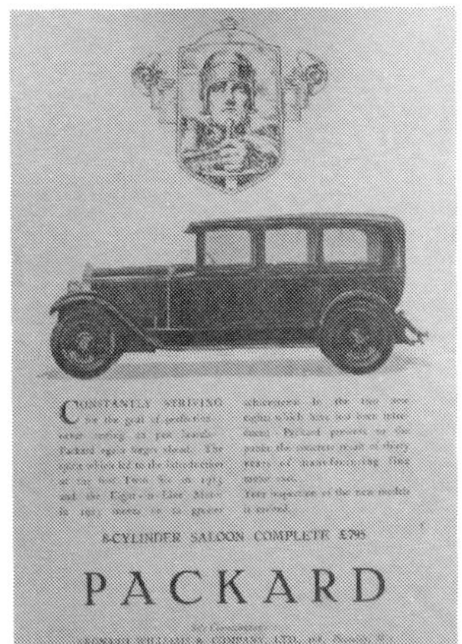

Packard, 8 cylinder saloon, 1929. £6

Crosse and Blackwell, 1920's. £5

Make Soup the Oxo Way, 1941. £5

Cadbury's Vogue Chocolates, 1938. £5

Atco, The Lawn Mark of Distinction, 1930's. £5

(Yesterdays Paper)

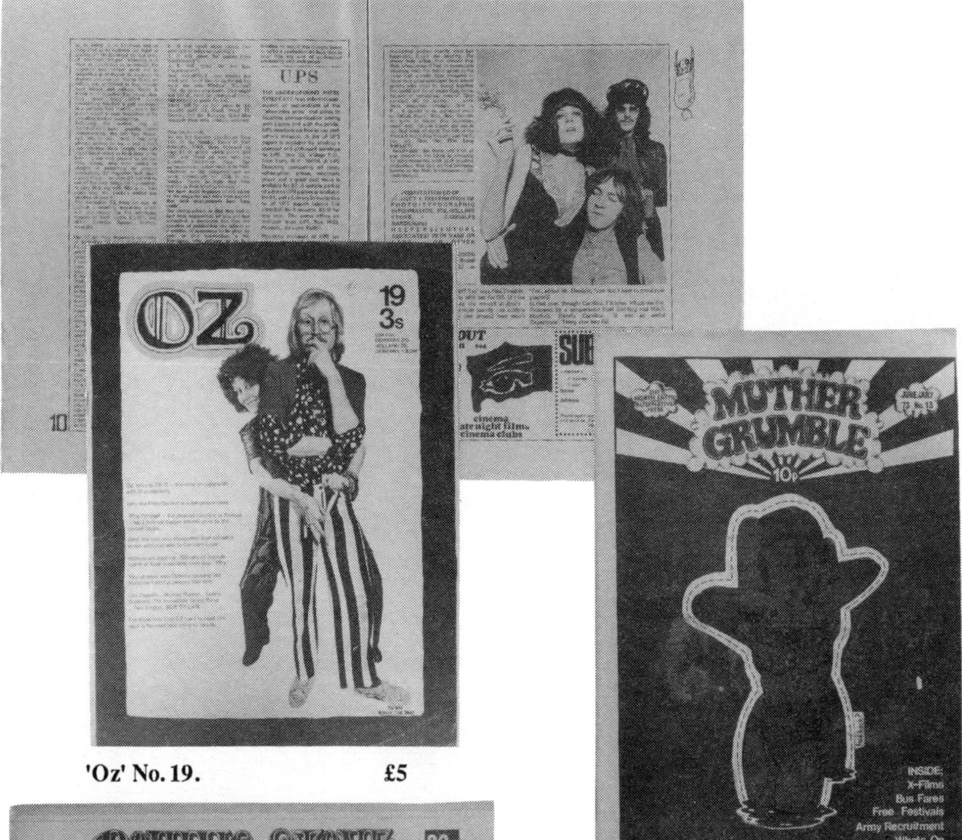

'Oz' No. 19. **£5**

Muther Grumble, June/July 1973. **£3**

Rolling Stone, 1972. **£6**

OZ – School Kids Issue. **£75**

(Yesterdays Paper)

The Running Man, 1968
No. 1. £5

International Times, 1972. £4

'Oz' No. 42, Inside Prisons. £6

Rolling Stone, 1972. £5

Street Life, No. 14, 1975. £3

(Yesterdays Paper)

An artist's album, circa 1890, wooden boards, the front decorated with a panel of cubic parquetry surrounded by a floral mosaic banding, initialled H.B., 9½in. wide. £700

Late 19th century Japanese photographic album with a finely painted frontispiece. £125

A small, fine quality embossed leather album with plated mounts and gilt decoration. £40

Late Victorian photographic album with finely printed mounts. £75

Late 19th century black lacquered album decorated with mother of pearl and ivory. £75

Early 20th century black leather album with finely cut silver plated mounts. £85

Late 19th century embossed brown leather album with floral decoration and gilt brass clasp, complete with photographs. £80

Edwardian tooled red leather album with gilded brass clasp, containing family photographs. £100

W. F. Cody, signed 2.25 x 3.5 card, also signed *Buffalo Bill*, rare, very slight smudging.
(Vennett-Smith) £320

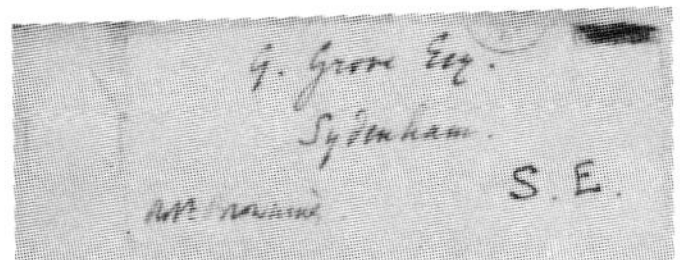

Robert Browning, portion of an autograph envelope signed, with complete address and signature, addressed to Sir George Grove, 1867.
(Vennett-Smith) £60

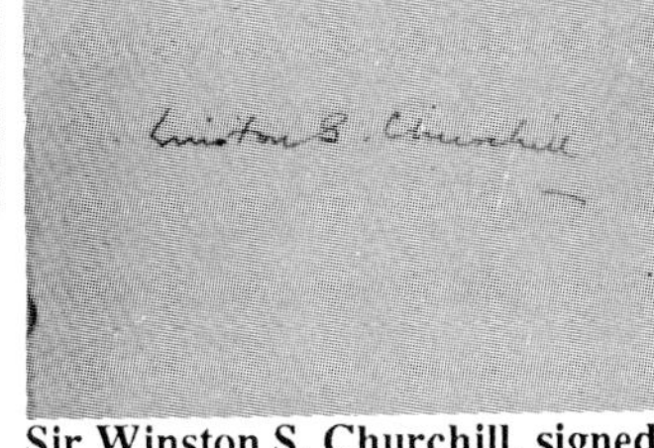

Sir Winston S. Churchill, signed album page, full signature.
(Vennett-Smith) £410

King George III, bold signature on piece, probably cut from a document.
(Vennett-Smith) £32

Joe Louis, signed album page, annotated in ink in another hand *Heavyweight Champion of the World 1948.*
(Vennett-Smith) £26

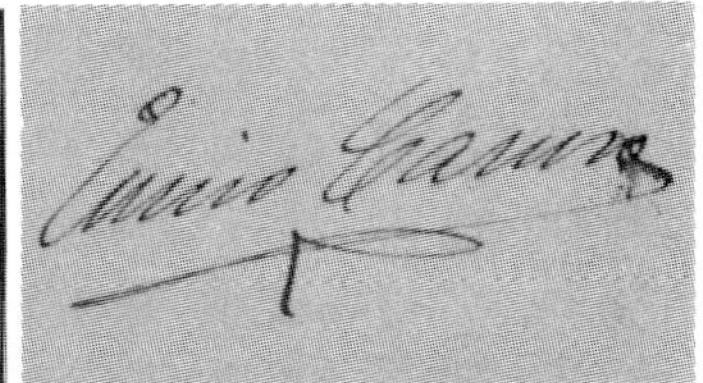

Enrico Caruso, signed piece, together with an unsigned colour cigarette card of Caruso, slight smudge.
(Vennett-Smith) £65

Irving Berlin, colour songsheet cover for 'Alexander's Ragtime Band', signed in green ink by Irving Berlin.
(Vennett-Smith) £125

A drawing of Mickey Mouse by Walt Disney, executed in grey crayon, signed and dedicated by the artist, 7½ x 4¾in.
(Sotheby's) £2,640

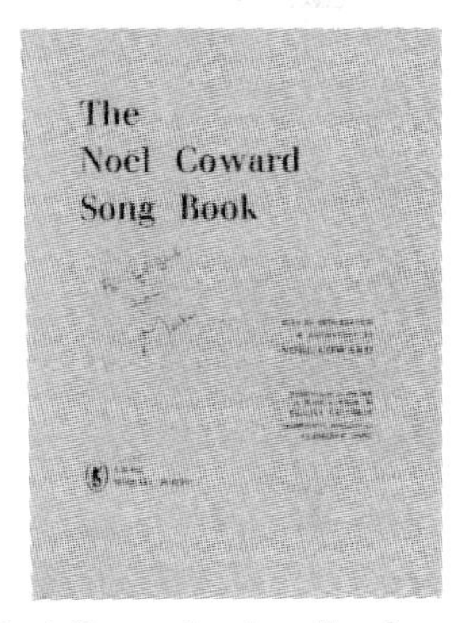

Noel Coward, a hardback edition of 'The Noel Coward Song Book', signed and inscribed to front title page, First Edition, 1953.
(Vennett-Smith) £45

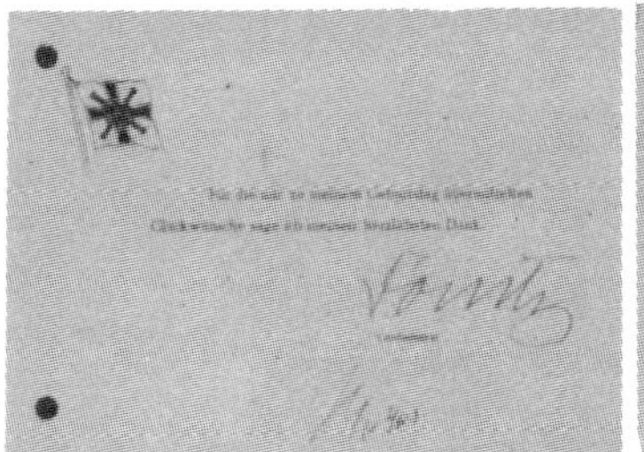

Admiral Karl Donitz, 6 x 4 printed card in German, giving thanks for birthday greetings, signed in ink by Donitz.
(Vennett-Smith) £60

Charles M. Schulz, signed colour 8 x 10 of Snoopy and friends from 'Snoopy Come Home'.
(Vennett-Smith) £100

Albert Schweitzer, signed 6 x 4 photograph to lower white border, being a photo of one of Schweitzer's hospitals.
(Vennett-Smith) £135

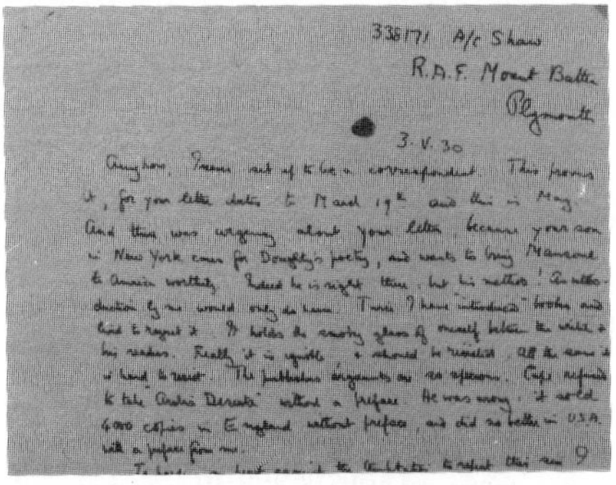
338171 A/c Shaw
R.A.F. Mount Batten
Plymouth
3.V.30

Thomas Edward Lawrence (1888–1935), a 2pp. a.l.s., by Lawrence, writing as T.E. Shaw, to H.M. Tomlinson, dated ***R.A.F. Mount Batten, Plymouth, 3.V.30***, discussing his reluctance to write prefaces.
(Christie's) £1,760

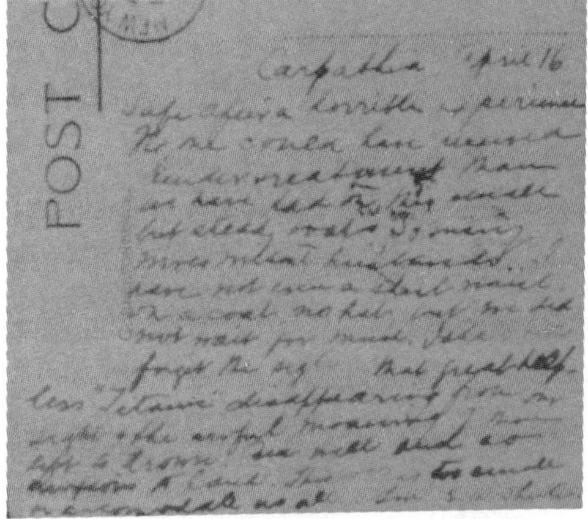

Carpathia April 16

Elizabeth W. Shutes (Survivor of the Titanic), a post-card from the "Carpathia" dated April 16th from Elizabeth Shutes to Mrs. Irving G. Mills saying *Safe again after a horrible experience.*
(Christie's) £880

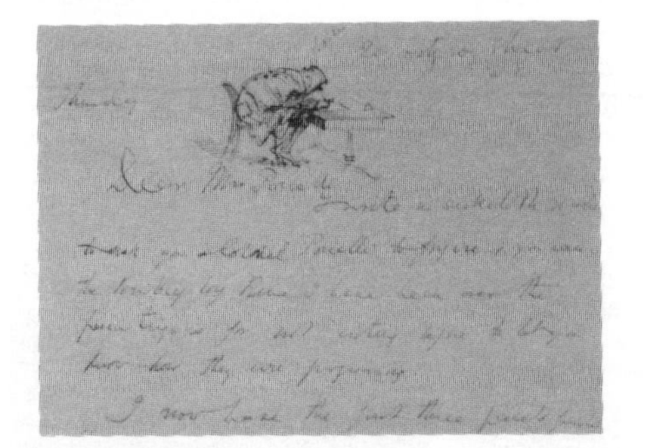

Rex Whistler (1905–44); Edwin Lutyens (1869–1944) a 2pp. a.l.s., by Rex Whistler, addressed *20 Fitzroy Street, W.1.*, to Mrs Porcelli, with a pen and ink drawing at the head of the paper of a figure crouched over a desk covered in a sackcloth and burning embers.
(Christie's) £385

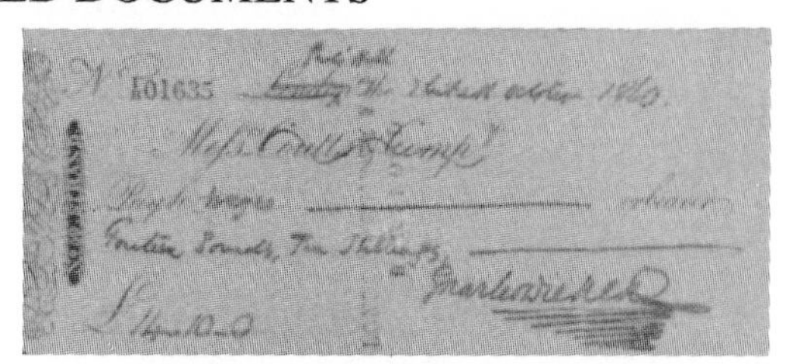
£01635

An autograph 'Coutts' cheque by Charles Dickens, dated *Gad's Hill, thirtieth October 1860*, for wages amounting to fourteen pounds, ten shillings; together with an envelope signed *Charles Dickens*.
(Christie's) £308

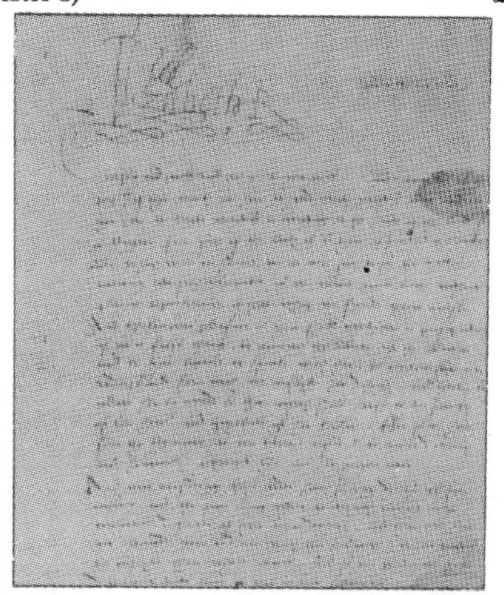

Elizabeth I, important letter signed Elizabeth R at head, to Sir Nicholas Throckmorton, her ambassador to Scotland, containing a major statement about Elizabeth's policy towards the fate of Mary Queen of Scots, July 1567.
£25,000

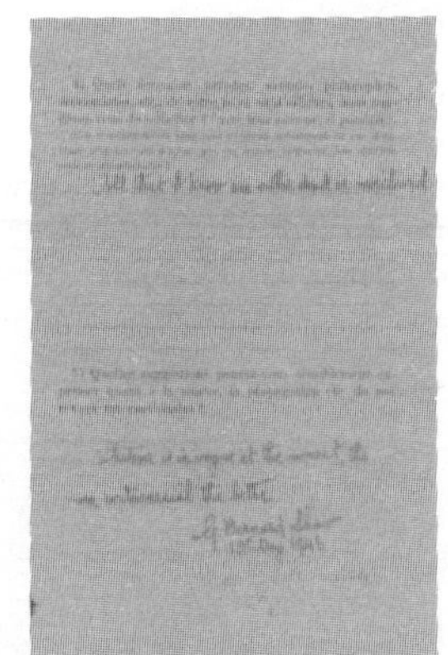

George Bernard Shaw (1856–1950), a 2pp. printed journalist's application questionnaire in French, evidently given to Shaw by the Belgian writer (?) Dotremont, which *Bernard Shaw, Vieillard sans futur* has taken literally, and responds with wit and flippancy.
(Christie's) £462

Felix Mendelssohn Bartholdy, the manuscript full score of Elijah, annotated throughout by Mendelssohn, sent by him in instalments from Leipzig to London, 1846, and used by the organist, Henry Gauntlett. (Phillips London) £88,000

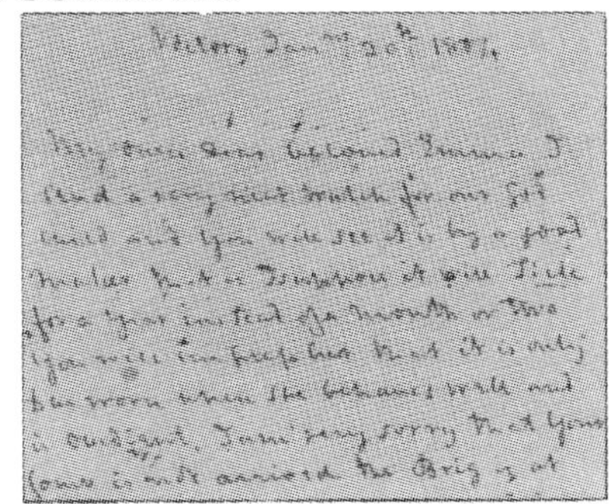

Horatio Nelson, fine autograph letter signed Nelson and Bronte to Emma Hamilton, 4 pages, quarto, sending a watch for their child and mentions that a comb is on its way to Emma etc., Victory, 20 January 1804. £3,000

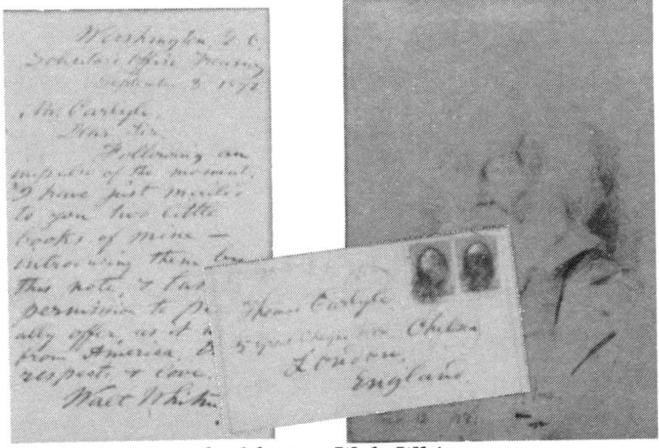

Autographed letter, Walt Whitman to Thomas Carlyle, signed and dated *September 3, 1872.* **(Skinner Inc.) £798**

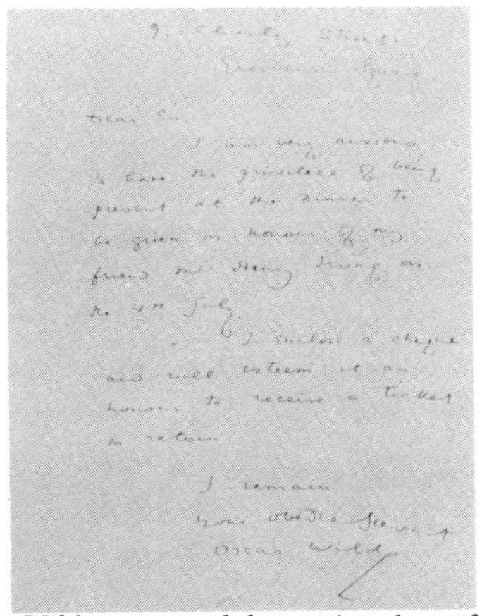

Oscar Wilde autograph letter signed, confessing himself *very anxious to have the privilege of being present at the dinner to be given in honour of my friend Mr Henry Irving on the 4th July,* **probably May 1883. (Phillips London) £1,450**

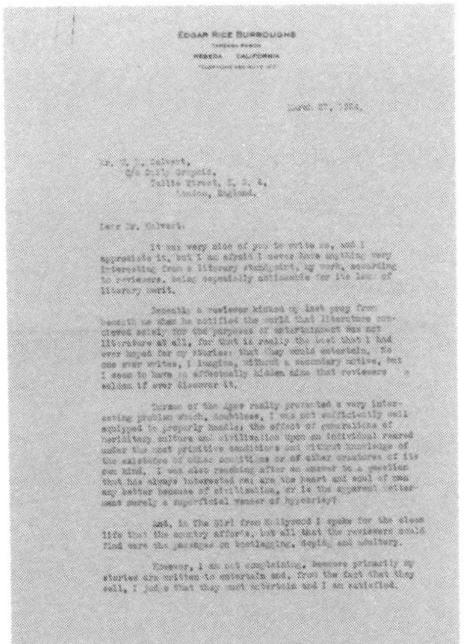

Fine typed letter signed by Edgar Rice Burroughs, about *Tarzan* **and the craft of fiction, to W. K. Calvert of the Daily Graphic, two page, slight paper-clip stain, Tarzania Ranch, California, 27 March 1924. (Phillips London) £1,150**

A fine document signed by Queen Victoria, printed on vellum in English and Samoan, seven page, Great Seal (cracked) attached by silver thread tassels, Windsor Castle, 26 February 1880. (Phillips London) £850

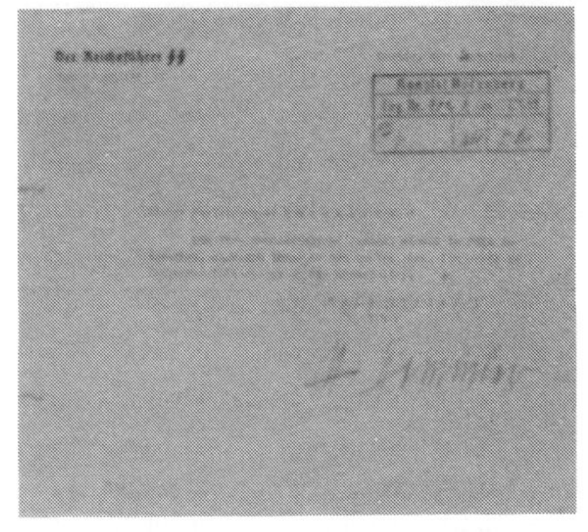

Heinrich Himmler (1900-1945), TLS 1 page 8vo, Berlin, 30th March 1938, to Nazi Politician Alfred Rosenberg. (Onslow's) £170

Agatha Christie, signed card, with a modern unsigned postcard, crease. (T. Vennett-Smith) £50

Identity cards carried by Mussolini, comprising that of Commandante Generale MVSN, with photo of Mussolini, card of the Associazione Nazionale Combattenti 1945, a card of the Presidenza Nazionale of the Opera and a card of the Istituto Nazionale Di Cultura Fascista. (Phillips London) £6,200

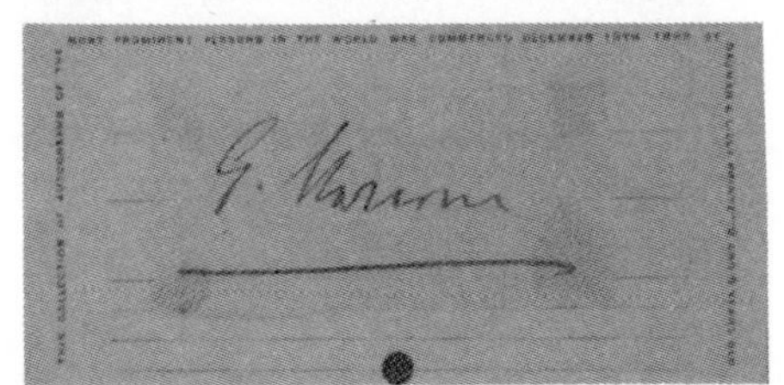

Guglielmo Marconi, signed piece, laid down to card, some staining to corners, just affecting underline of signature. (T. Vennett-Smith) £35

Lon Chaney Snr., small signed piece, cut from official document, rare, slight stain. (T. Vennett-Smith) £220

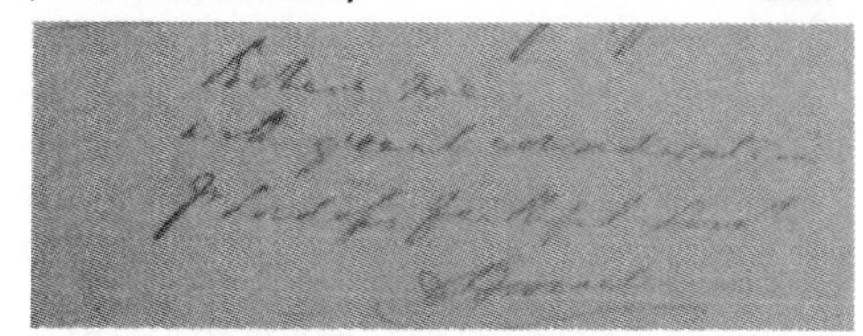

Benjamin Disraeli, signed piece, cut from end of letter, with nine words of text. (T. Vennett-Smith) £55

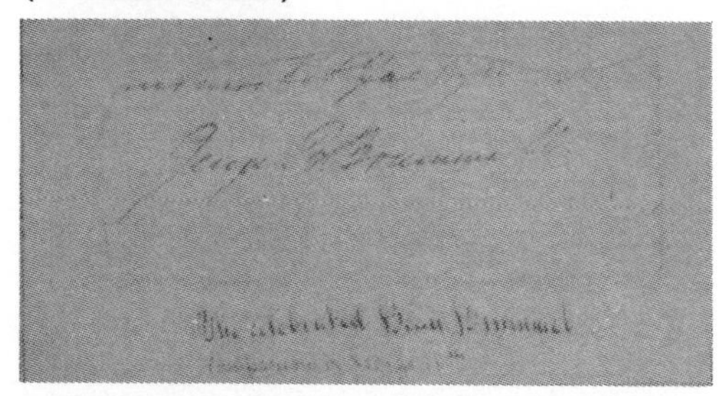

George B. Brummell, 'Beau Brummell', small signed piece, cut from end of letter. (T. Vennett-Smith) £38

Charles Darwin, autograph envelope, unsigned, addressed to Sir J. Paget, Bart, of Hanover Place, Hanover Square, London, postally cancelled 4th June 1881. (T. Vennett-Smith) £100

King George II, small signed piece, as King, cut from document, lightly laid down to card. (T. Vennett-Smith) £31

Robert Stephenson, Builder of the 'Rocket' Railway Engine, signed piece, cut from end of letter.
(T. Vennett-Smith) £40

George Stephenson, builder of the 'Rocket' Railway engine, signed piece, alongside modern colour postcard.
(T. Vennett-Smith) £130

Two political campaign pamphlets for the North West Manchester By-Election, 1906(?) each illustrated with a portrait photograph of Winston Churchill, one signed and inscribed *Winston S. Churchill 24 Ap. 1906*(?).
(Christie's S. Ken) £770

Louis Bleriot, signed postcard, showing three farm labourers watching Bleriot's aircraft passing above them.
(T. Vennett-Smith) £190

Louis Bleriot, small signed Savoy Hotel card, in pencil, also signed by Caproni (Italian Aero Designer), 1929.
(T. Vennett-Smith) £62

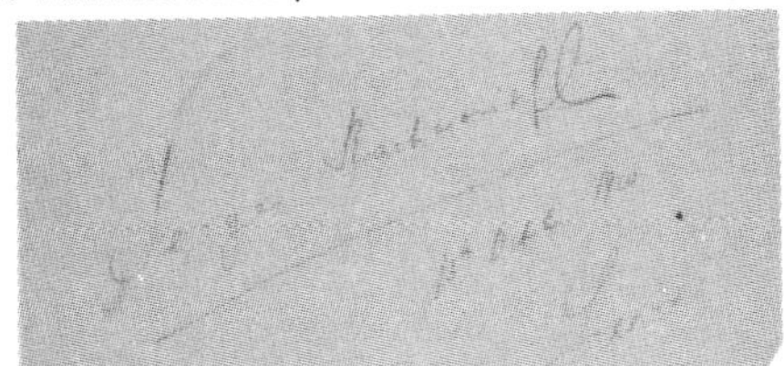

Sergei Rachmaninoff, signed album page, full signature, Leeds, 13th October 1910.
(T. Vennett-Smith) £120

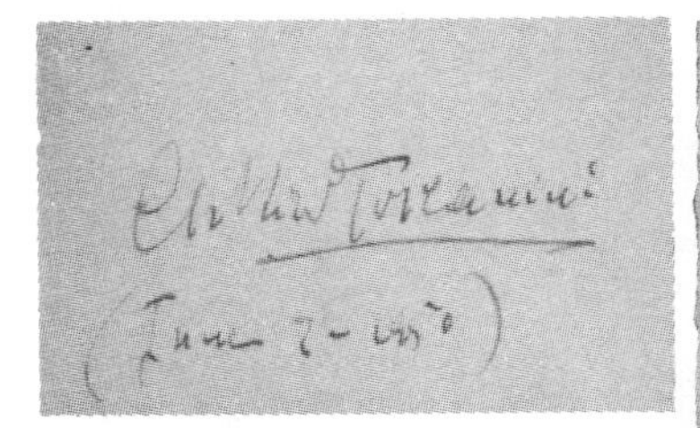

Arturo Toscanini, boldly signed card, in red ink, 2nd June 1950.
(T. Vennett-Smith) £70

Charles Chaplin, signed album page, annotated in another hand 'London Airport 29-10-52'.
(T. Vennett-Smith) £50

Leslie Howard, signed piece, 1933.
(T. Vennett-Smith) £42

King George I, small signed piece, as King, laid down to album page beneath contemporary engraving.
(T. Vennett-Smith) £65

Anna Pavlova, signed piece, overmounted beneath 5.5" x 7.5" reproduction photo.
(T. Vennett-Smith) £45

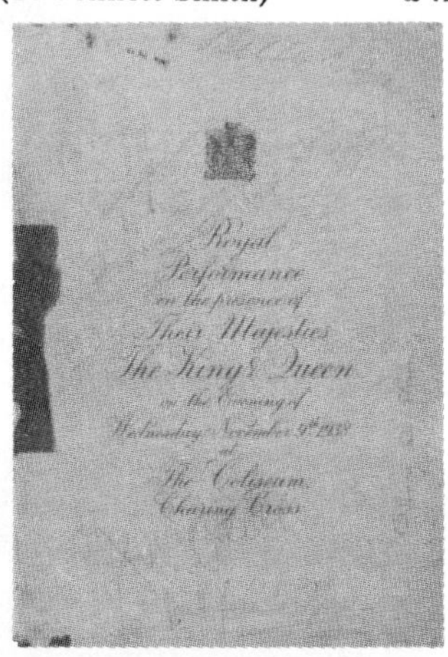

Gary Cooper, signed cover of Royal Performance Programme, at the Coliseum, Charing Cross, 9th November 1938.
(T. Vennett-Smith) £40

Ernest Hemingway, signed and inscribed edition of Look Magazine, to inside page, 26th January 1954 edition featuring large article about safari in Africa by Hemingway.
(T. Vennett-Smith) £470

Henry Longfellow, good signed piece, 1874, laid down to contemporary album page beneath contemporary sepia photograph.
(T. Vennett-Smith) £61

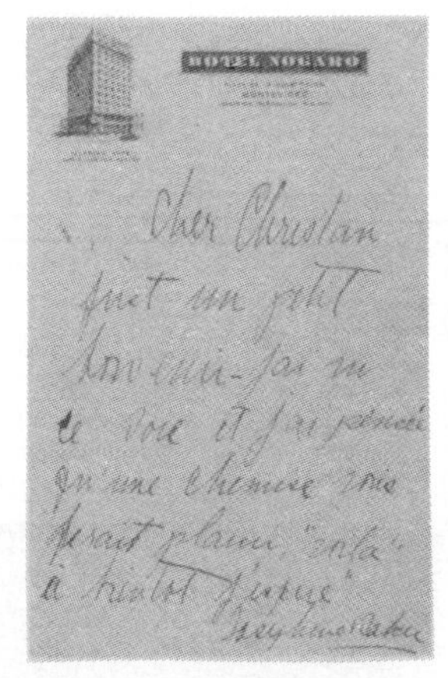

Josephine Baker, autograph letter, one page, in French, to 'Cher Christian' (her first theatrical hairdresser).
(T. Vennett-Smith) £75

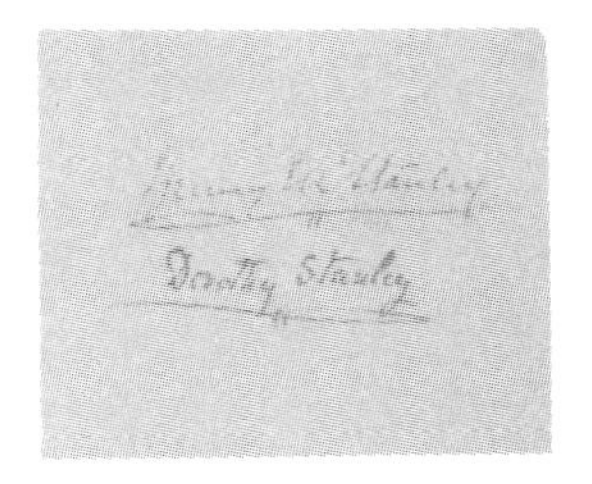

Henry M. Stanley, signed piece, also signed by his wife Dorothy Stanley, small stain.
(T. Vennett-Smith) £75

William Wordsworth, small signed piece, laid down.
(T. Vennett-Smith) £62

Georges Carpentier, signed album page.
(T. Vennett-Smith) £30

Anna Magnani, signed album page, with attached photo, overmounted beneath 7.5" x 9" reproduction photo.
(T. Vennett-Smith) £70

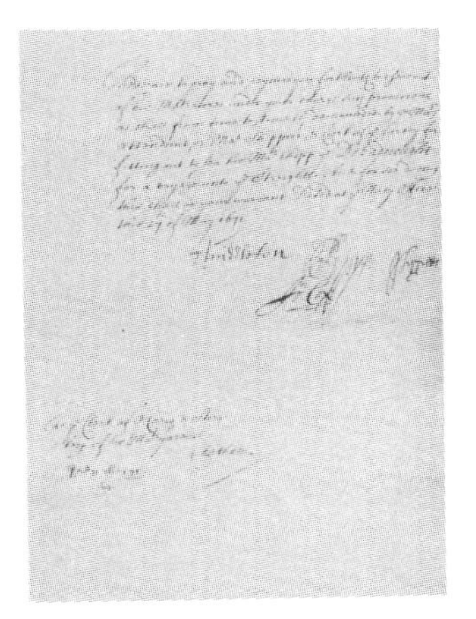

Samuel Pepys (1633–1703; Diarist and High Naval Officer, Secretary of the Admiralty under Charles II), one page, (London), 27 May 1671, being a warrant to the Clerk of the Stores at Chatham.
(T. Vennett-Smith) £620

John Garfield, signed album page, with small attached photo, overmounted beneath 9.5" x 7.5" reproduction photo.
(T. Vennett-Smith) £50

Maria Callas, signed postcard, to lower white border, head and shoulders, photo by Vivienne.
(T. Vennett-Smith) £180

To Dorothy Gardner
very sincerely
Leslie Howard
1935.

Leslie Howard, signed and inscribed sheet of Canadian Pacific Cruises headed notepaper, 1935, some creasing.
(T. Vennett-Smith) £45

Vivien Leigh, signed piece, overmounted beneath colour postcard, 6.25" x 11.25" overall.
(T. Vennett-Smith) £60

Merton May 7th 1802

My dear Sir

I am very sorry that you do not like your situation for it cost me more interest to obtain it for you than anything I could have asked, the Salary being fixed nothing I could say can alter it, but I agree with you that 100£ a year at Portsmouth is not equal ... in the Country you must Judge for yourself when you have a little more experience of the advantages the benefits from your place, I am always with every kind wish your sincere friend Nelson & Bronte

Horatio Nelson, autograph letter, 'Nelson & Bronte', one page, 7th May 1802, to Lieutenant Bromwich, in full "I am very sorry that you do not like your situation for it cost me more interest to obtain it for you than anything I could have asked."
(T. Vennett-Smith) £1,000

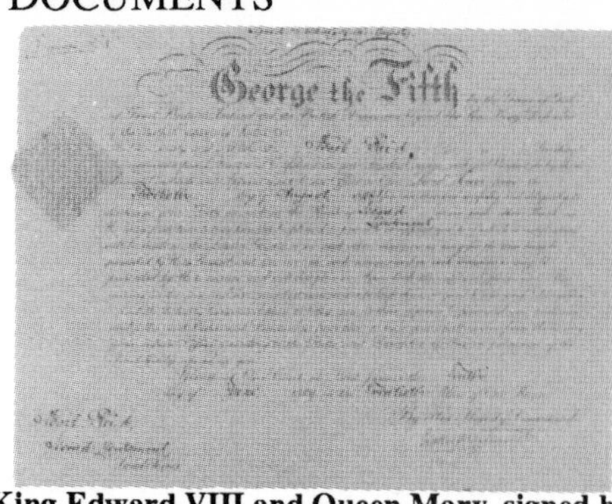

George the Fifth

King Edward VIII and Queen Mary, signed by both (Edward as Prince of Wales and Mary as Queen), on behalf of King George V, 10th June 1929, appointing Nevil Reid as Second Lieutenant in the Land Forces.
(T. Vennett-Smith) £165

Sir Winston S. Churchill, early autograph letter, one page, 16th December 1921, on Colonial Office headed notepaper, to the Irish political leader Tim Healy, "My dear Healy", "I am glad to tell you that a vacancy has occurred in the West African Custom Service"
(T. Vennett-Smith) £700

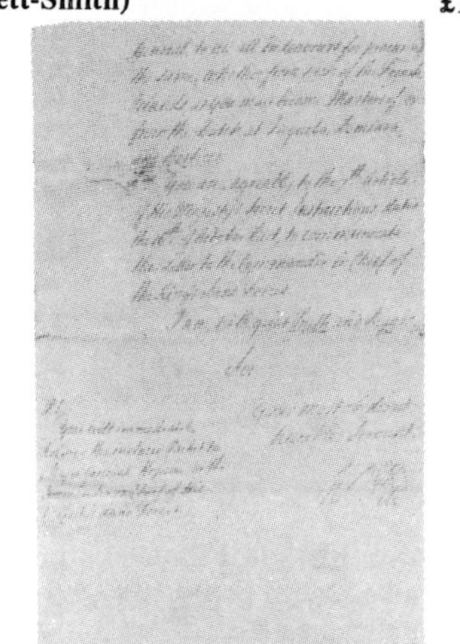

William Pitt, the Elder, interesting signed letter, nine pages, Whitehall, 9th March 1759, to Commodore Moore, marked 'Secret', stating that Captain Tyrrell had arrived with his despatch that had been immediately laid before the King.
(T. Vennett-Smith) £210

Queen Elizabeth II, signed Christmas card, beneath photo showing the Royal Family, accompanied by a Corgi, 1960.
(T. Vennett-Smith) £130

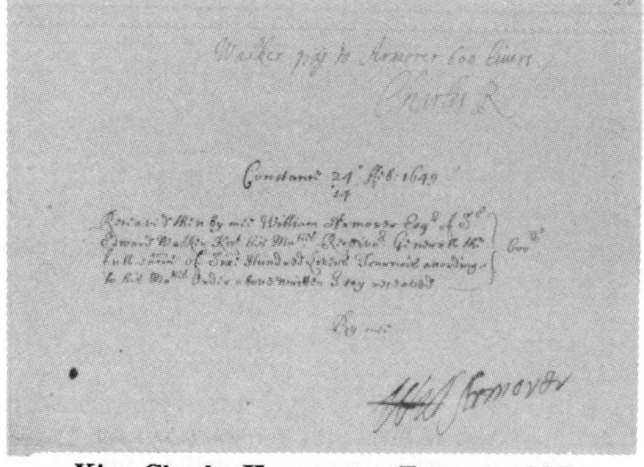

King Charles II, one page, February 1649, being an order of payment of six hundred livres from William Armourer Esq.
(T. Vennett-Smith) £360

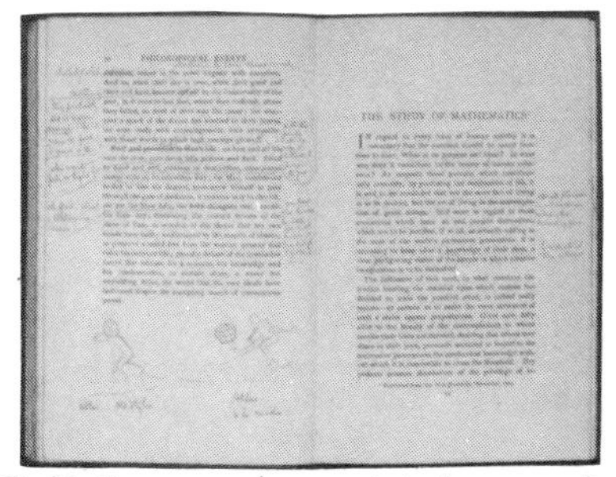

D. H. Lawrence's annotated copy of Bertrand Russell's Philosophical Essays, given to him by Lady Ottoline Morrell, inscribed by her in pencil on the fly-leaf *DHL from OM/1915*, 1910. (Phillips London) £4,400

Prince Charles and Princess Diana, attractive signed Christmas card by both, featuring a colour photograph of the Prince and Princess of Wales with their two children.
(T. Vennett-Smith) £1,000

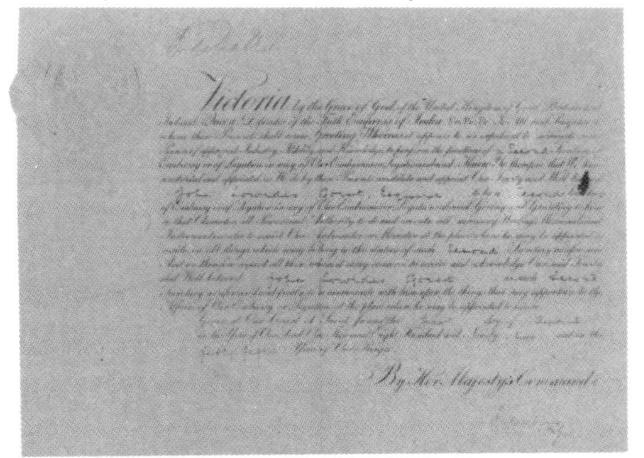

Queen Victoria, St. James's, 1st April 1892, being a document appointing John Lowndes Gorst a Second Secretary of Embassies or Legations abroad, countersigned by Salisbury.
(T. Vennett-Smith) £120

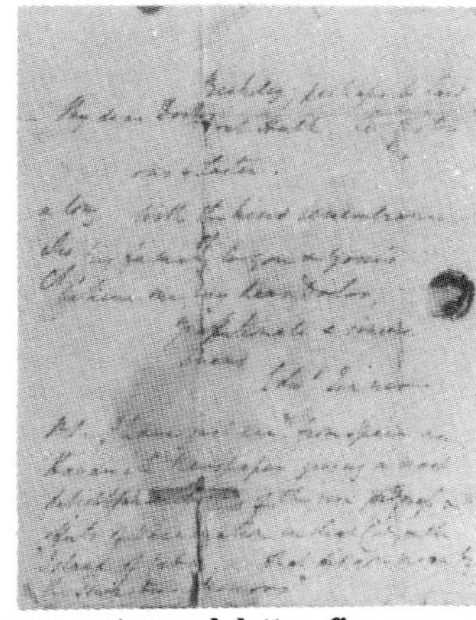

Edward Jenner, autograph letter, five pages, 'Friday Septr.' (26th added in another hand), to Dr. Worthington, the whole letter stained, torn at folds and generally fragile.
(T. Vennett-Smith) £380

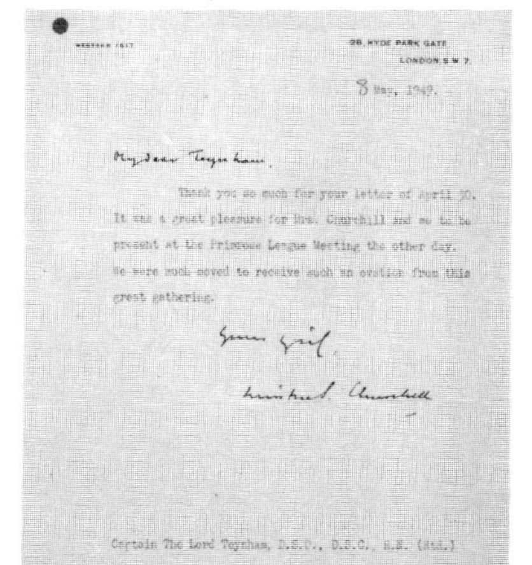

28, HYDE PARK GATE
LONDON S.W. 7.

8 May, 1949.

My dear Teynham,

Thank you so much for your letter of April 30. It was a great pleasure for Mrs. Churchill and me to be present at the Primrose League Meeting the other day. We were much moved to receive such an ovation from this great gathering.

Yours v[ery] t[ruly],

Winston S. Churchill

Captain The Lord Teynham, D.S.O., D.S.C., R.N. (Rtd.)

Sir Winston S. Churchill, typed letter signed, one page, 8th May 1949, to Captain The Lord Teynham, 'My dear Teynham', stating that "It was a great pleasure for Mrs. Churchill and me to be present at the Primrose League Meeting the other day."
(T. Vennett-Smith) £490

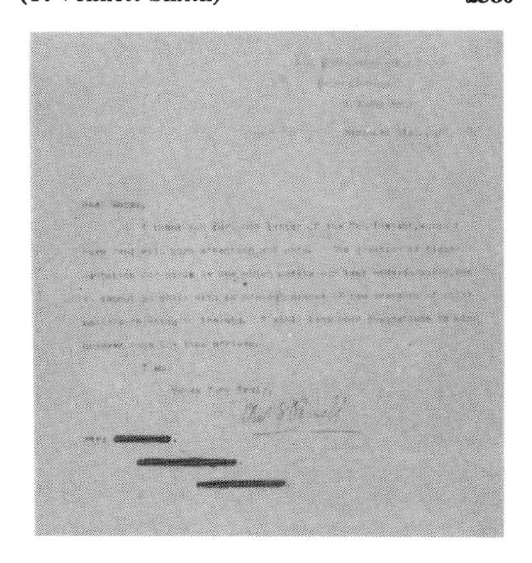

Charles S. Parnell, typed letter signed, one page, 31st December 1885, to a female correspondent thanking her for her letter.
(T. Vennett-Smith) £180

Malcolm Campbell postcard, inscribed *with my best wishes.*
(Onslow's) £200

A full length photograph of Winston Churchill seated on a horse 11 x $9^{1}/_{2}$in. mounted on card signed *W.S. Churchill, 1948.*
(Christie's S. Ken) £1,320

Richard Seaman signed postcard.
(Onslow's) £370

Tsar Nicolas II, a head and shoulders portrait photograph, signed and inscribed *Nicolas, Balmoral, Sept. 1896*, mounted on card, $11^{1}/_{2}$ x 7in.
(Christie's S. Ken) £1,870

Oscar Wilde, a head and shoulders portrait photograph, signed and inscribed *Bobbie, from his friend OW*, mounted on card, $9^{1}/_{2}$ x $7^{1}/_{4}$in.
(Christie's S. Ken) £1,650

A cabinet card studio portrait of the young Winston Churchill in tropical uniform probably taken in Egypt prior to the Omdurman campaign, 1898, signed *Winston*, 8 x 5in.
(Christie's S. Ken) £2,640

A three quarter length portrait photograph by Hugh Cecil of H.R.H. Prince Edward in Admiral's full dress uniform, signed and inscribed *Edward, 1939*, $12^{1}/_{2}$ x $10^{1}/_{2}$in.
(Christie's S. Ken) £308

Winston Churchill, a head and shoulders portrait photograph $5^{1}/_{2}$ x $4^{1}/_{2}$in. mounted on card signed *W.S. Churchill.*
(Christie's S. Ken) £660

A portrait photograph of H.M. Queen Victoria, by A. Bassano, signed and inscribed *Victoria R.I. 1899*, mounted on card, $12^{1}/_{2}$ x $10^{1}/_{2}$in.
(Christie's S. Ken) £770

Noel Coward — a three-quarter length portrait photograph by Dorothy Wilding, signed and inscribed *For Ginette with love always Noel 1903,* 9½ x 7in. (Christie's S. Ken) £165

Walter L Brock photograph in Bleriot cockpit, signed and dated September 18th 1913 by the subject.
(Onslow's) £170

HM Queen Victoria — a full length platinum print photograph by A. Bassano with photographer's credit, 21 x 15.5cm., signed and inscribed *Victoria R.I. 1886.* (Christie's S. Ken) £660

Galina Ulanova, signed 8" x 10", full length dancing.
(T. Vennett-Smith) £55

H.R.H.Edward Prince of Wales A half-length profile portrait photograph in his regalia as Prince of Wales, by Campbell Gray, signed and inscribed *'Edward 1911'.* 11½ x 9¾in. (Christie's S. Ken) £440

Tommy Sopwith, full length portrait standing beside aerodrome railings.
(Onslow's) £160

A full length photograph of HRH Princess Mary with her two eldest sons in Highland dress, signed and inscribed in Princess Mary's hand, *Victoria Mary 1906, Albert, Edward,* 7¾ x 6in. (Christie's S. Ken) £198

Marcus D Manton photograph seated in Farman biplane, signed and inscribed Hendon and dated 13-9-13.
(Onslow's) £100

A full length seated portrait photograph by Alice Hughes of Princess Mary with her three eldest children, signed and inscribed in Princess Mary's hand *Victoria Mary, Albert, Victoria, Edward 1897,* 6 x 4in. (Christie's S. Ken) £176

Lord Alfred Tennyson, signed carte-de-visite **photo, half length profile, rare in this form.**
(T. Vennett-Smith) £180

Sir Winston S. Churchill, signed piece, in full, laid down to blue card beneath original 10" x 8" photo of Churchill and the Queen outside 10 Downing Street.
(T. Vennett-Smith) £200

Gustave Carpentier (1860–1956; French Composer), good signed and inscribed 6" x 4.25", head and shoulders, 1924.
(T. Vennett-Smith) £140

Christine Keeler, signed and inscribed 8" x 10", a reproduction of the famous photograph by Lewis Morley showing Keeler, full length naked, sat on chair, signed and dated 1989.
(T. Vennett-Smith) £55

Anna Pavlova, boldly signed postcard, full length dancing with, but not signed by, Novikoff, in 'Amarilla'.
(T. Vennett-Smith) £130

Queen Elizabeth II and Prince Philip, signed Christmas card, 1957, signed beneath colour photo of The Queen and Prince Philip with Prince Charles, Princess Anne and two corgis.
(T. Vennett-Smith) £200

Josephine Baker, signed 4.25" x 5.75", full length.
(T. Vennett-Smith) £83

Gene Tunney, signed 7.5" x 9.5", head and shoulders, photo by Apeda of New York.
(T. Vennett-Smith) £80

Claudia Muzio, signed and inscribed 7" x 9.25", head and shoulders, Buenos Aires 1933.
(T. Vennett-Smith) £115

Edith Piaf, signed and inscribed postcard, in French, rare, slight corner creasing.
(T. Vennett-Smith) £131

Jascha Heifetz, signed and inscribed 12" x 7.5", head and shoulders playing violin, "To A.E. Warren, In rememberance of my first concert in Calcutta Jascha Heifetz", 1927.
(T. Vennett-Smith) £170

Enrico Caruso, signed postcard, Buenos Aires 1915.
(T. Vennett-Smith) £100

Anna Pavlova, signed postcard, full length dancing, slightly trimmed to edges, some foxing to image.
(T. Vennett-Smith) £60

Trapp Family, a rare signed and inscribed 8" x 10" of the Trapp Family Singers, shown seated around a table.
(T. Vennett-Smith) £260

Andrew Lloyd Webber, signed 8" x 10", head and shoulders, minor stain to image.
(T. Vennett-Smith) £75

Sir Winston S. Churchill, signed postcard, full signature, head and shoulders, as Minister of the Navy, photo by Elliott and Fry.
(T. Vennett-Smith) £500

Adolf Hitler, signed, in pencil, portrait profile, smiling, oval image, rare, apparently signed for Heinrich Heim, Martin Bormann's Adjutant.
(T. Vennett-Smith) £340

King George V, signed 6" x 8.25", full length in ceremonial dress, 1898, weaker signature.
(T. Vennett-Smith) £95

Rudyard Kipling, a good signed photograph.
(John Wilson) £550

King George V and Queen Mary, studio portrait photo, 14 x 18in., signed by both on mount, dated 1911. £150

Ulysses S. Grant, a good early signed photograph, 7 x 5 in.
(John Wilson) £1,200

Captain Robert F. Scott, signed 5.25" x 7.5", half length in uniform, photo by J. Thomson of London.
(T. Vennett-Smith) £400

Marc Chagall, signed magazine photo, in blue crayon, to lower white border.
(T. Vennett-Smith) £140

Richard Strauss, signed postcard, head and shoulders, in darker portion, corner clipped and slight tear to left of image.
(T. Vennett-Smith) £160

Charlie Chase, American comedian, a good signed and inscribed sepia 10½ x 14in.
(T. Vennett-Smith) £90

Babe Ruth, a rare early signed 6¾ x 4¾in. book photo, showing Ruth, full-length in action pose, 1927.
(T. Vennett-Smith) £600

Sir Winston S. Churchill, a good early signed 6 x 3.5 photograph to mount, full signature, half length standing, wearing a bowtie.
(Vennett-Smith) £520

David Lloyd George, signed 5 x 3½in., in later years.
(T. Vennett-Smith) £35

Jascha Heifetz, an 8 x 5½in. card featuring a photo of Heifetz playing the violin, dated *1935*.
(T. Vennett-Smith) £100

Vaclav Havel, President of Czechoslovakia, signed colour 7 x 5in.
(T. Vennett-Smith) £45

Colonel Gaddafi, signed colour 5.25" x 7.25", head and shoulders, scarce, corner crease.
(T. Vennett-Smith) £50

Richard Strauss (1864-1949), Composer, portrait photograph, inscribed and signed Vienna, 5th February 1931, 10 x 8in.
(Onslow's) £100

Nellie Melba, good signed sepia postcard, full length in costume as Margarette.
(T. Vennett-Smith) £140

King Edward VIII, a fine signed 11.5 x 14.5, 'Edward R.I.', as King, three quarter length in ceremonial uniform, 1936.
(Vennett-Smith) £400

Franz Lehar, a good signed postcard, featuring oval image of Lehar with printed musical quotation from 'The Merry Widow', 13th May 1909.
(Vennett-Smith) £140

Ayatollah Khomeini, signed colour 5 x 3½in., one of the rarest 20th century political autographs.
(T. Vennett-Smith) £360

Nicolae Ceaucescu, signed colour 5.5 x 8.75 photograph, to lower white border.
(Vennett-Smith) **£70**

Sir Winston S. Churchill, an excellent signed 7 x 9.5 photograph, with full signature, a slightly shaky example signed in later years.
(Vennett-Smith) £875

Andy Warhol, signed 8 x 10 to white border, half length.
(Vennett-Smith) £140

Mother Teresa, signed 8 x 10 photograph, half length standing with hands clasped together praying.
(Vennett-Smith) **£55**

An unusual 8.5 x 6.5 press photo of a policeman, Jack Gardner, full length walking towards the camera, signed at the base of the photo by Sir Winston S. Churchill and Clement R. Attlee.
(Vennett-Smith) £300

Mikhail Gorbachev, signed 8 x 10 photograph, also signed by Brian Mulroney, showing both Gorbachev and Mulroney stood amongst other World Leaders.
(Vennett-Smith) £240

Dame Margot Fonteyn, signed postcard, full-length dancing, on point.
(Vennett-Smith) £30

Jim Henson, signed 8 x 10 photograph, also signed by co-creator of the Muppets Frank Oz.
(Vennett-Smith) **£130**

John Philip Sousa, signed sepia postcard with additional two bars from 'The Diplomat', 1908.
(Vennett-Smith) **£170**

Richard Strauss, a fine signed postcard to lower white border, half-length seated writing at desk.
(Vennett-Smith) £310

J. Ramsay MacDonald, British Prime Minister, a good signed 12.5 x 10 photograph, full length standing in front of desk, sending New Year's greetings, 1933–34.
(Vennett-Smith) £75

General Francisco Franco, signed postcard, in uniform, rare.
(Vennett-Smith) £170

Harry Houdini, a signed and inscribed 10 x 8 photograph, the lengthy inscription reading *To my red Pal of Twenty years Dr. R. B. Lothian.*
(Vennett-Smith) £405

Muhammed Ali, signed colour 8 x 10 photograph, full length in ring standing over Sonny Liston.
(Vennett-Smith) £75

Maria Callas, an early signed and inscribed 9.5 x 7 photograph, looking downwards and holding her hands to her face, Buenos Aires, 1949.
(Vennett-Smith) £180

Anna Pavlova, signed postcard, full length, standing on point.
(Vennett-Smith) £105

King Edward VIII, a fine signed photograph 5.25 x 7.5 to lower white border, as Prince of Wales, three quarter length standing in uniform, 1922.
(Vennett-Smith) £350

Neil Armstrong, signed 8 x 10 photograph, half length in spacesuit, in profile.
(Vennett-Smith) £130

Brighton Equitable Co-operative Society, $1\frac{3}{4}$lb bag. 50p

Paper wrapper for Folley & Sons, Launceston. £1

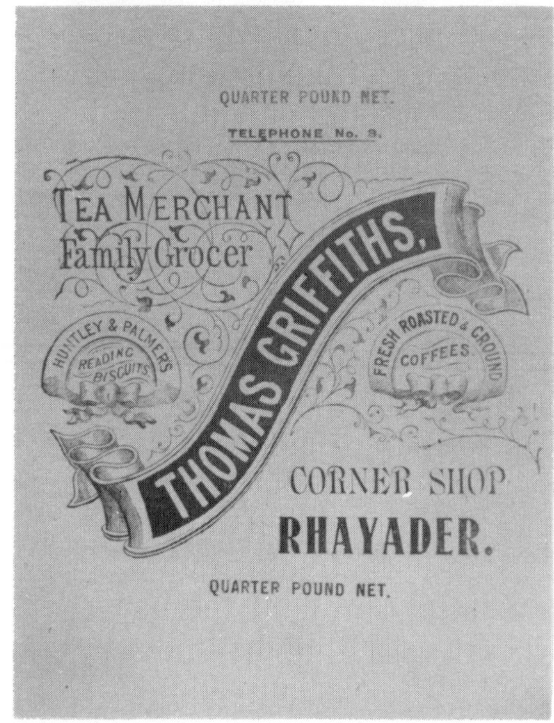

Paper wrapper for Thomas Griffiths, Tea Merchant. £1

Robertson's Silver Lemon and Golden Orange Jelly. £2

(Douglas Morgan)

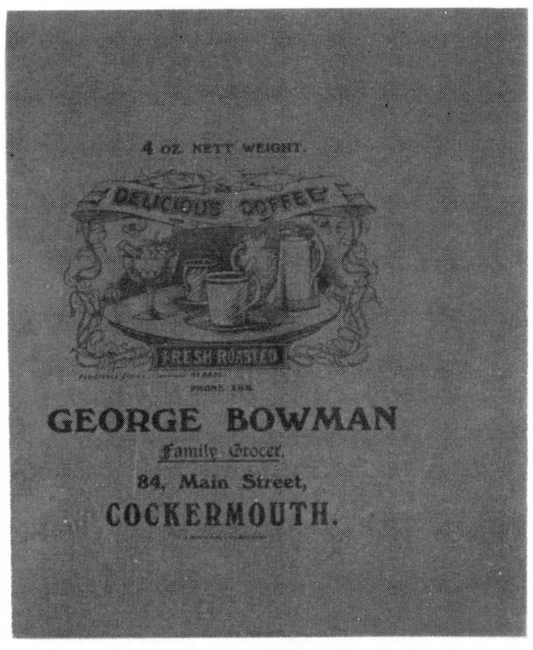

Paper wrapper for 4oz coffee by George Bowman. £1

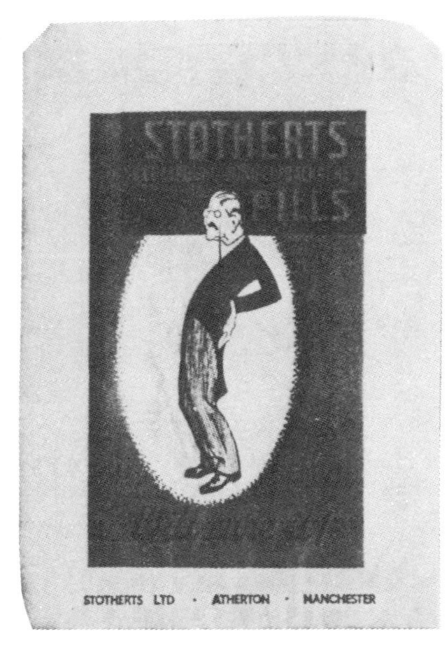

Stotherts compound juniper backache pills bag. 50p

Palethorpe's Sausages wrapper. £2

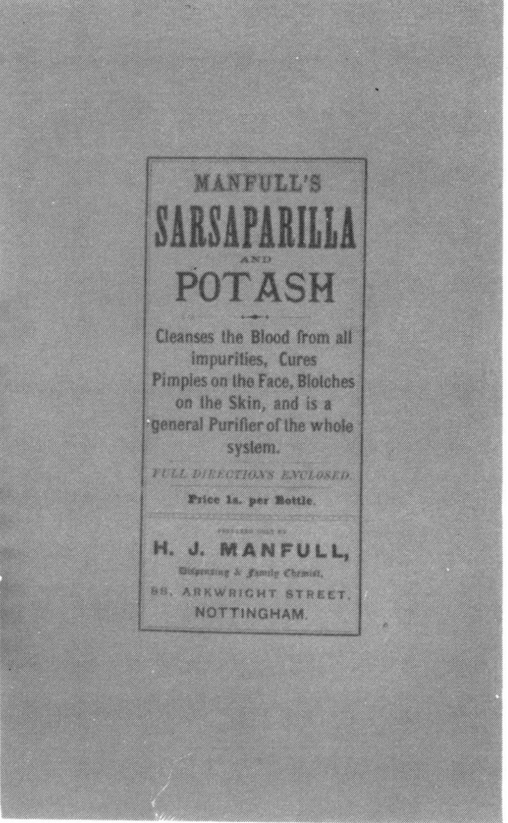

Paper bottle wrap for Manfull's Sarsaparilla. £1

(Douglas Morgan)

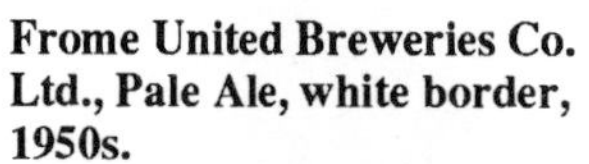
Frome United Breweries Co. Ltd., Pale Ale, white border, 1950s. £5

Harvey's Oat-Malt Stout, Recommended for Invalids. £4

St Anne's Well Brewery, Exeter, Brown Ale, 1950s. £2

Hyde's Anvil Strong Ale, yellow lettering, 1970s. 50p

Macardle's H.B. Brown Ale, bottled by Vendor, 1920s. £5

Pierrette Brand Superior Quality Light Beer, 1930s. £10

Hambridge Brewery Ltd., Curry Rivel, Somerset, Pale Ale, 1940s. £7

Unicorn Bitter, Brewed & Bottled by Johnson & Phipps Ltd., Wolverhampton, 1940s. £5

Light Pale Ale, John Aitchison & Co. Ltd., Edinburgh, 1890s. £15

(Michael Jones)

Whitakers Cock o' the North Standard Stout, 1940s. £3

J.W. Lees & Co. Brown Ale with portrait, 1940/50s. £2

T.V. Ale, Brewed & Bottled by the Ely Brewery Co. Ltd., Ely, Cardiff, 1950s. £4

Harvey & Son (Lewes) Ltd., India Pale Ale, 1940s. £4

Old English Ale Special Xmas Brew, Shanklin Brewery, 1950s. £8

Ely Coronation Ale, 1953, £4

Lamb Brewery Ltd., Frome, Stingo, Full of Life, 1950s. £5

West Country Ale, Brewed & Bottled by Cheltenham & Hereford Breweries Ltd., 1950s. £1

Lady Brand Special Light Beer, Brewed and Bottled in Edinburgh, 1930s. £10

(Michael Jones)

Magpie Pale Ale, W. B. Reid & Co. Ltd., Newcastle on Tyne, named after the local football team in red and black on white. £8

Coronation Ale, David Roberts and Sons Ltd., Aberystwyth, red, white and blue on cream. £8

Young & Co's Pale Ale, an attractive label from a company which still keeps rams, in red and black on white. £8

Nicholsons' Double Nick Strong Ale, in red, black, gold and yellow on white. £8

Paine & Co's Old English Ale, an attractive 1930's label in red, yellow and black on pink. £4

Hambridge Brewery Ltd., Home Brewed Ale, a 1930's label showing the trademark in red, with blue and black lettering on white. £6

Gilmour Sheffield Shield Extra Stout, an attractive 1950's label in brown, buff and green on white. £8

Isleworth Stout, The Brewery, Isleworth, a 1940's label on a buff ground. £4

King & Barnes Ltd., Festive Ale, a 1960's label in red, yellow and black on white. £1

(Michael Jones)

Brickwoods Light Bitter Ale, a 1940's label in blue, yellow and red on white. £3

Coronation Year, '53 Ale, Drybrough & Co. Ltd., Edinburgh, multicoloured label on white, a popular event for brewers. £6

Bent's Coronation Ale, Liverpool and Stone, in the patriotic colours of red, white and blue on a cream ground. £3

Thwaites Big Ben Strong Ale, named after Ben, the Brewery's founder, in red, blue and black on white. £2

Dog's Head, British Lager Beer, Export Bottlers Ltd., in blue, orange and black on white. £1

Mackie's Nut Brown Ale, an attractive 1950's bottlers label, in brown and red on white. £2

Festivale Gold Medal Ales by Eagle Brewery, Leicester, produced for the Festival of Britain in 1951, in green and black on white. £8

Jenner's Double Nut Brown Ale, an attractive 1930's label in green, brown and black on buff. £10

Salt & Co's East India Pale Ale, an attractive label from 1894, in black and yellow on white. £35

(Michael Jones)

Preston Breweries P.B. Sparkling Bitter Special Ale, 1950s. £8

Hyde's Anvil Ale, 1970s. 50p

Belhaven, Dudjeon & Co's Export, 1890s. £15

Greene King Burton Ale, 1930s. £3

Chelt Brown Ale, Brewed & Bottled by Cheltenham & Hereford Breweries Ltd., 1950s. £1

Greene King Suffolk Ale 1799, 1930s. £3

Thompson & Son Ld., Walmer Brewery Stout, with vignette, The Friendly Light, 1920s. £12

Rayment's Coronation Ale, The Queen God Bless Her, 1950s. £8

The Workington Brewery Company Limited John Peel Old Ale, 1940s. £3

(Michael Jones)

Shrewsbury & Wem Brewery Coronation Ale, with vignette of Windsor Castle, 1950s. £8

India Pale Ale, Brewed and Bottled by S.H. Higgs Ltd., Lion Brewery, Reading, 1930s. £12

J.W. Lees & Co. Pale Ale, red label with portrait 1940/50s. £2

Thompson & Son Ld., Walmer Brewery Stout, with vignette of lighthouse, 1920s. £12

Hunt Edmunds Best Bitter, 1960s. £1

'333' Brand Special Light Beer, Brewed and Bottled in Edinburgh, Scotland. £10

Extra Stout, John Aitchison & Co. Ltd., Edinburgh, 1890s. £15

Hyde's Anvil Stout, 1970s, green label. 50p

Hambridge Extra Stout, Hambridge Brewery Ltd., 1940s. £7

(Michael Jones)

Worksop and Retford Brewery Co. Ltd., No 5, 1953. £3

T. Hoskins Ltd., No. 1, 1938 £3

William Younger & Co. Ltd., No 5, 1934. £3

Buckingham Palace, British Brewery Export, 1950's. £5

British Overseas Airways Corporation. 50p

Stella Artois, Belgian, 1980's. 25p

Dale's Cambridge Ales, 1935. £20

Holden's Black Country Bitter, 1980's. 25p

Bullard's Ales, 'Strength and Quality', 1930's. £15

Hope & Anchor Breweries Ltd., No. 4, 1951. £1.50

The Rewarding Experience, Aston Manor Brewery Co. Ltd., 1970's. 50p

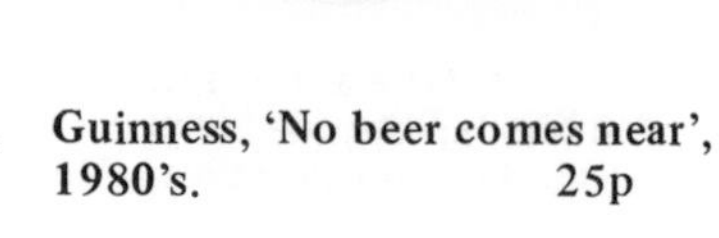

Guinness, 'No beer comes near', 1980's. 25p

(Tim Stannard)

Moors '& Robson's Brilliant Beers, late 1940's. £10

Aitchison's Export Ale, British Brewery, 1960-64. £1

Germania Munster, Westfalen, 1960's. 25p

Baksor, East European, 1930's. £2

Hanson's Special Stout, 1960's. 50p

The West Auckland Brewery Co. Ltd., 1934. £30

M & B, Woodbine — the great little cigarette, 1950's 25p

J. Wray & Nephew Ltd., Rum, Appleton, 1950's. 25p

Whiteways Cyder, Pure Devon, 1930's. £4

Richard Clarke & Co. Ltd., Mild Ale, Stockport, 1936. £25

The Swan, The Romance of Inn Signs, 1960. 50p

(Tim Stannard)

Ogden's Juggler Tobacco, 1930's. £6

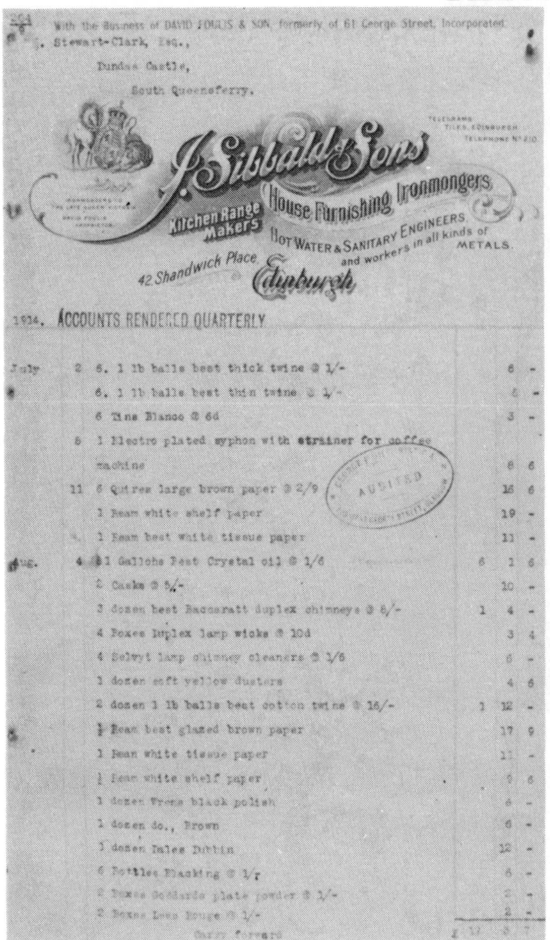

With the Business of DAVID FOULIS & SON, formerly of 61 George Street, Incorporated.

J. Stewart-Clark, Esq.,
Dundas Castle,
South Queensferry.

J. Sibbald & Sons
Kitchen Range Makers
House Furnishing Ironmongers
Hot Water & Sanitary Engineers and workers in all kinds of Metals.
42 Shandwick Place, Edinburgh

1914. ACCOUNTS RENDERED QUARTERLY

			£	s	d
July	2	6. 1 lb balls best thick twine @ 1/-		6	-
		6. 1 lb balls best thin twine @ 1/-		6	-
		6 Tins Blanco @ 6d		3	-
	8	1 Electro plated syphon with strainer for coffee machine		8	6
	11	6 Quires large brown paper @ 2/9		16	6
		1 Ream white shelf paper		19	-
		1 Ream best white tissue paper		11	-
Aug.	4	81 Gallons Best Crystal oil @ 1/6	6	1	6
		2 Casks @ 5/-		10	-
		3 dozen best Baccaratt duplex chimneys @ 8/-	1	4	-
		4 Boxes Duplex lamp wicks @ 10d		3	4
		4 Selvyt lamp chimney cleaners @ 1/6		6	-
		1 dozen soft yellow dusters		4	6
		2 dozen 1 lb balls best cotton twine @ 16/-	1	12	-
		½ Ream best glazed brown paper		17	9
		1 Ream white tissue paper		11	-
		½ Ream white shelf paper		9	6
		1 dozen Wrens black polish		6	-
		1 dozen do., Brown		6	-
		1 dozen Dales Dubbin		12	-
		6 Bottles Blacking @ 1/-		6	-
		2 Boxes Goddards plate powder @ 1/-		2	-
		2 Boxes Loss Rouge @ 1/-		2	-
		Carry forward	£ 13	3	7

AUDITED

J. Sibbald & Sons, Kitchen Range Makers, billhead, 1914. £2

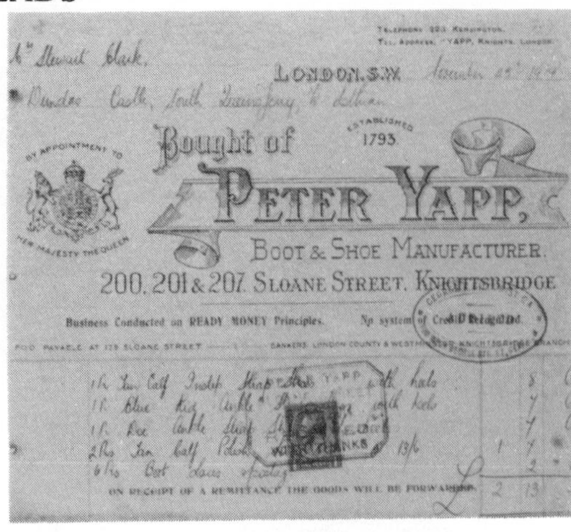

Peter Yapp, Boot and Shoe manufacturer, billhead 1914. £3

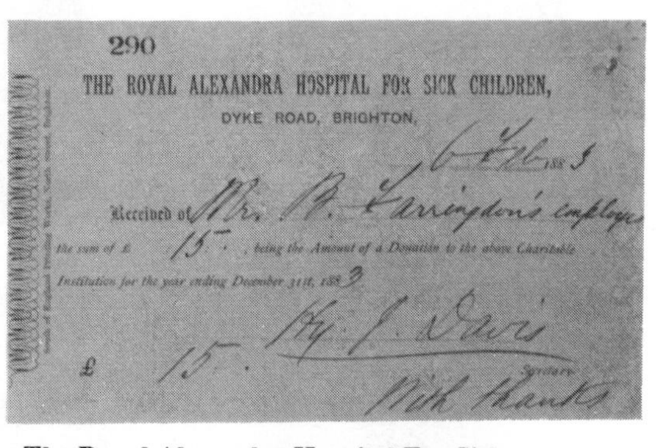

The Royal Alexandra Hospital For Sick Children receipt, February 1885. £1

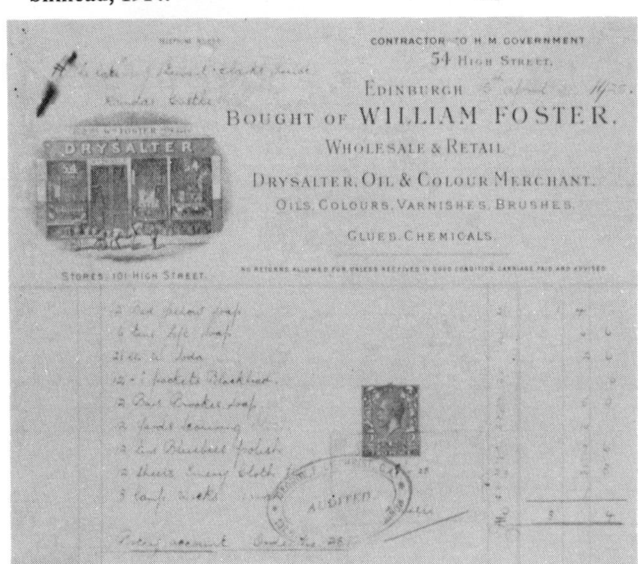

William Foster, Drysalter Oil and Colour Merchant, 1925. £3

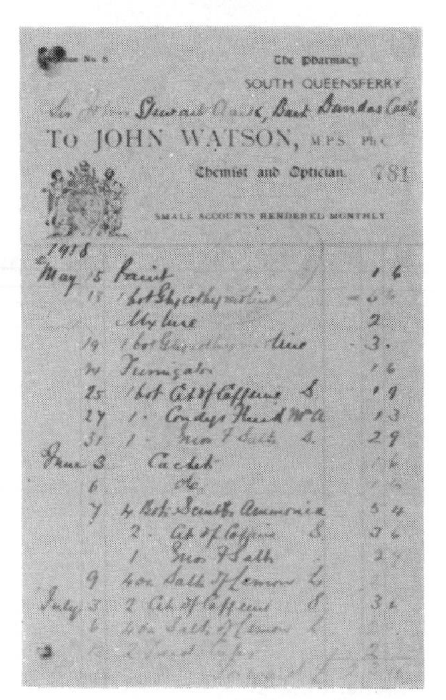

John Watson, Chemist and Optician, billhead, 1918. £2

(Yesterdays Paper)

Bought of HORNER, SON & Co. LIMITED. HOME & EXPORT
MANUFACTURING CLOTHIERS. Goodman Street Leeds

Horner, Son & Co., Leeds, (Manufacturing Clothiers), 1917. £8

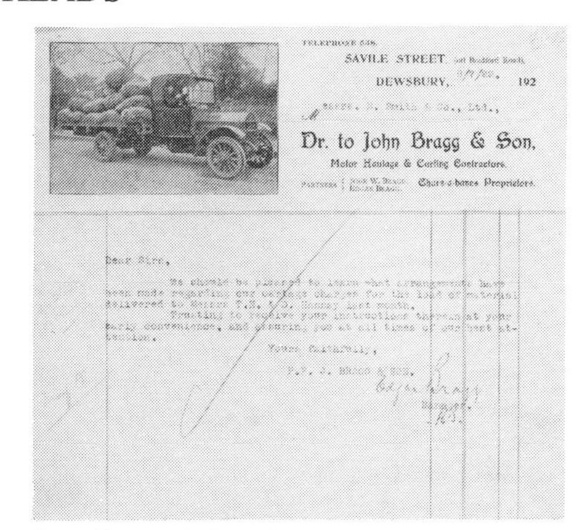
SAVILE STREET, DEWSBURY, 192
Dr. to John Bragg & Son,
Motor Haulage & Carting Contractors.
Chars-a-banc Proprietors.

John Bragg & Son, Dewsbury, (Motor Haulage and Carting Contractors) 1922. £5

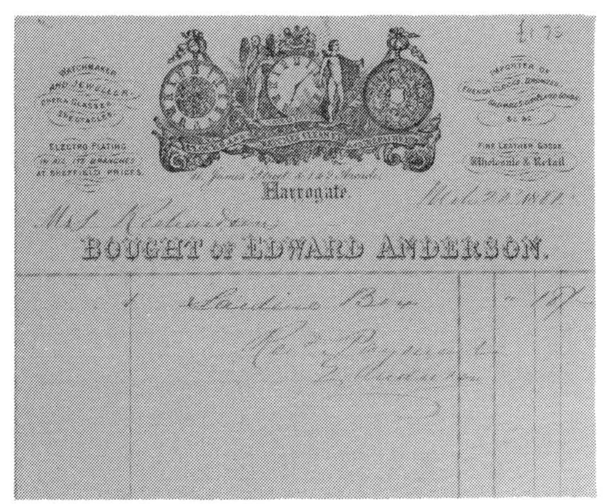
Harrogate.
BOUGHT of EDWARD ANDERSON.

Edward Anderson, Harrogate, (Watchmaker), March 28th, 1880. £4

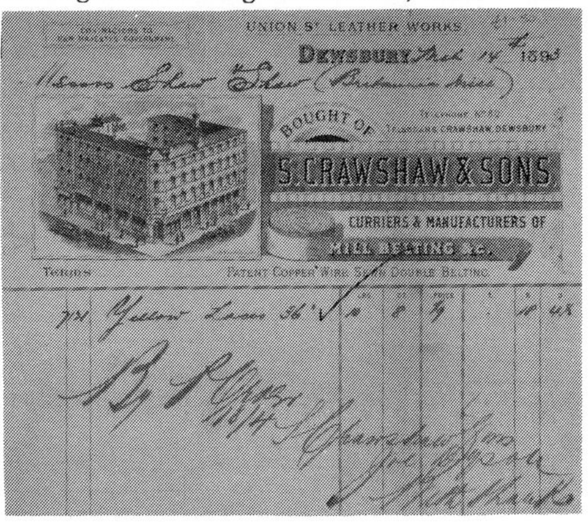
UNION St LEATHER WORKS
DEWSBURY
BOUGHT OF
S. CRAWSHAW & SONS
CURRIERS & MANUFACTURERS OF
MILL BELTING &c.

S. Crawshaw & Sons, Dewsbury, (Carriers), March 14th, 1893. £3

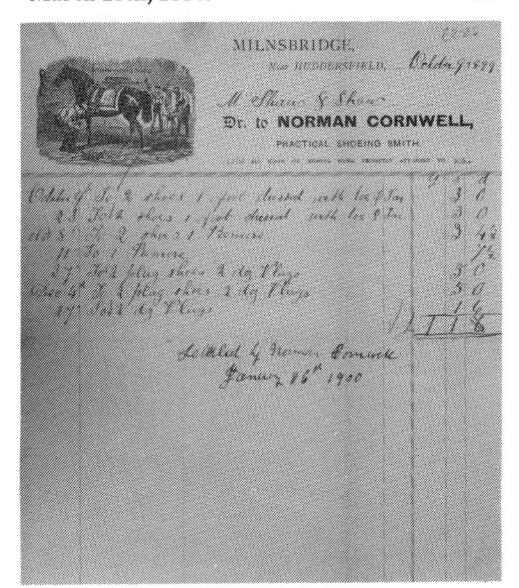
MILNSBRIDGE,
Near HUDDERSFIELD,
Dr. to NORMAN CORNWELL,
PRACTICAL SHOEING SMITH.

Norman Cornwell, Huddersfield, (Shoeing Smith), Oct. 9th, 1899. £5

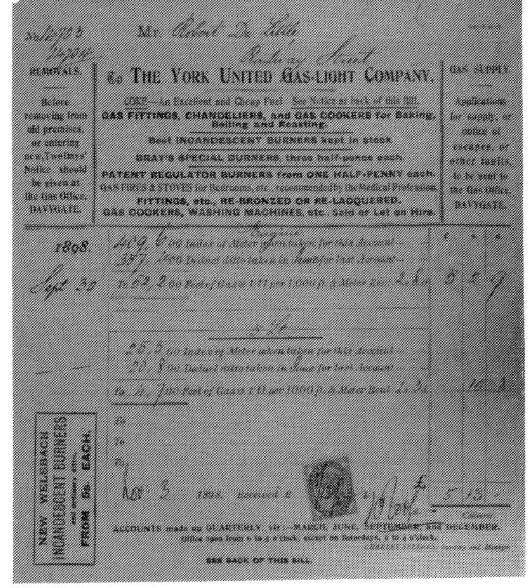
Mr.
To THE YORK UNITED GAS-LIGHT COMPANY.
REMOVALS.
GAS SUPPLY.
COKE—An Excellent and Cheap Fuel
GAS FITTINGS, CHANDELIERS, and GAS COOKERS for Baking, Boiling and Roasting.
Best INCANDESCENT BURNERS kept in stock
BRAY'S SPECIAL BURNERS, three half-pence each.
PATENT REGULATOR BURNERS from ONE HALF-PENNY each.
FITTINGS, etc., RE-BRONZED OR RE-LACQUERED.
GAS COOKERS, WASHING MACHINES, etc. Sold or Let on Hire.
NEW WELSBACH INCANDESCENT BURNERS FROM 5s EACH.
ACCOUNTS made up QUARTERLY, viz:—MARCH, JUNE, SEPTEMBER, and DECEMBER.
SEE BACK OF THIS BILL.

The York United Gas Light Company, Sept. 30th, 1898. £3

(Yesterdays Paper)

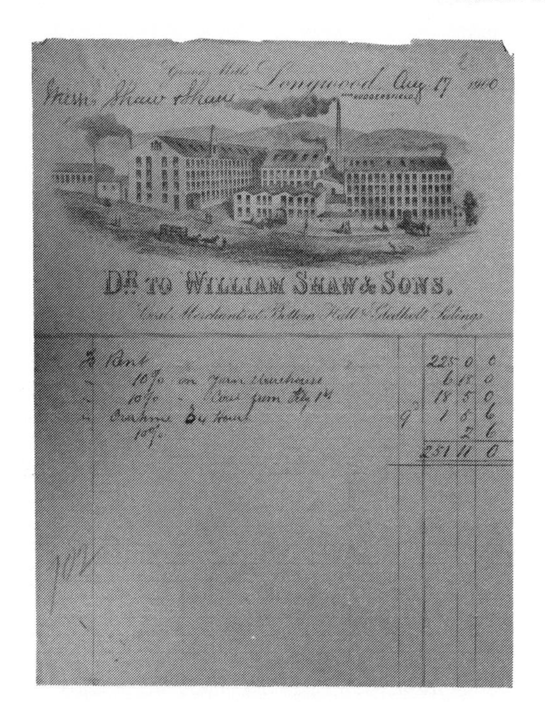
Dr. TO WILLIAM SHAW & SONS,

William Shaw & Sons, Huddersfield, (Coal Merchants), Aug. 17th, 1900. £5

GRAVEL LANE SOUTHWARK, S.E.
LONDON,
BOUGHT OF
Parsons, Fletcher & Co LIMITED
Manufacturers of
PRINTING INKS AND ROLLERS
Varnishes, Dry Colours &c.
Order No.

Parsons Fletcher & Co. Ltd., London, (Printing Inks), June 17th, 1904. £3

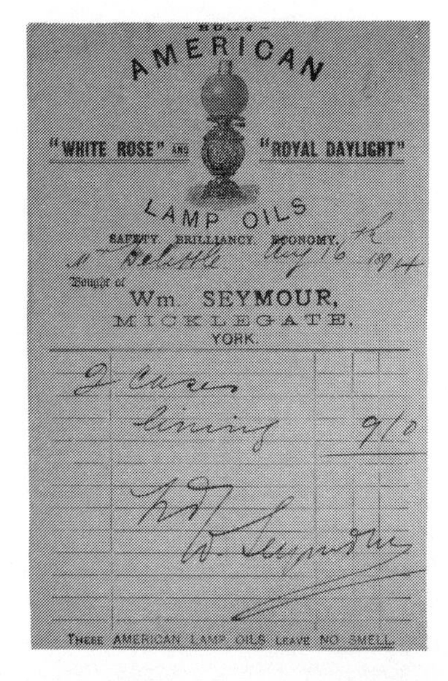
AMERICAN
"WHITE ROSE" AND "ROYAL DAYLIGHT"
LAMP OILS
SAFETY. BRILLIANCY. ECONOMY.
Bought of
Wm. SEYMOUR,
MICKLEGATE,
YORK.
THESE AMERICAN LAMP OILS LEAVE NO SMELL.

Wm. Seymour, York, (Lamps), Aug. 16th, 1894. £2

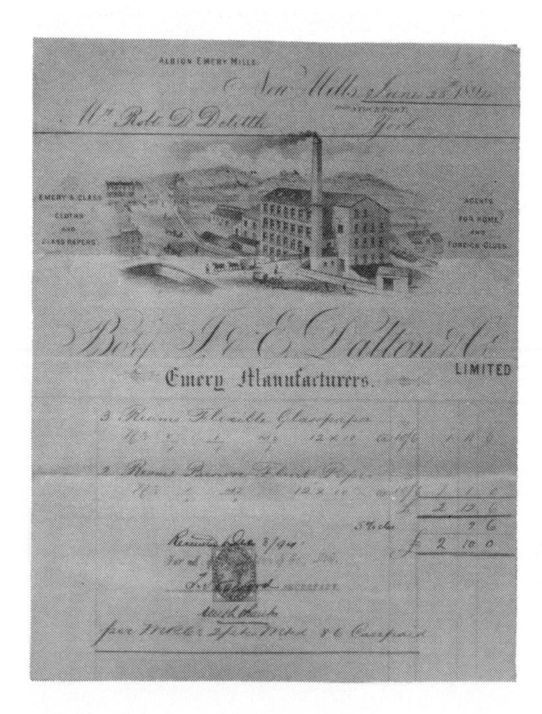
ALBION EMERY MILLS
Emery Manufacturers.
LIMITED

J. & E. Dalton & Co. Ltd., York, (Emery Manufacturers), June 25th, 1894. £6

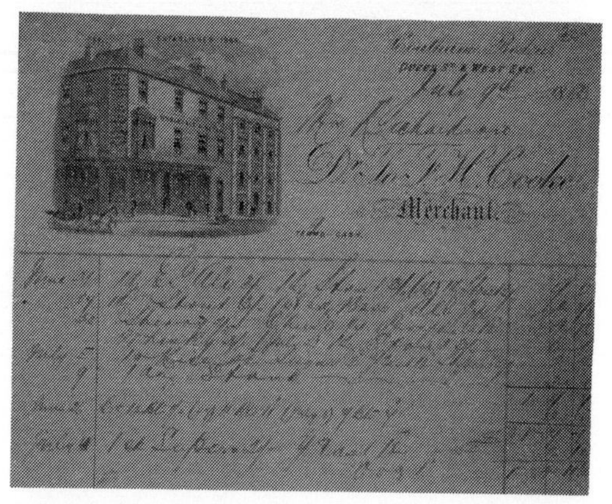
Merchant.

F. H. Cooke, Redcar, (Merchants), July 9th, 1883. £5

(Yesterdays Paper)

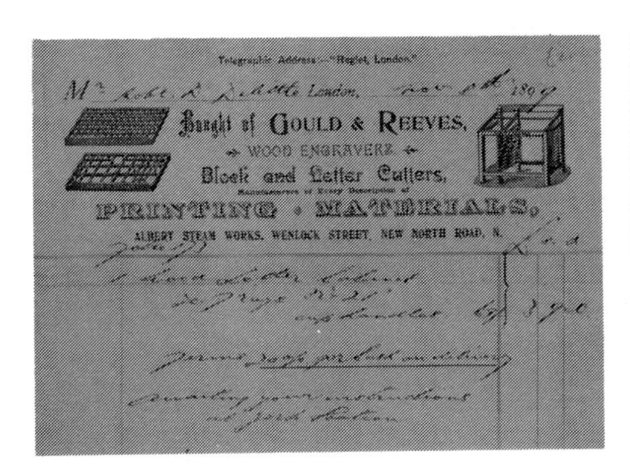

Gould & Reeves, London, (Printing Materials), Nov. 8th, 1899. £4

Pioneer Matches, The Best You'll Ever Strike. £3

Preston Brothers & Co., Huddersfield, (Printers), Oct. 1st, 1896. £5

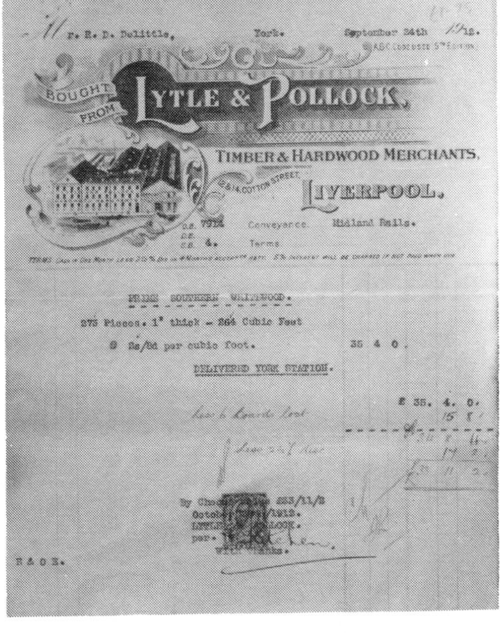

Lytle & Pollock, Liverpool, (Timber Merchants), Sept. 24th, 1912. £3

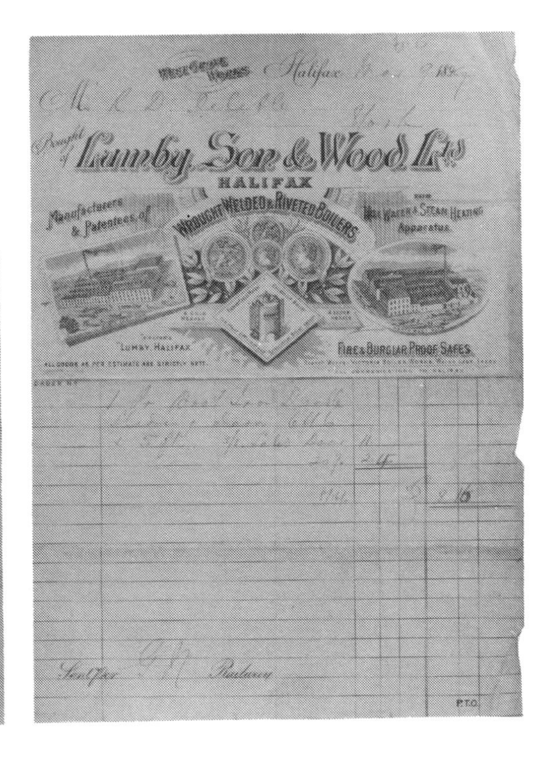

Lumby Son & Wood Ltd., Halifax, (Boilers), March 9th, 1899. £4

(Yesterdays Paper)

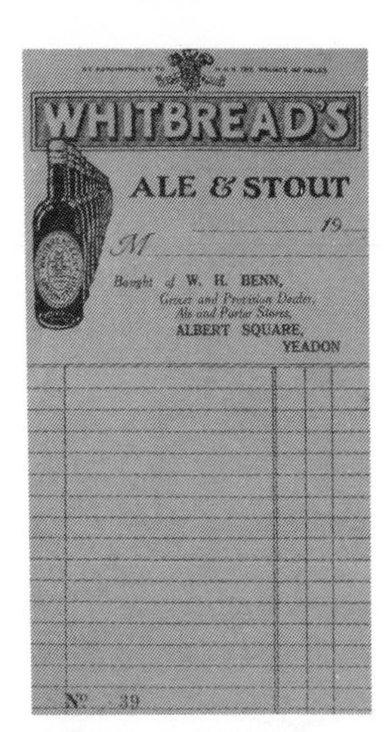

WHITBREAD'S
ALE & STOUT
M 19
Bought of W. H. BENN,
Grocer and Provision Dealer,
Ale and Porter Stores,
ALBERT SQUARE,
YEADON
No. 39

Whitbread's Ale & Stout. £2

THE YORK CABINET WORKS,
YORK
BOUGHT OF ALFRED CHAPMAN.

Alfred Chapman, York, (Cabinet Maker), Nov. 20th, 1890. £6

MOIR'S
IN TINS & GLASSES
FAMOUS SOUPS
SOLD BY ALL GROCERS.
190
JAMES T. LUCAS
Bot of HIGH STREET, CONGLETON.

James T. Lucas, Congleton, (Moir's Soups). £3

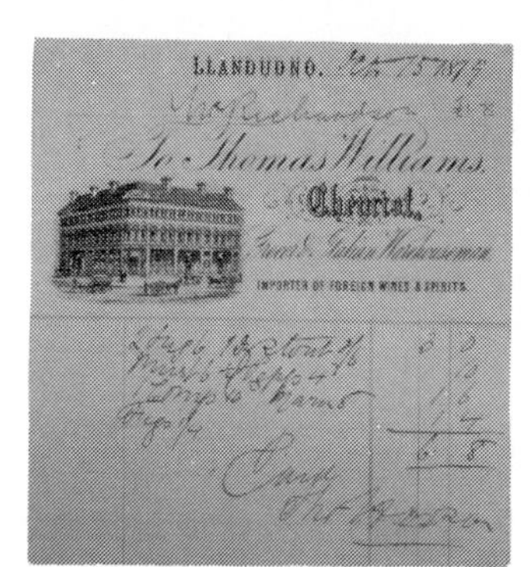

LLANDUDNO.
To Thomas Williams.
Chemist,
IMPORTER OF FOREIGN WINES & SPIRITS.

Thomas Williams, Llandudno, (Chemist), Oct. 15th, 1879. £4

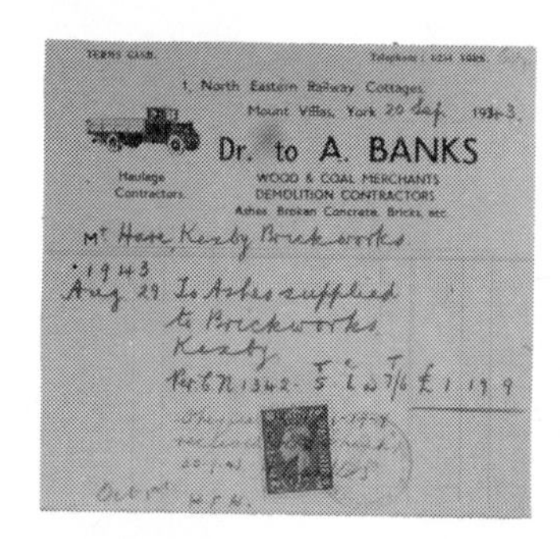

1, North Eastern Railway Cottages
Mount Villas, York
Dr. to A. BANKS
Haulage Contractors.
WOOD & COAL MERCHANTS
DEMOLITION CONTRACTORS
Ashes Broken Concrete Bricks, etc.

A. Banks, York, (Coal Merchants), Sept. 20th, 1943. £2

MILNSBRIDGE,
Nr Huddersfield
Dr. to WILLIAM MATTHEWS,
SKIP AND HAMPER MAKER.

William Matthews, Huddersfield, (Hamper Maker), 14th April, 1892. £2

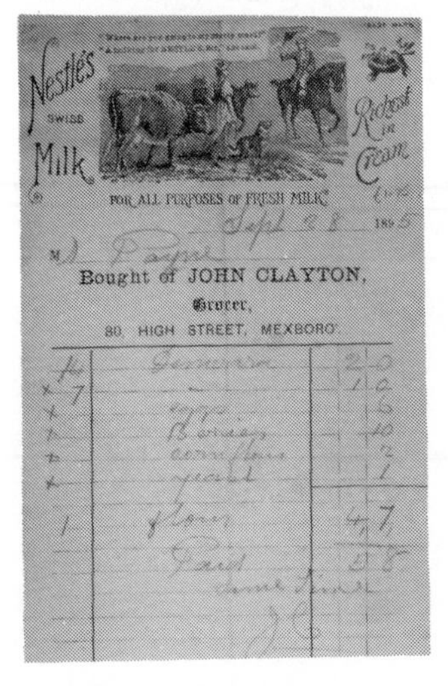

FOR ALL PURPOSES OF FRESH MILK.
1895
Bought of JOHN CLAYTON,
Grocer,
80, HIGH STREET, MEXBORO'

John Clayton, Mexborough, (Nestle's Milk), Sept. 28th, 1895. £5

M 19
Bought of C. & E. DANIEL,
High-class Tobaccos and Confectionery
47 CASTLE STREET,
ABERDEEN
Punch Matches

Punch Match, British Made. £3

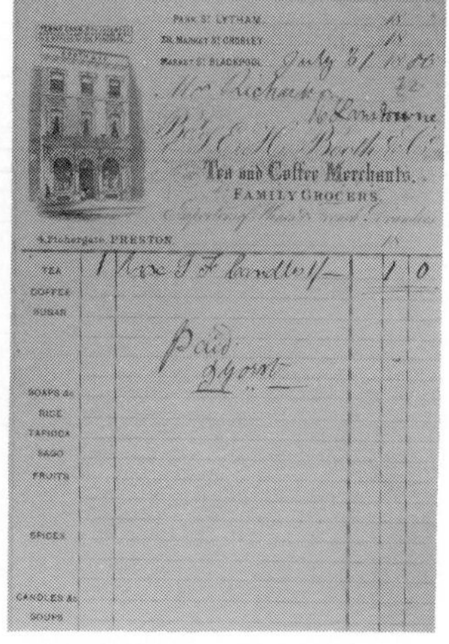

PARK ST LYTHAM
TEA
COFFEE
SUGAR
SOAPS &c
RICE
TAPIOCA
SAGO
FRUITS
SPICES
CANDLES &c
SOUPS
Tea and Coffee Merchants.
FAMILY GROCERS
PRESTON
Paid

E. H. Booth & Co., Preston, (Family Grocers), July 31st, 1886. £4

(Yesterdays Paper)

Lots of Games, Happy Birthday. £4

May You Have Jolly Times. £8

5 Today, Birthday Greetings. 50p

Best Wishes for this Happy Birthday. 50p

To My Sweetheart With Love. £3

Birthday, Many Happy Returns. £3

To My Sweetheart On His Birthday. £1

A Big Wish For A Big Occasion. 50p

Happy Birthday To My Darling. £1

Mickey Mouse Birthday Card, by Valentine, 1930's. £10

My Best Wishes Are With You. £6

Don't Forget, We Are Having A Party. £6

(Yesterdays Paper)

Russia, Riazan-Uralsk Railway Co., 4½% loan, 1893, bond for 5000 roubles, mauve (D/H 1107d), lacks coupons. £120

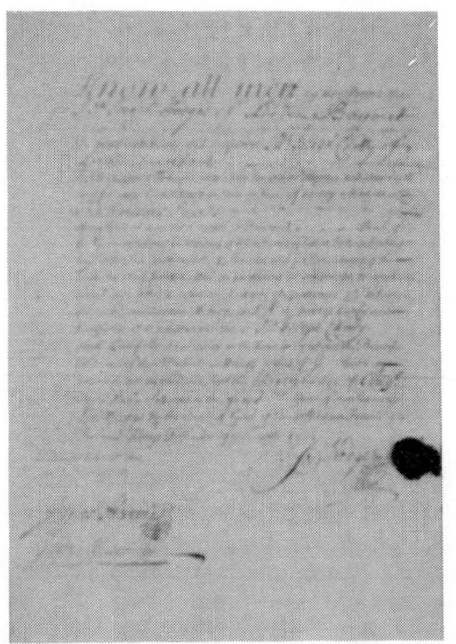

South Sea Company, printed form of power of attorney, 1714, empowering Joseph Chitty, a London Merchant, to deal with stock belonging to Sir Joseph Hodges, Baronet, signed and sealed by Hodges and witnessed by two others, 3 embossed revenue stamps. £600

Chinese Central Government Loan of £300,000 sterling, March 1913 (Arnhold Karberg Loan III) £1,000 bond No. 167, possibly the rarest Chinese bond. (Phillips London) £2,100

Peru, Oroya Railroad and Cerro de Pasco Mining Co. 1878, £100 shares (50 examples). (Phillips London) £420

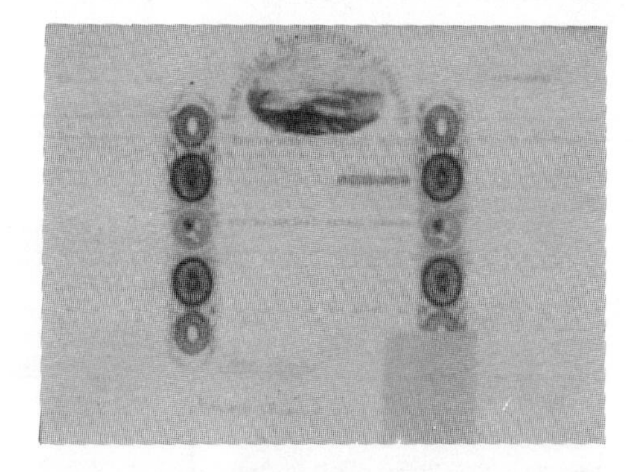

Australian Agricultural Company, incorporated by Royal Charter in 1824, certificate for 5 x £100 shares dated 14th June, 1825. Elegant and decorative piece with a vignette of Sydney Harbour from the Observatory area. (Phillips London) £4,500

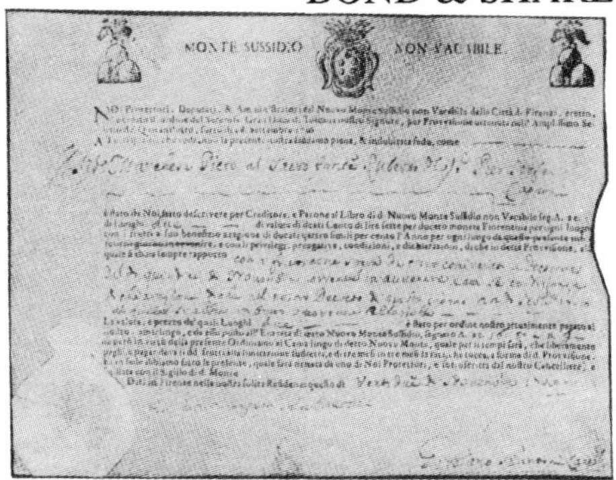

Italy: Monte Sussidio Non Vacabile della Citta di Firenze 22nd November 1700, an interest bearing deposit receipt di Luoghi "Due", paying 4% per annum.
(Phillips) £320

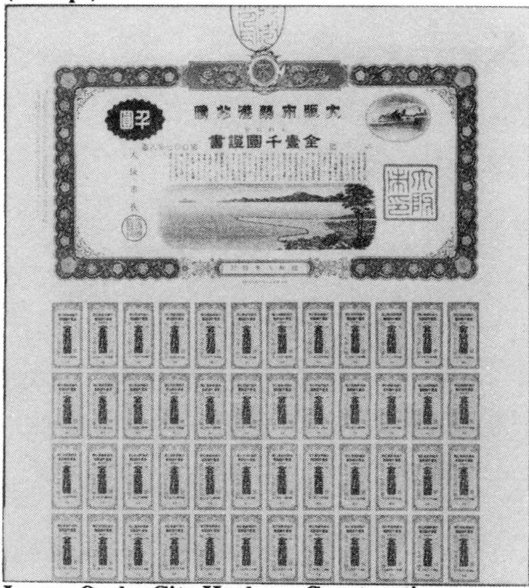

Japan: Osaka City Harbour Construction Loan 6%, 1933. 1,000 Yen bearer bond with coupons, attractive vignettes of Osaka Bay and Castle.
(Phillips) £500

Italy: Monte Della Citta di Firenze 6th July 1752, an interest bearing deposit receipt di Luoghi "Quattro", paying 3% per annum.
(Phillips) £380

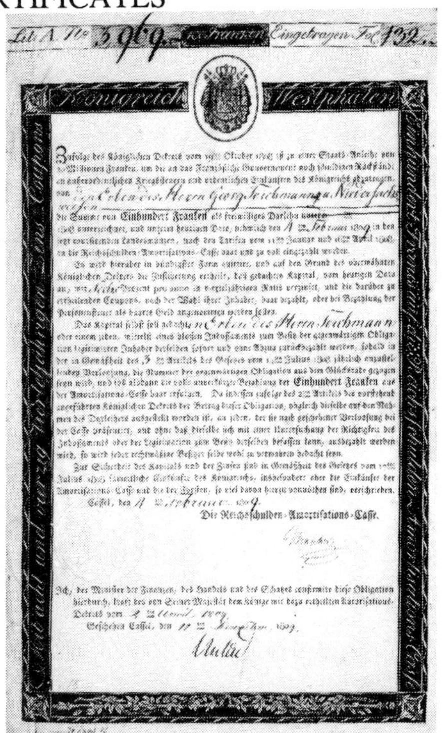

Germany, Kingdom of Westphalia, 1808 Loan, 100 frank bond, dated 1809, ornate border, black, with numerous coupons. £250

Republic of China 6% 2 Year Gold Treasury Notes 1919. $1,000 bond with original coupons and 14 script certificates attached.
(Phillips) £280

Palestine, The Jewish Colonial Trust (Juedische Colonialbank) Ltd. 1900, 1st year of issue, Cert No. 340 for 1 x £1 ordinary share. (Phillips London) £200

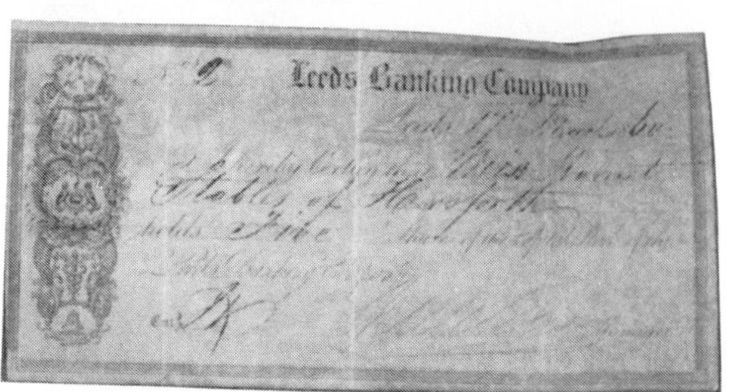

Leeds Banking Co. 18609, Certificate No. 2 for five shares, attractive vignette, on vellum.. (Phillips) £120

Australian Agricultural Company, incorporated by Royal Charter in 1824, Certificate for ten subscribers shares of £100 each dated 1829, trimmed possibly in the 19th century due to change of directors. (Phillips London) £1,700

China: Gold Loan 1908 (Anglo-French) £20, a rare bond, seldom seen in this condition. (Phillips) £580

The Stockton & Darlington Railway Co., 1858, one £25 Class A Preferential share. (Phillips London) £1,250

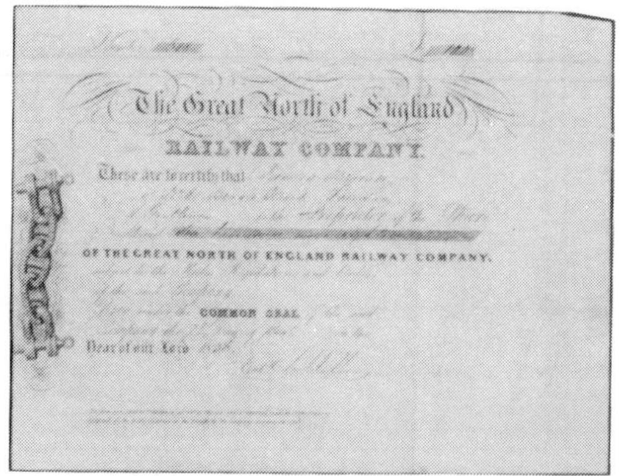

The Great North of England Railway Company 1836, £100 share. (Phillips London) £210

Italy: Monte Redimibile Secondo della Citta di Firenze 14 July 1734, an interest bearing deposit receipt di Luoghi "Ventidue", paying $3^1/_2$% per annum.
(Phillips) £280

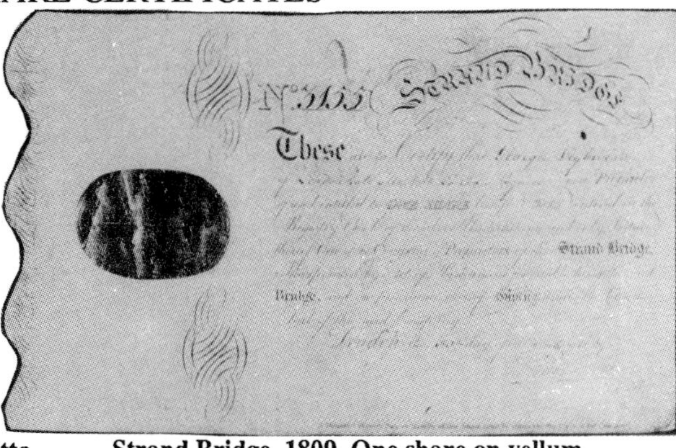

Strand Bridge, 1809. One share on vellum. Large gold embossed seal depicting the bridge.
(Phillips) £370

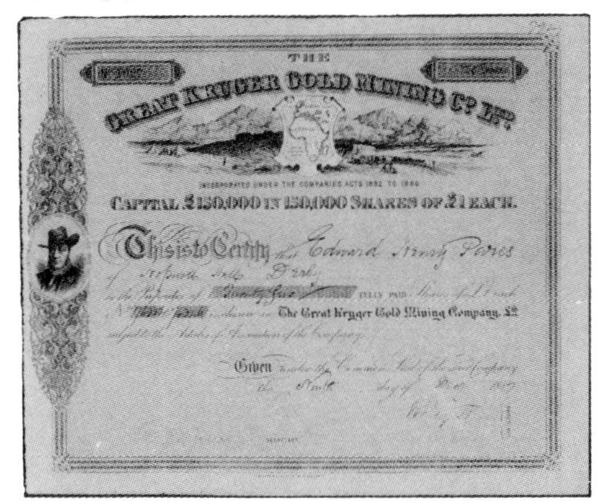

South Africa: The Great Kruger Gold Mining Co. Ltd. 1889. £1 shares, several attractive vignettes.
(Phillips) £200

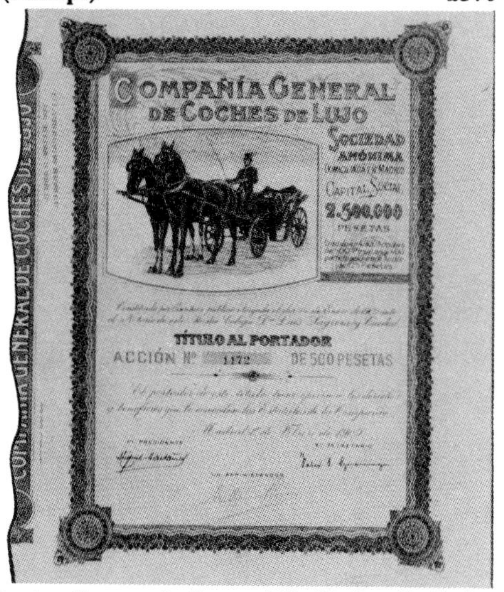

Spain: Compania General De Coches De Lujo. Madrid 1909, bearer share cert. for 1 x 500 Pesetas, large vignette of coach and horses.
(Phillips) £100

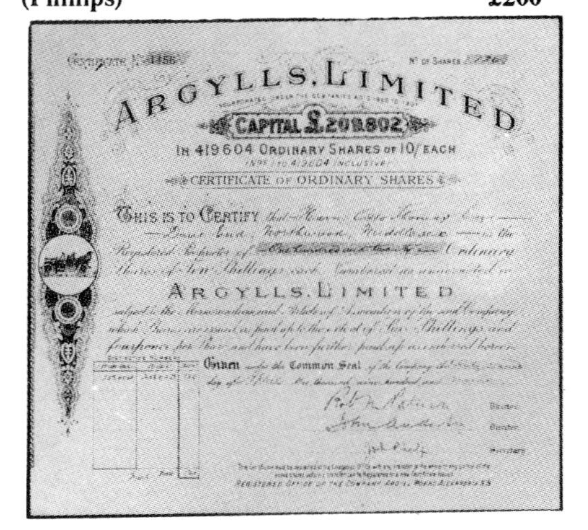

Argylls, Ltd. 1909. Ord. 10/- shares, very early car manufacture, vignette of car of that period, embossed seal depicting the car.
(Phillips) £75

Whitehead Aircraft (1917) Ltd. 1919. Deferred 1/- Ordinary shares. Vignettes of biplanes and busy airfield, also large biplane in R.A.F. markings on underprint. Yellow/black on white. (Phillips) £240

The Currant Recipe Book by Sylvia Wayne. £1

Atora Book of Old Time Christmas Customs, Games and Recipes 1933. £4

The Recipe Book of 'Atora'. £1

Recipes 'pee Tree Salmon'. £1

The Good Neighbour Cookery Book by Jean Conil. £2

Two Hundred War-Time Recipes by Ambrose Heath, 1941. £4

Ideal Milk, a book of recipes by Helen Tress. £2

Rowntree's Recipes , Chocolate and Jelly Dainties. £3

McDougall's Cookery Book. £3

Revo Recipe Book, March 1931. £2

The 'Oxo' Cook Book, 'The mighty Atom'. £6

Good Things to Cook and Eat by Revo. £1

(Yesterdays Paper)

Radiation Recipe Book by Mrs C. S. Peel. £2

Simple Home Cookery by the Check Apron Girl. £5

National Mark Recipes New and Old. £2

Just read what you can make with Creamola. £2

Splits and Parfaits, Walls Ice Cream. £1

Edwardsburg Recipe Book, the Canada Starch Company Ltd. £3

Golden Shred, Some Everyday Dishes. £3

Homepride Cookery Book. £1

60 recipes for flavouring with Lyons Extract. £2

Borwick's Baking Powder, 250 recipes by Elizabeth Craig. £2

Be-Ro Home Recipes. £1

(Yesterdays Paper)

Potato Recipes by Elizabeth Craig. £2

The Northern Assurance Company Limited. £4

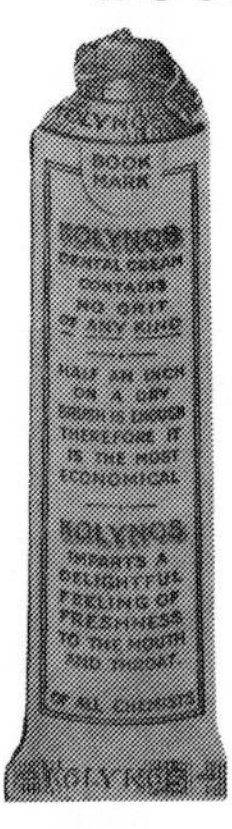

Kolynos Dental Cream. £8

Cherry Blossom Nunnicer. £5

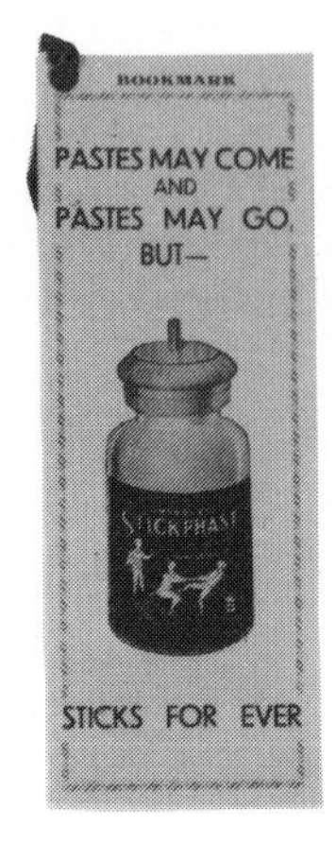

Stickphast, Sticks For Ever. £5

Hall's Distemper, Hull. £2

Lloyd's Weekly News, the Best Family Paper. £8

Theatre Royal, Manchester, Little Women with Katharine Hepburn. £3

St Ivel Cheese, the Pride of the West Countrie. £5

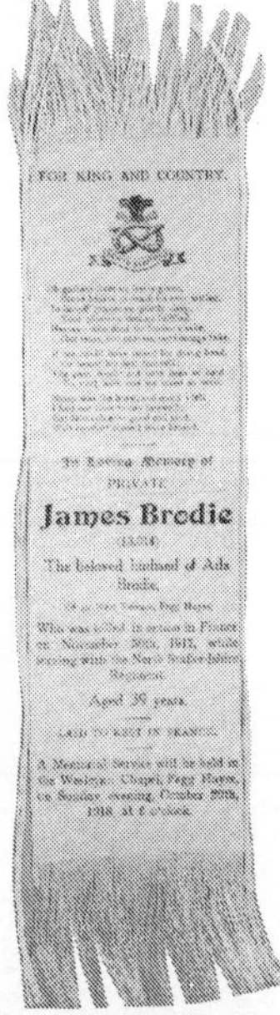

Silk bookmark, 'In loving memory of Private James Brodie', 1918. £8

Fry's Milk Chocolate, Pull up his head. £12

Brown & Polson's Cornflour, nearly 40 years world wide reputation. £6

Maison Lyons Turkish Delight. £8

(Yesterdays Paper)

Hoyts German Cologne bookmark, Lowell, Mass. £6

Cherry Blossom, bookmark, Perfume Toilet Powder and Soap, 1890. £12

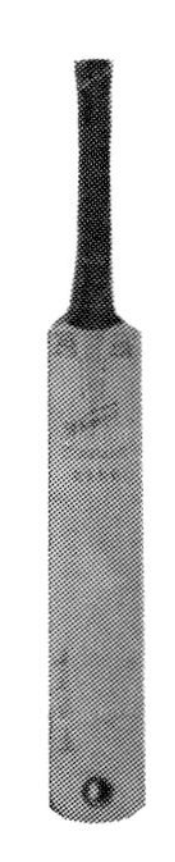

Wisden's Exceller Bat bookmark, from the 1936 Wisden's. £5

Wright's Coal Tar Soap. £5

Hall's Distemper, Hull. £2

Keen's D.S.F. Mustard, 1902. £10

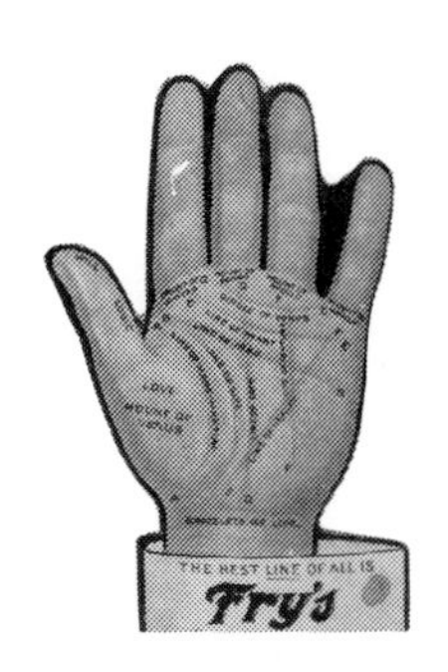

Fry's Cocoa and Chocolates, The Best Line of All is Fry's. £5

The Heritage Policy. £1

Wright's Coal Tar Soap, the seal of health and purity. £6

Kleen-eze Brush Co. Ltd., Royal Silver Jubilee souvenir bookmark, 1935. £3

Sons of the Empire, with compliments Dr Lovelace's Soap. £6

Singer's bookmark with portrait of Lt. Col. R.S.S. Baden-Powell. £10

(Yesterdays Paper)

Unix. £2

Penguin Nature Guides. 75p

Les Gitanes. £3

1879 Book Mark calendar. £4

Pear's Soap, Purity Itself. £10

The Central Hall Picture house, Souvenir of the opening, 23 December 1913. £10

'National Savings will give you a Wider Horizon'. £1

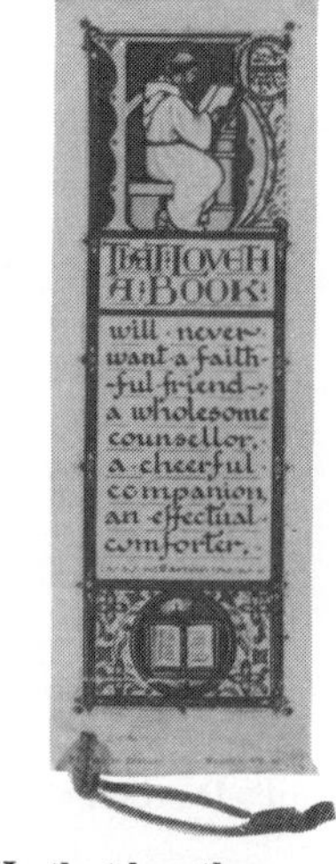

'He that loveth a Book'. £2

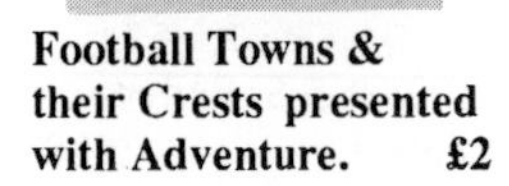

Football Towns & their Crests presented with Adventure. £2

'Consider History'. £2

The Scottish Widows Fund. £1

'There are better ways of getting here', William Pitts cake shop. £1

(Spread Eagle Antiques)

Ex Libris, Cat. £3

This Book Belongs To. £1

Ex Libris 'Pegasus'. £1

Ex Libris. £1

Aluredi Baronis De Braye. £5

Ex Libris 'Monk'. £1

Ex Libris, Water Meadows, Huntington. £3

The New Era Publishing Co. Ltd. £1

Upper Chine School Shanklin. £1

Ex Libris 'Humpty Dumpty'. £1

Pintail, Duck and Drake, Peter Scott. £1

James Gordon Shenton F.G.A. £1

(Yesterdays Paper)

'Superman in the Jungle', 1968, A. & B.C. Chewing Gum Ltd. £20

'Footballer', 1960/61 Season, A. & B.C. Chewing Gum Ltd. £10

'Mars Attacks', 1962, Bubble Inc. £100

'Captain Scarlet', 1968, Anglo Confectionery Ltd. £15

'All Sport', 1954, A. & B.C. Chewing Gum Ltd. £15

'SkyHy', 1954, Parrs, Southern Food Products Ltd. £30

'Land of the Giants', 1969, A. & B.C. Chewing Gum Ltd. £25

'The Beatles' Yellow Submarine', 1968, Anglo Confectionery Ltd. £15

'Space Cards', 1959, A. & B.C. Chewing Gum Ltd. £20

(Mike Johnson)

'Tarzan', 1967, Anglo Confectionery Ltd. £2

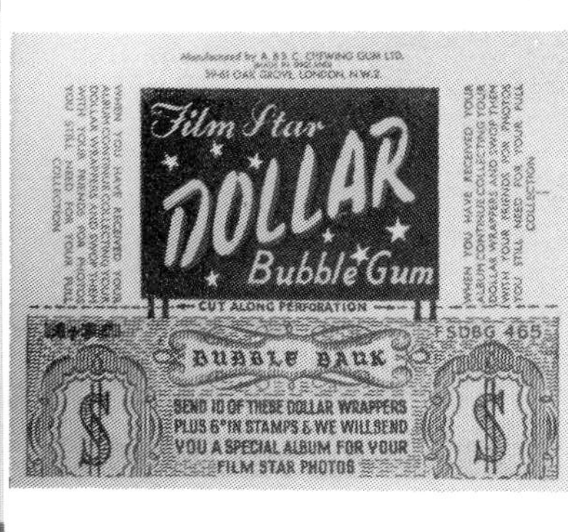

'Dollar', 1953, A. & B.C. Chewing Gum Ltd. £10

'Legend of Custer', 1968, A. & B.C. Chewing Gum Ltd. £15

'Cliff Richard', 1959, Leaf Ltd. £20

'My Chum' (Popeye), 1945, Klene's, Holland, imported. £30

'Monkees', 1967, A. & B.C. Chewing Gum Ltd. £10

'Outer Limits', 1964, Bubble Inc. £25

Cinema, 1955, A. & B.C. Chewing Gum Ltd. £20

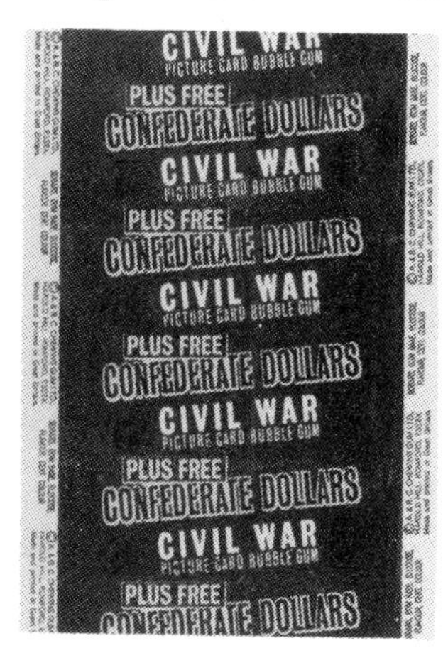

'Civil War News', 1965, A. & B.C. Chewing Gum Ltd. £15

(Mike Johnson)

'A.T.V. Stars', 1961, A. & B.C. Chewing Gum Ltd. £20

'Football', 1954, Chix Confectionery Co. Ltd. £10

Star Trek, Topps Chewing Gum, 1979. £3

'Hocus Pocus', 1955, Wow Productions Ltd. £30

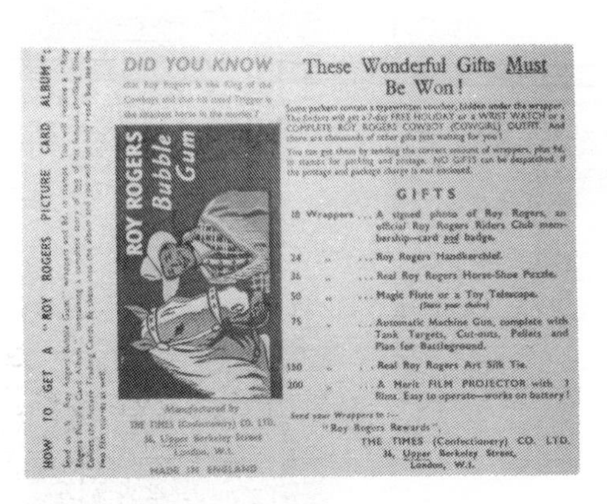

'Roy Rogers;, 1955, Times Confectionery Co. Ltd. £20

Superman, Topps Ireland Ltd, 1978. £2

(Mike Johnson)

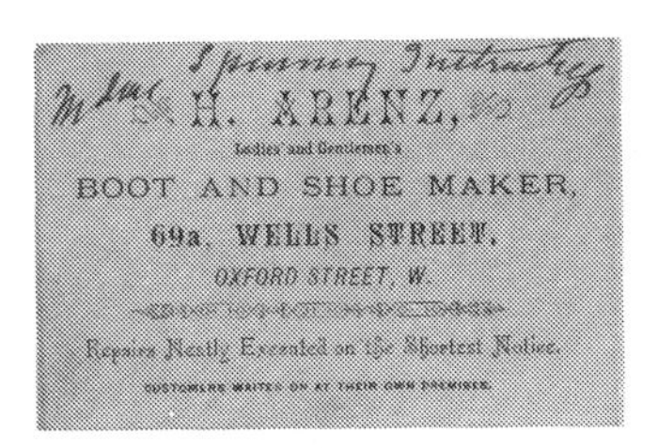

H. Arenz, Boot and Shoe Maker, Oxford Street. £3

Marchant Bros., Drapers, Hyde Park London. £4

Kennedy, Crosby Street, Maryport. £6

H. A. Johannesen, Compass Adjuster, Grimsby. £4

H. French, Baker, Kingston upon Thames, 1855. £3

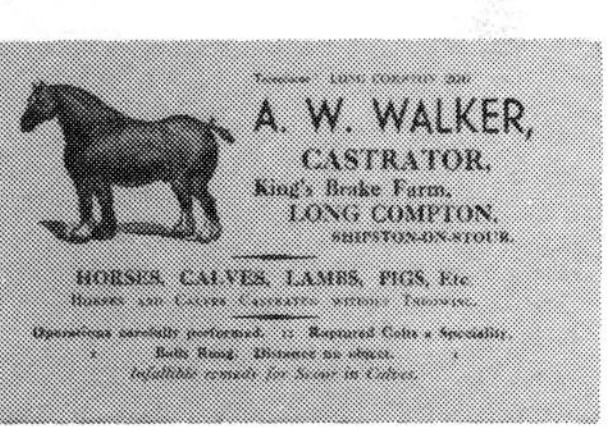

A. W. Walker, Castrator, Shipston-on-Stour. £5

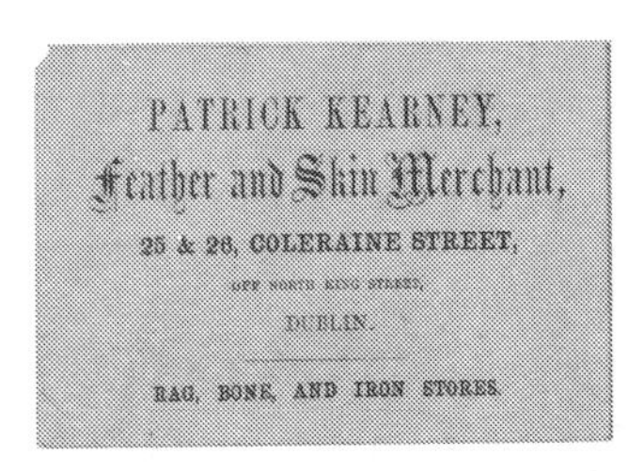

Patrick Kearney, Feather and Skin Merchant. £3

Cohen Bros., Tailor Made Costumes, Skirts, Jackets. £4

Servants' Institute, Glasgow. £3

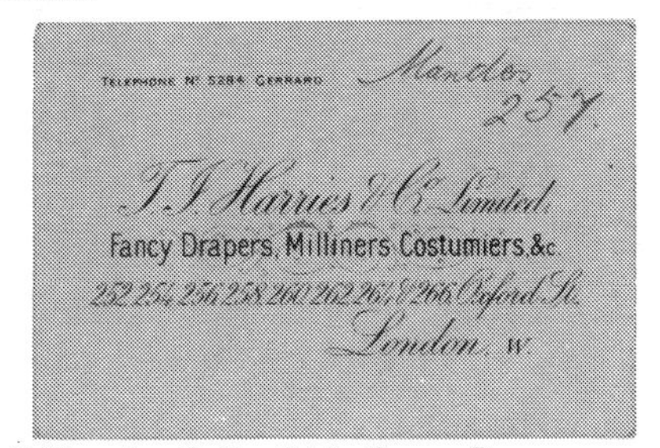

T. J. Harries & Co. Ltd., Fancy Drapers, Milliners, Costumiers. £3

(Yesterdays Paper)

Norman Thelwell calendar, 1982. £3

Plated tin calendar for Charles Lightowler, Hunslet Printing Sheds, Leeds, 1929. £55

1930's novelty calendar, Folks hevn't changed much since the good old days. £8

Tin sign for John Haig's Glenleven Whisky with calendar for 1910, 17" x 13". £130

Ruth in the Field of Boaz, Calendar 1899. £10

W.H. Moss & Sons, Printers, 1933. £4

(Dave Lewis)

Thos. Forman & Sons, Calendar for 1905–05. £3

Die cut Royal Flowers calendar for 1900. £12

D.C.L. Malt Extract & Malt and Oil, 1939. £3

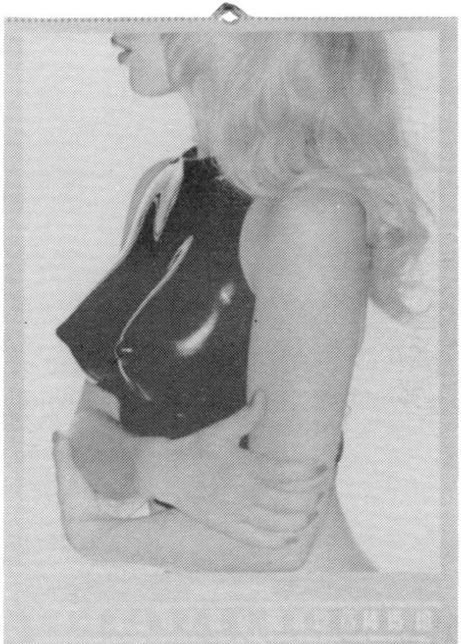

The Pirelli Pin-up Calendar, 1973. £140

Varga Calendar, 1948, with verses by Earl Wilson. £40

Calendar for 1900 by E.P. Dutton & Co., with a moving ship operated with a string. £35

Playboy 'Playmate Calendar', 1978. £7

CHRISTMAS

'May nothing floor your happiness this Christmas', Davidson Bros., London. £3

A Happy Christmas. £3

'To Greet You, with loving Christmas greetings'. £5

Happy Tune record Christmas Card, 'Hark the Herald Angels Sing'. £4

The Seasons Greetings. £7

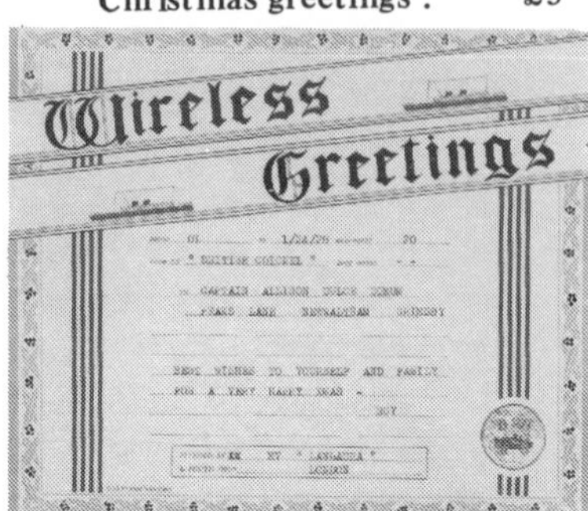

Wireless Greetings, received by M.V. Landaura from London. £5

Conveying Good Wishes, Christmas, 1934. £2

'May your Christmas be Happy'. £7

Loving Christmas Greeting and Best Wishes. £6

Jolly Xmas Crushes and Sweet Xmas Jams. £5

The first Christmas card sent to Henry Cole by William Makepeace Thakeray. (Phillips) £2,500

'Like merry robin redbreasts, we ring our roundelay'. £2

NEW YEAR

A Happy New Year Be Before Thee. £1.50

A Happy New Year. £2

Wishing You A Happy New Year. £1.50

A Bright And Happy New Year. £3.50

A New Year Greeting With Love. £1

The Season's Remembrances. £2

Happiest Wishes. £4.50

To Greet My Little Friend This New Year. £6

A Happy New Year To You. £3.50

Wishing You A Glad New Year. £2

A Bright And Happy New Year. £2

Much Fun And Merriment. £7.50

A fine portrait study of the Duke of Edinburgh. £10

Australian carte de visite portrait study of a man in a bowler hat by A. Lomer and Co., Brisbane. £3

H.R.H. The Prince of Wales, later Edward VII. £10

A fine portrait study of Queen Victoria in the 1890's. £10

Portrait study of a country gentleman, with a typical pictorial reverse back, by M. Boak, Bridlington. £5

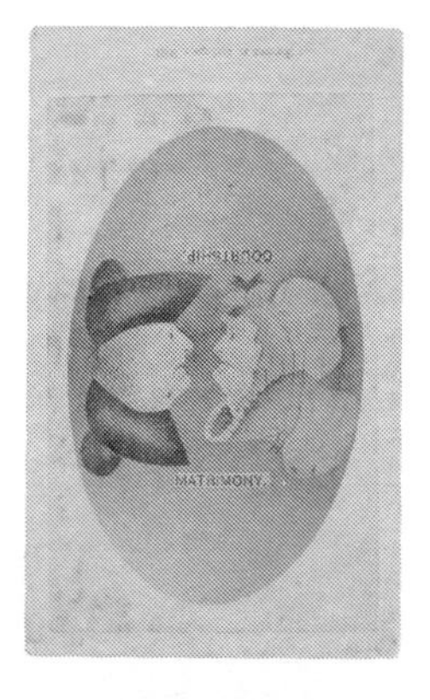

'Fun' type carte de visite of Matrimony and Courtship by Perry and Co., London. £12

Portrait study of a bearded gentleman by W. J. Welsted and Son, 'Photographers of the Prince and Princess of Wales'. £3

Envelope containing two cartes de visite posted from David Rees, Clapham Road, London, Certified Artist and Photographer – Prize Medal Awarded, 1872, bearing penny red stamp. £8

His Grace the Archbishop of Canterbury, Dr Tait, by the London Stereoscopic and Photographic Co. (Prize medal for portraiture Vienna Exhibition 1873.) £10

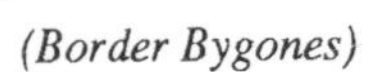

(Border Bygones)

How to Draw Caricatures, by Compton Bennett, 1945. £4

Giles Cartoons, Daily Express, 1946. £50

The Pop Annual, 1930's. £8

Fragments from France, No. 7, by Bruce Bairnsfather, 1918. £8

Bristow, by Frank Dickens, Evening Standard, 1966. £8

Life With Andy Capp, 1959, Daily Mirror. £8

The Pop Annual, 1920's. £10

Drawing Secrets, by Jack Greenall. £6

(Yesterdays Paper)

Romeo Brown, Daily Mirror, 1954. £15

Garth, Daily Mirror, 1976  £8

Andy Capp 'Spring Tonic', Daily Mirror, 1959. £8

Nipper Annual, Daily Mail, 1937. £20

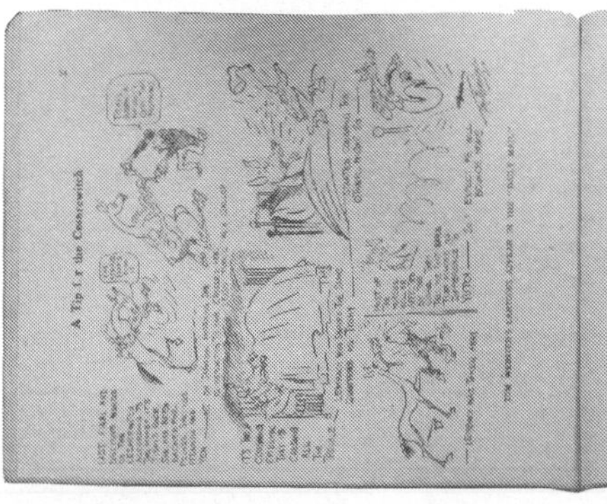

Tom Webster's Annual, Daily Mail, 1922. £15

The Perishers, No. 17, Daily Mirror, 1975. £4

Special War Cartoons, No. 4, Daily Graphic, 1918. £6

(Yesterdays Paper)

The Gambols, No. 1, Daily Express. £25

What a Life by Gilbert Wilkinson, Daily Herald, 1946. £8

Roy Ullyett Cartoon Annual, Daily Express, No. 19. £5

Farewell to Jane, Daily Mirror, 1959. £10

Giles Cartoons, Daily Express, 1947. £50

Fosdyke Saga Six, Daily Mirror, 1977. £5

Tidy's World, 1969. £4

(Yesterdays Paper)

Lloyds Bank Ltd., Tonbridge, unused cheque form dated 1883. £8

Colonial Bank, Kingston, Jamaica, unusual piece dated 1909. £10

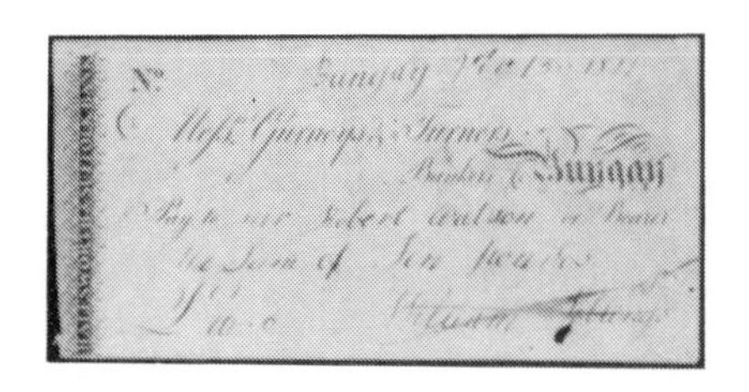

Gurneys & Turners, Bungay, famous banking group which became part of Barclay in 1896. This cheque dated 1811. £20

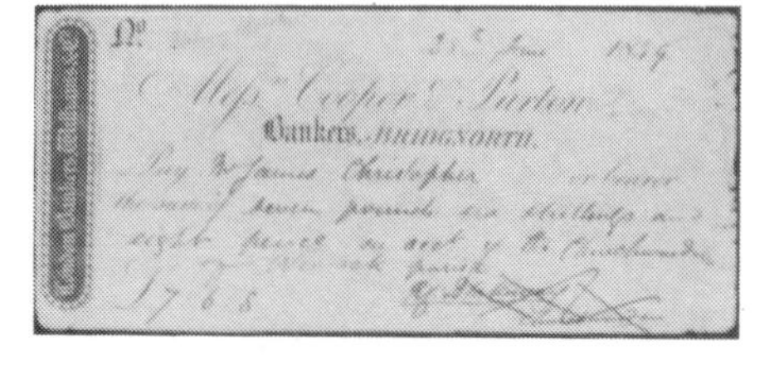

Cooper & Purton, Bridgnorth, 1849, an example of one of the many private banks that failed during the last century. £10

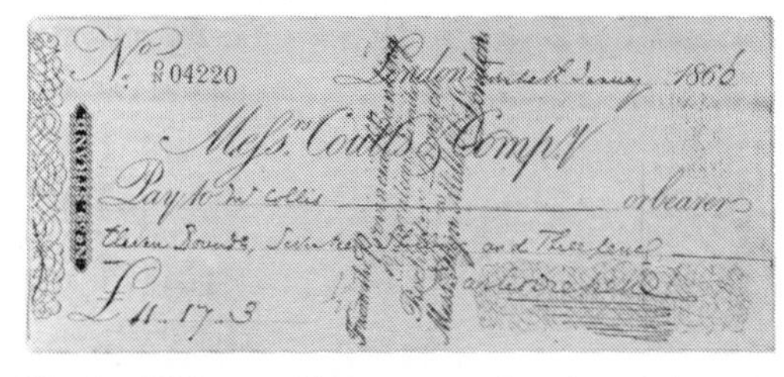

Charles Dickens, Cheque completed and signed, 1866. £350

Central Bank of New Jersey, 1873. £6

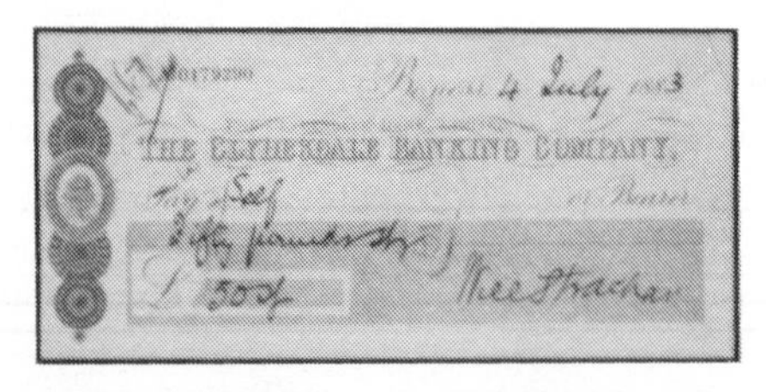

Clydesdale Banking Company, 1883, with overprint of new bank name, Clydesdale Bank Limited, when it was re-registered under Limited liability laws. £8

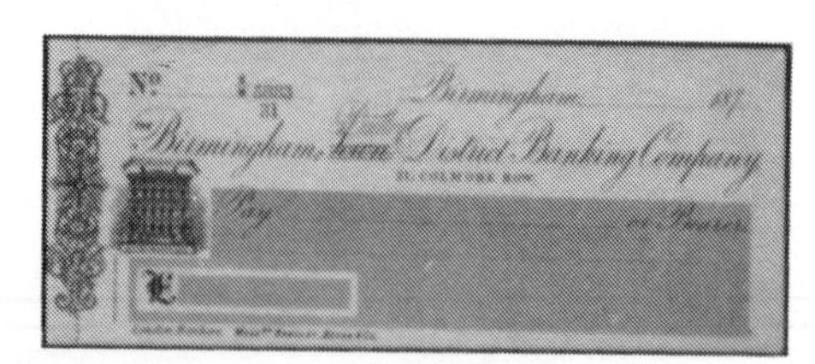

Birmingham, Town & District Banking Company, 1870's, with Town replaced by Dudley on amalgamation with a competitor, this cheque also unusual as it sports a fine vignette of the bank building. £15

First National Bank, Cooperstown, New York, 1895. £5

National Bank of the Republic, private cheque for the New York and New Haven Railroad Co., dated 1865. £10

(M. Veissid & Co.)

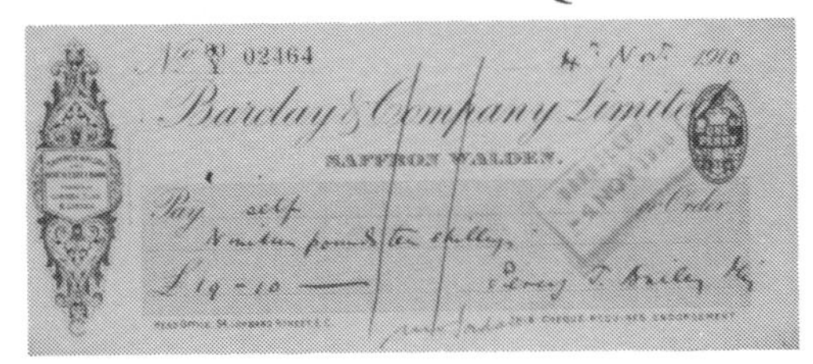

Barclay & Co. Ltd., Saffron Walden, 1910. £3

Bank of Otterville, Missouri, cheque dated 1901. £5

Midland Bank Ltd. , overprinted on London Joint City & Midland Bank Ltd., Brigg, 1924. £3

Messrs. Gosling & Sharpe, now part of Barclays, cheque dated 1831. £10

The Brazil Bank, Indiana, 1873 cheque on this American Bank. £10

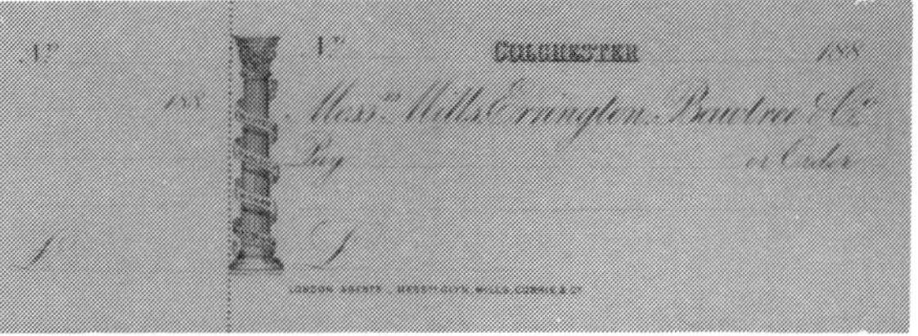

Mills, Errington, Bawtree & Co. , Colchester, unused cheque form dated 1880. £10

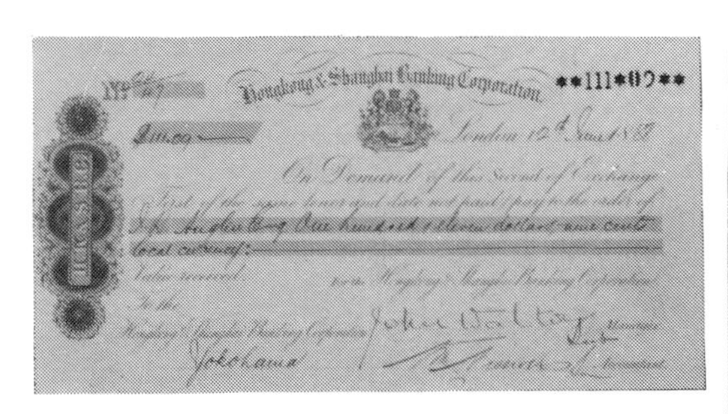

Hongkong & Shanghai Banking Corporation, London, bank draft on the Yokohama branch, 1888. £15

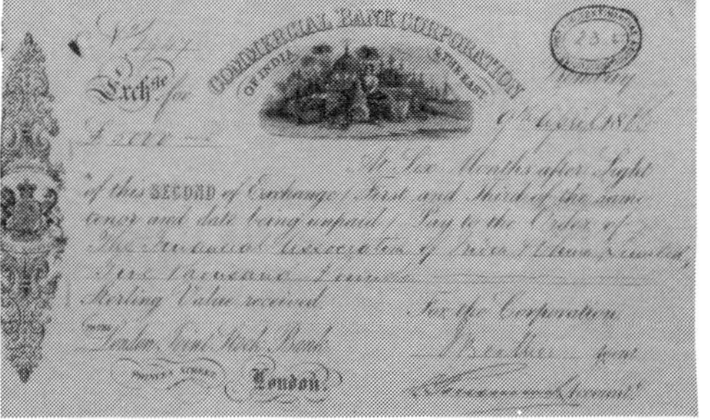

Commercial Bank Corporation of India & The East, draft from Bombay to their correspondents in London, dated 1866. £20

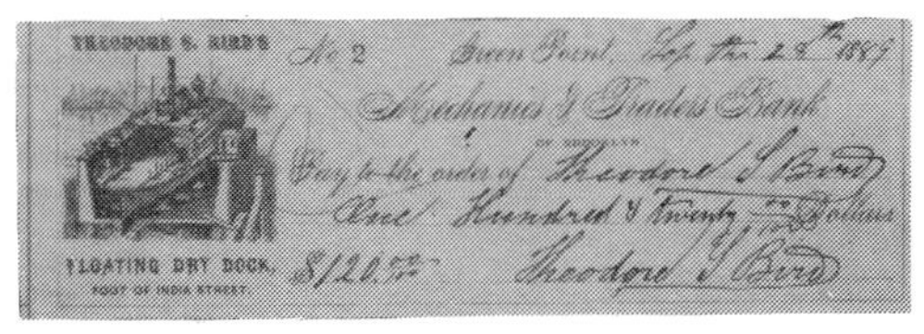

Mechanics & Traders Bank of Brooklyn, privately printed 1889 cheque for Theodore S. Bird's Dry Dock. £10

Blackstone National Bank, Boston, U.S.A., 1875. £6

(M. Veissid & Co.)

Musical Box Annual. £7

Louis Wain's Annual 1908, a paperback annual published by Bemrose & Sons. (Phillips) £110

Nister's Holiday Annual. £25

'PC49' Eagle Strip Cartoon Book 1950. £15

'The Wizard Book For Boys 1938'. £20

'The Tom Merry's Own', 1950. £10

Sunbeam Annual 1933. £12

'Film Fun Annual', 1941. £25

'Archie Andrews Annual 1952'. £8

(Yesterdays Paper)

'More Adventures of Rupert', Daily Express 1947. £45

'Girls' Crystal Annual 1952'. £8

'The Jolly Gnomes Annual', 1951. £15

'The Lone Ranger Annual 1964'. £8

'Tiger Annual 1961', Fleetway Publications. £4

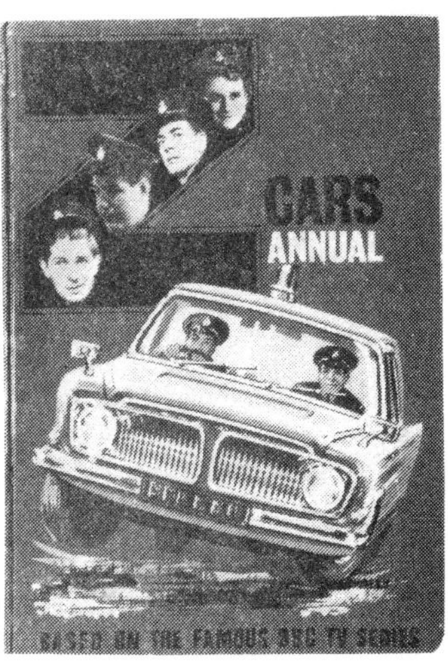

'Z' Cars Annual 1964'. £5

'Radio Fun Annual', 1957. £12

'Rainbow Annual 1957'. £8

'The Beezer Book 1979'. £5

(Yesterdays Paper)

'The Beano Book', D. C. Thompson. £15

'The Dandy Monster Comic', 1948. £30

'The Beano Book', 1968. £10

'Girls' Crystal Annual 1953'. £8

'Mickey Mouse Annual', 1947. £18

The Oojah Annual. £12

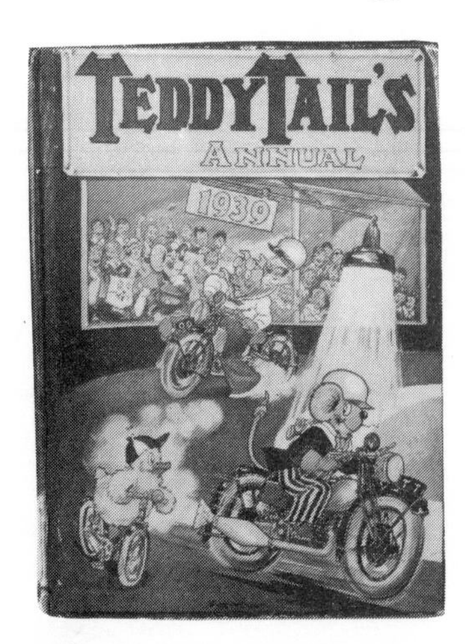

'Teddy Tail's Annual', 1939. £10

'Buck Jones Annual', 1958. £10

Playbox Annual 1918. £25

(Yesterdays Paper)

'The Willie Waddle Book', 1930's. £25

'Eagle Annual Number One', 1952. £20

School Girl's Annual volume 3. £10

'Knockout Fun Book', 1955. £12

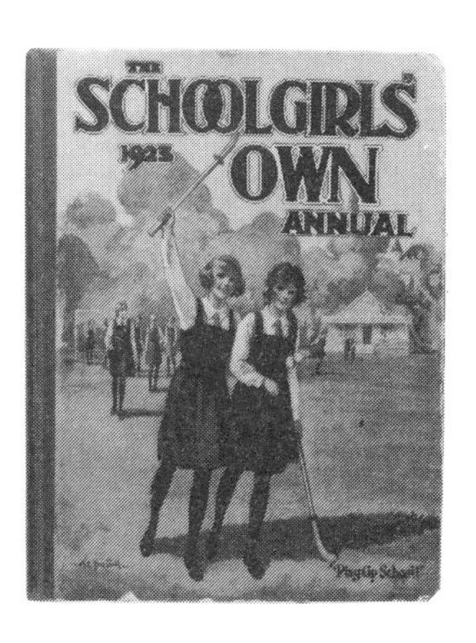

'The Schoolgirls' Own Annual 1923. No. 1'. £15

'News and Chronicle Boys' & Girls' Annual', by Enid Blyton. £10

Pip and Squeak Annual 1931. £30

'The Companion Annual', 1924. £10

'Lucie Attwell's Annual.' £10

(Yesterdays Paper)

'Girl Annual Number 8', 1960. £8

Wilfred's Annual 1930. £25

'Mickey Mouse Annual 1944'. £25

'The Book of Blue Peter 1965'. £12

'The Girl's Own Annual 1934'. £20

(Yesterdays Paper)

'Chatterbox 1914', Wells, Gardner, Barton & Co. Ltd. £10

Rainbow Annual 1924. £15

'The Greyfriars Holiday Annual 1929'. £20

'Emergency Ward 10' Girls' Annual'. £5

'Daily Mirror 'Jimpy' Annual 1952'. £18

(Yesterdays Paper)

Child's Companion Annual
1934. £10

Cassell's Children's Annual
1920 – illustrations include
Anne Anderson, Harry Rountree and C. E. Brock. £15

Hotspur Book for Boys 1937.
£12

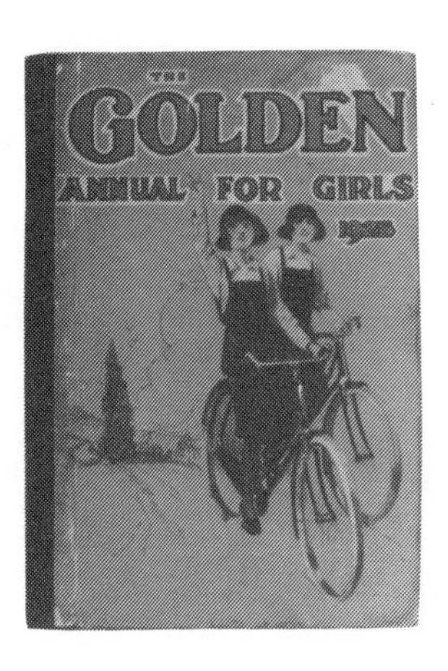

Golden Annual for Girls
1925. £12

'Swift Annual', 1962. £4

Blackie's Girls' Annual
1930. £7

Madge Williams Children's
Annual. £7

Blackie's Children's Annual
1922 – illustrations include
Honor Appleton, H. M. Brock,
Ruth Cobb, A. E. Jackson.
£15

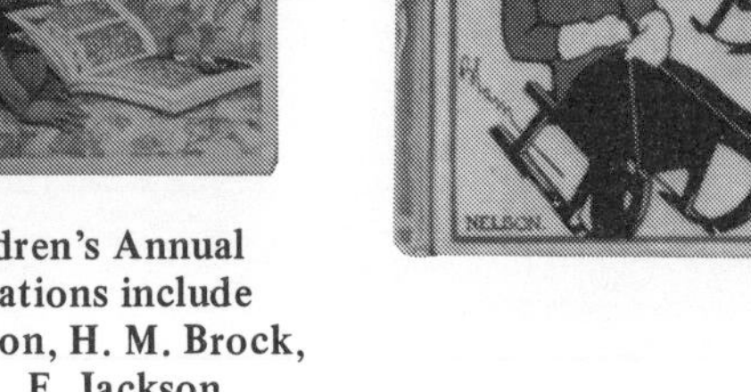

The Jolly Book 1919. £15

(Yesterdays Paper)

Teddy Tail's Annual 1937. £12

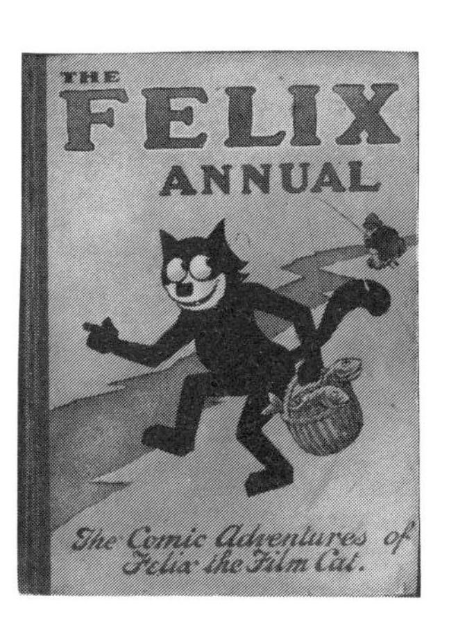

'The Felix Annual', 1930's. £12

My Favourite Annual 1933. £15

Greyfriars Holiday Annual 1921. £30

Chums Volume 1, 1892. £40

Noah's Ark Annual 1935. £8

Chatterbox 1907. £12

Bubbles, Volume 7. £25

'Okay Adventure Annual', Boardman & Co. £12

(Yesterdays Paper)

Make Believe Story Book 1924. £20

Sunbeam's Picture Book 1926. £5

Nelson's Chummy Book 1933. £14

Modern Boy's Book of True Adventure. £10

Adventure Land 1938. £12

Book of Great Adventurers. £8

Mrs Strang's Annual for Children 1914. £20

The Prize for Boys and Girls Volume 66. £7

Children's Stories from the Poets 1940 – ill. Frank Adams. £12

(*Yesterdays Paper*)

Lawson Wood's Merry Monkeys. £12

Master Charlie 1899. £15

Pets and Playmates. £12

Lawson Wood Nursery Rhyme Book. £12

The Bunty Book – published by G. Heath Robinson & J. Birch Ltd. Illustrations include Louis Wain and Gordon Browne. £25

'Jill the Reckless', Eighth Printing, 1928. £5

Blackie's Granny's Old Stories – ill. Hassall 1939. £15

Boys Illustrated Book of the War 1917. £8

Cicely Mary Barker's Flower Fairy Picture Book. 40 illustrations. £8

(Yesterdays Paper)

'Under Wellington's Command', by G.A. Henty, 1907. £6

Gulliver's Travels – ill. John Hassall. £15

'Robinson Crusoe', Nister Publications, circa 1900. £20

'Treasure Hunt', Puzzle Book, circa 1940. £8

'Railways For All', 1950's, Painting Book. £8

(Yesterdays Paper)

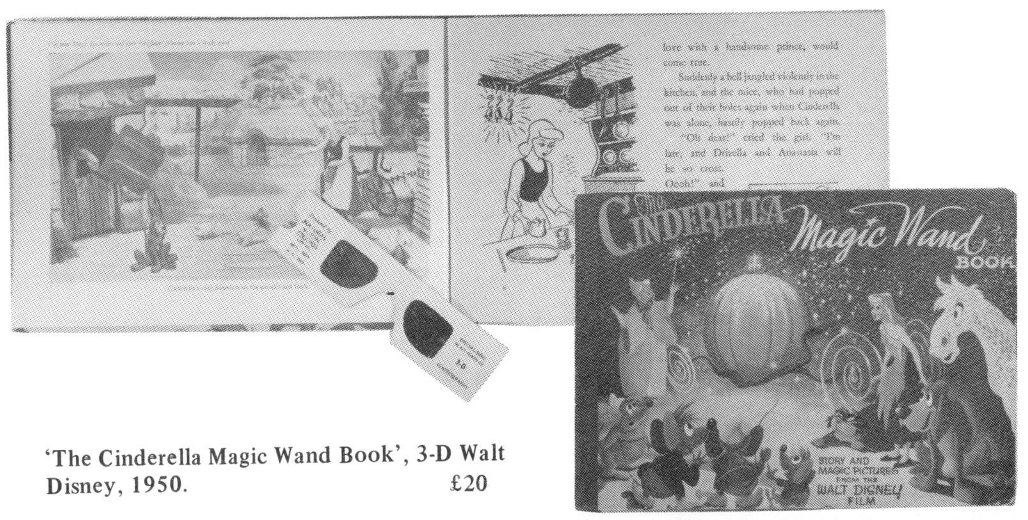

'The Cinderella Magic Wand Book', 3-D Walt Disney, 1950. £20

Grand Jubilee Volume of Little Folks 1921. £10

'The Birds' Alphabet', 1946. £10

'Our Darlings', circa 1910. £20

(Yesterdays Paper)

'Boys Who Became Famous', by F.J. Snell, 1924. £5

'Rosy Cheeks', Nister Untearable. £20

'The Arabian Nights', Hodder & Stoughton, 1949. £30

'Andersen's Fairy Tales', Anne Anderson Illustrations, 1930's. £12

'Teddy Tail of the Daily Mail', £12

'The Alphabet Book', 1880's. £30

(Yesterdays Paper)

'Dan Dare's 'Anastasia' Jet Plane', by Wallis Rigby. £35

'Billy Bunter's Treasure Hunt', 1961, 1st Edition. £10

'The Animal ABC', Deans Diploma Series No. 28. £15

'The Big Book for Girls', 1927. £8

'Walt Disney's Pinocchio', 1940. £20

(Yesterdays Paper)

'The Mystery of the Spiteful Letters', Enid Blyton, 1949. £6

'Horace and the B.B.C.', by Harry Hemsley. £20

'The Quest for the Perfect Planet', W. E. Johns, 1961. £8

'The Book of Soldiers', E. P. Dutton & Co. £20

'Run-Away Dick', by Harry Eliott, 1936. £12

'Some Farm Friends', circa 1900. £20

'Little Wide Awake 1890'. £35

'Merry Hearts 1896'. £45

(Yesterdays Paper)

'Bunter Keeps It Dark', 1960, 1st Edition. £10

'Noah's Ark', Peepshow Book, by Nancy Spain. £8

'The Adventures of Larry the Lamb', 1940's. £10

'Under One Flag', Tuck, circa 1900. £8

'The House That Jack Built', George Routledge & Sons. £35

'With Joffre At Verdun', by Captain Brereton, 1st Edition. £10

Infants Magazine 1903. £12

(Yesterdays Paper)

'The Young Fur Traders', by R.M. Ballantyne. £5

'Roy Rogers', Adprint Ltd., 1952. £5

Tiny Tot's Picture Book 1934 – 80 pages of pictures including Rountree, Beaman and Gordon Robinson. £15

'Blown to Bits', by R. M. Ballantyne, 1889. £5

Peter Pan and Wendy – illustrated by Mabel Lucie Attwell. £30

'Diamond Dick', The Boys Best Weekly, 1900. £8

Water Babies 1938 – illustrated by Jessie Wilcox Smith. £35

'The Splendid Savage', by Conrad H. Sayce. £5

Treasure Island 1929 – illustrated by Rowland Hilder. £15

Peggy and Joan – illustrated by Honor Appleton. £12

(Yesterdays Paper)

The Magic Doorway. £15

Peek-a-Boo Japs – ill. Chloe Preston 1916. £20

'Billy Bunter's Own'. £8

Arabian Nights – illustrated by A. E. Jackson. £25

Big Book of Mother Goose, has revolving disk of hunt scene in cover. £18

'Mrs Tickler's Caravan', Cecil Aldin, 1931. £20

My Book of Ships 1913. £10

Les Vacances de Nane 1924. – ill. Henry Morin. £8

Armchair Story Book 1937. £12

(Yesterdays Paper)

'The Master Book of Magic', by J.C. Cannell, 1935. £8

'Ethel Graham's Victory', by Mrs H.B. Paul, 1882. £5

'The Dandy's Desperate Dan', 1954. £20

'The Children's Encyclopedia', by Arthur Mee, Set of Ten. £20

'Oscar Danby, V.C. ', by Rowland Walker. £5

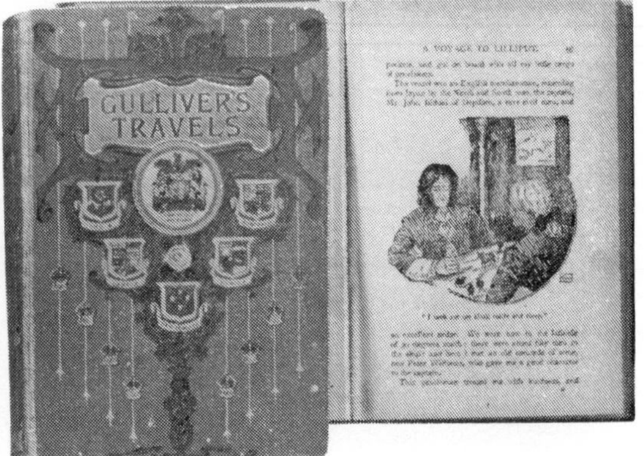

'Gulliver's Travels', Illustrations by R.R. Russell. £5

(Yesterdays Paper)

The Children's Treasury.
£5

'Little Frolic', 1930's. £15

'The Children's Hour', Lilian Rowles. £8

'The Blue Muffin Book', 1951. £10

'The Topper Book', 1958. £10

(Yesterdays Paper)

Hans Anderson's Fairy Tales – ill. Harry Clarke. **£5**

'Joey the Clown and his dog Spot', by P. A. Purton. **£8**

'Both Sides the Border', G.A. Henty, 1922. **£5**

'The Big Book Of Shops', fold-over book, 1930's. **£35**

'Honours for Heroes', Tuck Painting Book. £8

'Teddy Tar and the Gipsies', circa 1960. **£3**

(Yesterdays Paper)

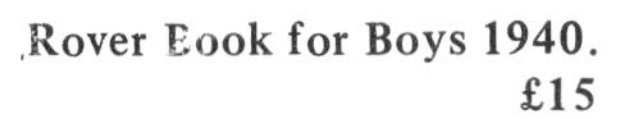

Rover Book for Boys 1940. £15

'The Little Ebony Elephant', by Fitz. £8

'Biggles Works It Out', Hodder & Stoughton, 1952. £4

'Dan Dare's Spacebook', 1953. £30

'Tintin Destination Moon', 1959. £10

'Nursery Fun', Dean's Picture Book. £3

'Sunny Sammy Smiler', circa 1910. £20

(Yesterdays Paper)

'The Ship of Adventure', Enid Blyton, 1st Edition, 1950. £18

'Children's Outdoor Games', by G. B. Crozier, 1910. £12

'Alice in Wonderland', Pears Illustrations. £8

'The Mickey Mouse Fire Brigade, 1936'. £40

'From Many Lands, America', Father Tuck Series, 1904. £25

'Ameliaranne and the Green Umbrella', 1939. £18

'ABC for Little Willie', Daily News Ltd. £10

'The Brave Little Tailor', 1923. £15

(Yesterdays Paper)

The Broadway Book of Railways of the World. £3

Beezer Broadway Book, All About the Circus. £3

The Beezer Broadway Books, The World's Railway Engines of every kind. £5

Hotspur Handy Books No. 10 the World's Lost Cities. £5

Adventure Vest Pocket Library No. 2 Black Morgan's Island. £5

Adventure Vest Pocket Library No. 3 Erik the Viking. £5

The Circus Tenderfoot No. 1 The Big Vest Pocket Storybooks, 1926. £10

The Big Vest Pocket Book No. 2, The Skyway School, 1926. £10

Gold Star Broadway Book, What Every Boy Should Know. £3

The Diana Book of Singing and Dancing, No. 32, 28 September 1963. £3

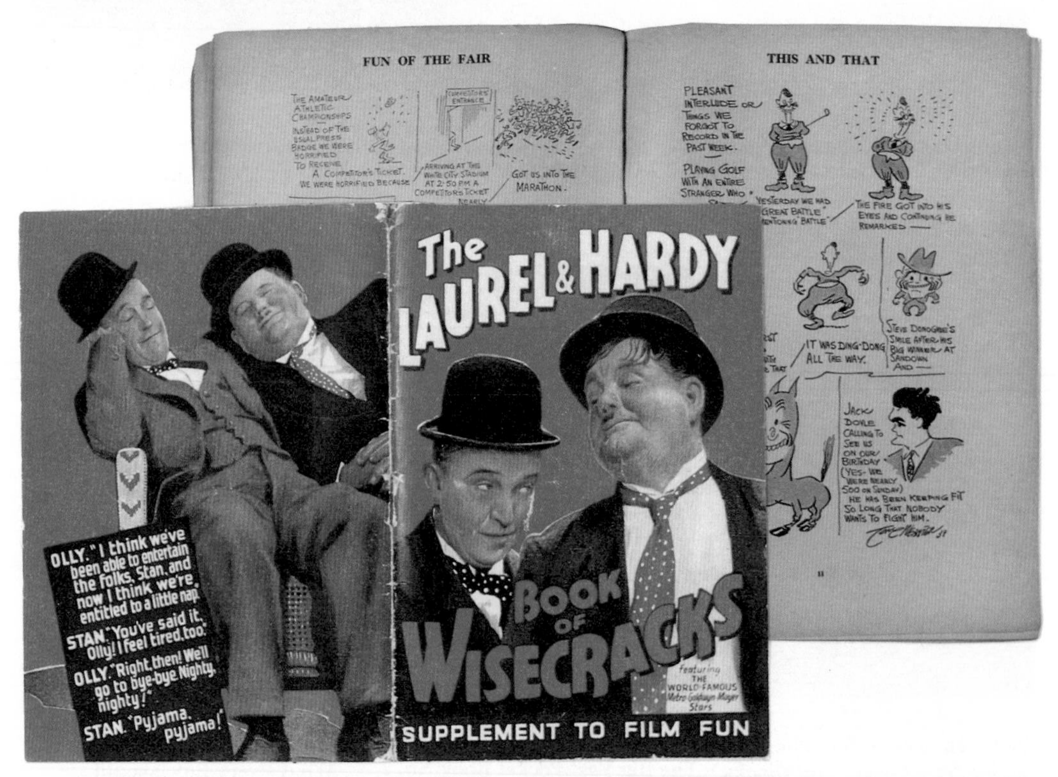

The Laurel and Hardy Book of Wisecracks, a free gift with Film Fun Comic, 1936. £200

(Denis Gifford)

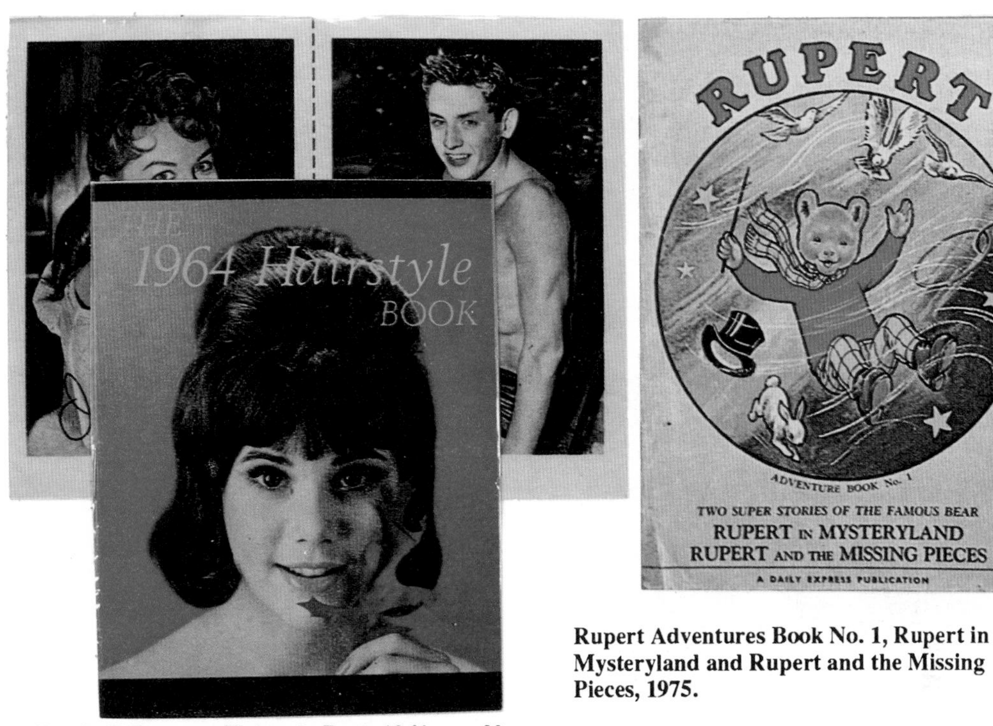

The D C Thomson Hairstyle Book 1964. £3

Rupert Adventures Book No. 1, Rupert in Mysteryland and Rupert and the Missing Pieces, 1975. £3

The Charlie Chaplin Fun Book, 1915, first Chaplin book. £100

(Denis Gifford)

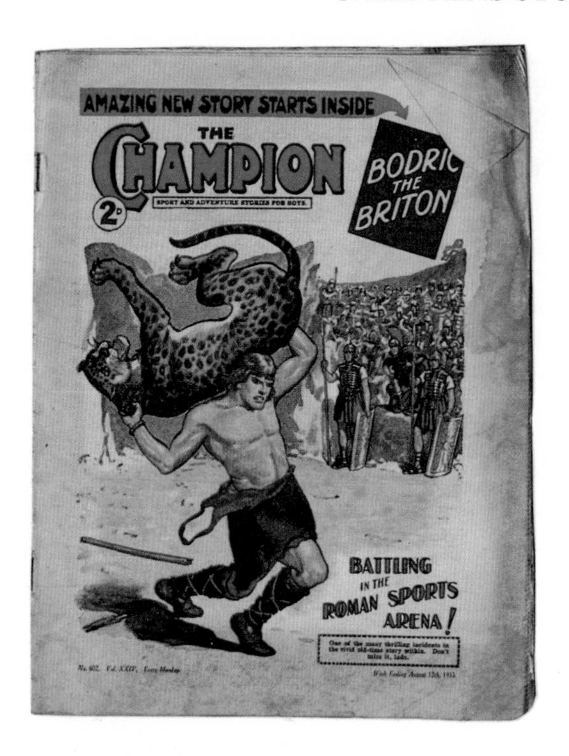

The Champion, August 12, 1933. **£15**

The Rover No. 607, December 23, 1933. **£15**

The Wizard No. 557, December 23, 1933. **£18**

The Hotspur No. 12, November 18, 1933. **£15**

(Spread Eagle Antiques)

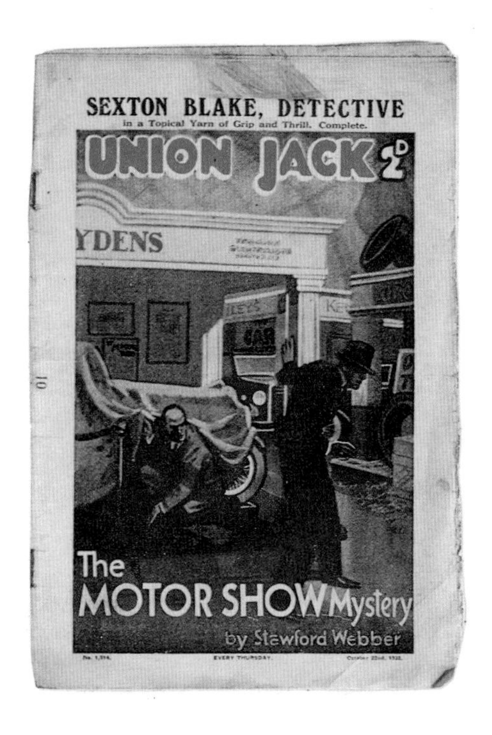

Union Jack, October 22, 1932, with Sexton Blake. £15

Peg's Paper No. 278, Sold Into Slavery. £15

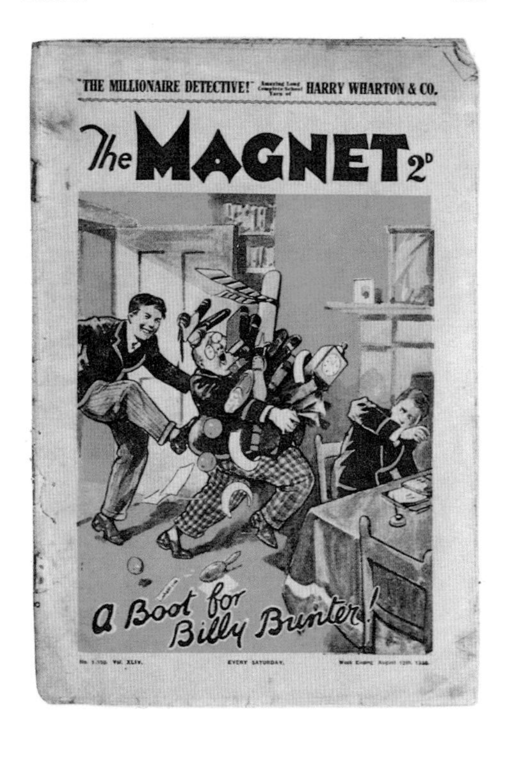

The Magnet, August 12, 1933. £20

The Gem, December 31, 1932. £20

(Spread Eagle Antiques)

The Triumph, Another Dandy free Gift Inside!, No. 137, June 4 1927. £4

The Magnet, 'Harry Wharton's Double', May 18th 1935. £7

Boys' & Girls' Weekly, December 18, 1880, USA. £10

The Hotspur, January 28th 1950. £4

The Rover No. 816, with free gift of Pre-No. 1 Dandy Comic December 4 1937. £100

The Magnet Grand Christmas Number, 1937. £10

THE BOY'S OWN PAPER

No. 1.—Vol. I. SATURDAY, JANUARY 18, 1879. Price One Penny. (ALL RIGHTS RESERVED.)

MY FIRST FOOTBALL MATCH.

BY AN OLD BOY.

IT was a proud moment in my existence when Wright, captain of our football club, came up to me in school one Friday and said, "Adams, your name is down to play in the match against Craven to-morrow."

I could have knighted him on the spot. To be one of the picked "fifteen," whose glory it was to fight the battles of their school in the Great Close, had been the leading ambition of my life—I suppose I ought to be ashamed to confess it—ever since, as a little chap of ten, I entered Parkhurst six years ago. Not a winter Saturday but had seen me either looking on at some big match, or oftener still scrimmaging about with a score or so of other juniors in a scratch game. But for a long time, do what I would, I always seemed as far as ever from the coveted goal, and was half despairing of ever rising to win my "first fifteen cap." Latterly, however, I had noticed Wright and a few others of our best players more than once lounging about in the Little Close where we juniors used to play, evidently taking observations with an eye to business. Under the awful gaze of these heroes, need I say I exerted myself as I had never done before? What cared I for hacks or bruises, so only that I could distinguish myself in their eyes? And never was music sweeter

Boy's Own Paper No. 1, Vol. 1, January 18, 1879. £8

The Champion, February 18th 1950. £4

Nestle's Crackermilk Milk Chocolate, late 1940's. £3

Fry's 6d Chocolate Cream, Giant Size, late 1950's. £3

Nestle Milk Chocolate, late 1940's. £3.50

Fry's Bristol chocolate bar, late 1940's. £3

Milk Chocolate Coffee Crunch by Tobler, 6d bar, early 1960's. £1.50

Fry's Crunch Milk Block, 6d, mid 1950's. £3

Rowntree's Motoring Fruit & Nut Milk Chocolate with picture of grapes and nuts, circa 1960. £4

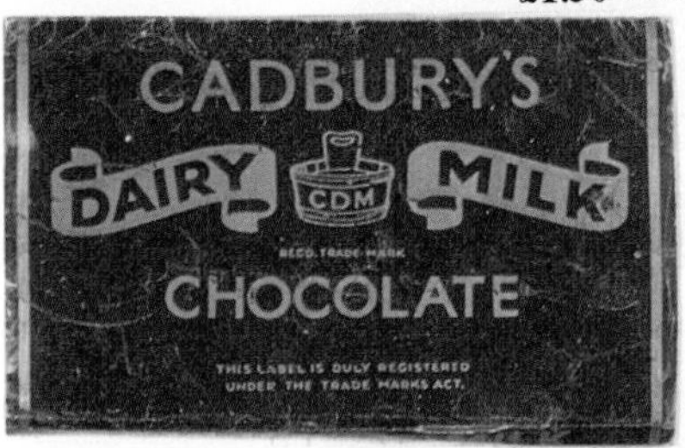

Cadbury's Dairy Milk Chocolate, mid 1940's. £3.50

Needlers' Kreema Pineapple Flavour Milk Chocolate, late 1950's. £1

Rowntree's 1953 Coronation Aero. £5

Nestle Rupert Milk Chocolate, with picture of Rupert and Algy sledging, 1975. £2

Lindt Suvretta, Milch Schokolade mit feinen Mandel-Haselnuss und Praline-Suvretta Füllung, early 1960's. £1

Fry's Double Milk Sandwich 6d bar, mid 1950's. £3

Fry's 4d Chocolate Cream Christmas Bar. £4

Fry's Five Boys Wrapper, Desperation, Pacification, Expectation, Acclamation, Realisation, It's Fry's, late 1950's £8

(Paul Surridge)

Fry's Milk Chocolate Wrapper, Makers to the King, 300 Gold Medals, No. 1902, 1900's. £28

KitKat 50th Anniversary, 1937–1987. 50p

CWS Blended Chocolate, late 1940's. £0.50

Rowntree's Peppermint Cracknel, 6d, mid 1950's. £3

Caley Double Fruit in Rich Milk Chocolate, late 1950's. £4

Nestle's Milky Bar, Made with Full Cream Milk, early 1960's. £2

Terry's Devon Milk Chocolate with Nuts, early 1960's. £1.50

Nestle's Blended Chocolate, late 1940's. £3

Rowntree's Motoring Fruit & Nut Chocolate, Rowntree's Motoring with Fruit and Nuts, early 1950's. £5

Nestle Rupert Milk Chocolate, with picture of Rupert and Podgy on beach, 1975. £2

Cadbury's Dairy Milk Chocolate, 80th Anniversary, 1935–1985, Free Anniversary Mug, 200g bar, 1985. 50p

Cadbury's Fruit & Nut Milk Chocolate, 6d bar, early 1960's. £2.50

Bond's of Bristol Chocolate Variety Block, late 1950's. £1

Rowntree's 1953 Coronation KitKat. £5

Cadbury's Caramello, Covered with Blended Chocolate, mid 1940's. £3.50

(Paul Surridge)

Cadbury's Dairy Milk, 6d bar, circa 1960. **£2.50**

Galaxy New-Style Fruit & Almond Milk Chocolate, 10d bar, early 1960's. **£2**

Fry's Tiffin with Biscuits & Fruit, Delicious and Satisfying, late 1950's. **£3**

Cadbury's Milk Tray Block, Covered with Blended Chocolate, circa 1960. **£3**

Cadbury's Bournville Plain Chocolate, 1/3 bar, 1/4 lb, early 1960's. **£2**

Cadbury's Bournville Fruit & Nut, mid 1940's. **£3.50**

Cadbury's The Wombles Dairy Milk Chocolate with picture of Tomsk, mid 1970's. **£1**

Menier Finest Milk Chocolate, Alpages, early 1960's. **£1**

Cadbury's Dairy Milk, New 1/- bar, early 1960's. **£2.50**

Terry's Devon Milk Chocolate, early 1960's. **£1.50**

Nestle's Milk Chocolate Grapefruit, 1/- bar, early 1960's. **£2**

Kunzle Blended Chocolate Cream Fudge Filled Tablet, late 1950's. **£1**

(Paul Surridge)

Rowntree's Card Display, with samples of KitKat, Aero, Peppermint Aero and Nux bars, late 1950's. £70

Cadbury's Display with range of 1/– bars, early 1960's. £80

Cadbury's Bar Six, Milk Chocolate Wafer Bar, early 1960's. £2.50

Tobler Mandarinette, Chocolate for Adults, Chocolat au Lait Fourré Truffe Mandarin Liqueur, early 1960's. £1.50

Fry's Double Milk Sandwich, 1/– bar, late 1950's. £3

Van Houten Orange Milk Chocolate, 1958. £1

Suchard Milka Full Cream Milk Chocolate, 100 gm, early 1960's. £1

Nestle's Superfine Chocolate, 2½d, late 1940's. £3.50

(Paul Surridge)

Man of War Cigarettes by Cope Bros. of Liverpool, pack of 10, 1900–20. £18

At Ease Cigarettes by Cope Bros. & Co., packet of 10, 1900–20 £20

Champion Cigarettes by Cope Bros. & Co., pack of 5, 1900–10. £18

Life Guard Cigarettes by Wm. Clarke & Sons, pack of 5, 1900–20. £20

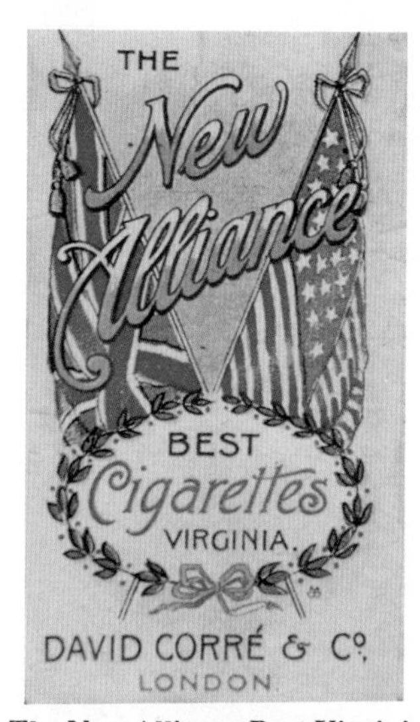

The New Alliance Best Virginia Cigarettes by David Corre & Co., pack of 5, 1900–20. £16

Circus Girl Cigarettes by Cohen, Weenen & Co., pack of 5, 1900–20. £20

Raspberry Buds Cigarettes, by Salmon & Gluckstein, pack of 7, 1900–20. £16

Star of the World Cigarettes by the J.L.S. Tobacco Co., pack of 5, 1900–20. £18

Rich Uncle Cigarettes, by S.J. Gore & Co., London, pack of 5, 1900–20. £20

(Hilary Humphries)

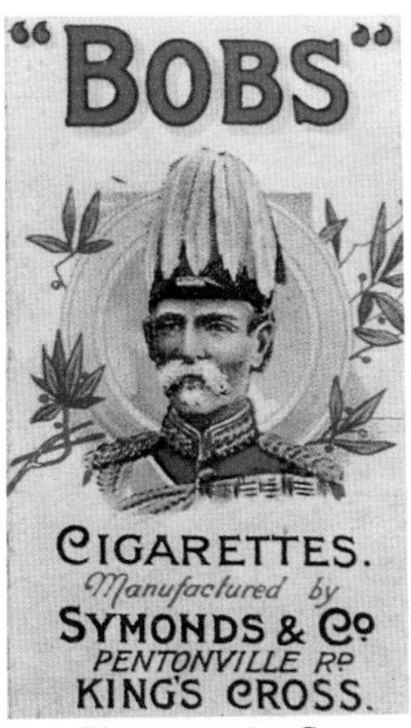

'Bobs' Cigarettes by Symonds & Co., King's Cross, pack of 5, 1900–20. £20

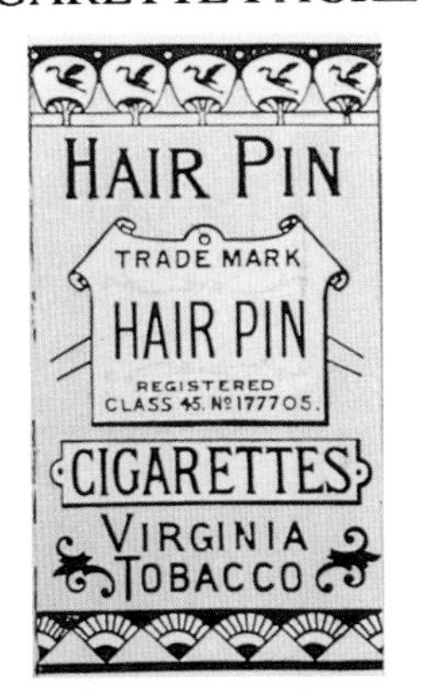

Hair Pin Virginia Cigarettes, pack of 10, 1900–20. £17

Dandy Dan Cigarettes, by A.H. Franks & Sons, pack of 5, 1900 -20. £20

Faulkner's Grenadier Cigarettes, pack of 5, 1920–40. £8

Pear Blossom Compressed Cigarettes, by A. Baker & Co., London, pack of 5, 1900–20. £18

The 'Don' Cigarettes by J.J. Holland, London, pack of 5, 1900–20. £15

'Jolly Briton' Hand Made Cigarettes by T.P. & R. Goodbody, pack of 5, 1900–20. £18

Ocean Prince Cigarettes by Adkin & Sons, pack of 5, 1900–20. £15

All Gay Cigarettes by Harris of London, with 'handsome coloured photo', pack of 5, 1900–20. £20

(Hilary Humphries)

Steve Samson, Roman Invasion, No. 26, 1955. £3

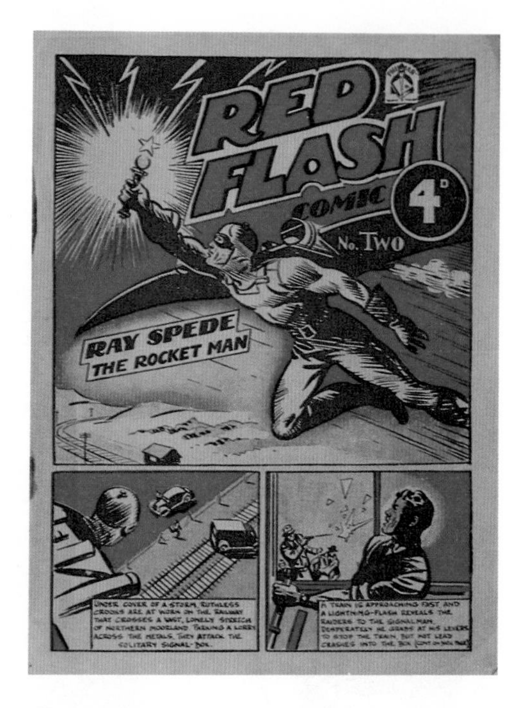

Red Flash No. 2. £5

Red Dagger Twisty, No. 1. £1.50

Battle Squadron. £4

(Bryan Whitworth)

Blue Bolt, No. 18, 1953. £4

Captain Marvel, No. 12, 1953. £10

Bat Man No. 61, Batman the Magician, 1950s. £4

Black Magic, No. 13, 1952. £10

(Bryan Whitworth)

Indian Fighter, 1951. **£3**

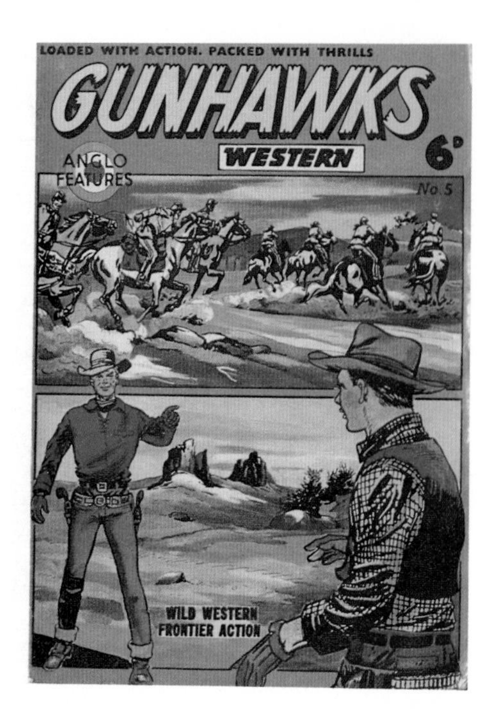

Gunhawks Western No. 5.  **£3**

Fighting Outlaws, No. 10, early 1950s. **£4**

Westworld Foursome Comic, No. 5. **£6**

(Bryon Whitworth)

Cheyenne Kid, No. 16. **£4**

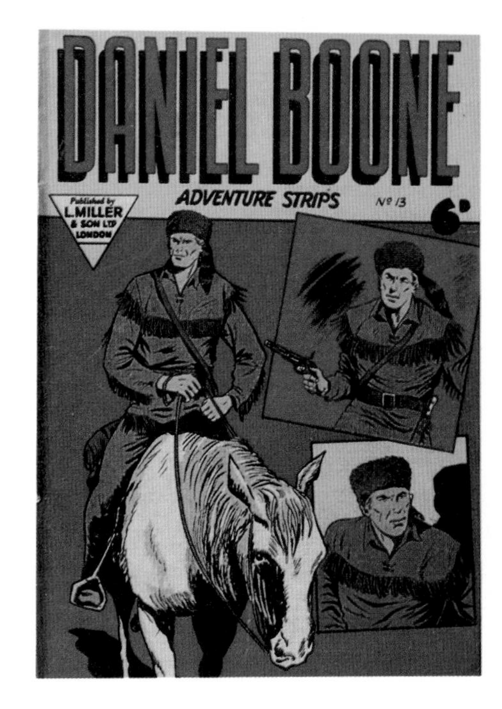

Daniel Boone, No. 13, 1957/8. **£3**

Rocky Mountain King Western Comic No. 23. **£3**

The Crimson Comet, No. 41. **£4**

(Bryon Whitworth)

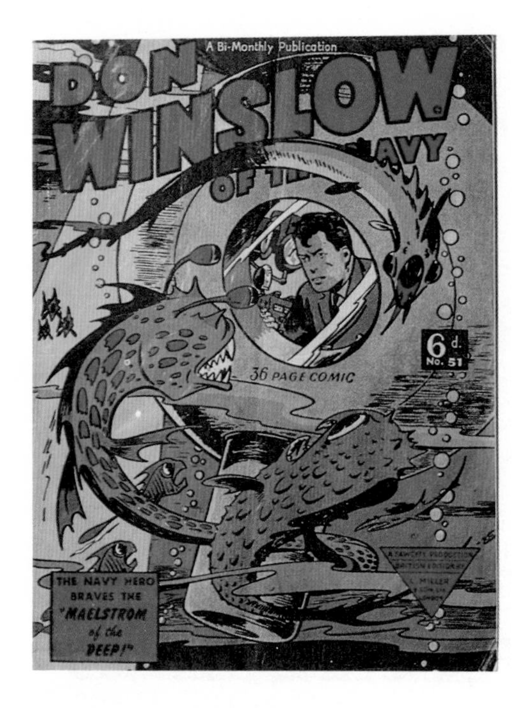

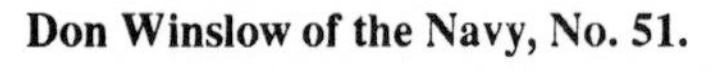
Don Winslow of the Navy, No. 51. £4

Mandrake The Magician No. 24, early 1960s. £2

Comet, featuring Buffalo Bill, No. 338, January 8 1955. £3

Sun, Billy the Kid, No. 323, April 16 1955. £3

(Bryon Whitworth)

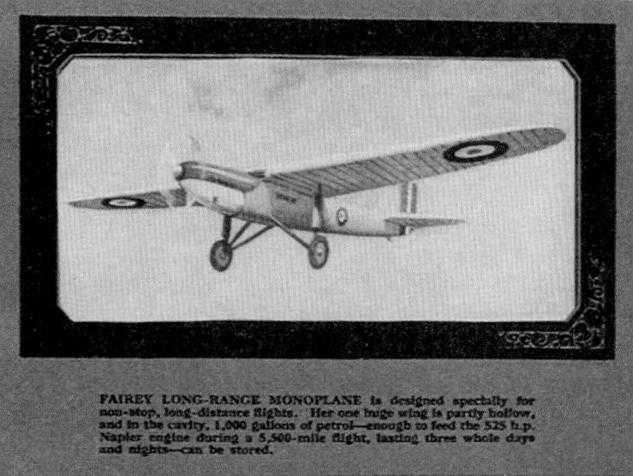

The Modern Boy Album of Up-to-Date Aeroplanes, presented with The Modern Boy, 25 January 1930. £15

The Oink Song, free with Oink. £2

The Beano Gnasher Snapper No. 1970. £1.50

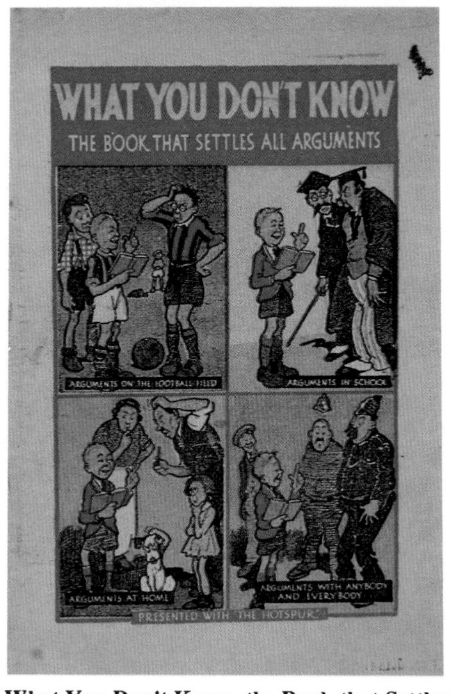

What You Don't Know, the Book that Settles All Arguments, presented with The Hotspur, 17 October 1936. £5

(Bryon Whitworth)

The Union Jack Album of World Famous Aircraft, presented with Union Jack, November 15 1930. £12

Whizzer & Chips 2 in 1 Joke Book. £1.50

Forces in Combat cards, presented with Combat. 50p

The Dandy Thunder Bang, No. 2106. £1

Beano No. 2202, Dennis Stickers. 50p

(Bryon Whitworth)

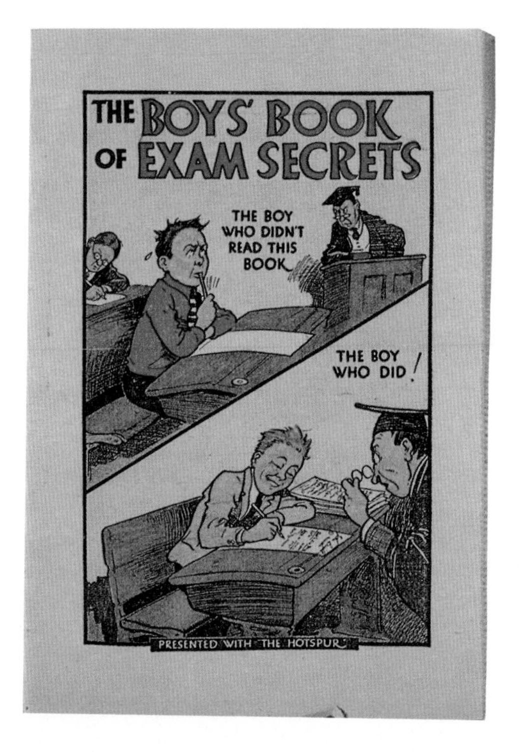

The Boys' Book of Exam Secrets, presented free with Hotspur, 24 October 1936. £6

The STAMP HUNTER'S GUIDE

PRESENTED WITH "THE HOTSPUR"

EVERY boy, from 9 to 90, can be a stamp-hunter. He can roam the world collecting wild animals, savage native tribesmen, aeroplanes, engineering marvels—and all without leaving his own home!

If you have never thought of becoming a stamp-hunter before, you will find that stamps are not just pieces of paper, they are passports to adventure. And even if you already have a good-going stamp collection, you'll find lots of thrilling things you didn't know about stamps in these pages.

First of all, before you take the great stamp trail, you must check your kit, like every good hunter.

For stamp hunting you don't need guns and packs, but the kit you do need is just as essential as the kind used by the bring-'em-back-alive boys.

First you need a stockade, a corral for keeping your captures in, in other words an ALBUM. Start off with a general-type album, with the name of each country at the top of the page and squares for the stamps. As your catch gets bigger, you can get a larger and more specialised album.

When you have caught your stamps, you don't just bung 'em in the album any old how. Be like the hunter—cage each one separately. Here's where STAMP MOUNTS come in. These are thin, gummed, transparent pieces of paper slightly less in size than an ordinary stamp. You fold them over, lightly gum one end to the stamp, and fix the other end in your album.

The marksman needs a rifle with a telescopic sight, you need a MAGNIFYING GLASS. And for the same reason—to check the detail of your game, your stamp, before you decide to take it.

Have you ever stopped to consider the fact that a big-game hunter does not go out and capture a lot of animals and then wait for someone to come along and buy them? No, he has orders for the animals first. You need an order book, a CATALOGUE, to tell you what stamps there are to go after, and what they look like. You can easily buy the rest of your stamp-hunting kit yourself, but here's a tip, get your dad to buy you the catalogue, as a New Year's present, and ask him to get a simplified one.

Now you are ready to start your great adventure. Off you go, and the best of luck!

The Stamp Hunter's Guide Book, presented with The Hotspur, No. 897. £4

ERIC LANGTON—CYCLONE SPEEDSTER

ERIC KEMP LANGTON, captain of the England and Belle Vue speedway teams, has broken records galore in the cinder-sport.

Yet this round-faced, curly-headed young man of 28, whose face always wears a confident and perky smile, is one of the safest riders in the game.

Eric Langton never takes undue risks. Steady riding, aided by perfectly-tuned bikes, has put him in the forefront.

He is the man who has done most to give Belle Vue her wonderful run of consistent success. For the past three years, the Manchester track has finished at the head of the Speedway League, and this summer Langton has been a wonderful captain.

Born at Leeds, Eric Langton has been reared in an atmosphere of petrol and oil. In his earlier days, he indulged in every form of motor-cycle sport, including the T.T. races.

When the speedway sport came to Britain, Eric and his brother Oliver—another valued member of the Belle Vue side—decided to try their luck. That was at Leeds, where Eric rode for ten shillings a meeting.

Since then, Langton has set up dozens of records. At one time he held every Belle Vue record for standing start, clutch start and flying start together with the Lancashire mile record of 87 secs., set up in October, 1933.

Eric Langton has also set up many remarkable performances in Test matches against Australia.

In the Fifth and Final Test at West Ham, in 1934, he not only equalled the previous four-laps record for the track, but he beat it with a speed of 44.1 m.p.h.—in successive heats, too.

This year, the Belle Vue captain has again been in wonderful form for England, and under his leadership the "Ashes" have been regained from the Australian riders.

It is not only in this country that he has set up records. Last winter Eric had a great time in Australia and New Zealand and showed the fans 'down under' some of his skill and his colossal speed. Eric will also be spending this winter abroad, in America, and perhaps Australia, too.

(24)

OUR UNDER-WATER WONDER SHIP

CAN you imagine a massive armoured warship diving under perfect control beneath the sea? Perhaps not. Yet Submarine X1—one of the finest craft in the British Navy—is a veritable cruiser.

She is the only one of her class and is the biggest submarine in our fleet.

This under-water cruiser was built at Chatham Dockyard and cost £941,794. Later, she was altered slightly and her total cost was something like £1,044,158. Her first trials were held in January, 1924, and X1 was completed by September, 1925.

Britain's largest submarine is completely armoured from stem to stern, and was designed for deep-sea diving. She is 350 ft. long, 29 ft. wide and 17 ft. deep. Her
Diesel en
develop
horse-powe
she can
along at 19
on the surfa
9 when she
merged.

Her w
varies. C
surface X
tonnage of
But when
speeding
under wat
weighs 3,6
—due to
She carr
and other
She can
under wate
X1 is fitte
For a sul
guns and s
England
water crui

The Champion Album of Record Breakers, large free booklet complete with all it's coloured stick-in stamps, 1935/6. £15

(Bryon Whitworth)

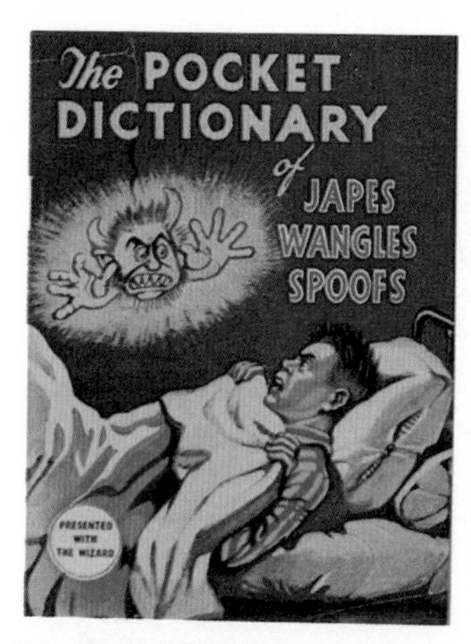

The Pocket Dictionary of Japes, Wangles & Spoofs, presented with the Wizard. £5

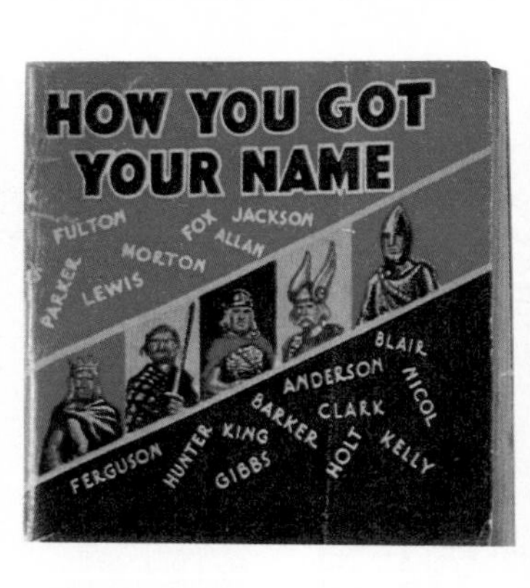

Hotspur Handy Books No. 8 How You Got Your Name. £5

Mighty Monsters of the Wilds, presented free with The Rover. £5

Hotspur Handy Books No. 4, My Own Easter Logbook. £5

The Modern Boy Pocket Stamp Album 1938, presented with The Modern Boy, September 23 1937. £8

Hotspur Handy Books No. 1 Forward The Rescue Squad. £5

The Bright Boys' Album of Motor Cars, supplement to The Skipper. £15

Triumph Album of Railways, presented free with Triumph (no cards). £8

The Skipper Full Colour Book of Flags, presented with The Skipper, damaged, but rare. £8

(Bryon Whitworth)

Our Forefathers Were Cavemen, presented with The Wizard. **£5**

Hotspur Handy Books No. 12 Big Blows & Blasts. **£5**

1000 Years from Now, presented with Adventure. **£15**

Hotspur Handy Books No. 2, My Own Highway Log-Book, pre 1940. **£5**

The Wizard Wonder Album of Sea and Air, No. 1 presented with The Wizard, 1932. **£15**

The Rover Album of Ships, presented with The Rover, 1 November 1924. **£15**

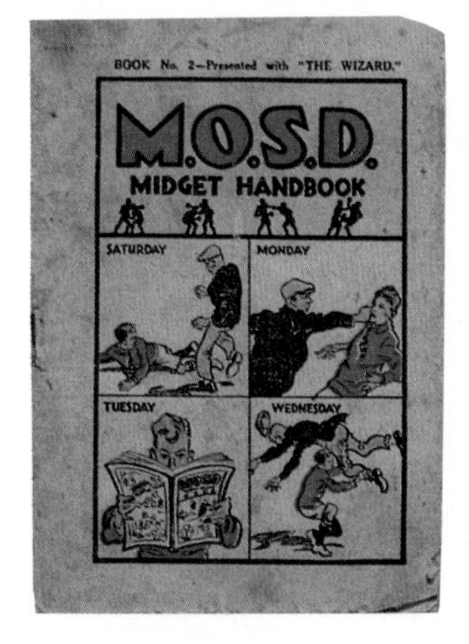

My Own Self Defence Midget Handbook No. 2, presented with The Wizard, 1932. **£5**

The Triumph Album of What Every Boy Wants To Know About Ships, with 9 of the original colour plates. **£10**

HotspurHandy Books No. 3, Dodger Drew, Everything Happens to Him. **£5**

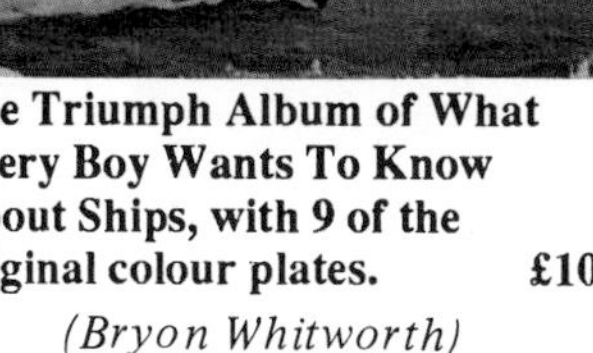

(Bryon Whitworth)

Stickers presented with Warlord No. 121. 50p

Instant Disguise Kit presented with Whizzer & Chips 1970. £2

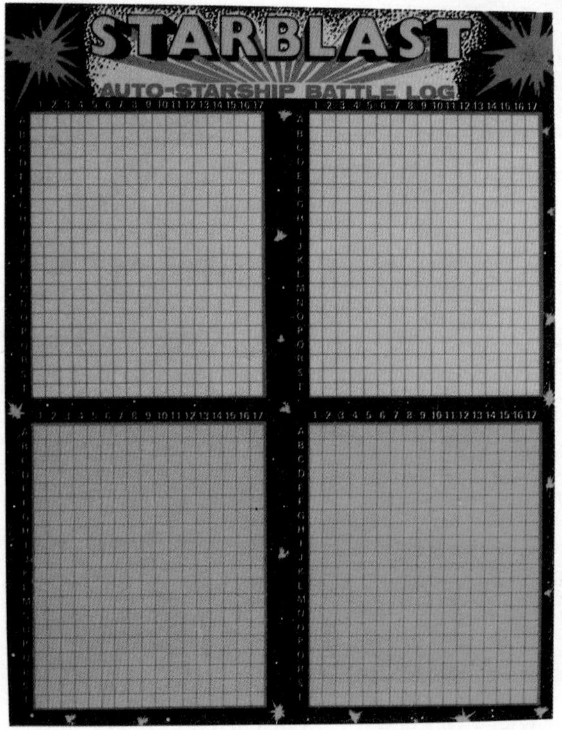

Starblast data Sheet presented with Star Lord No. 3. £2

Wheel of Fortune wallet presented with Misty No. 2. £2

(Bryon Whitworth)

Desperate Dan's Pie Eater's Club, wallet and two badges. £2

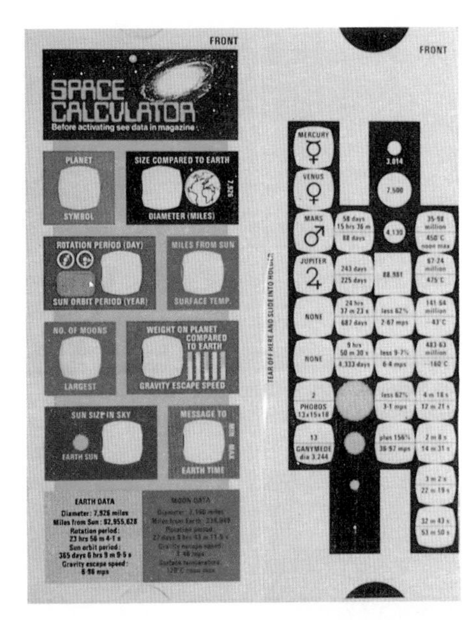

Star Lord No. 2 Space Calculator. £2

Action Invasion Game, free inside Action Comic 29 May 1976. £2

Korky Glow Mask, No. 2240, presented with The Dandy. £1

(Bryon Whitworth)

Pip Squeak and Wilfred, Printing and Colouring Outfit, circa 1925. £50

Ally Sloper china bust with the Arms of Brixham, circa 1890. £75

Ally Sloper carved wood pipe bowl, circa 1885. £40

Bonzo board game, Sausages and Ladders, circa 1925. £50

The Bruin Boys Jolly Ring Game from Rainbow Comic, circa 1930. £75

Felix the film cat, small china jug, circa 1922. £75

(Denis Gifford)

The Bruin Boys Crackers, circa 1930. £150

Teddy Tail Party Invitations, circa 1935. £75

Ally Sloper clay pipe, circa 1885. £50

Ally Sloper's Jubilee Purse complete with the original box, 1887. £10

Popeye Pipe Toss Game, 1935. £75

Ally Sloper tobacco jar with removable hat, circa 1890. £200

(Denis Gifford)

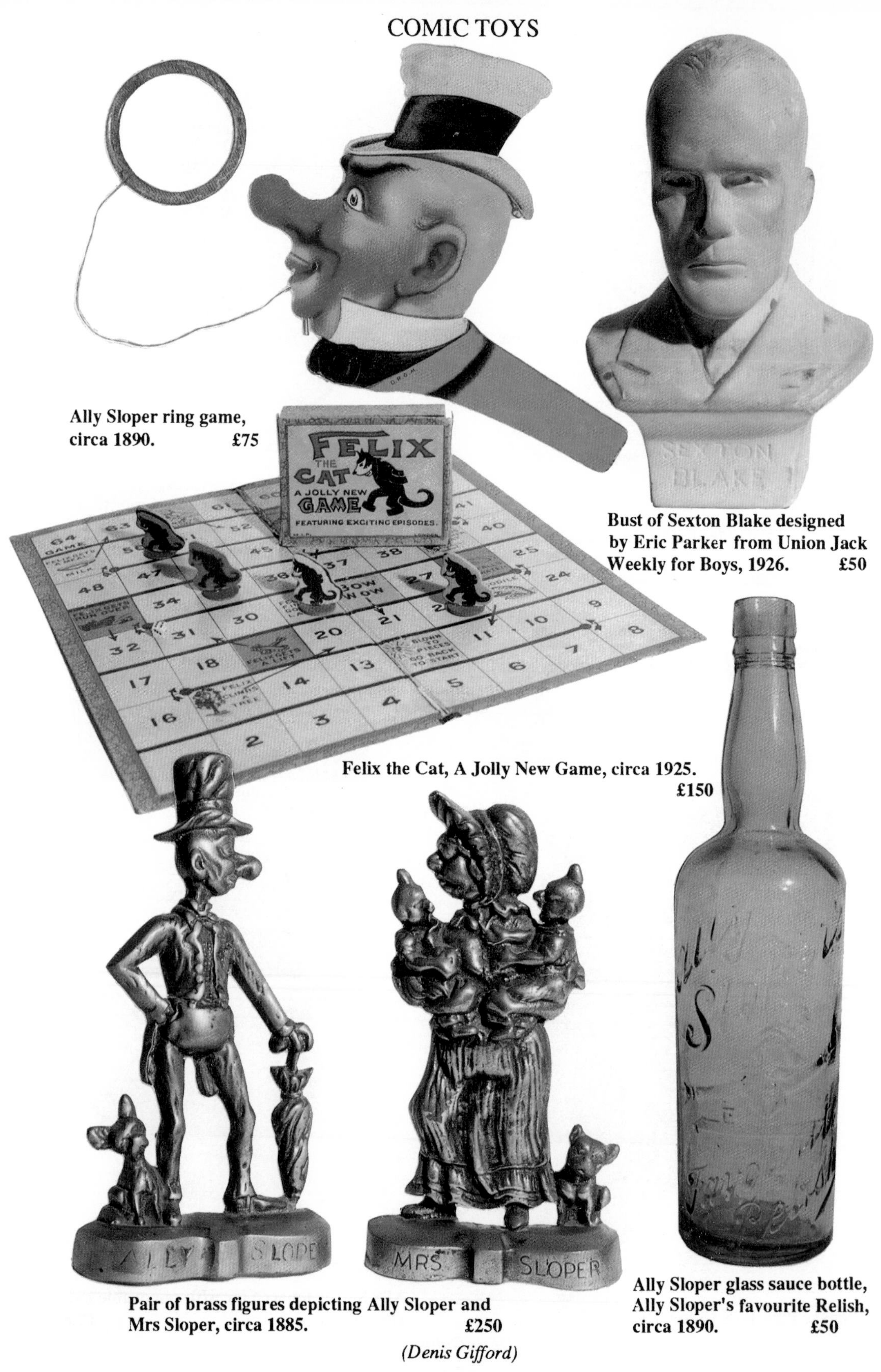

Ally Sloper ring game, circa 1890. £75

Bust of Sexton Blake designed by Eric Parker from Union Jack Weekly for Boys, 1926. £50

Felix the Cat, A Jolly New Game, circa 1925. £150

Pair of brass figures depicting Ally Sloper and Mrs Sloper, circa 1885. £250

Ally Sloper glass sauce bottle, Ally Sloper's favourite Relish, circa 1890. £50

(Denis Gifford)

Detective Comics No. 27, Starting This Issue, the Amazing and Unique Adventures of The Batman, May 1939, about 100 copies known extant, of which 6 in UK. £75,000

Detective Comics No. 1, March 1937, about 30 copies known extant, of which 2 in UK. £15,000

More Fun Comics No. 53, Another Thrilling Adventure of The Spectre, March 1940, about 65 copies known extant, of which 1 in UK. £8,000

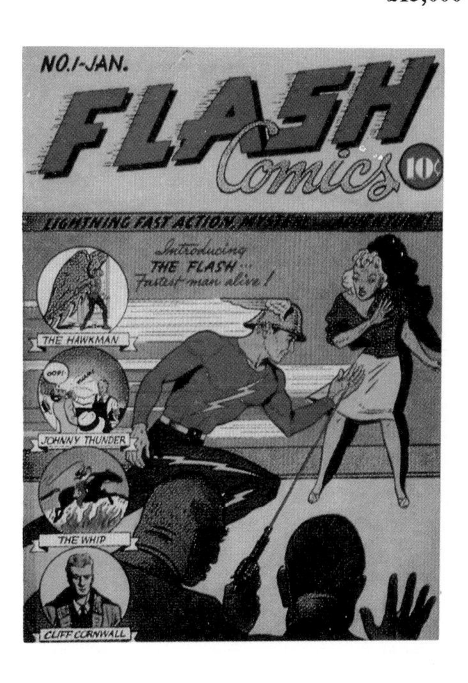

Flash Comics No. 1, Introducing The Flash, Fastest Man Alive, January 1940, about 135 copies known extant, of which 3 in UK. £17,500

(Duncan McAlpine)

All-American Comics No. 16, introducing The Green Lantern, July 1940, about 55 copies known extant of which 2 in UK. £15,000

Batman No. 1, the Brand New Adventures of Batman and Robin the Boy Wonder, spring 1940, about 300 copies known extant, of which 8 in UK. £20,000

Detective Comics No. 31, Batman versus The Monk, September 1939, about 90 copies known extant of which 5 in UK. £7,000

All Star Comics No. 3, stamped Justice Society of America, winter 1940, about 160 copies known extant, of which 3 in UK. £9,000

(Duncan McAlpine)

More Fun Comics, No. 52, first issue to feature the Spectre, February 1940, about 65 copies known extant, of which 1 in UK. £12,000

Detective Comics No. 23, Another Thrilling Adventure of The Batman, November 1939, about 90 copies known extant, of which 3 in UK. £10,000

Adventure Comics No. 40, first issue to feature The Sandman, July 1939, about 55 copies known extant, of which 2 in UK. £5,500

Captain Marvel Adventures No. 1, 64 Pages of New Captain Marvel Adventures, March 1941, about 140 copies known extant, of which 1 in UK. £9,500

(Duncan McAlpine)

Detective Comics, No. 29, July 1939, featuring 'The Batman', about 85 copies known to be extant, 3 known in UK. £7,000

New Fun, the Big Comic Magazine, No. 1, February 1935, featuring Jack Woods on cover, about 17 copies extant. £8,000

Superman No. 1, the Complete Story of the Daring Exploits of the One and Only Superman, summer 1939, about 200 copies known extant, 12 in UK. £40,000

Marvel Comics No. 1, November 1939, about 100 copies known extant, of which 3 in UK. £35,000

(Duncan McAlpine)

Whiz Comics No. 1, featuring Captain Marvel, February 1940, about 150 copies known extant, of which 1 in UK. £25,000

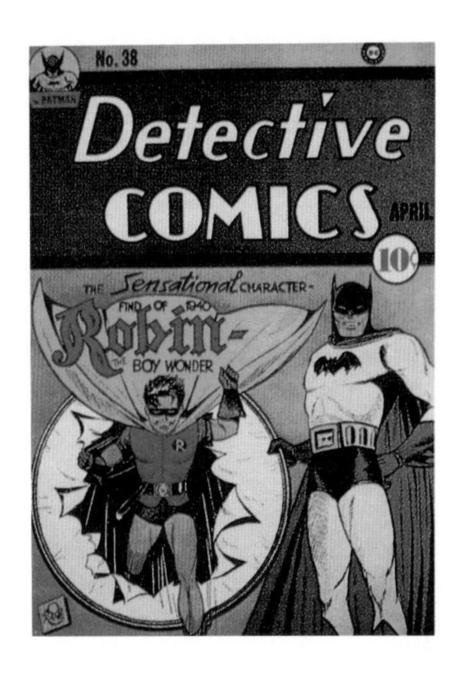

Detective Comics No. 38, featuring Robin, the Boy Wonder, April 1940, about 90 copies known extant of which 5 in UK. £11,000

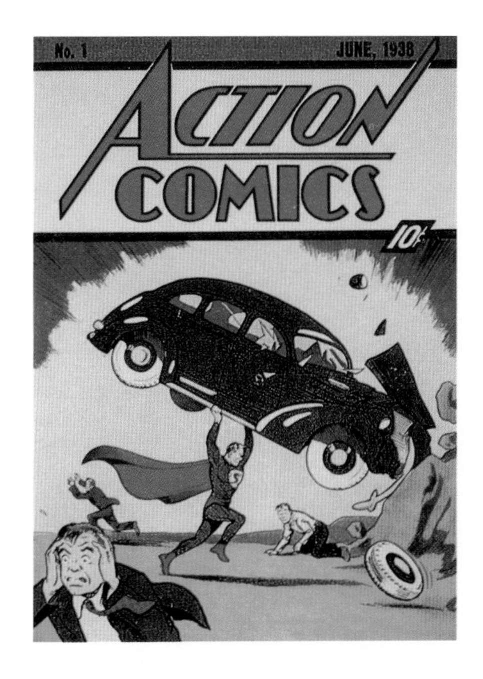

Action Comics No. 1, the first to feature Siegel & Schuster's creation Superman, June 1938, about 100 copies extant, 6 in UK. £60,000

Captain America No. 1, 45 Thrilling Pages of Captain America, March 1941, about 175 copies known extant, of which 5 in UK. £15,000

(Duncan McAlpine)

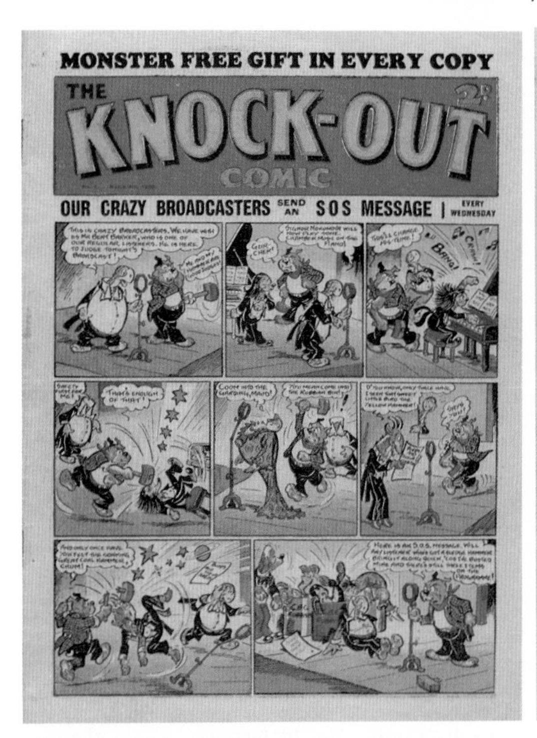

The Knock-Out-Comic, with free 'Tuck Hamper' of assorted biscuits, March 4th 1939, No. 1. £200

2000 A.D., featuring the new Dan Dare, with free Space Spinner, 26th February 1977, No. 1. £30

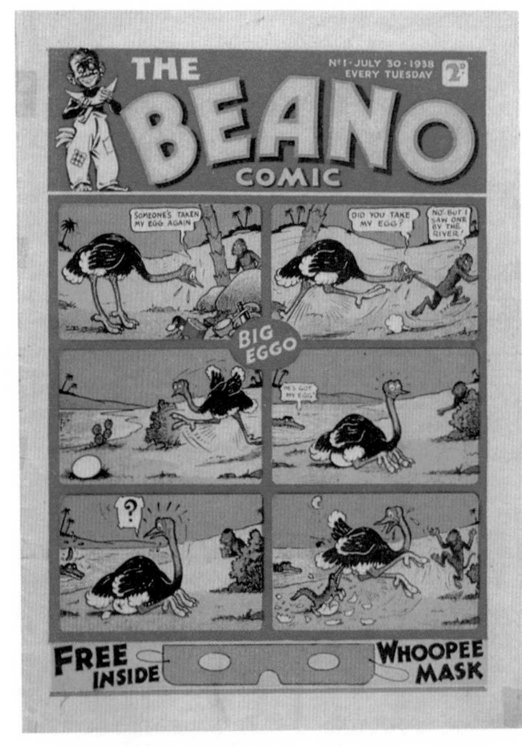

The Beano Comic, with free Whoopee Mask, July 30th 1938, No. 1. £1,000

Radio Fun, Just out with grand free gift, October 15th 1938, No. 1. £175

(Denis Gifford)

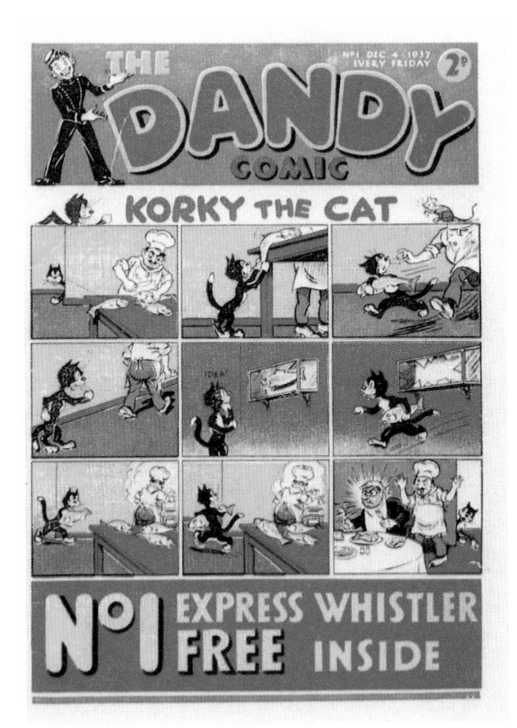

The Dandy Comic, featuring Korky the Cat, with free Express Whistler, 4th December 1937, No. 1. £1,000

Girl, Sister paper to Eagle, with free Princess Elizabeth poster, November 2nd 1951, No. 1. £20

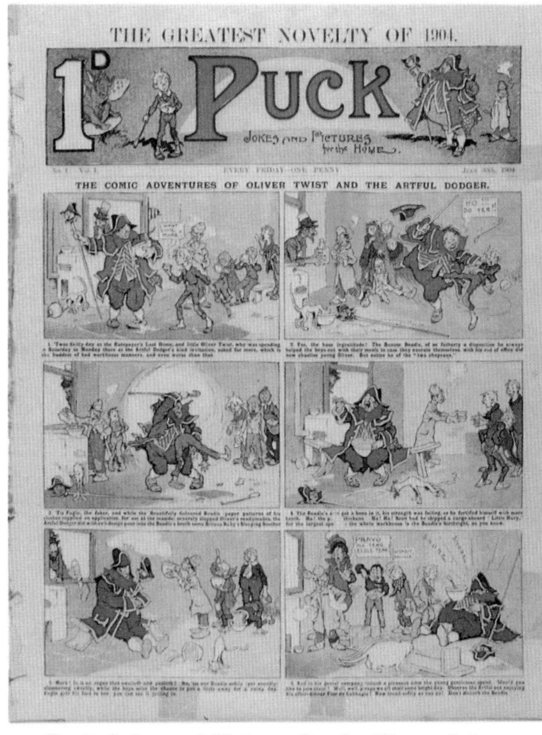

Puck, Jokes and Pictures for the Home, July 30th 1904, No. 1, first successful coloured comic. £80

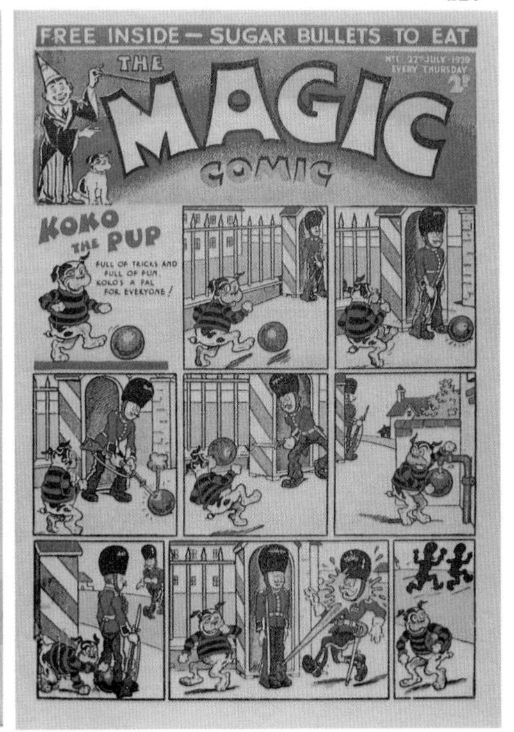

The Magic Comic, with free Sugar Bullets to Eat, July 22nd 1939, No. 1 £700

(Denis Gifford)

The Rainbow, A splendid toy model given free with this number, February 14th 1914, No. 1. £100

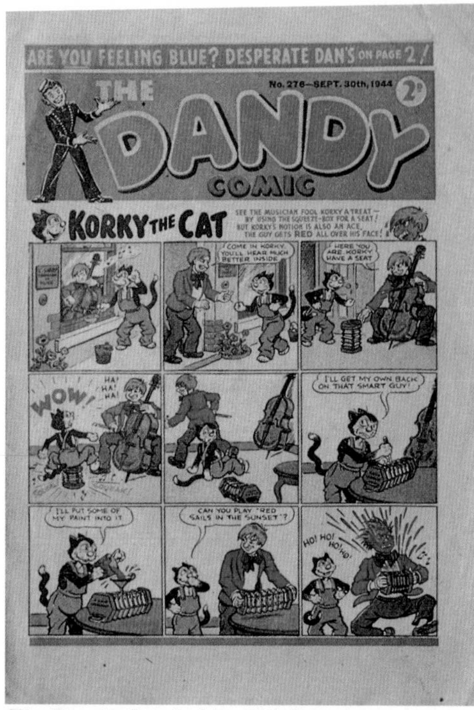

The Dandy Comic, No. 276. September 30 1944. £35

Happy Days At Chimpo's Circus, with free propelling pencil, notebook and eraser, October 8th 1938, No. 1. £200

Mickey Mouse Weekly, Fun for the whole family, with free 'Post Toasties Post' Newspaper, February 8th 1936, No. 1. £500

(Denis Gifford)

Tiger, The Sport and Adventure Picture Story Weekly, with free Space Gun, September 11th 1954, No. 1. £30

TV Century 21, Adventure in the 21st Century, with free Top Secret Codebook, January 23rd 2065 (1965), No. 1. £50

Eagle, the New National Strip Cartoon Weekly, April 14th 1950, No. 1. £75

Buster, Son of Andy Capp, with free Buster's Balloon Bleeper, May 28th 1960, No. 1. £40

(Denis Gifford)

Sparky No. 1 of a Great New Comic for Boys and Girls, with free Flying Snorter, January 23 1965. £7.50

The Rover Special Christmas Number, No. 1694, 14 December 1957. £4

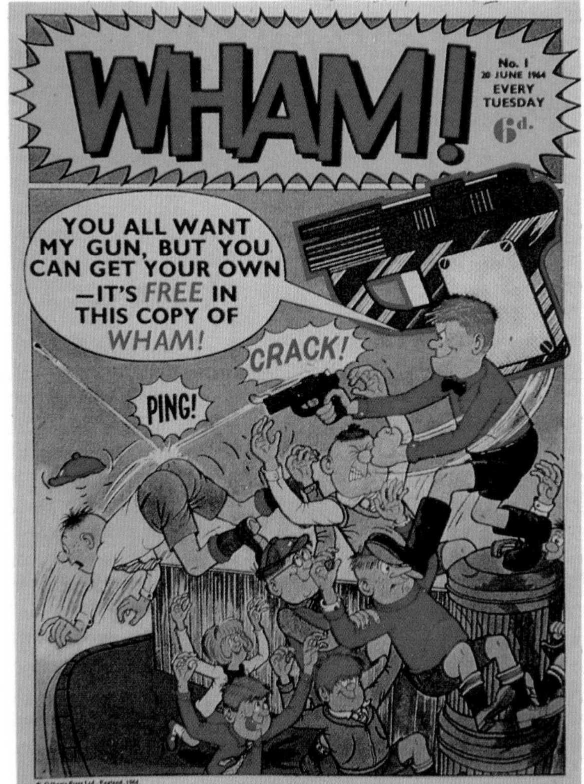

WHAM! No. 1, 20 June 1964. £25

The Beano, No. 354, May 1 1948. £20

(Bryon Whitworth)

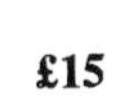

Sharp's **Dorothy assorted toffee. £15**

Sharp's Kreemy Toffee. £3

Cremona Dairy Cream Toffee. £7

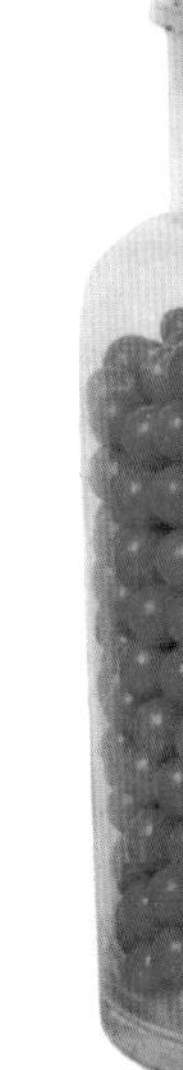

Huntley and Palmers Chocolate Bar, Soldier Series. £4

The Eagle, High Class Confectionery. £10

Superfine Violet Powder by Burdall's. £5

Uncle Joe's Mintballs by Wm. Santus & Co Ltd. £12

Pascall Home Sweets. £12

Radiance Devon Cream Toffee. £25

(Douglas Morgan)

Rowntree's mixed pastilles. £3

George V and Queen Mary Coronation souvenir tin by Fry's Chocolate. £25

Brown Bros Superior Butter Drops. £15

Huntley and Palmers Rialto chocolate bar, 1937. £4

Squirrel Confections Clear Gums. £8

Tucker's of Totnes Butter Scotch. £6

Squirrel Confections tin. £15

Harlow's Mintoes, a seller all the year round. £12

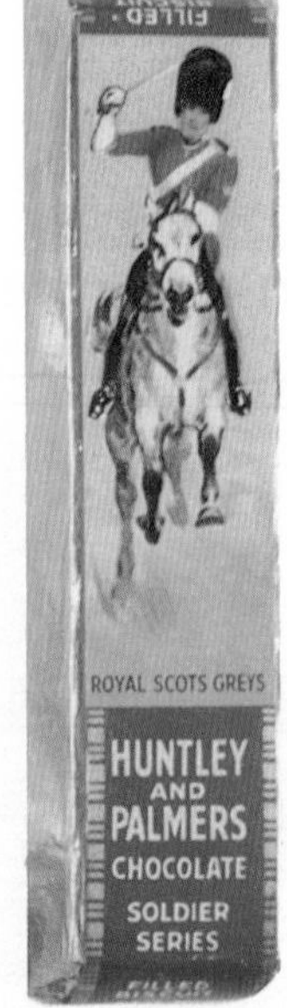

Huntley and Palmers Chocolate Bar, Royal Scots Greys. £4

(Douglas Morgan)

Kellogg's Corn Flakes Cockerel design, with 8d coupon inside for Pop-Tarts, The New Pastry Treat, 1968. £8

Shredded Wheat packet with picture of factory, Britons Make It – It Makes Britons, late 1930's. £20

Weetabix, More Than A Breakfast Food, Serve With Milk, Hot or Cold, late 1930's. £30

Kellogg's Rice Krispies, Vitamin Enriched, with Rose Bush Offer, 1961. £8

Kellogg's Rice Krispies, 1988 Diamond Jubilee Pack, with free model van offer, 1988. 75p

Force Wheatflakes, Sunny Jim design, mid 1930's. £30

Large Display Corn Flakes pack, peaches and bowl of Cornflakes design, 1955. £6

Nabisco Welgar Shredded Wheat, Free Model Inside, Kings & Queens of England, late 1960's. £8

Kellogg's Rice Krispies, Snap, Crackle, Pop, circa 1950. £20

(Paul Surridge)

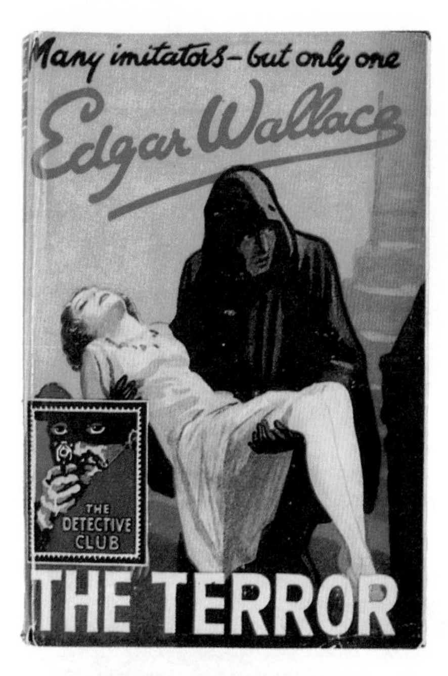

The Terror by Edgar Wallace, the first talkie horror film, Warner, 1928. £50

Scarlet Adventuress featuring Magda's New Arabian Knight, May 1936, Number One Issue. £30

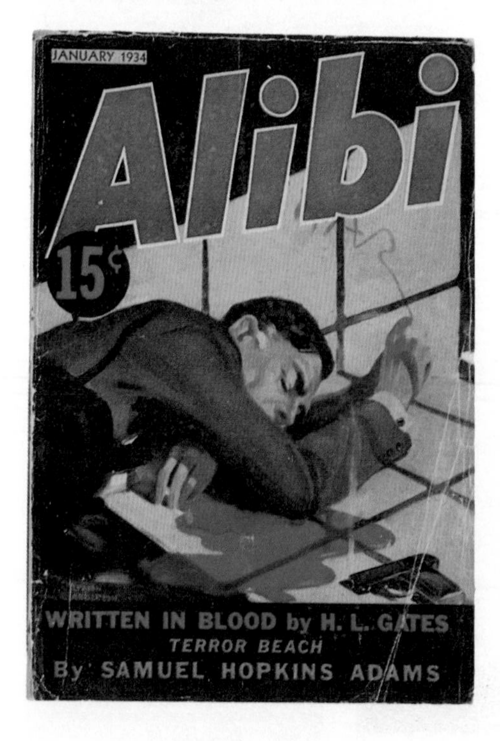

Alibi, January 1934 featuring Written in Blood by H. L. Gates, Number One Issue. £50

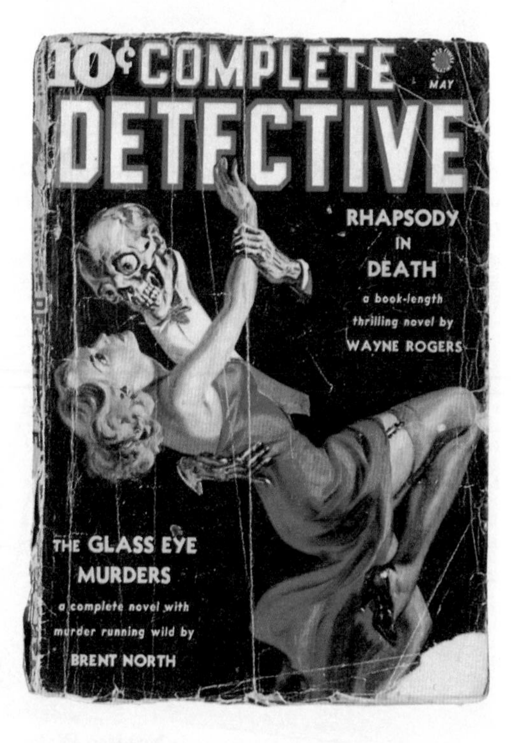

Complete Detective, May 1938, featuring Rhapsody in Death by Wayne Rogers, Number One Issue. £40

(Denis Gifford)

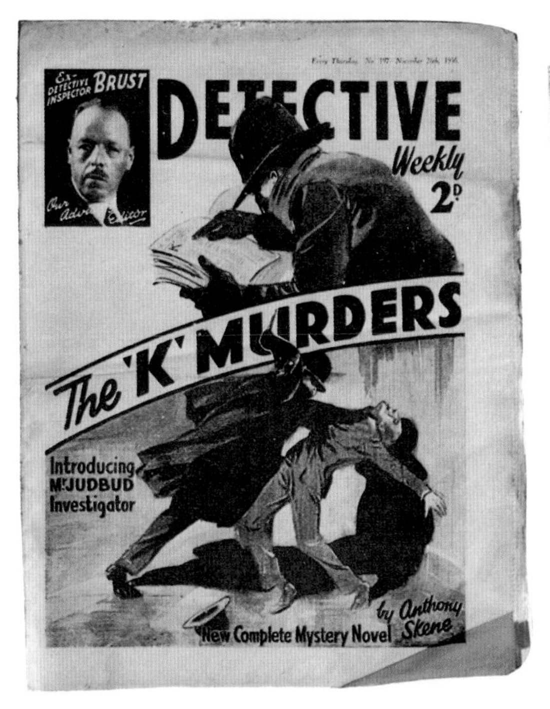

Detective Weekly, November 28, 1936, The 'K' Murders. £12

Complete Mystery Novelettes, December 1931, featuring The Tower Room Mystery by Arthur W. Patterson, Number One Issue. £50

All Aces Magazine, April 1936, featuring Under Sealed Orders by Hugh Pendexter, Number One Issue. £40

Prison, Life Stories featuring Federal Agents by J. Edgar Hoover, September 1935, Number One Issue. £25

(Denis Gifford)

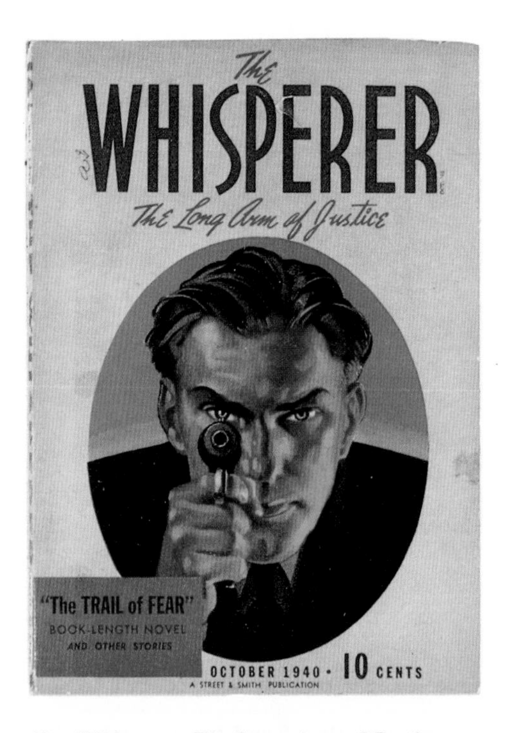

The Whisperer, The Long Arm of Justice, October 1940, Number One Issue. £40

Detective Tales, August 1935 featuring Heartbreak House by Franklin H. Martin, Number One Issue. £50

G-Men, The Federals in Action, October 1935, Number One Issue. £50

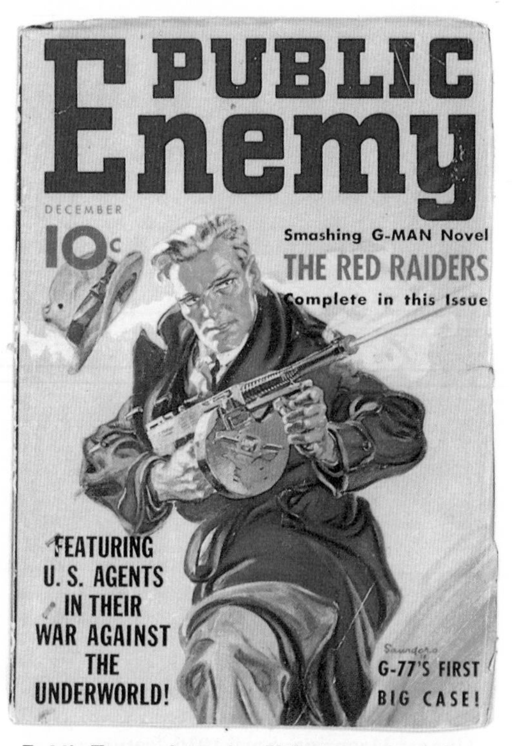

Public Enemy featuring U.S. Agents in their War against the Underworld, December 1935, Number One Issue. £50

(Denis Gifford)

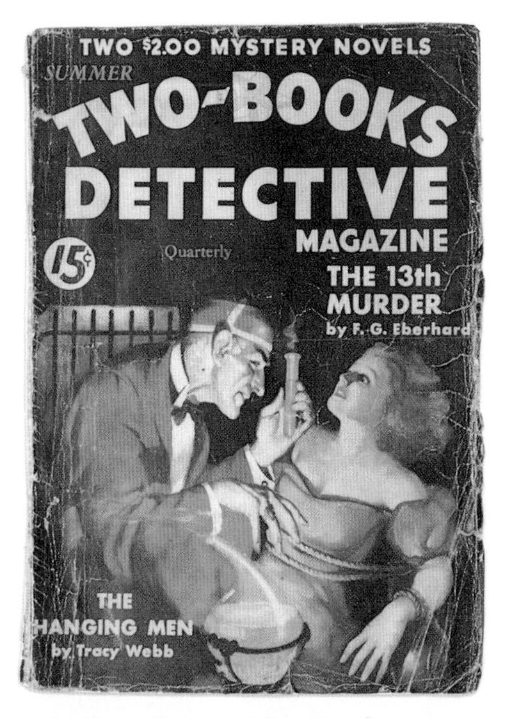

Two-Books Detective Magazine, Summer 1933, featuring The 13th Murder by F. G. Eberhard, Number One Issue. £50

Murder Mysteries featuring The Mystery of the Armless Men by Francis Welch, July 1935. £5

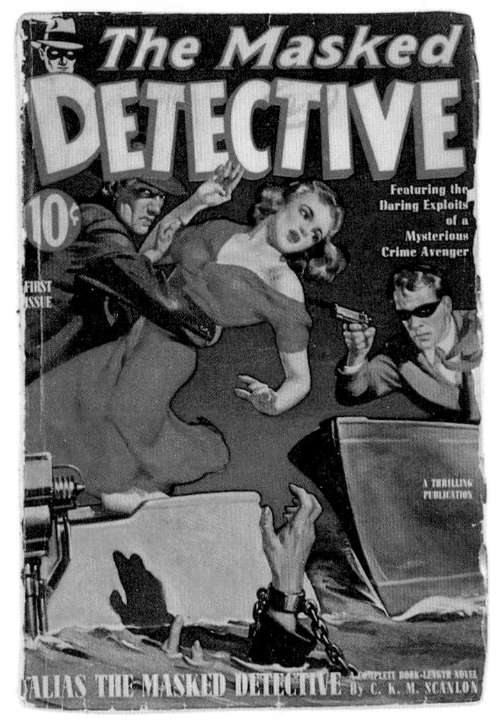

The Masked Detective featuring the Daring Exploits of a Mysterious Crime Avenger, 1940, Number One Issue. £40

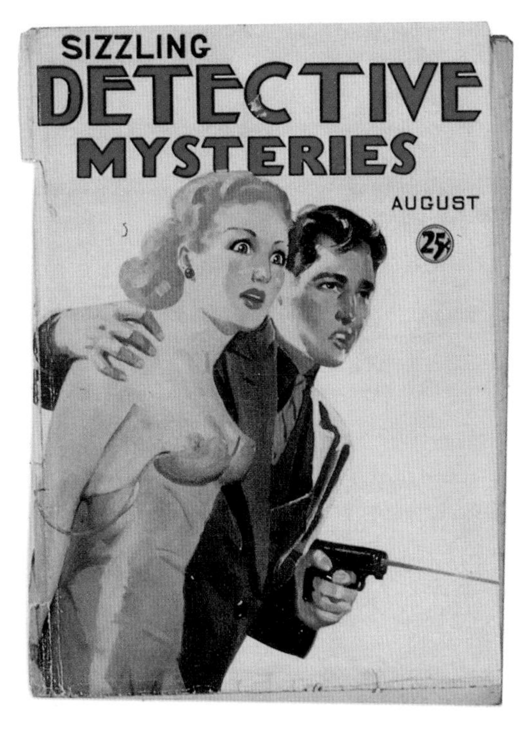

Sizzling Detective Mysteries, August 1935. £5

(Denis Gifford)

French perfume box by Sebellen & Despiney. £12

Chelsea Royal Boot Dubbin. £6

Swan Ink, for fountain and steel pens. £2

Blakey's Boot Protectors. £2

Snowene white cleaner, bottle and contents. £8

Glamour Talcum Powder. £8

Wax Floor Polish, Grand Hotel Quality, with contents. £5

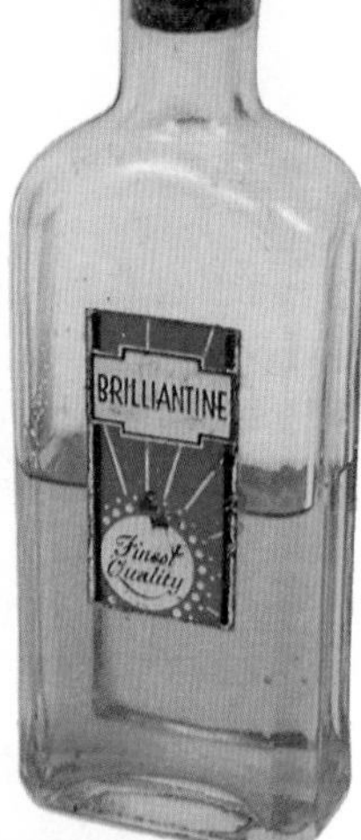

Brilliantine, Finest Quality. £3

Duofil Double filament lamps, 110 V, 40 W, 1930's. £6

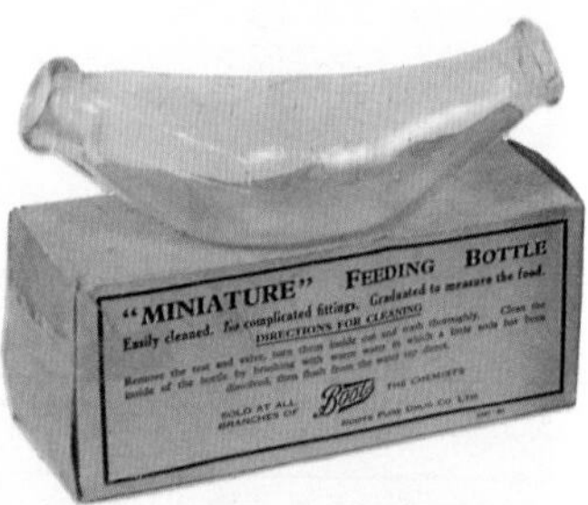

Miniature Feeding Bottle by Boots. £12

Borax Shaving Cream, The Pride O' the Morn. £5

Newey's Bar Loop Hooks and Eyes. £2

(Douglas Morgan)

Indian Cerate by Reade Brothers. £5

Yardley Old English Lavender. £15

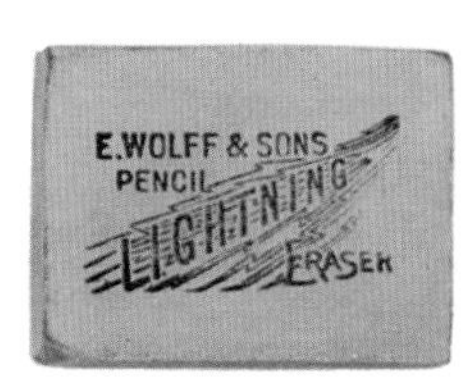

Lightning eraser by E. Wolff & Sons. £1

Field's ink bottle and contents. £3

Town Talk Silver Polish, Clean, Harmless, Quick, Lasting. £5

Carr's Dubbing, A relief to chapped hands. £7

Dunlop Rubber Solution. £6

Edison Bell gold moulded record. £3

Bryant & May match box case. £6

Cherry Blossom Snowene white cleaner and contents. £5

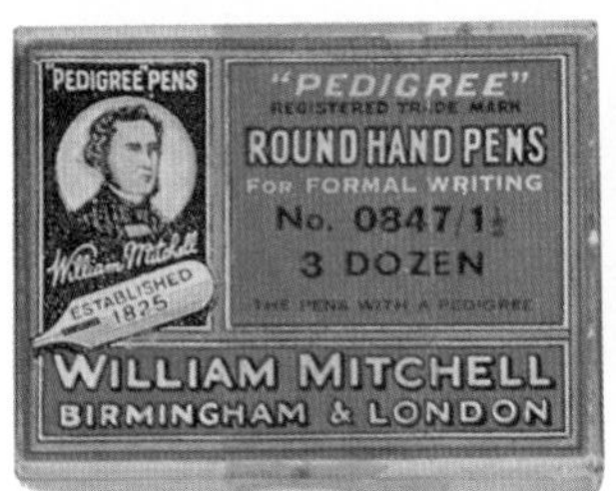

Pedigree Round Hand Pens by William Mitchell. £1

Fairy Segs Shoe Studs. £2

Trower's Shell Sand for all kinds of cage Birds. £4

(Douglas Morgan)

Slippery Elm Food prepared by Dr Thompson's. £6

Heinz Dried Sage. £3

Matte $^1/_2$ lb pack with contents. £4

Dr Watson's Tonic Stout with contents, circa 1920. £7

Birds Custard Powder sachet, Wartime Issue. £3

Fryco Sparkling Orange. £7

Blue sugar bag $1^1/_2$ lbs. £6

George Murray packet of tea. £6

Lyle's Golden Syrup, 2 lb tin. £13

L. Cook Fruit Grower, box for marmalade. £3

(Douglas Morgan)

Peacock's Angela Burdette Plums. £7

Bovril Fluid Beef jar with contents. £15

Colman's superfine compound Mustard. £4

Burdall's Gravy Salt. £8

Edwards Desiccated Soup. £20

Bird's Golden Raising Powder. £5

Hill Evans & Co pure malt vinegar. £12

Orlox Beef Suet, 1 lb box. £7

Edwards Desiccated Soups, packet. £1

Camp coffee and chicory essence, 1930's. £10

Pitman Vitanut Flakes. £3

(Douglas Morgan)

Snowene white cleaner and contents. £7

Veritas Mantles for Strength and Brilliancy. £6

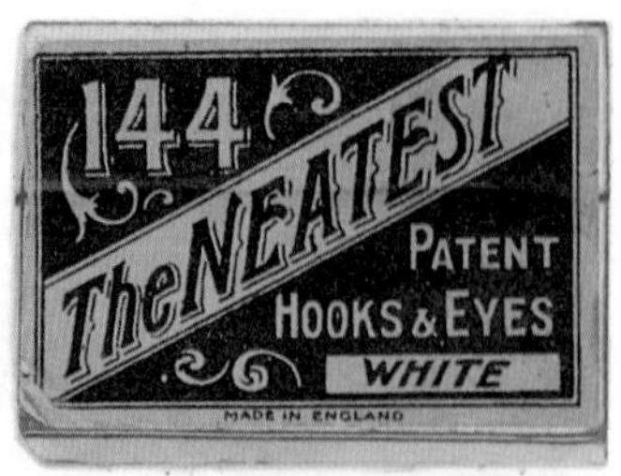

The Neatest, Patent Hooks & Eyes. £2

Ivy Drawing Pins, Superior quality. £2

Dura-glit metal polish, wartime pack, together with contents. £15

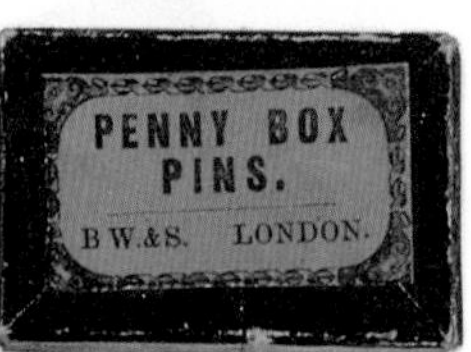

Penny Box Pins by BW&S London. £2

Kirby's Diamond Polished Darning Needles. £2

Waverley Pennibs, 3007 Newspapers recommend them. £3

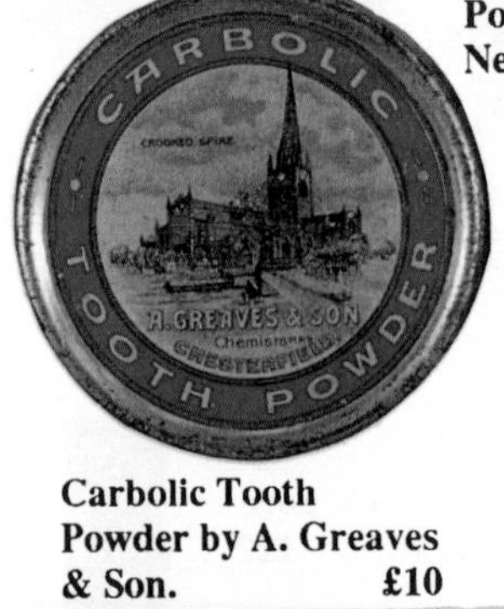

Carbolic Tooth Powder by A. Greaves & Son. £10

Oil of Rosemary by Potter & Clark. £10

Stag gummed jam pot covers. 50p

(Douglas Morgan)

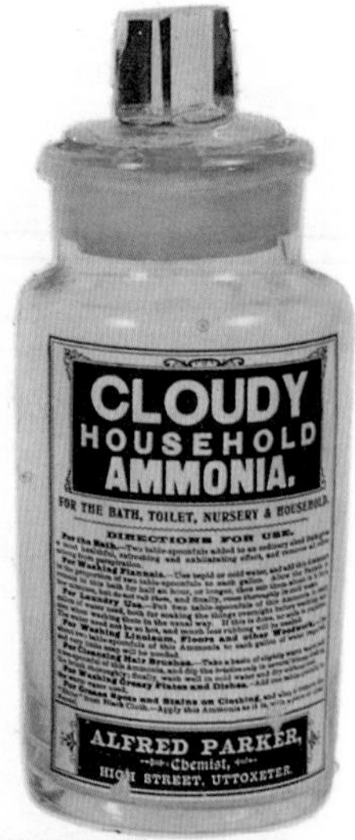

Cloudy Household Ammonia by Alfred Parker. £15

Corn Silk packet and contents by Alfred Parker. £2

Sanitas Moth Tablets including contents. £5

Doto Crystal double filament lamps, 105 V, 25 W, 1930's. £6

Perseverance Japanned Pins. £2

Oasaloid Nickel Plated Darning Needles. £2

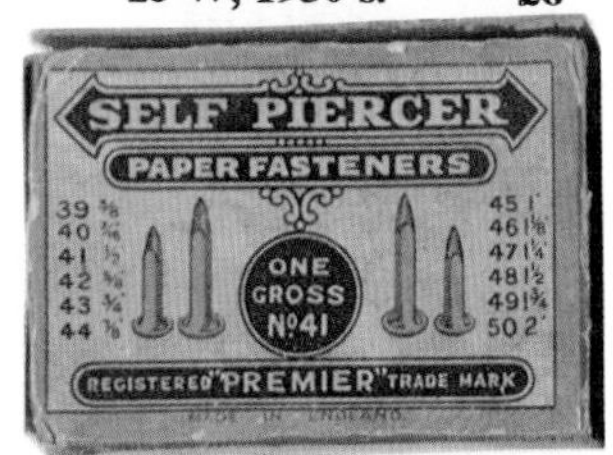

Self Piercer Paper Fasteners, Premier. £2

Lane's Superfine Wax Boot Polish. £4

Lektra, Brilliant Plate Powder. £3

Butterfly Brand Mending Tape. £2

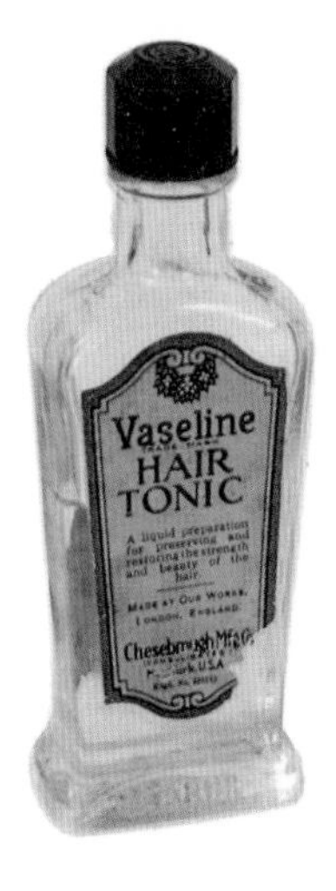

Vaseline Hair Tonic. £3

Harlene Camomile shampoo sachet. £6

(Douglas Morgan)

Octim, makes water work wonders, 1948. £4

Screen Chills and Macabre Stories, 1960, No. 1. £15

Film Fiction, from the month's best pictures, August 1921, No. 1. £50

Screen Pictorial, Britain's only film Magazine, July 1935, No. 1. £20

(Denis Gifford)

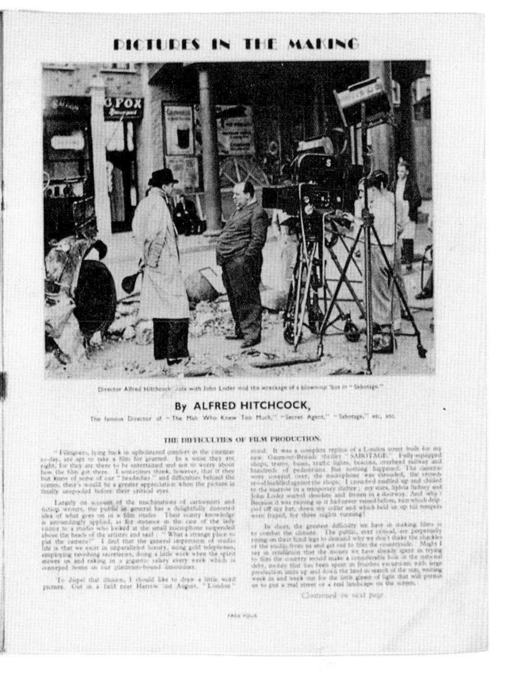

British Screen, featuring Jessie Matthews, March 1937, No. 1. £25

Talkie Topics, available only to members of the Lux Toilet Soap Movie Club, 1938, No. 1. £35

(Denis Gifford)

The Shadow Stage, the Foremost Motion Picture Magazine in the Kingdom, July 1919, No. 1. £25

Picture Plays, featuring Miss Alma Taylor, November 15th 1919, No. 1. £35

Picturegoer Monthly, January 1921, No. 1. £35

(Denis Gifford)

Film Pictorial, with free Star Portrait Album, February 27th 1932, No. 1. £35

Picturegoer Weekly, featuring Marlene Dietrich, May 30th 1931, No. 1. £35

(Denis Gifford)

The Cinegoer, A study of Charlie Chaplin in private life, February 26th 1916, No. 1. £25

The Picturegoer, The Picture Theatre Weekly Magazine, October 11th 1913, No. 1. £50

(Denis Gifford)

The Picture Show, For people who go to the pictures, with free art plate of Mary Pickford, May 3rd 1919, No. 1. £40

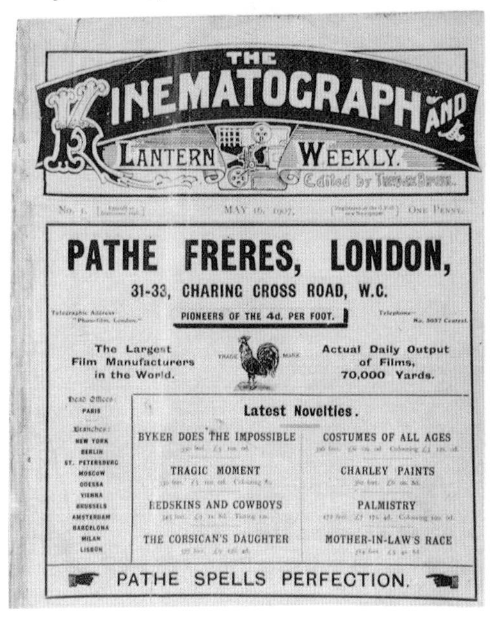

The Kinematograph And Lantern Weekly, May 16th 1907, No. 1. £100

Cinema Chat, with free plate of Pearl White, 26th May 1919, No. 1. £30

(Denis Gifford)

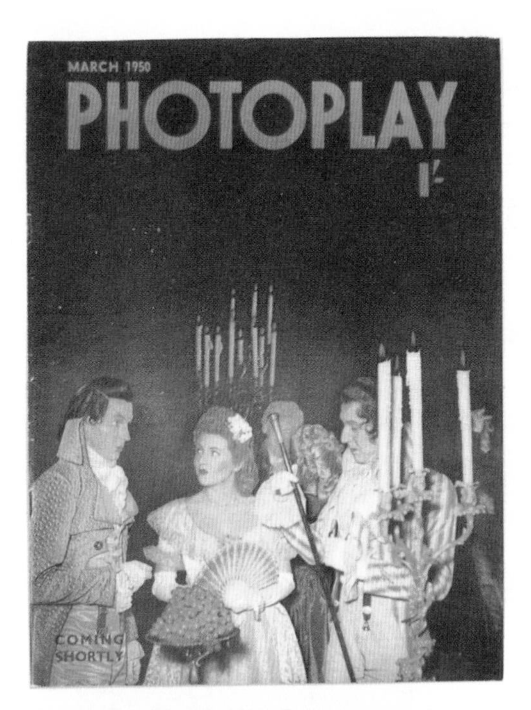

Photoplay, March 1950, British Series, No. 1. £25

Girls' Cinema No. 212, November 1, 1924. £20

A.B.C. Film Review featuring Dennis Price and Gisele Preville, January 1949, No. 1. £15

(Denis Gifford)

Standard 6d Aeroplane, Not to be Held, early 1960's. £4

Standard Fireworks Poster, with Firework Man, 1960's. £8

Wizard 4½d Golden Glory, late 1950's. £3

Standard 1d Robot Signal, early 1960's. £4

Standard 1/5 (7p) Sky Rocket, 1970. £3

Standard British Made Sparklers, ½d packet, early 1960's. £4

Standard Fireworks Poster, early 1960's. £8

(Paul Surridge)

Standard Giant Sparklers, 1½ minutes Continuous Display, 6d pack, mid 1950's. £8

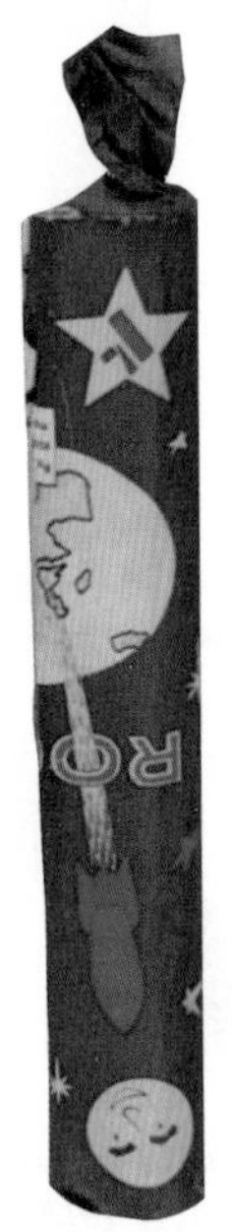

Wizard 1/- Rocket, late 1950's. £3

Standard Robot Signal Showcard, Traffic Signals in Fireworks!, 2d, early 1960's. £5

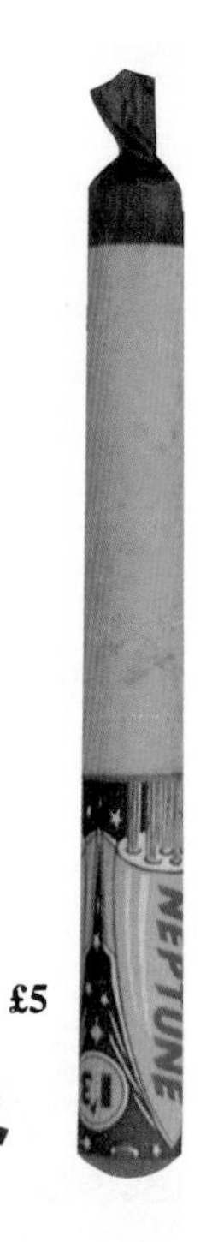

Brock's 1/3 Neptune Rocket, late 1950's. £4

Brock's 2/- Space Rocket, late 1950's. £4

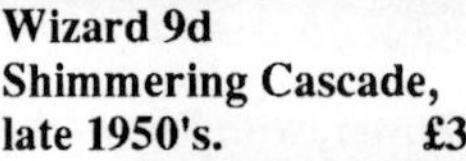

Wizard 9d Shimmering Cascade, late 1950's. £3

Guy's Assorted Fireworks Showcard, 6 Assorted Fireworks 1/-, early 1960's. £5

Brock's Mini Rockets, with Launching Pad, 6 for 1/9, early 1960's. £5

Standard Super 1/- Sparklers, Must Not be Held Near Clothing, early 1960's. £4

Standard 3d Roman Candle, early 1960's. £2

Display Box of Brock's Fireworks, 10/- box, late 1950's. £5

(Paul Surridge)

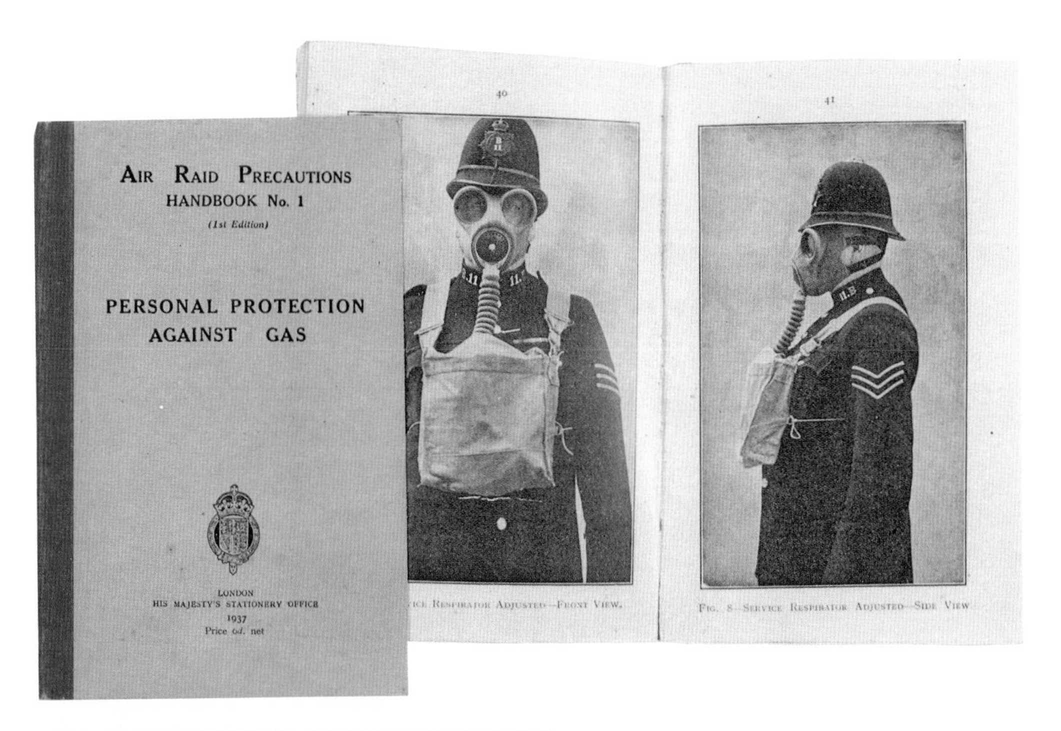

Air Raid Precautions, No. 1, Personal Protection against Gas, H.M.S.O. £5

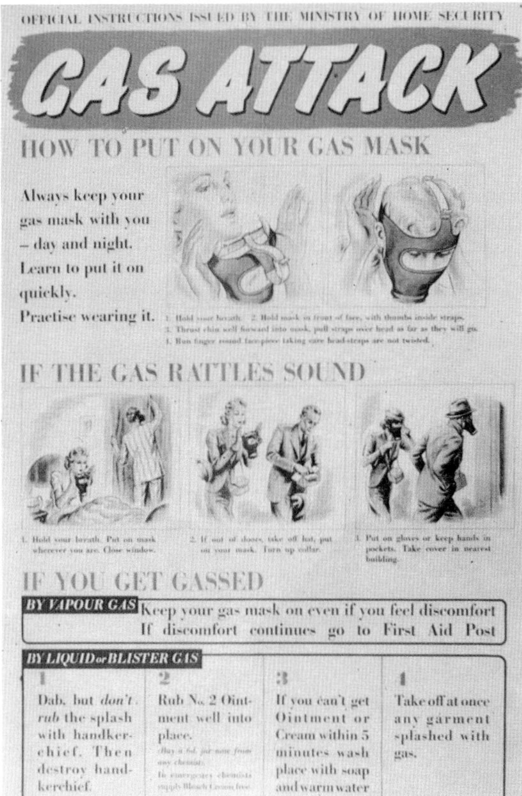

Gas Attack poster issued by The Ministry of Home Security. £8

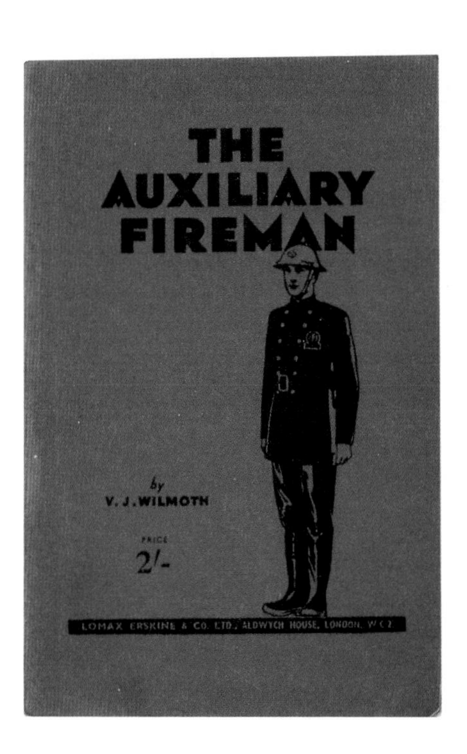

The Auxiliary Fireman by V. J. Wilmoth. £5

(Douglas Morgan)

National Registration Identity Card, 1940. £1

Clothing Book 1946–47. £1

SPOON MEASURE

WHERE spoon measures are required it is very necessary that a standard type should be used. At the foot of this page you will see oval shaped diagrams in three sizes. They represent the outside measurements of the recognised standard size teaspoon, dessertspoon, and tablespoon. Place your own spoons over these patterns and they should fit exactly. You can then safely use these for your smaller measures. For a level spoonful fill the spoon to edge level and smooth off any surplus with a knife. This will

MOF

HOW TO MAKE A HANDY KITCHEN MEASURE

WAR-TIME food shortages and the advent of new foods like dried eggs and household milk mean that the housewife has to try her hand at many new recipes. Good results cannot be expected unless the ingredients are measured out accurately. But war-time shortages also extend to kitchen equipment and many households are unable to obtain proper scales or measures. Following out recipes by guesswork or by using cupfuls or handfuls as measurements is liable to lead to disappointment. This can be avoided if a handy kitchen measure is made from a 2 lb. jam jar as described in the following pages. Housewives will find the measure saves time and labour and avoids waste.

Ministry of Food Leaflet How to make a handy kitchen measure, 1940. £2

Selo film wallet. £2

Kodak film wallet. £2

(Douglas Morgan)

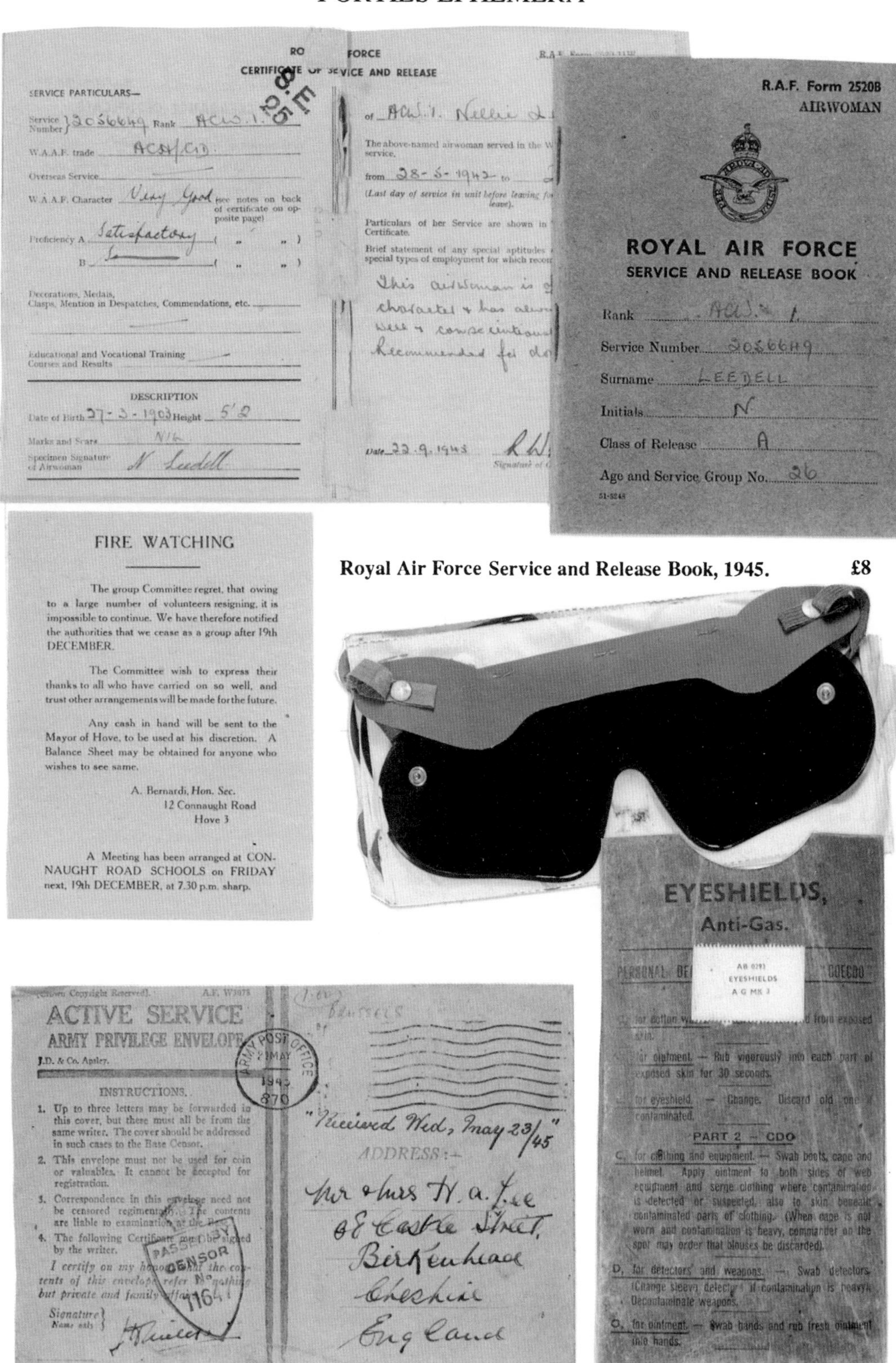

ROYAL AIR FORCE
CERTIFICATE OF SERVICE AND RELEASE

SERVICE PARTICULARS—

Service Number 2056649 Rank ACW.1

W.A.A.F. trade ACH/GD

Overseas Service

W.A.A.F. Character Very Good (see notes on back of certificate on opposite page)

Proficiency A Satisfactory („ „)

B („ „)

Decorations, Medals, Clasps, Mention in Despatches, Commendations, etc.

Educational and Vocational Training Courses and Results

DESCRIPTION

Date of Birth 27-3-1903 Height 5'2

Marks and Scars Nil

Specimen Signature of Airwoman N Leedell

of ACW.1 Nellie L...

The above-named airwoman served in the W... service.

from 28-5-1942 to ...

(Last day of service in unit before leaving for ... leave).

Particulars of her Service are shown in ... Certificate.

Brief statement of any special aptitudes ... special types of employment for which recom...

This airwoman is of ... character & has alw... well & conscientious... Recommended for do...

Date 22.9.1945

R.A.F. Form 2520B
AIRWOMAN

ROYAL AIR FORCE
SERVICE AND RELEASE BOOK

Rank ACW. 1

Service Number 2056649

Surname LEEDELL

Initials N

Class of Release A

Age and Service Group No. 26

FIRE WATCHING

The group Committee regret, that owing to a large number of volunteers resigning, it is impossible to continue. We have therefore notified the authorities that we cease as a group after 19th DECEMBER.

The Committee wish to express their thanks to all who have carried on so well, and trust other arrangements will be made for the future.

Any cash in hand will be sent to the Mayor of Hove, to be used at his discretion. A Balance Sheet may be obtained for anyone who wishes to see same.

A. Bernardi, Hon. Sec.
12 Connaught Road
Hove 3

A Meeting has been arranged at CONNAUGHT ROAD SCHOOLS on FRIDAY next, 19th DECEMBER, at 7.30 p.m. sharp.

Royal Air Force Service and Release Book, 1945. £8

EYESHIELDS,
Anti-Gas.

AB 0291
EYESHIELDS
A G MK 2

PART 2 — CDO

C. for clothing and equipment. — Swab boots, cape and helmet. Apply ointment to both sides of web equipment and serge clothing where contamination is detected or suspected, also to skin beneath contaminated parts of clothing. (When cape is not worn and contamination is heavy, commander on the spot may order that blouses be discarded).

D. for detectors and weapons. — Swab detectors. (Change sleeve) detector if contamination is heavy. Decontaminate weapons.

O. for ointment. — Swab hands and rub fresh ointment into hands.

(Crown Copyright Reserved) A.F. W3078

ACTIVE SERVICE
ARMY PRIVILEGE ENVELOPE

J.D. & Co. Apsley.

INSTRUCTIONS.

1. Up to three letters may be forwarded in this cover, but these must all be from the same writer. The cover should be addressed in such cases to the Base Censor.
2. This envelope must not be used for coin or valuables. It cannot be accepted for registration.
3. Correspondence in this envelope need not be censored regimentally. The contents are liable to examination at the Base.
4. The following Certificate must be signed by the writer.

I certify on my honour that the contents of this envelope refer to nothing but private and family affairs.

Signature (Name only)

ARMY POST OFFICE 21 MAY 1945 870

PASSED BY CENSOR No 11641

"Received Wed, May 23/45"

ADDRESS:—
Mr & Mrs W. A. Lee
8E Castle Street,
Birkenhead
Cheshire
England

Active Service Army Privilege envelope, 1945. £1

Anti-Gas Eyeshields, pack of six, clear & opaque. £5

(Douglas Morgan)

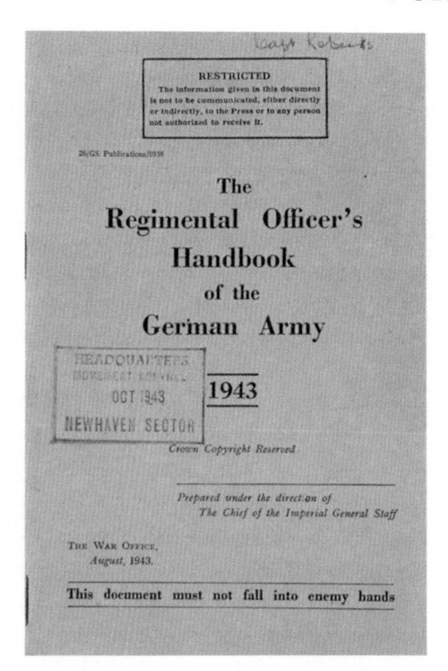

RESTRICTED
The information given in this document is not to be communicated, either directly or indirectly, to the Press or to any person not authorized to receive it.

26/GS. Publications/1038

The
Regimental Officer's
Handbook
of the
German Army
1943

HEADQUARTERS
OCT 1943
NEWHAVEN SECTOR

Crown Copyright Reserved

Prepared under the direction of
The Chief of the Imperial General Staff

The War Office,
August, 1943.

This document must not fall into enemy hands

The Regimental Officer's Handbook of the German Army, 1943. £4

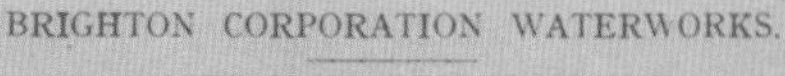

BRIGHTON CORPORATION WATERWORKS.

WATER SUPPLY IN EMERGENCY.

Should heavy bombing cause widespread damage to Watermains, supplies will be maintained by means of Tanks carried on Lorries. The Lorries will patrol the affected areas during daylight hours and will at intervals sound one short and two long blasts on their horns as a signal that water is available. The ration of water under such circumstances, will be limited to two gallons per person, per day.

Should the supply to your house be affected, conserve the contents of your Hot-water Tanks and Cisterns as a standby and ration accordingly.

A. B. CATHCART,
Waterworks Engineer.

12, Bond Street,
Brighton, 1.
April, 1943.

A61213. 70m. 4/43.

Water Supply in Emergency, information leaflet, April, 1943. £1

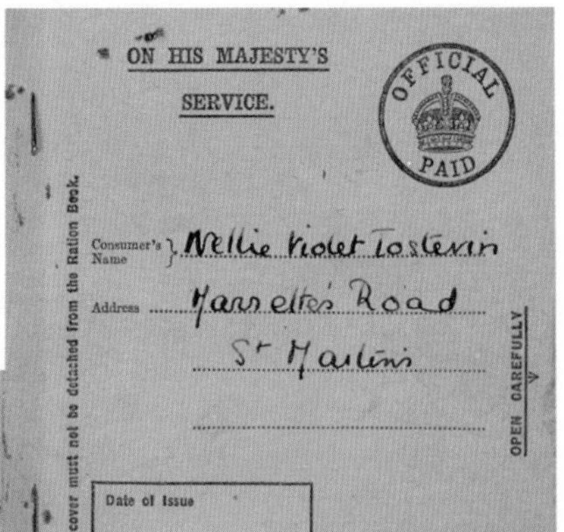

ON HIS MAJESTY'S SERVICE.

OFFICIAL PAID

Consumer's Name Nellie Violet Tostevin

Address Marrettes Road
St Martins

This cover must not be detached from the Ration Book.

OPEN CAREFULLY

Date of Issue

IF FOUND, RETURN TO
GUERNSEY
FOOD OFFICE.

Serial Number of Book.

JD 383165

R.B. 1. [General]

Ration Book for Guernsey, 1940's. £2

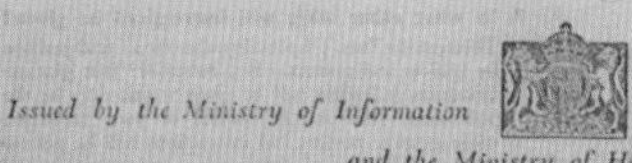

Issued by the Ministry of Information in co-operation with the War Office and the Ministry of Home Security

Beating the INVADER

A MESSAGE FROM THE PRIME MINISTER

If invasion comes, everyone—young or old, men and women—will be eager to play their part worthily. By far the greater part of the country will not be immediately involved. Even along our coasts, the greater part will remain unaffected. But where the enemy lands, or tries to land, there will be most violent fighting. Not only will there be the battles when the enemy tries to come ashore, but afterwards there will fall upon his lodgments very heavy British counter-attacks, and all the time the lodgments will be under the heaviest attack by British bombers. The fewer civilians or non-combatants in these areas, the better—apart from essential workers who must remain. So if you are advised by the authorities to leave the place where you live, it is your duty to go elsewhere when you are told to leave. When the attack begins, it will be too late to go; and, unless you receive definite instructions to move, your duty then will be to stay where you are. You will have to get into the safest place you can find, and stay there until the battle is over. For all of you then the order and the duty will be: "STAND FIRM".

This also applies to people inland if any considerable number of parachutists or air-borne troops are landed in their neighbourhood. Above all, they must not cumber the roads. Like their fellow-countrymen on the coasts, they must "STAND FIRM". The Home Guard, supported by strong mobile columns wherever the enemy's numbers require it, will immediately come to grips with the invaders, and there is little doubt will soon destroy them.

Throughout the rest of the country where there is no fighting going on and no close cannon fire or rifle fire can be heard, everyone will govern his conduct by the second great order and duty, namely, "CARRY ON". It may easily be some weeks before the invader has been totally destroyed, that is to say, killed or captured to the last man who has landed on our shores. Meanwhile, all work must be continued to the utmost, and no time lost.

The following notes have been prepared to tell everyone in rather more detail what to do, and they should be carefully studied. Each man and woman should think out a clear plan of personal action in accordance with the general scheme.

Winston S. Churchill

STAND FIRM

1. What do I do if fighting breaks out in my neighbourhood?

Keep indoors or in your shelter until the battle is over. If you can have a trench ready in your garden or field, so much the better. You may want to use it for protection if your house is damaged. But if you are at work, or if you have special orders, carry on as long as possible and only take cover when danger approaches. If you are on your way to work, finish your journey if you can.

If you see an enemy tank, or a few enemy soldiers, do not assume that the enemy are in control of the area. What you have seen may be a party sent on in advance, or stragglers from the main body who can easily be rounded up.

Ministry of Information leaflet for Beating the Invader, 1940. £2

THIS IS TO CERTIFY that
Mrs N E WILSON
of 74 Hurst Rd
is a member of a fire-fighting party organised by the Eastbourne Borough Council and possesses the powers of entry and of taking steps for extinguishing fire or for protecting property, or rescuing persons or property, from fire, which are conferred by the Fire Precautions (Access to Premises) (No. 2) Order, 1941.

Town Clerk

Fire Precautions Identity Card, 1941. £1

(Douglas Morgan)

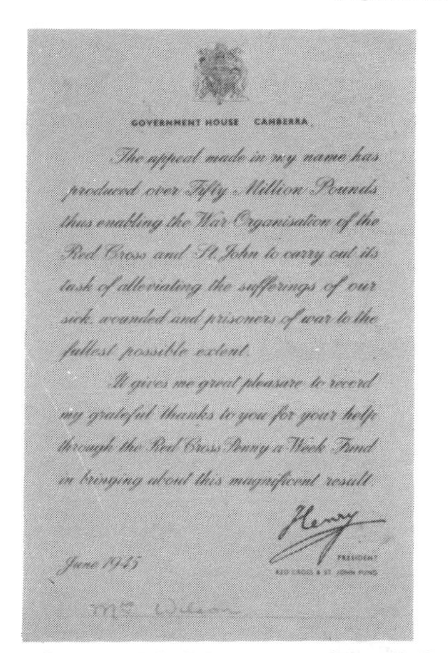
GOVERNMENT HOUSE CANBERRA

The appeal made in my name has produced over Fifty Million Pounds thus enabling the War Organisation of the Red Cross and St. John to carry out its task of alleviating the sufferings of our sick, wounded and prisoners of war to the fullest possible extent.

It gives me great pleasure to record my grateful thanks to you for your help through the Red Cross Penny a Week Fund in bringing about this magnificent result.

Henry
PRESIDENT
RED CROSS & ST. JOHN FUND

June 1945

Red Cross and St John appeal, June 1945. £1

Hygienic Domestic
SANDBAG
LINEN LINED

Hygienic Domestic Sandbag, linen lined, 1940's, 20 ins x 14 ins. £5

McGlennon's Book of choruses. £1.50

POST OFFICE SAVINGS BANK BOOK
KEEP THIS BOOK IN A SAFE PLACE
Its loss may cause you trouble

Post Office Savings Bank Book, 1941. £3

Lewisham Thanksgiving Celebrations Programme, 1945. £8

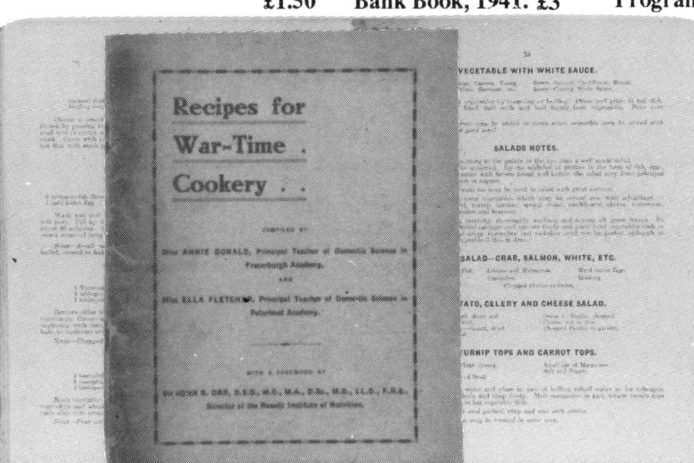

'Recipes for War-Time Cookery ' by Annie Donald and Ella Fletcher. £6

Speedway at Newcross programme, 1947 season. £12

(Douglas Morgan)

'In Affectionate Remembrance', embossed porcelain wreath embellishment, circa 1910, 4" high. £6

In Memoriam, Bacup Cemetery, 1913. £5

'A Token of Respect', embossed porcelain wreath embellishment, circa 1910, 4" high. £6

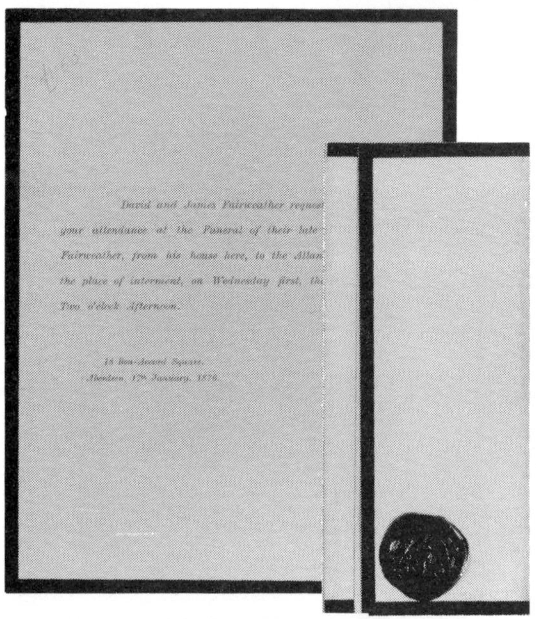

Funeral, Allanvale Cemetery, Aberdeen, 1876. £3

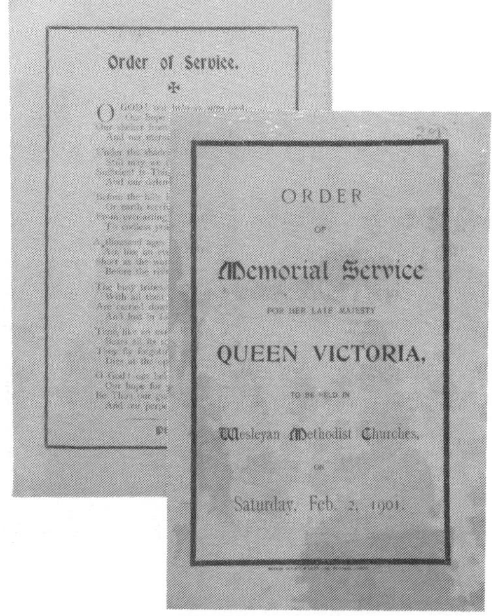

Memorial Service for Queen Victoria, Wesleyan Methodist Churches, 1901. £2

Funeral Hymns. £2

'A Token of Respect' embossed porcelain wreath embellishment, circa 1910, 4½" diameter. £6

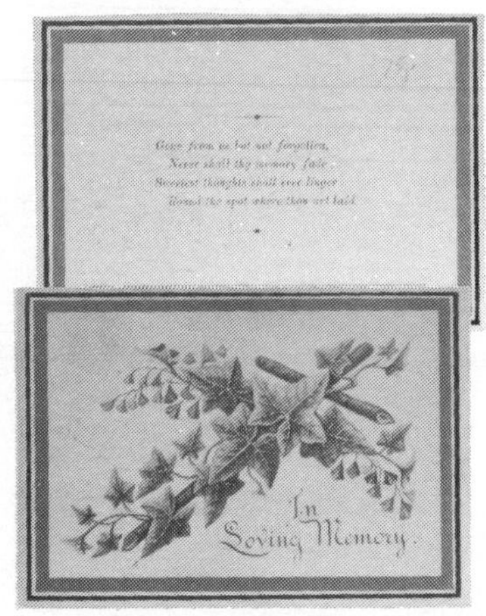

In Loving Memory, Gone From Us But Not Forgotten. £2

(Yesterdays Paper)

General Interest 1899, 'King – Manager of Chinese Telegraphs who witheld despatches from European legations'. £3

No. 200 Actresses 1900. Lily Langtry, her latest creation and success in 'The Degenerates'. £7

General Interest, white panel base D 1900, H.R.H. The Prince of Wales. £2

Large format Boer War Base D 1900, Admiral Kempff, U.S. Commander in Chief on China Station. £3

Large format Theatre Artistes 1899, Monnie Emerald by Webber, Lancaster. £5

General Interest unnumbered 1898, Col. Baden-Powell. £3

No. 839 1900, Actresses, Alexandra Dagmar. £3

No. 254 1899, General Interest, Statesman and Leaders, The Rt. Hon. Sir Frank Cavendish Lascelles, G.C.B. £2

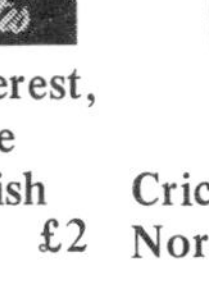

A. GREENWELL
NORTHUMBERLAND.
Ogden's Guinea Gold Cigarettes

Cricketers 1898, A. Greenwell, Northumberland. £10

(Border Bygones)

Hobby Horses, With Riders By Guinness. £30

Prodigies and Prodigals, 1946. £20

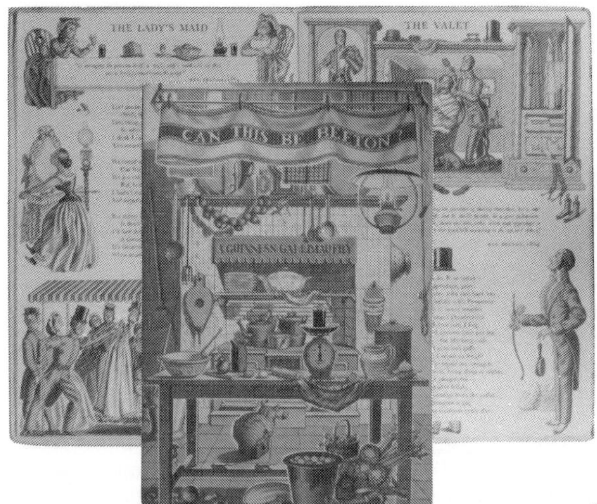

A Guinness Gallimaufry 'Can This Be Beeton?'. £30

Guinness Dublin, History of the Company 1939. £8

Album Victorianum. £25

A Guinness Sportfolio. £25

(Yesterdays Paper)

A 19th century cotton handkerchief printed in black and red depicting four children playing lawn tennis, 13½ x 14in. (Christie's S. Ken) £462

Polychrome printed silk commemorative handkerchief, America, circa 1866, 32 x 30in. (Skinner) £913

Arsenal Football Club, Season 1930-31. Holders of the English Cup, **a commemorative cotton handkerchief, 15 x 15in. (Christie's S. Ken) £143**

An early 19th century ivory silk handkerchief printed with Hackney Coach and Cabriolet Fares, Regulations and Acts of Parliament, 88 x 92cm., circa 1833. (Phillips) £120

Le Tennis, a crepe handkerchief, printed in green with figures playing tennis, signed *Raoul Dufy,* 15in. square, circa 1918-1924. (Christie's S. Ken) £935

Early 19th Century printed handkerchief Apotheosis of George Washington, England, 26 x 19½in. £800

'The Reformers attack on the Old Rotten Tree – of the Foul Nests of our Morants in Danger', handkerchief printed in colour on silk, circa 1830. £300

Declaration of the Independence of the United States of America, July 1776, a printed cotton handkerchief depicting the scene with the protagonists listed, 30 x 31in., circa 1840. (Christie's) £605

'A representation of the Manchester Reform Meeting dispersed by the Civil and Military Powers, August 16, 1819', handkerchief on linen, 20 x 22in. £425

Weird Shorts, G. Swan Publication, 1940's. £7

Seven Strange Stories, Glasgow Publication, 1940's. £3

Occult, G. Swan Publications, 1940's. £6

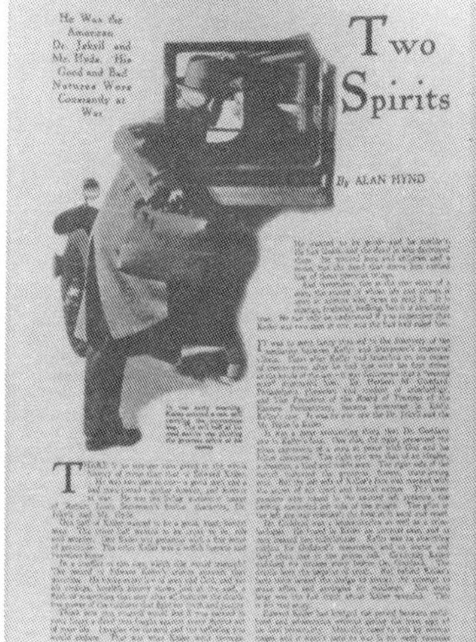

He Was the American Dr. Jekyll and Mr. Hyde. His Good and Bad Natures Were Constantly at War

Two Spirits Fierce Warred within His Soul

By ALAN HYND

True Strange Stories, Vol. 1, No. 1, March 1929. £20

Tales of Terror, Worlds Work Publication, 1937. £20

Strange Tales, by Hugh B. Cave, January 1933. £20

(Yesterdays Paper)

Tales of Magic and Mystery, March 1928. £20

Haunted and Hunted, Dublin Publication, 1940's. £4

Strange Tales, Second Selection, Utopian Publications, 1940's. £6

Strange Tales, Utopian Publication, 1940's. £6

The Witch's Tales, Vol. 1, No. 2, Dec. 1936. £15

Tales of the Uncanny, No. 2, British Publication, 1937. £15

Weird Tales, H. P. Lovecraft Stories, June 1938. £25

Ghost Stories, Uncanny, Spooky, Creepy Tales, July 1929. £15

(Yesterdays Paper)

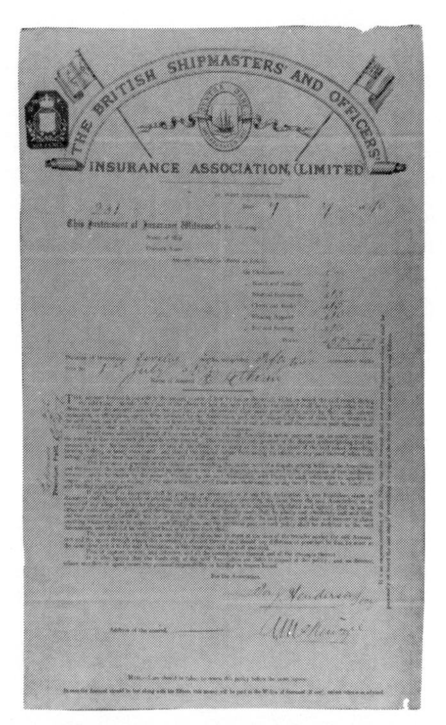
THE BRITISH SHIPMASTERS' AND OFFICERS' INSURANCE ASSOCIATION, LIMITED

British Shipmasters' and Officers Insurance Association Ltd., Policy covering effects dated 1890. £15

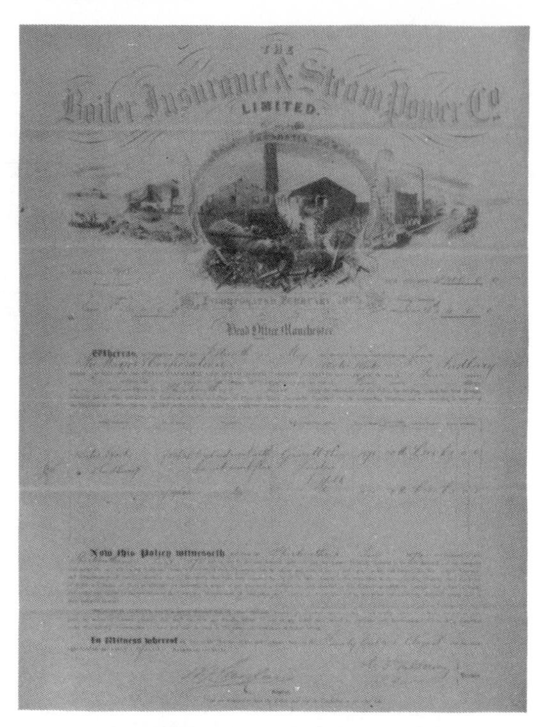
THE Boiler Insurance & Steam Power Co LIMITED

Head Office Manchester

Whereas

Now this Policy witnesseth

In Witness whereof

Boiler Insurance & Steam Power Co. Ltd., Policy for Sudbury Water Works dated 1874. £25

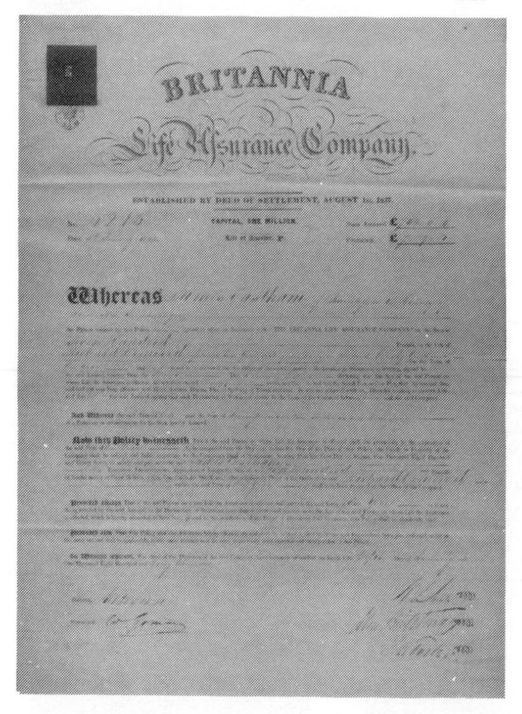
BRITANNIA

Life Assurance Company.

Whereas

Britannia Life Assurance Co., 1843, Policy for the Life of another, Large document on vellum. £45

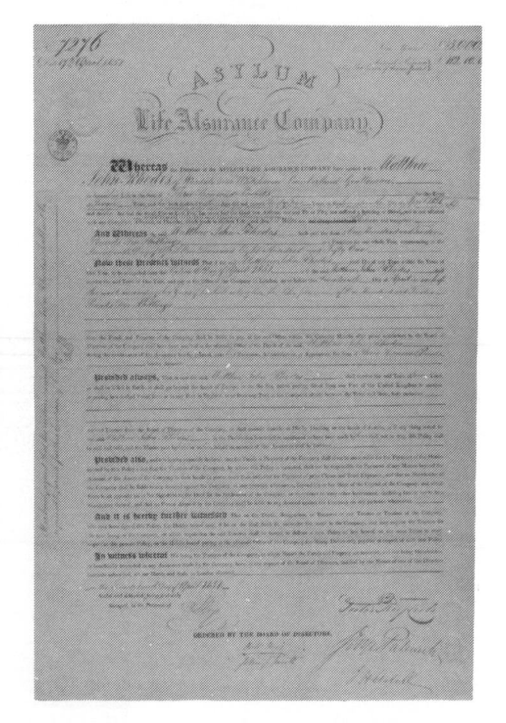
ASYLUM

Life Assurance Company

Whereas

Asylum Life Assurance Company, Policy dated 1851. £30

(M. Veissid & Co.)

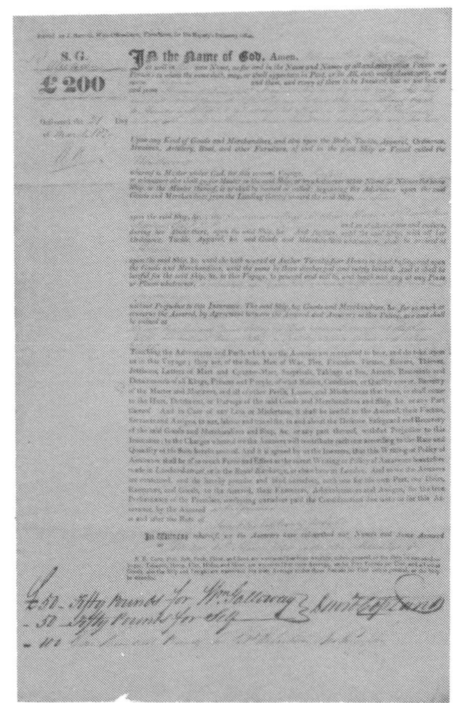
In the Name of God, Amen.

£200

An early Marine Policy dated 1829. £25

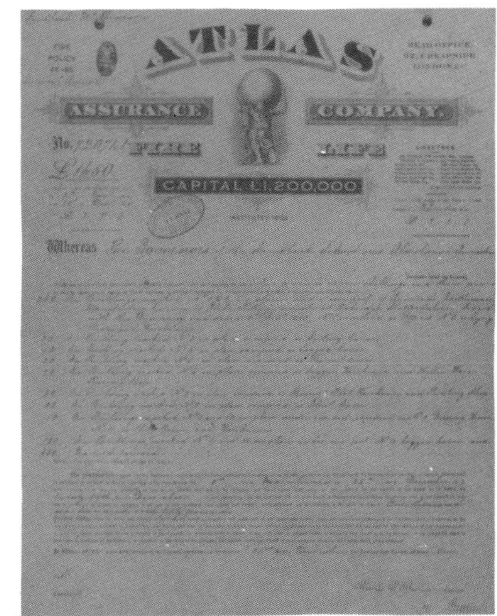
ATLAS ASSURANCE COMPANY

FIRE LIFE

CAPITAL £1,200,000

Whereas

Atlas Assurance Co., Fire Policy covering School buildings, 1892. £18

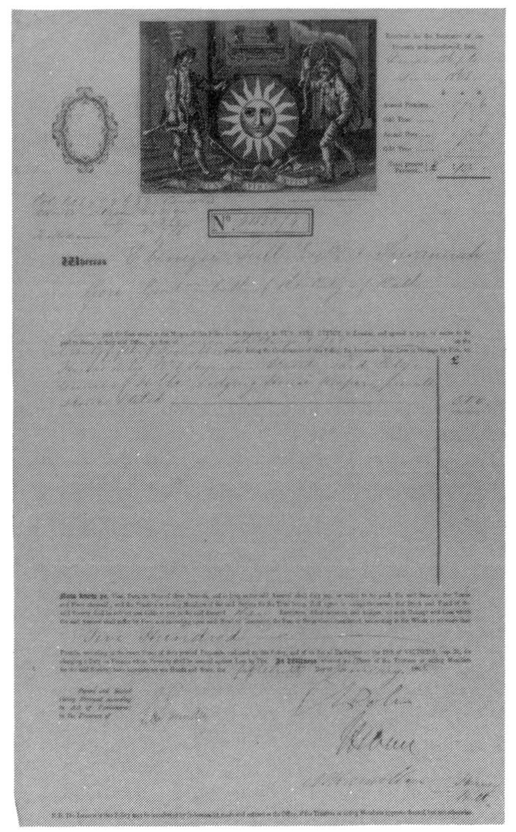
Whereas

Sun Fire Office, Policy dated 1868. £20

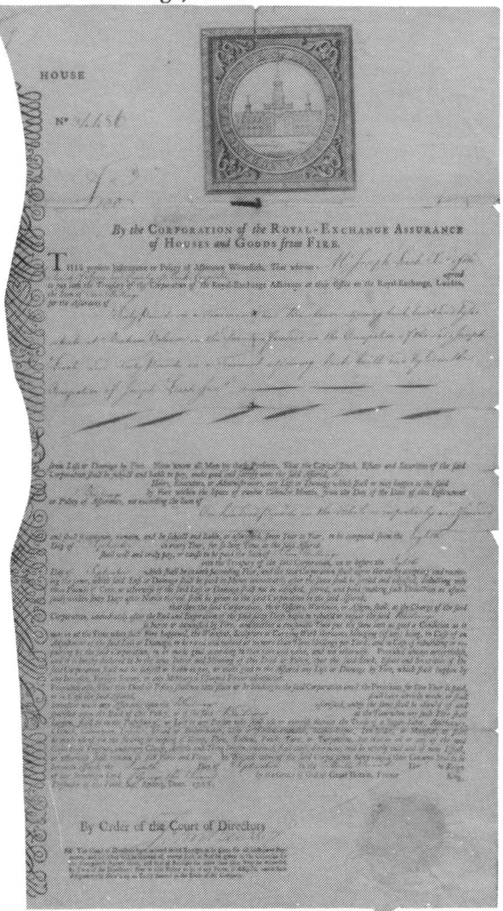
HOUSE

By the Corporation of the Royal-Exchange Assurance of Houses and Goods from Fire.

By Order of the Court of Directors

Corporation of the Royal Exchange Assurance of Houses and Goods from Fire, very early Policy covering a private house in 1758. £75

(M. Veissid & Co.)

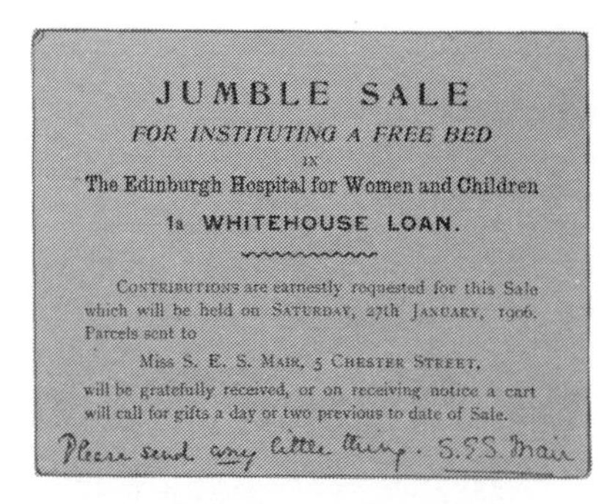

JUMBLE SALE
FOR INSTITUTING A FREE BED
IN
The Edinburgh Hospital for Women and Children
1a WHITEHOUSE LOAN.

CONTRIBUTIONS are earnestly requested for this Sale which will be held on SATURDAY, 27th JANUARY, 1906.
Parcels sent to
Miss S. E. S. MAIN, 5 CHESTER STREET,
will be gratefully received, or on receiving notice a cart will call for gifts a day or two previous to date of Sale.

Jumble Sale for Edinburgh Hospital for Women and Children, 27th Jan. 1906. £4

DEVONSHIRE HOUSE,
PICCADILLY, W.

FRIDAY, MAY 20TH 1910.
ADMIT BEARER.

GARDEN ENTRANCE, BERKELEY STREET, W.
52

Devonshire House, Friday 20th May 1910, Admit Bearer. £3

THE OFFICERS, N.C.O.'S AND AIRMEN
OF THE
ROYAL AIR FORCE, KISUMU
REQUEST THE PLEASURE OF THE COMPANY OF

AT AN
ALL RANKS DANCE
TO BE HELD IN
THE AIRMEN'S CANTEEN
ON
FRIDAY, 18TH AUGUST 1944.
AT 8-30 P.M.

Royal Air Force, Kisumu, 18th August 1944, 'All Ranks Dance'. £2

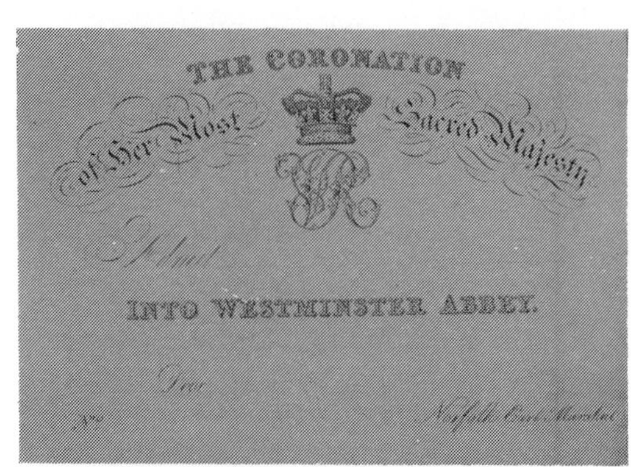

THE CORONATION
of Her Most Sacred Majesty
Admit
INTO WESTMINSTER ABBEY.

Invitation for the Coronation of Queen Victoria. £10

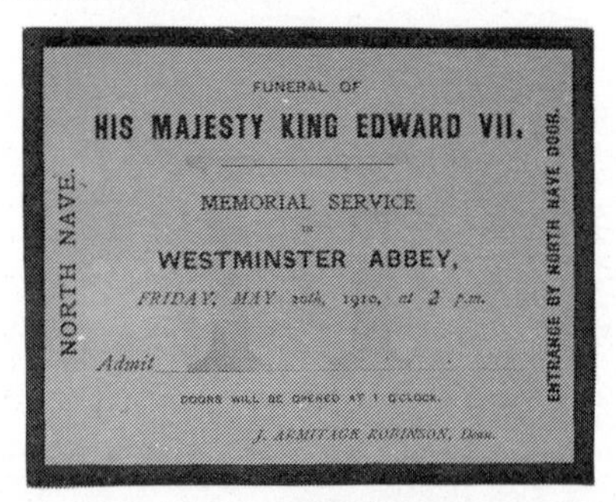

FUNERAL OF
HIS MAJESTY KING EDWARD VII.
MEMORIAL SERVICE
IN
WESTMINSTER ABBEY,
FRIDAY, MAY 20th, 1910, at 2 p.m.
Admit
DOORS WILL BE OPENED AT 1 O'CLOCK.
J. ARMITAGE ROBINSON, Dean.
NORTH NAVE.
ENTRANCE BY NORTH NAVE DOOR.

Funeral of His Majesty King Edward VII, Westminster Abbey, May 20th 1910. £6

Cottingley Coronation Festivities,
THURSDAY, JUNE 22nd, 1911.

You are cordially invited to join in the PROCESSION which will start from Main Street, Cottingley, at 1.0 o'clock prompt, and also in the SPORTS and GALA on the Plain.

Invitation to Cottingley Coronation Festivities, June 22nd 1911. £3

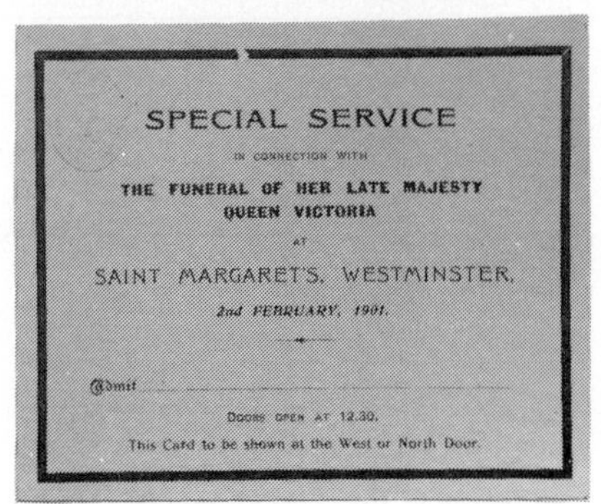

SPECIAL SERVICE
IN CONNECTION WITH
THE FUNERAL OF HER LATE MAJESTY
QUEEN VICTORIA
AT
SAINT MARGARET'S, WESTMINSTER,
2nd FEBRUARY, 1901.

Admit

DOORS OPEN AT 12.30.
This Card to be shown at the West or North Door.

Special Service for Her Late Majesty Queen Victoria, 2nd February 1901. £4

CORONATION
OF
HIS MAJESTY KING EDWARD VII.
THURSDAY, JUNE 26th, 1902.
PASS THE BEARER
TO
WESTMINSTER HALL.
In accordance with the Police Regulations.
Serjeant-at-Arms.

Pass to Westminster Hall for Coronation of Edward VII, June 26th 1902. £4

(Michael Moon)

Carlton Club, 'Admit One Lady', 27th June 1902. £3

Scotland v. England Ticket, Hampden, 17th April 1937. £3

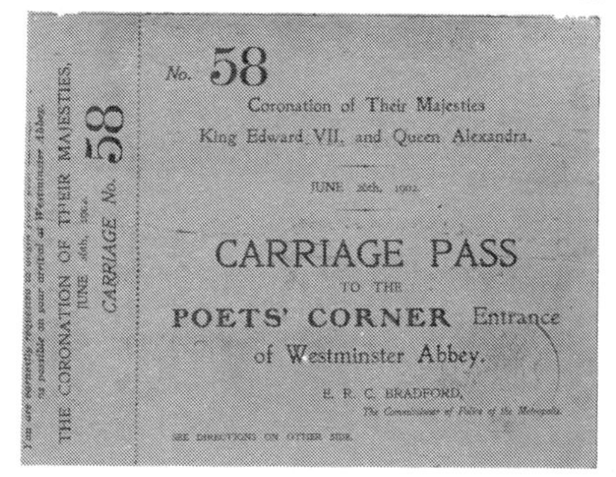

Carriage Pass to Coronation of King Edward VII, June 26th 1902. £6

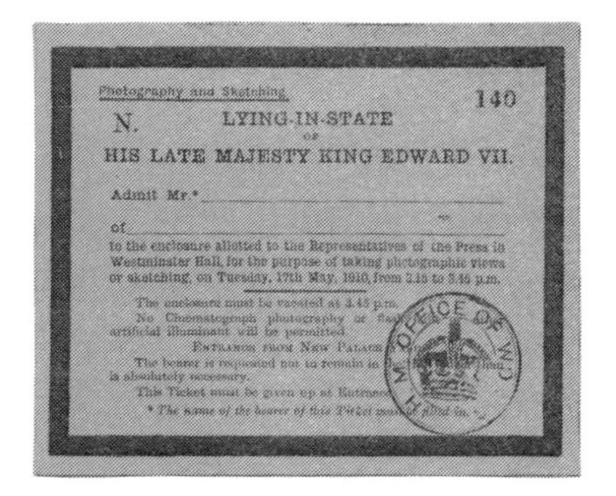

Lying-in-State of His Late Majesty King Edward VII, Photography & Sketching. £6

Scarborough Cricket Club, MCC v. Yorkshire, 2nd September 1953. £2

Coronation Procession, 27th June 1902, Grand Stand Charing Cross Station. £8

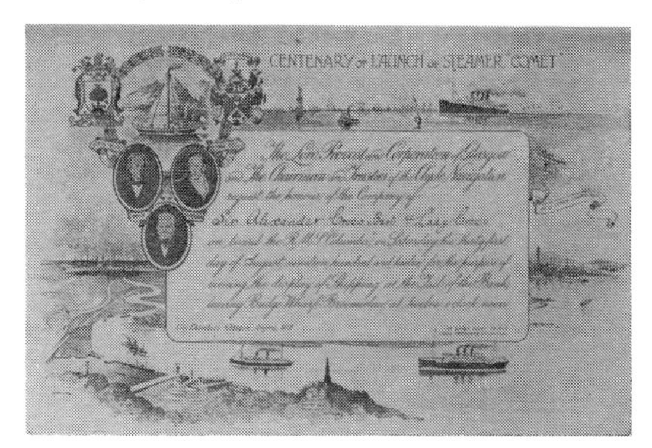

Centenary of Launch of Steamer 'Comet', 31st August 1912. £8

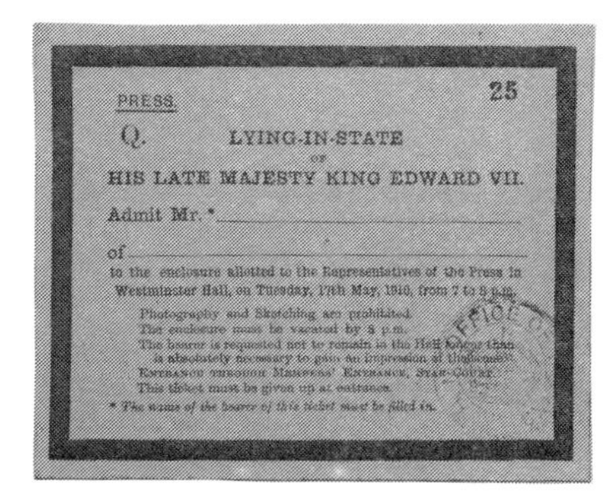

Lying-in-State of His Late Majesty King Edward VII, 'Press'. £4

(Michael Moon)

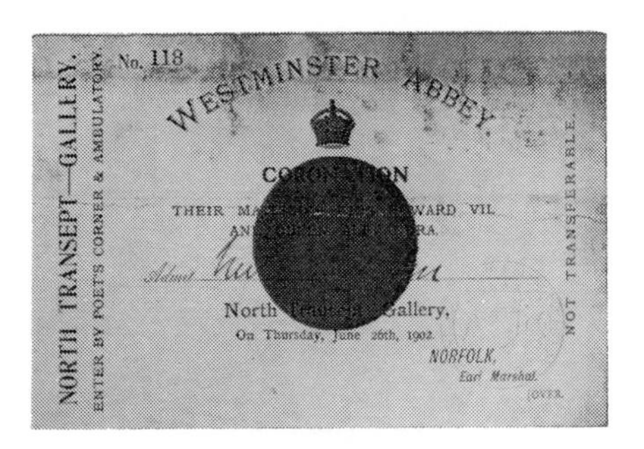

Invitation to Coronation of King Edward VII, June 26th 1902. £7

Royal Opera Covent Garden – Gala Performance, July 7th 1903 for the President of France. £6

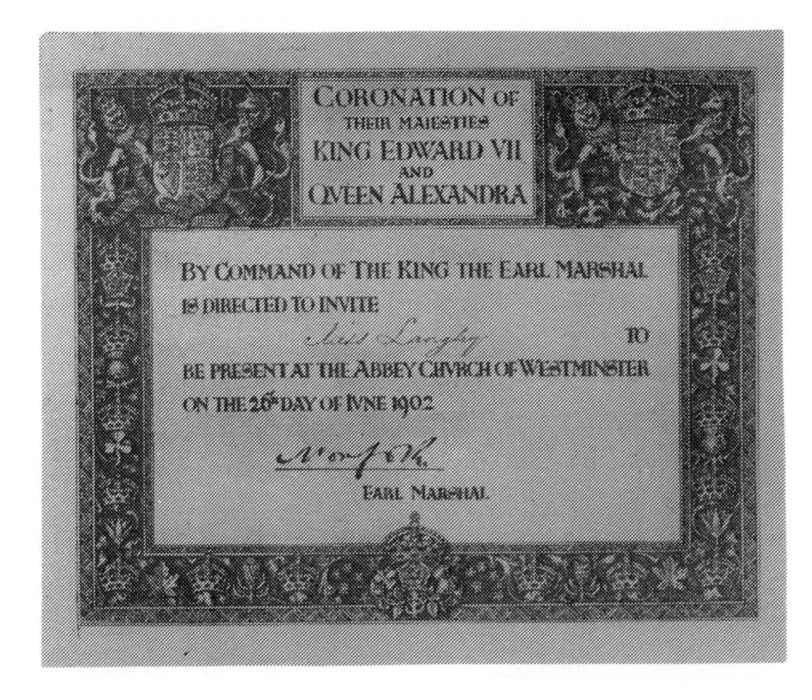

Coronation Invitation to the daughter of Miss Lilly Langtry, 26th June 1902. £10 

Alert Eagle Fire Society invitation, dated Boston Feb. 25, 1800, signed in plate D. Staniford del and S. Hill SC 1800, 7½ x 6½in. (Skinner) £543

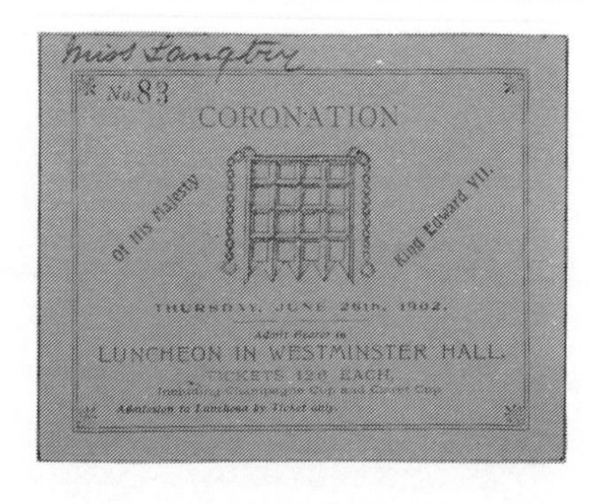

Coronation of His Majesty Edward VII, June 26th 1902. £6

(Michael Moon)

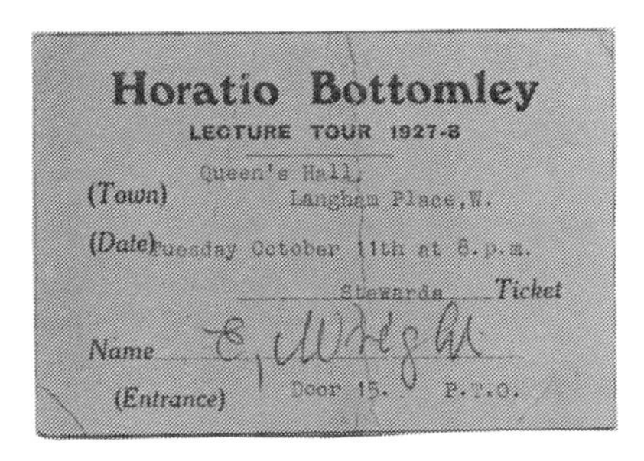
Horatio Bottomley
LECTURE TOUR 1927-8
(Town) Queen's Hall, Langham Place, W.
(Date) Tuesday October 11th at 8.p.m.
Stewards Ticket
Name E. Wright
(Entrance) Door 15. P.T.O.

Horatio Bottomley Lecture Tour, 1927–28. £3

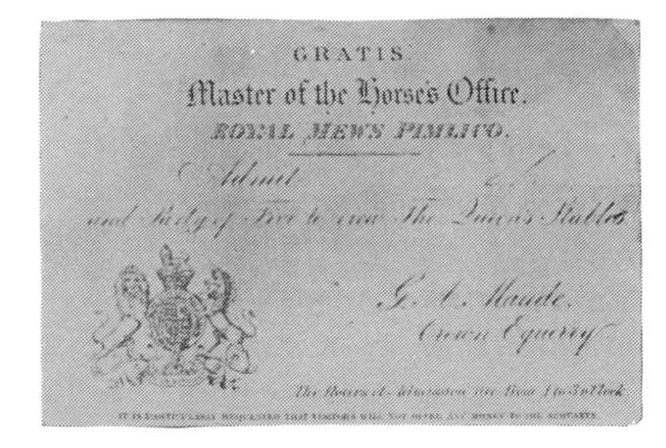
GRATIS
Master of the Horses Office.
ROYAL MEWS PIMLICO.
Admit
G. A. Maude.
Crown Equerry

Invitation to View the Queen's Stables. £4

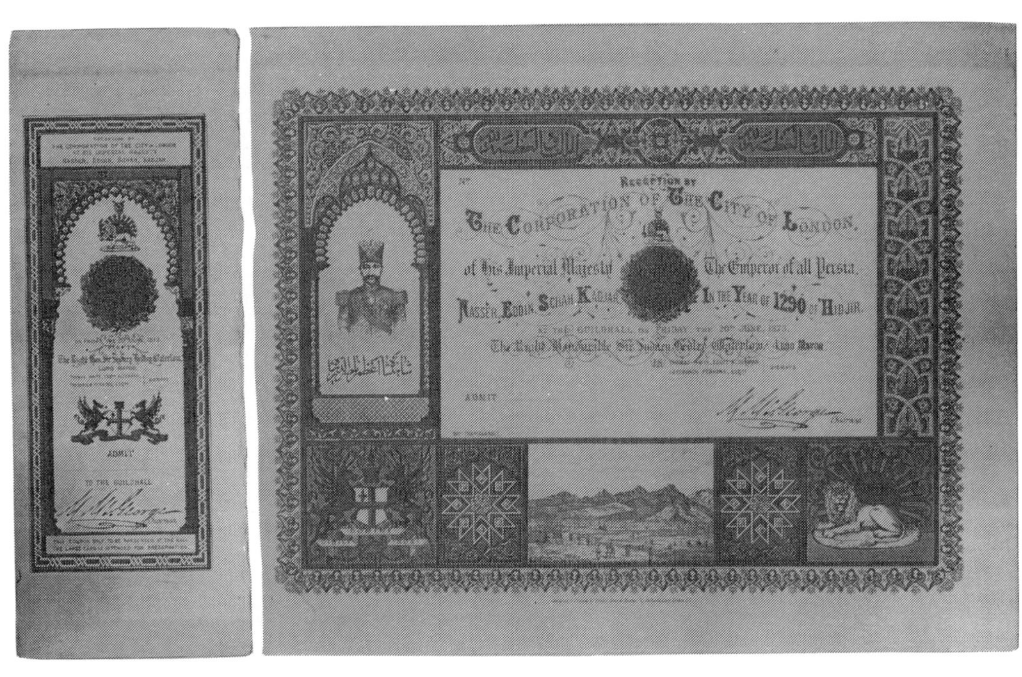
Reception by
The Corporation of The City of London,
of His Imperial Majesty The Emperor of all Persia.
Nasser Eddin Shah Kadjar In the Year of 1290 of Hidjir.
ADMIT

An extremely large invitation for a Reception for His Imperial Majesty the Emperor of all Persia at the Guildhall, 20th June 1873. £15

FUNERAL OF
Her late Majesty Queen Victoria.
ADMIT BEARER TO MALL STAND.
BLOCK F
No. 50
Esher

Funeral of Her Late Majesty Queen Victoria. £4

Opening of the David Lewis Northern Hospital Liverpool, 13th March 1902. £7

(Michael Moon)

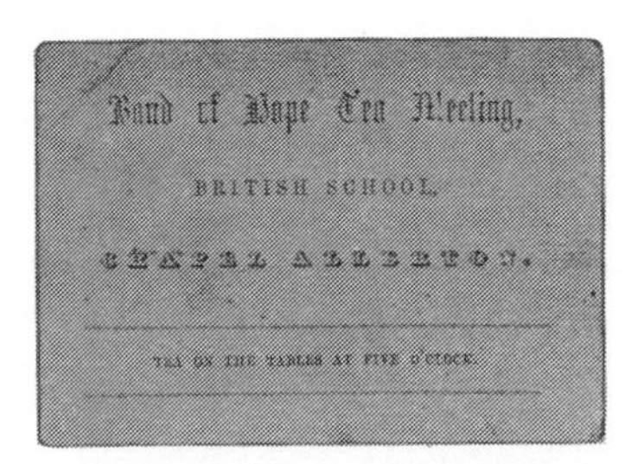
Band of Hope Tea Meeting,
BRITISH SCHOOL,
CHAPEL ALLERTON.
TEA ON THE TABLES AT FIVE O'CLOCK.

Band of Hope Tea Meeting. £2

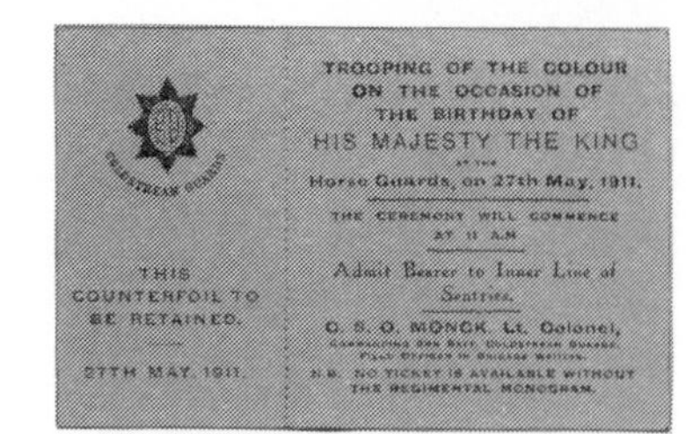
TROOPING OF THE COLOUR
ON THE OCCASION OF
THE BIRTHDAY OF
HIS MAJESTY THE KING
Horse Guards, on 27th May, 1911.
THE CEREMONY WILL COMMENCE
AT 11 A.M.
Admit Bearer to Inner Line of
Sentries.
C. S. O. MONCK, Lt. Colonel,
N.B. NO TICKET IS AVAILABLE WITHOUT
THE REGIMENTAL MONOGRAM.
THIS
COUNTERFOIL TO
BE RETAINED.
27TH MAY, 1911.

Trooping of the Colour, 27th May 1911. £4

irmingham Society of Arts
SCHOOL OF ART
CONVERSAZIONE

Birmingham School of Art, Invitation to a Conversazione. £5

The Manor of Birmingham.
requests the pleasure of the Company of
at the Town Hall
on Tuesday Evening February 11th 1879.

The Manor of Birmingham Invitation, February 11th 1879. £5

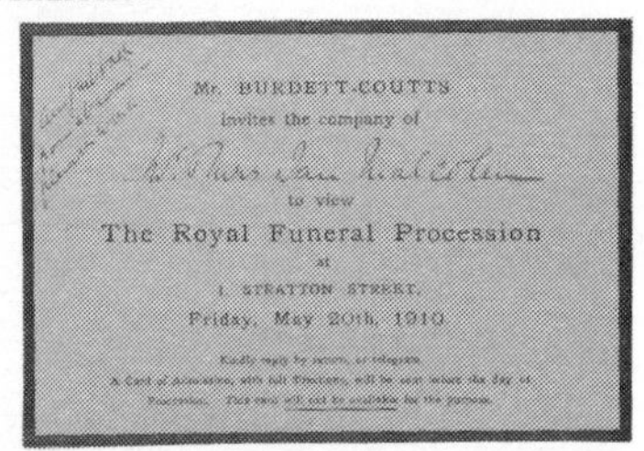
Mr. BURDETT-COUTTS
invites the company of
to view
The Royal Funeral Procession
at
1, STRATTON STREET,
Friday, May 20th, 1910.

The Royal Funeral Procession, May 20th 1910. £4

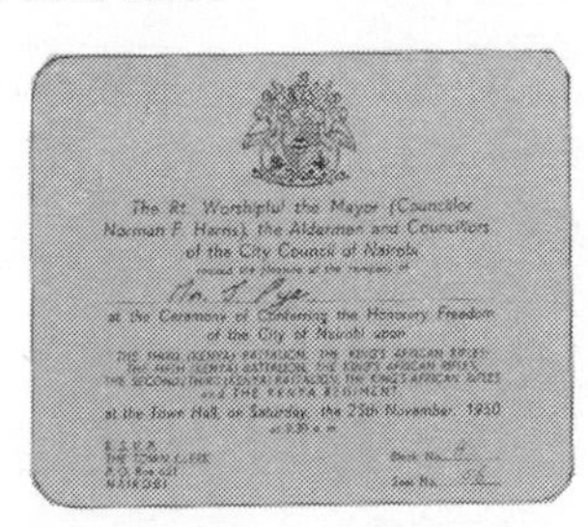
The Rt. Worshipful the Mayor (Councillor
Norman F. Harris), the Aldermen and Councillors
of the City Council of Nairobi
at the Ceremony of Conferring the Honorary Freedom
of the City of Nairobi upon
at the Town Hall, on Saturday, the 25th November, 1950

Freedom of the City of Nairobi, 25th November 1950. £3

No 232
OPENING OF THE
NEW COAL EXCHANGE
BY
HER MAJESTY.
ADMIT ONE PERSON TO THE PLATFORM ON THE
CUSTOM-HOUSE QUAY,
On Tuesday the 30th of October, 1849,
JOHN WOOD, Chairman.

Opening of the 'New Coal Exchange' by Queen Victoria, 30th October 1849. £8

FREE WEST CHURCH.
1 Sitting in No. 36 GALLERY, One Year, £ - 10 s -
From Martinmas, 1859 to Do. 1860.

Free West Church, Martinmas 1859. £3

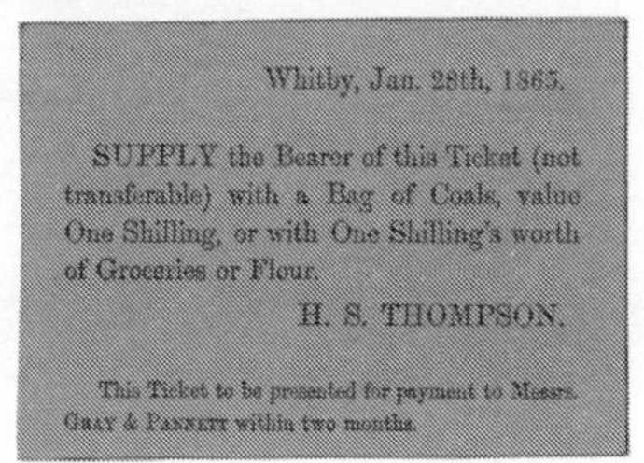
Whitby, Jan. 28th, 1865.
SUPPLY the Bearer of this Ticket (not transferable) with a Bag of Coals, value One Shilling, or with One Shilling's worth of Groceries or Flour.
H. S. THOMPSON.
This Ticket to be presented for payment to Messrs. Gray & Pannett within two months.

Ticket for a Bag of Coal, Jan. 28th 1865, Whitby. £4

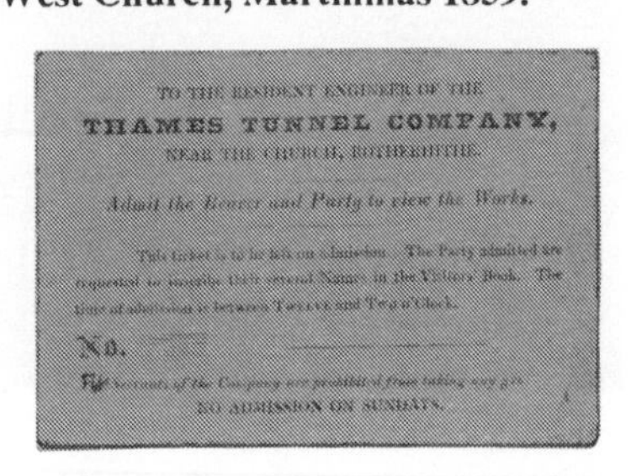
TO THE RESIDENT ENGINEER OF THE
THAMES TUNNEL COMPANY,
NEAR THE CHURCH, ROTHERHITHE.
Admit the Bearer and Party to view the Works.
No.
NO ADMISSION ON SUNDAYS.

Thames Tunnel Company, 'View of Works'. £5

(Michael Moon)

Thames Tunnel Company Incorporation, 24th June 1924. £5

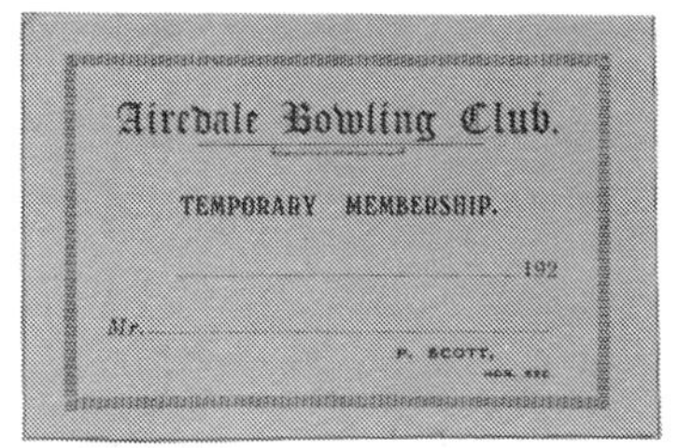

Airedale Bowling Club 'Temporary Membership'. £2

University of Edinburgh, Summer Session 1889. £4

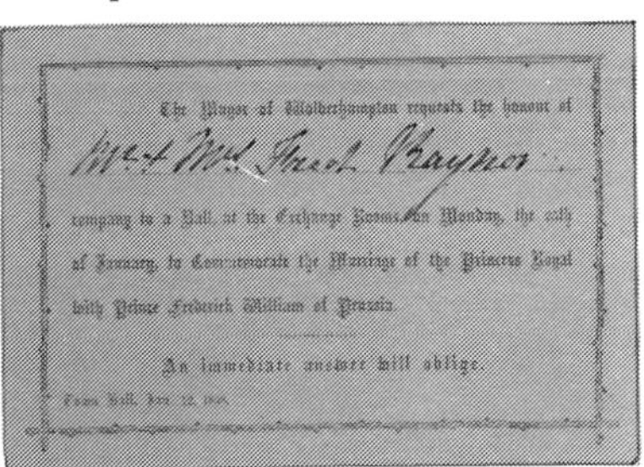

Manor Of Wolverhampton, 'Invitation to a Ball', January 12th 1858. £3

Unveiling Ceremony for the Queen Victoria Memorial, 16th May 1911. £6

Stonehouse Coronation Festivities, June 26th 1902. £2

First International Rodeo, Empire Stadium, June 24th. £2

Invitation to Dinner at the Palais de Ras-El-Fine, 1914. £3

Keighley Skating Rink, Complimentary Ticket. £1

Dame Christabel Pankhurst Speech, April 12th, Leicester. £3

(Michael Moon)

Extrait Concentre Aux Fleurs. £2

Late 19th century American Speaking Dog and Stump Speaker lithographic labels, the larger 5 x 3¼in. £300

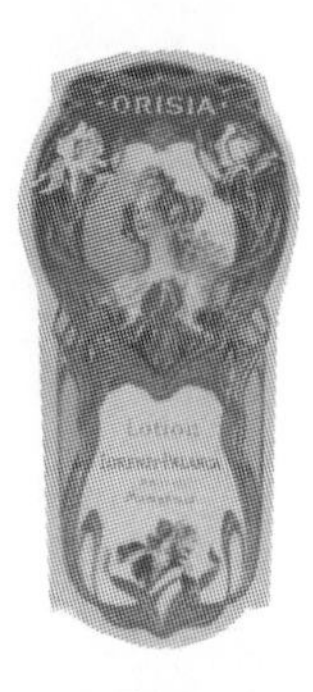

Orisia Lotion, Paris, 1920's. £5

Textile label Bayete, registered in South Africa. £5

Columbia Belle Apples, Wenatchee, Washington, 1950's. £3

Raspberryade, Haworth & Sons. 75p

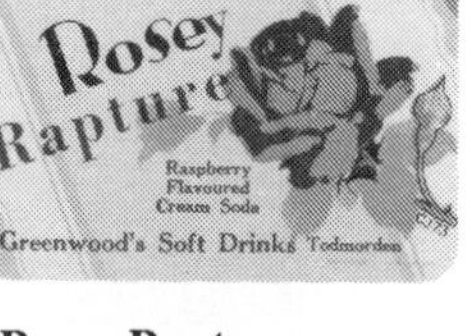

Rosey Rapture, Cream Soda. £1

Worm Powders, W.H. Laverack & Son. 75p

Haworth's Pineapple Crush. 75p

Seltzer Water Hopkinson & Co. 75p

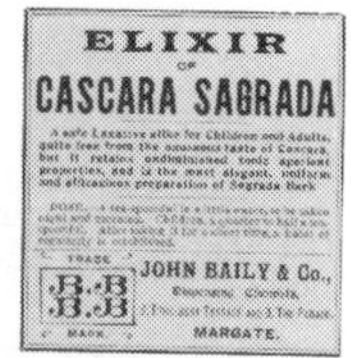

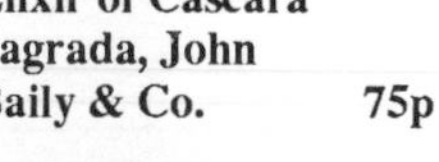

Elixir of Cascara Sagrada, John Baily & Co. 75p

Textile label Agrada registered in India, 1930's. £3

Peter Gabler, Long Hill, Conn., 'Gabler's Judge'. £5

Habana, Flor de Lopez Hermanos. £4

(Yesterdays Paper)

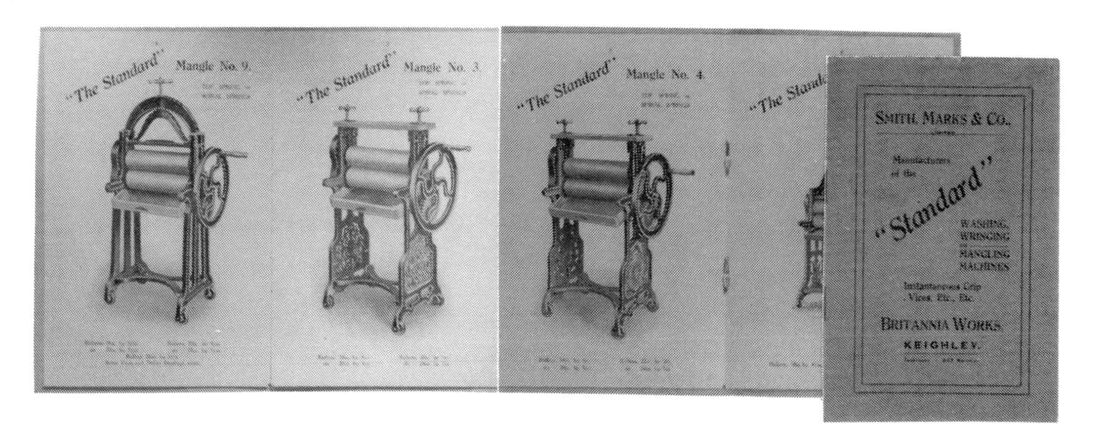

Smith, Marks & Co., Keighley, 'Standard' Catalogue. £10

Murton & Varley Ltd., Keighley, 'Premier Grade Washing Machines', List No. 2. £4

'You And Your Laundry', by Mrs. Christine Frederick 1923. £6

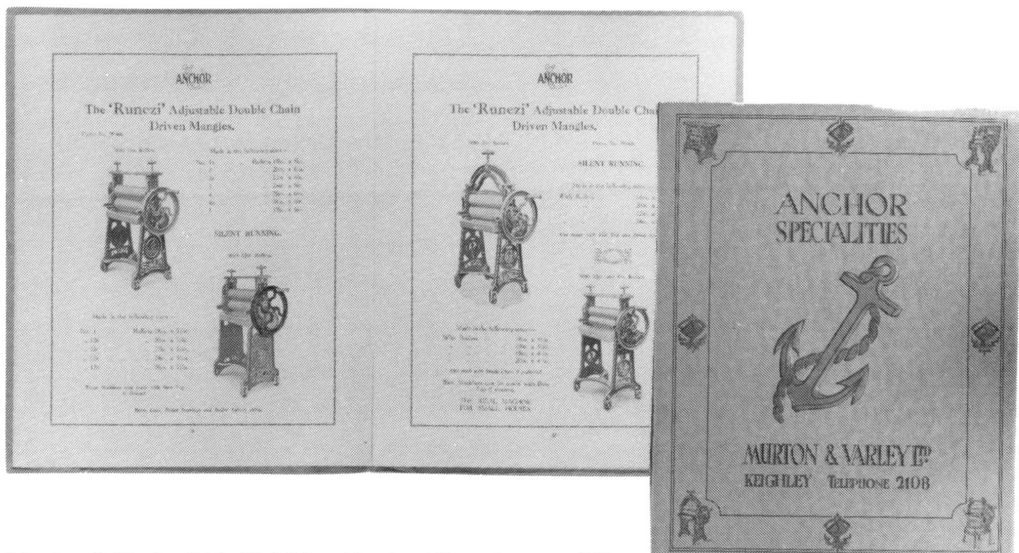

Murton & Varley Ltd., Keighley, 'Anchor' Brand. £12

(Yesterdays Paper)

PICTORIAL

Hotwell House & Clifton Suspension Bridge. £4

Windsor Castle and the drive by J. & F. Harwood. £5

St. Vincent Rocks, Leigh Woods & The River Avon. £5

Buxton From Corber. £3

Hebden Bridge Church & Adjacent Scenery. £4

South Shore, Blackpool. £4

Manchester Royal Lunatic Hospital. £6

(Yesterdays Paper)

PICTORIAL

Torquay From The Rock Walk. £4

Palace of Holyrood, Edinburgh. £4

Edinburgh Castle From The Princess Street Gardens. £4

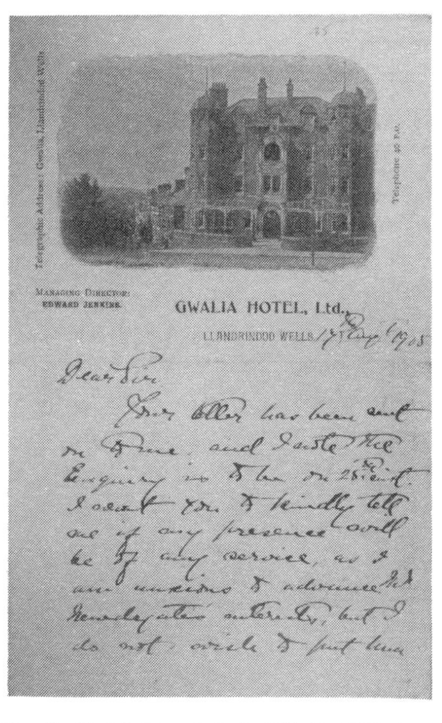

MANAGING DIRECTOR:
EDWARD JENKINS.

GWALIA HOTEL, Ltd.,

LLANDRINDOD WELLS, 19 Aug 1905

Dear Sir,

Your letter has been sent on to me, and I note the Enquiry is to be on 23rd inst. I want you to kindly tell me if my presence will be of any service, as I am anxious to advance the [illegible] interests, but I do not wish to put [illegible]

Gwalia Hotel, Llandrindod Wells, 19th Aug. 1905. £5

Entrance to Scarborough. £6

Windsor Castle by J. & F. Harwood, London. £5

(Yesterdays Paper)

TRADE

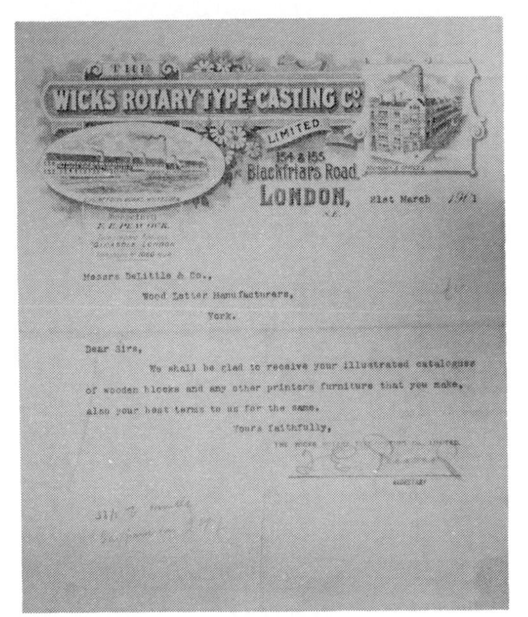

THE WICKS ROTARY TYPE-CASTING Co LIMITED
154 & 155 Blackfriars Road
LONDON, S.E. 21st March 1901

Messrs DeLittle & Co.,
Wood Letter Manufacturers,
York.

Dear Sirs,

We shall be glad to receive your illustrated catalogues of wooden blocks and any other printers furniture that you make, also your best terms to us for the same.

Yours faithfully,

Wicks Rotary Type-Casting Co., London, 21st March 1901. £3

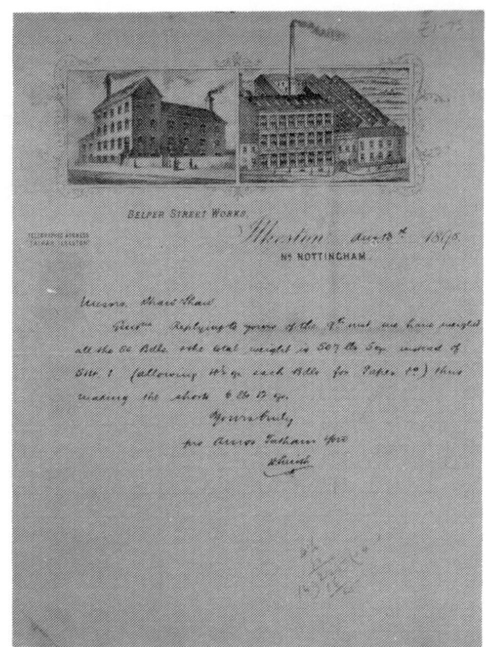

BELPER STREET WORKS.
Ilkeston Aug 13th 1895
Nr NOTTINGHAM

Yours truly,
per Amos Tatham

Tatham, Ilkeston, Aug. 13th 1895. £4

BARNSLEY. March 4th 1897
From
WILSONS & Co. BARNSLEY, Ltd.

To Messrs Shaw & Shaw,
Milnsbridge.

Dear Sirs,

We are obliged for your enquiry and have pleasure in quoting prices as below viz:-
20 gross Short Collar Tubes 10" x 9" lift x 1¾" barrel ⅞" Spindle fitted with 1¾" diameter Steel Driver Shield only and plain head at top......13/6 per gross
If fitted with 1¾" diam.Steel Hoop at top 14/- "

Tubes painted ends and varnished all over or varnished only as may be required.

Carriage paid usual terms. If favoured with your order we can commence delivery in 2/3 weeks and complete in 4 weeks.

Your commands will oblige.

Yours obediently,
for WILSON & CO. Barnsley, Ltd.
J. Birtles Director

Specialities.

Wilsons & Co., Barnsley, March 4, 1897. £3

ARUNDEL & Co
MACHINE MAKERS,
Sovereign Works,
STOCKPORT

Feb: 26th, 1904

Messrs. Shaw & Shaw,
Britannia Mills,
Milnsbridge.

Dear Sirs,

We are duly in receipt of yours of the 25th. inst, and beg to inform you, that we have arranged with the Railway Co to warehouse your machine for a few days, until you are ready to receive it, and we shall be glad if you will kindly let us know, when you will be ready to receive the machinery, so that we can arrange to dispatch the remaining portion from our Works; We regret that owing to an oversight, a portion of this machine was dispatched before writing you, and trust same will not cause you any inconvenience.

We remain,
Yours truly,

Arundel & Co. Ltd., Stockport, (Machine Makers), Feb. 26th 1904. £3

(Yesterdays Paper)

TRADE

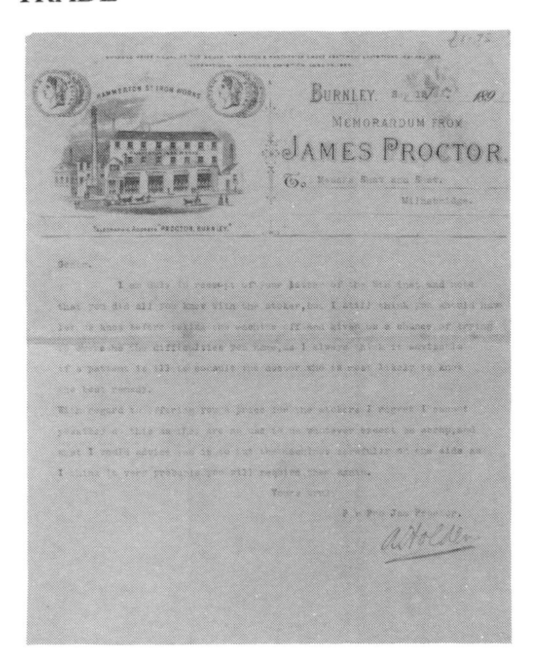

BURNLEY

MEMORANDUM FROM

JAMES PROCTOR

James Proctor, Burnley, Sept. 12th 1893. £4

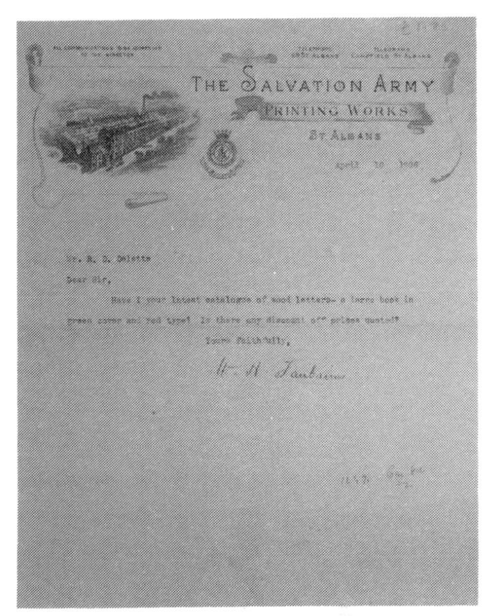

THE SALVATION ARMY

PRINTING WORKS

ST ALBANS

Dear Sir,

Yours faithfully,

The Salvation Army Printing Works, St. Albans, April 10, 1906. £4

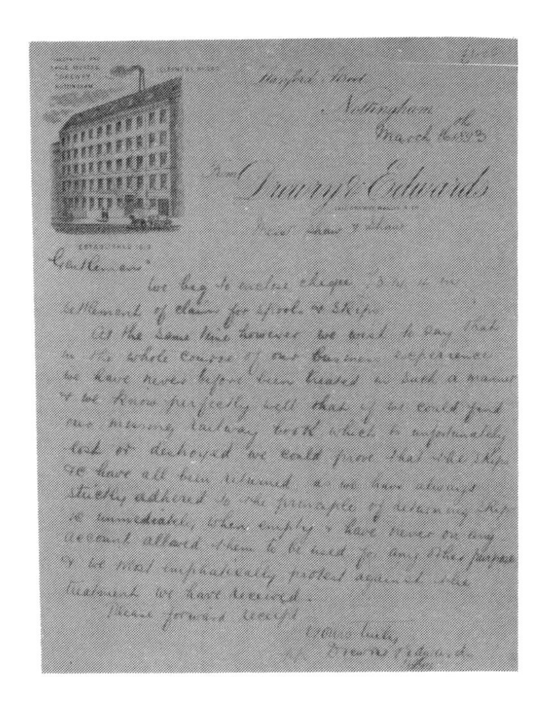

Nottingham

March 16th 93

Drewry & Edwards

Gentlemen

We beg to enclose cheque [illegible] in settlement of claim for Spools & Skips. At the same time however we wish to say that in the whole course of our business experience we have never before been treated in such a manner & we know perfectly well that if we could find our missing railway book which is unfortunately lost or destroyed we could prove that the Skips &c have all been returned as we have always strictly adhered to the principle of returning Skips &c immediately when empty & have never on any account allowed them to be used for any other purpose & we most emphatically protest against the treatment we have received.

Please forward receipt

Yours truly,

Drewry & Edwards

Drewry & Edwards, Nottingham, March 16th 1893. £3

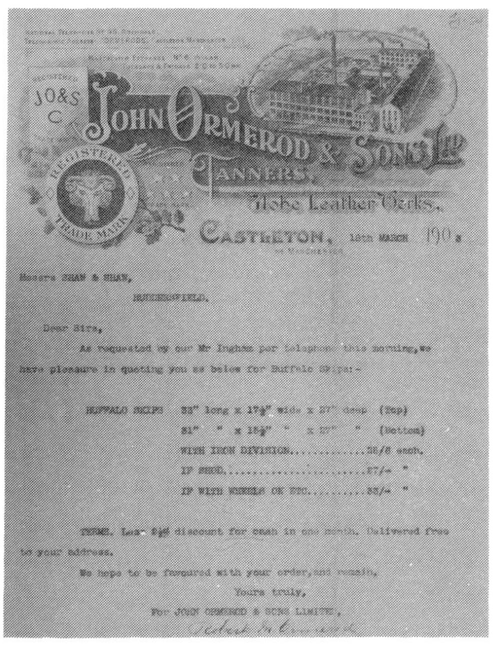

JOHN ORMEROD & SONS LTD

TANNERS,

Globe Leather Works,

CASTLETON, 18th MARCH 190

Messrs SHAW & SHAW,

HUDDERSFIELD.

Dear Sirs,

As requested by our Mr Ingham per telephone this morning, we have pleasure in quoting you as below for Buffalo Skips:-

BUFFALO SKIPS

WITH IRON DIVISION

We hope to be favoured with your order, and remain,

Yours truly,

For JOHN ORMEROD & SONS LIMITED,

John Ormerod & Sons Ltd., Castleton, (Tanners), 18th March 1903. £3

(Yesterdays Paper)

TRADE

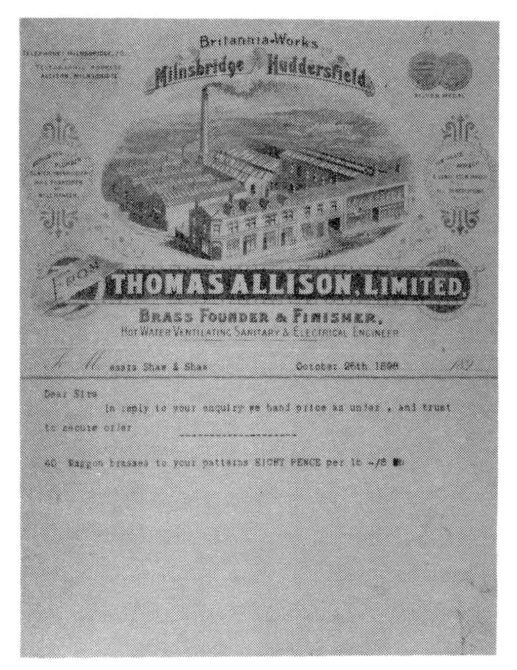

Britannia-Works
Milnsbridge Huddersfield.
FROM THOMAS ALLISON, LIMITED.
BRASS FOUNDER & FINISHER,
HOT WATER VENTILATING SANITARY & ELECTRICAL ENGINEER

To Messrs Shaw & Shaw   October 25th 1898   189

Dear Sirs
In reply to your enquiry we hand price as under, and trust to secure order

40 Waggon brasses to your patterns EIGHT PENCE per lb -/8

Thomas Allison, Limited, Huddersfield, (Brass Founders), Oct. 25th, 1898. £3

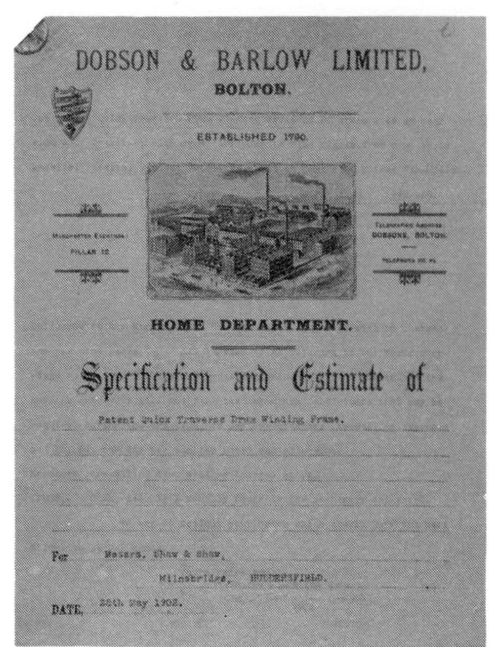

DOBSON & BARLOW LIMITED,
BOLTON.
ESTABLISHED 1790.
HOME DEPARTMENT.
Specification and Estimate of
Patent Quick Traverse Drum Winding Frame.

For Messrs. Shaw & Shaw,
Milnsbridge, HUDDERSFIELD.

DATE. 28th May 1902.

Dobson & Barlow Limited, Bolton, 28th May 1902. £3

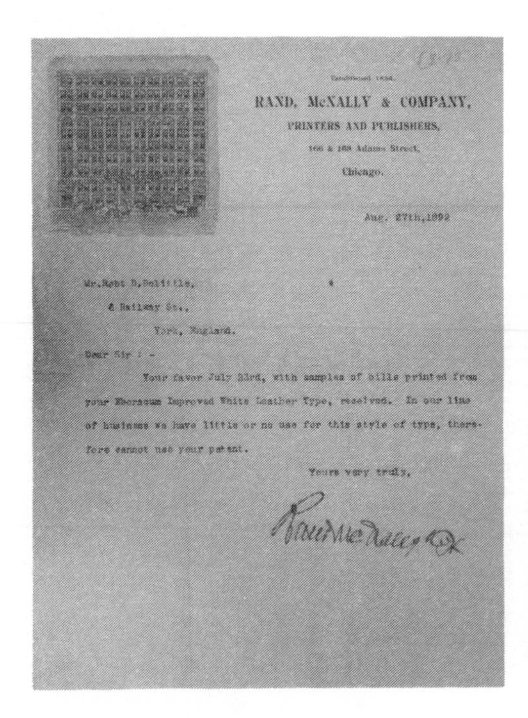

RAND, McNALLY & COMPANY,
PRINTERS AND PUBLISHERS,
166 & 168 Adams Street,
Chicago.

Aug. 27th,1892

Mr.Robt D.Dolittle,
6 Railway St.,
York, England.

Dear Sir : -
Your favor July 23rd, with samples of bills printed from your Eboracum Improved White Leather Type, received. In our line of business we have little or no use for this style of type, therefore cannot use your patent.

Yours very truly,

Rand McNally & Co

Rand, McNally & Company, Chicago, (Printers), Aug. 27th 1892. £6

JAMES KENWORTHY & SON.
RAILWAY WAGONS
WHEELS RE-TURNED
NEW TYRES PUT ON

James Kenworthy & Son, Huddersfield, (Railway Wagons), July 14th 1899. £5

(Yesterdays Paper)

TRADE

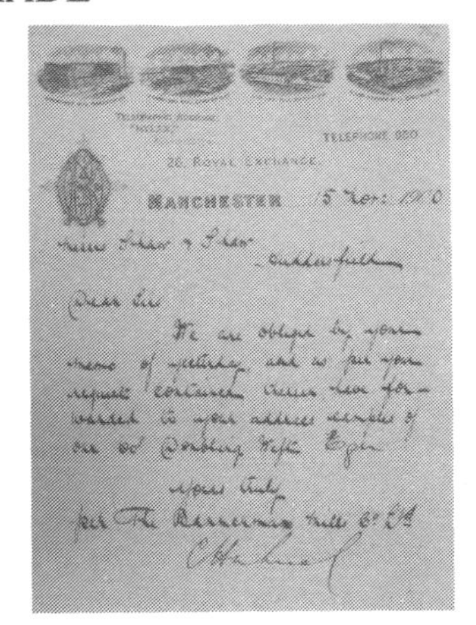

20, ROYAL EXCHANGE,

MANCHESTER 5 Nov: 1900

Hylax, Manchester, 15th Nov. 1900. £2

Huddersfield May 8 1895

Fisher & Company

Fisher & Company, Huddersfield, May 8th 1895. £4

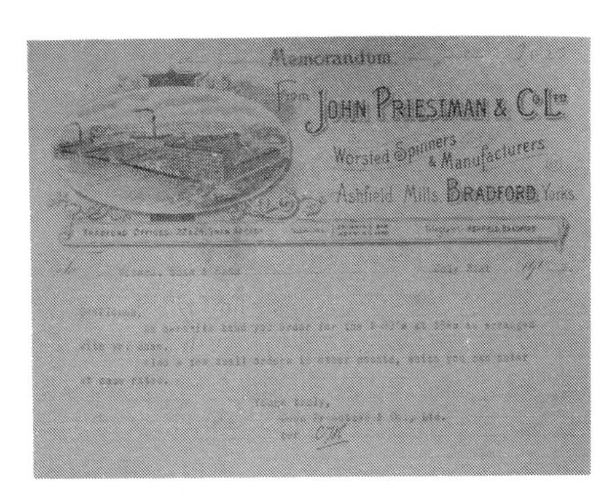

Memorandum.

From John Priestman & Co. Ltd.

Worsted Spinners & Manufacturers

Ashfield Mills, Bradford, Yorks.

John Priestman & Co. Ltd., Bradford, (Spinners), July 31st, 1903. £3

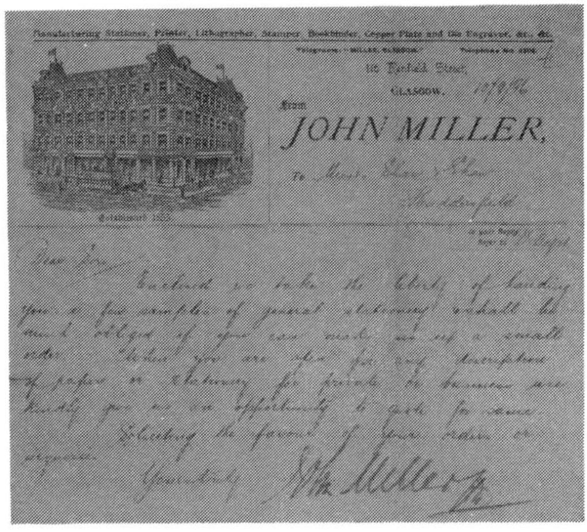

Manufacturing Stationer, Printer, Lithographer, Stamper, Bookbinder, Copper Plate and Die Engraver, &c. &c.

Glasgow. 10/9/96

From JOHN MILLER,

John Miller, Glasgow, (Printers), 10/9/96. £3

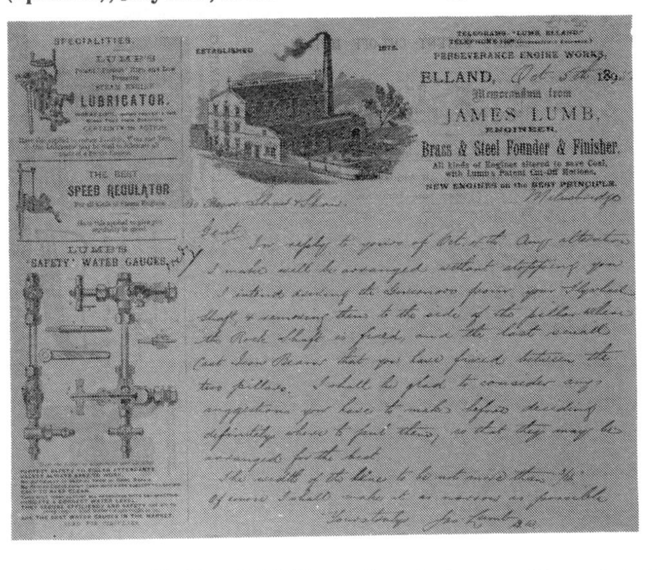

SPECIALITIES.

LUMB'S LUBRICATOR.

THE BEST SPEED REGULATOR

LUMB'S "SAFETY" WATER GAUGES.

ESTABLISHED 1875.

PERSEVERANCE ENGINE WORKS,

ELLAND, Oct 5th 189

Memorandum from

JAMES LUMB,

ENGINEER.

Brass & Steel Founder & Finisher.

All kinds of Engines altered to save Coal, with Lumb's Patent Cut-Off Valves.

NEW ENGINES on the BEST PRINCIPLE.

James Lumb, Huddersfield, (Brass Founder), Oct. 5th 1895. £4

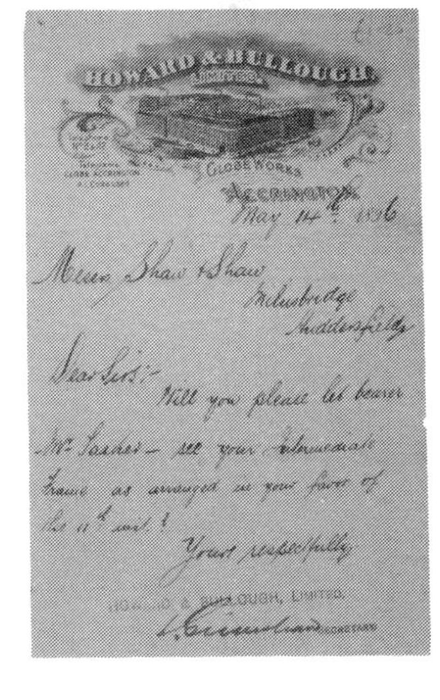

HOWARD & BULLOUGH, LIMITED.

GLOBE WORKS

ACCRINGTON, May 14th 1896

Messrs Shaw & Shaw

Milnsbridge

Huddersfield

Dear Sirs:-

Yours respectfully,

HOWARD & BULLOUGH, LIMITED.

Howard & Bullough Ltd., Accrington, May 14th 1896. £3

(Yesterdays Paper)

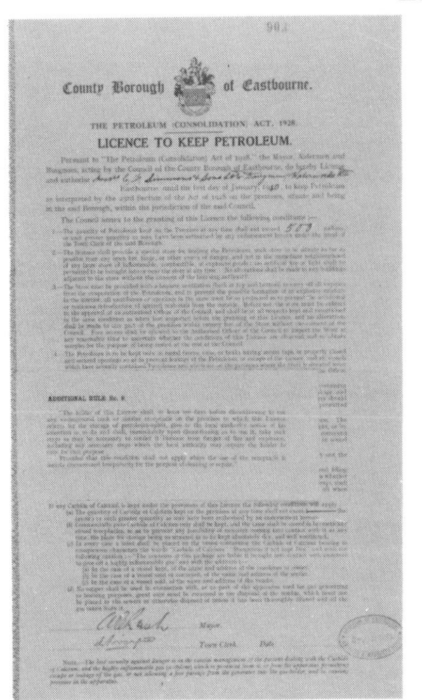
County Borough of Eastbourne.

THE PETROLEUM (CONSOLIDATION) ACT, 1928.

LICENCE TO KEEP PETROLEUM.

Licence to Keep Petroleum issued by the County Borough of Eastbourne, 1940. £5

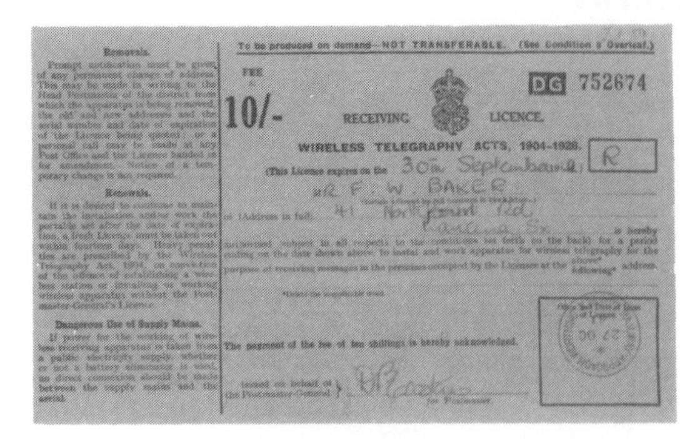
To be produced on demand—NOT TRANSFERABLE. (See Condition s Overleaf.)

FEE 10/- RECEIVING LICENCE. DG 752674

WIRELESS TELEGRAPHY ACTS, 1904-1926.

MR F. W. BAKER

Receiving licence to comply with the wireless Telegraphy Acts 1904–1926. £2

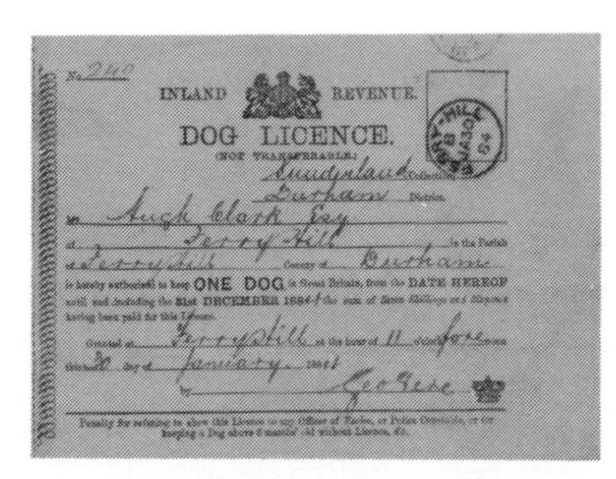
INLAND REVENUE.

DOG LICENCE.

(NOT TRANSFERABLE.)

is hereby authorised to keep ONE DOG in Great Britain, from the DATE HEREOF until and including the 31st DECEMBER 1884

Dog Licence, January 1884, Durham. £3

Control Commission for Germany, Car Licence. £2

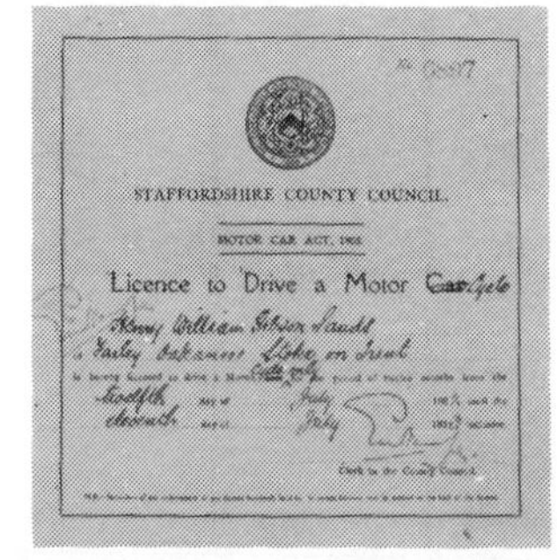
STAFFORDSHIRE COUNTY COUNCIL.

MOTOR CAR ACT, 1903.

Licence to Drive a Motor Cycle

Staffordshire Licence to Drive a Motor Cycle, 1922. £4

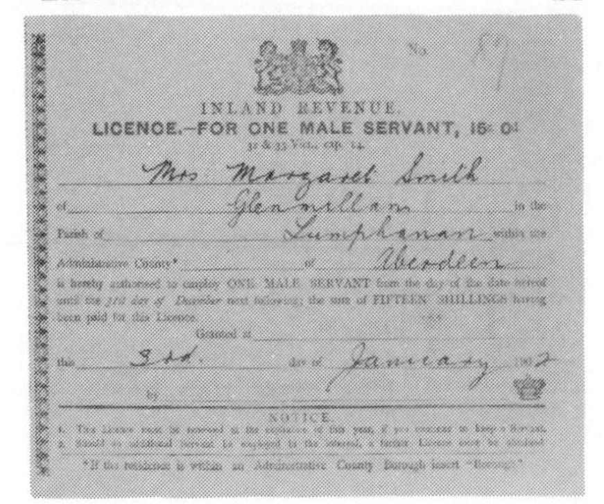
INLAND REVENUE.

LICENCE.—FOR ONE MALE SERVANT, 15s 0d

Mrs Margaret Smith

of Glenmillan in the Parish of Lumphanan within the Administrative County of Aberdeen

is hereby authorised to employ ONE MALE SERVANT from the day of the date hereof until the 31st day of December next following; the sum of FIFTEEN SHILLINGS having been paid for this Licence.

this 3rd day of January 1902

NOTICE.

Licence for One Male Servant, January 1902, Aberdeen. £6

Dog Licence, February 1898, Cumberland. £5

(Yesterdays Paper)

Monkey Brand, 'Won't Wash Clothes'. £7

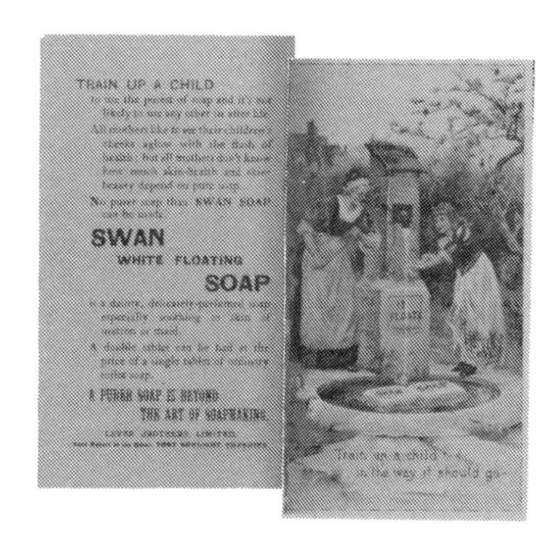

Swan Soap, 'Train Up A Child In The Way It Should Go'. £8

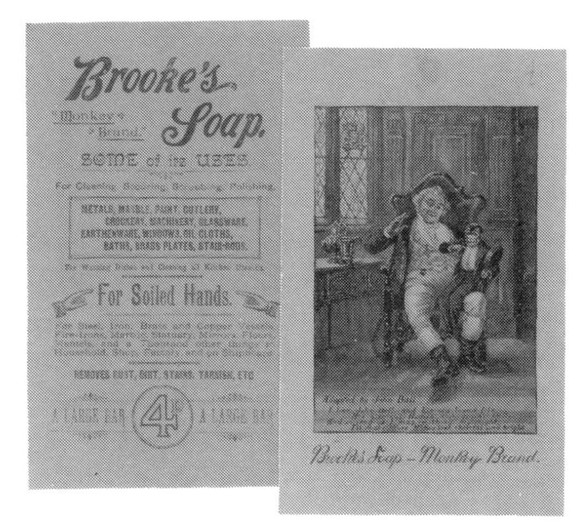

Brooke's Soap, 'For Soiled Hands'. £3

Sunlight Soap, 'The Great Labour Saver'. £8

Sunlight Soap, 'Labour Light, Clothes White – Sunlight'. £8

Brooke's Soap, 'For All Kitchen Utensils'. £4

(Yesterdays Paper)

Harlene For The Hair, 'Prevents It Falling Off'. **£6**

Marvo, 'The Shine Of The Time'. **£3**

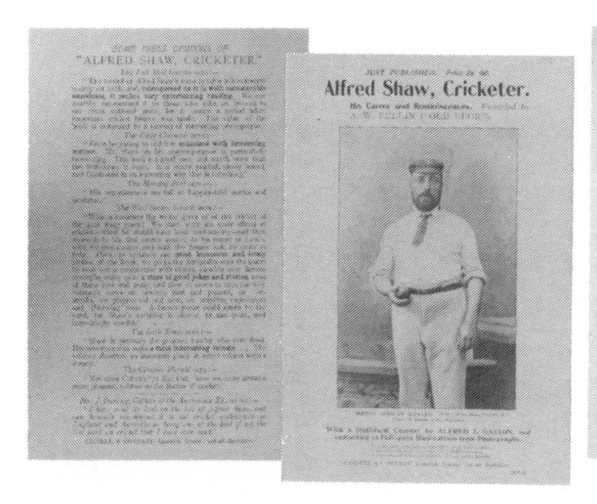

Alfred Shaw, Cricketer, 'Just Published'. **£2**

Angier's Emulsion, 'I've Got The Right One'. **£3**

Colman's Mustard/Cake Royal. **£6**

Chappell & Co's. 'New High Class English Pianofortes'. **£2**

(Yesterdays Paper)

Stowers Lime Juice Cordial, 'No Musty Flavour'. £6

Webb, Williams & Company, 'Remarkable Value In Tailor-Made'. £1

International Fur Store/Hewetsons, Milner. £3

A SEASIDE HOME
THAT CAN BE MADE TO
PAY FOR ITSELF
UNBEATABLE!
£395 SEASIDE HOME
IT CAN BE MADE TO
PAY FOR ITSELF
£5 INITIAL PAYMENT SECURES £5
PRINTED PAPER RATE
THE MANAGER,
THE MOUNT ESTATE,
SALTDEAN,
BRIGHTON
SUSSEX

A Seaside Home, Saltdean, Brighton. £2

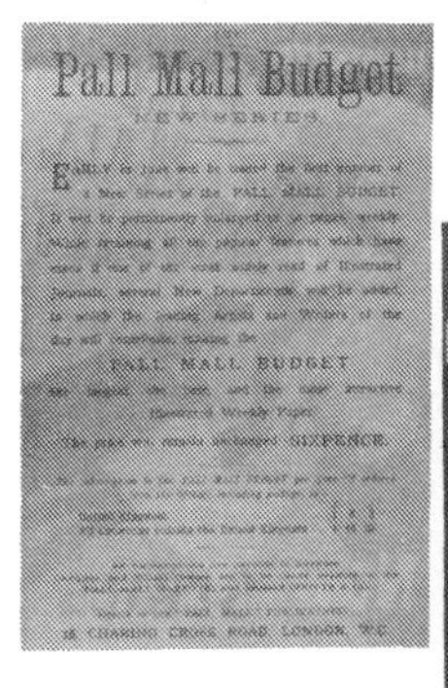

Pall Mall Budget 'New Series'. £3

Charming miniature on porcelain, Artistic Photographic Co. £4

(Yesterdays Paper)

Butlins 'For Your Holiday'. £1

The New Vimto Book, Knowledge Is Power. £3

'The Triumph', A Magnificent Blend of India, China and Ceylon Tea'. £2

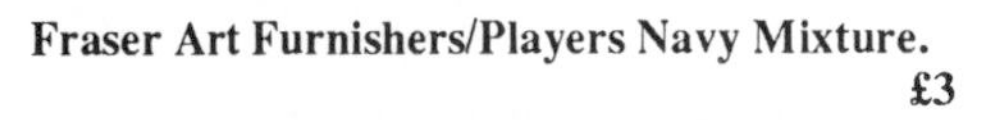

Fraser Art Furnishers/Players Navy Mixture. £3

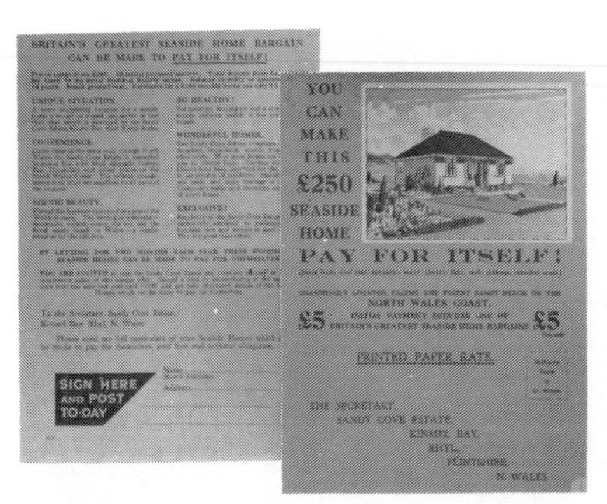

Sandy Cove Estate, Rhyl, Flintshire. £2

Cadbury's, 'Over 10,000 Prizes', 1933. £2

(Yesterdays Paper)

Vim, 'Handy, Speedy, Economical'. £4

Nernstlamp, The Electrical Company Limited. £10

Spode China, W. T. Copeland & Son. £5

Eno's Fruit Salt, 'It Might Have Been'. £5

Sadler's Old English Mustard, 1869. £3

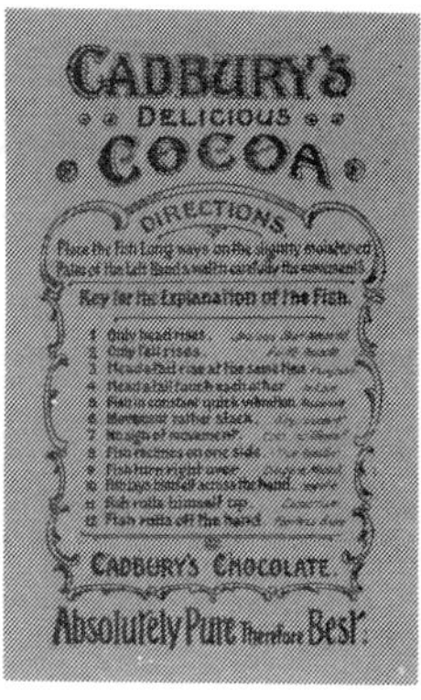

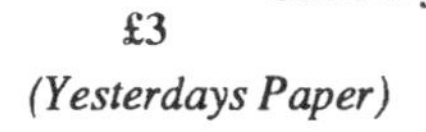

Cadbury's Cocoa, 'Explanation Of The Fish'. £7

(Yesterdays Paper)

INSURANCE

London & Lancashire Fire Insurance Company. **£1**

Royal Insurance Company. **£3**

Liverpool & London & Globe Insurance Company. **£3**

Rock Life Assurance Company. **£1**

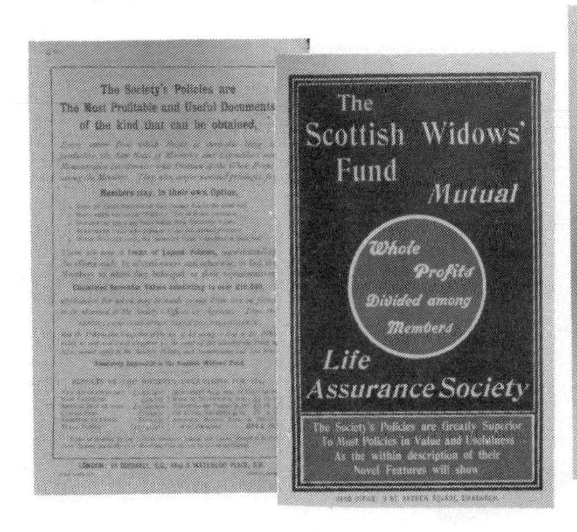

The Scottish Widow's Fund. **£1**

Liverpool & London And Globe Insurance Company. **£1**

(Yesterdays Paper)

SOAP

Sunlight Soap, 'Good Old Sunlight Done Dis Job'. £8

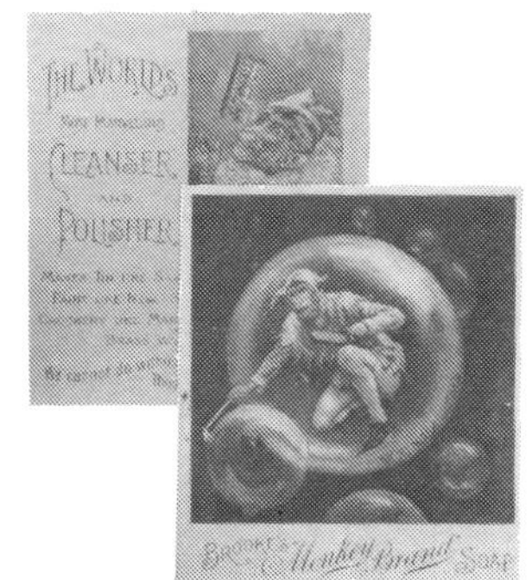

Brooke's Monkey Brand Soap, 'We Cannot Do Without It'. £6

Plantol Soap, 'Made From Fruit And Flowers'. £8

Lux, 'Why Don't They Use Lux'. £7

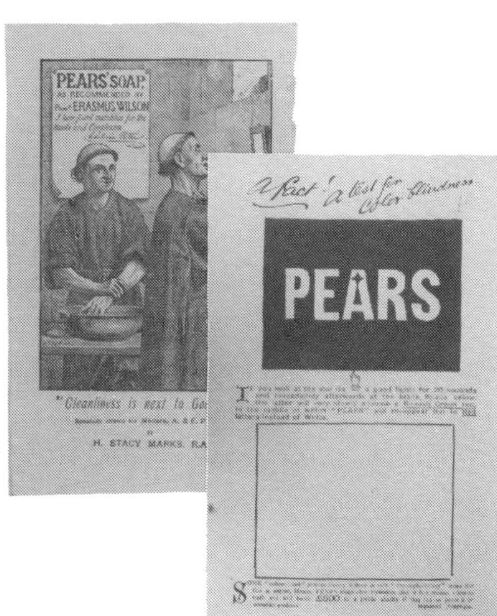

Pears' Soap, 'Colour Blindness Test'. £6

Pears' Soap, 'Bubbles', by Sir John E. Millais. £4

Lifebuoy Soap, 'Grateful Mothers'. £8

Lifebuoy Soap, 'Rescue Yourself And Others From Contagion And Disease'. £6

(Yesterdays Paper)

Lux, 'Won't Shrink Woollens'. £8

SOAP

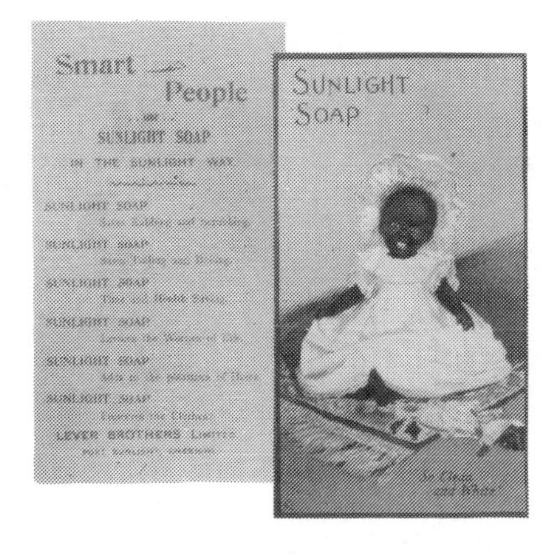

Sunlight Soap, 'So Clean and White'. £8

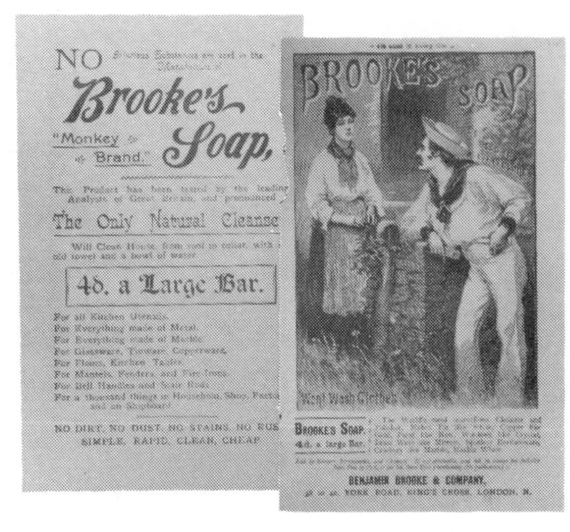

Brooke's Soap, 'The Only Natural Cleanser'. £5

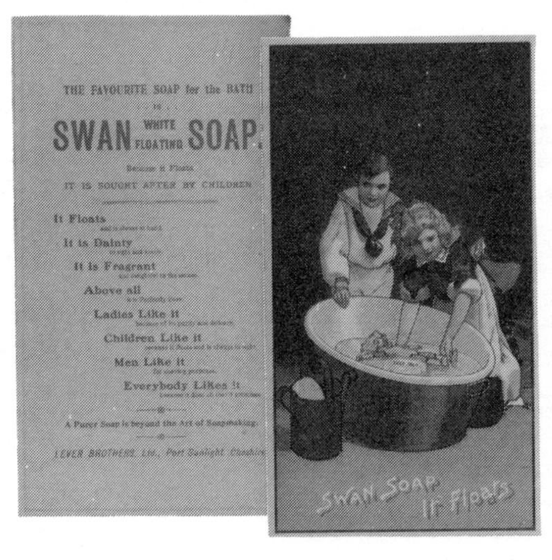

Swan Soap, 'It Floats'. £8

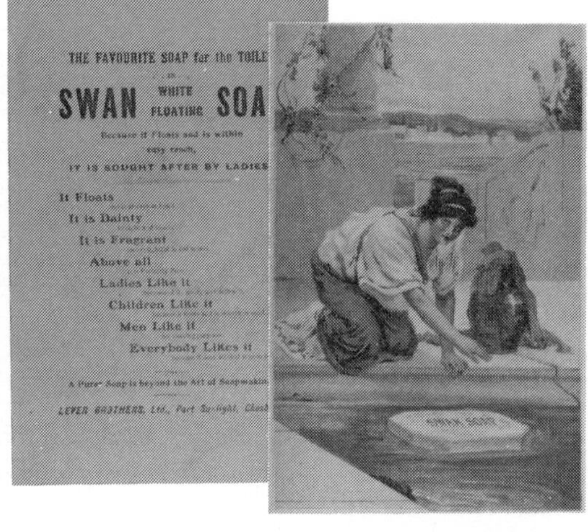

Swan Soap, 'It Is Sought After By Ladies'. £7

Ivy Soap, 'Going To The Bath'. £7

Brooke's Soap, Monkey Brand, 'Brightens Home Like A Baby's Smile'. £5

(Yesterdays Paper)

SOAP

Lux 'Won't Shrink Woollens'. £5

Sunlight Soap 'Is a friend in need'. £10

Lifebuoy Soap 'Saved!'. £5

Powder Monkey 'The Introduction'. £5

Vim Brings Brightness Closer. £6

Lifebuoy 'The Life Saver'. £5

(Spread Eagle Antiques)

Maclean's Canada's National Magazine, March 1958. £2

To-day, the New National Weekly, No. 1, May 28th, 1938. £5

L'Indiscret, Le Lapin et Lepine, 5th November, 1902. £8

Weekly Illustrated, November 27th, 1937, King and Queen's busy season. £9

Farmer and Stock-breeder, 8th December 1959. £3

Les Corbeaux, L'Emente clericale a Louvain, 26th June 1904. £7

(Yesterdays Paper)

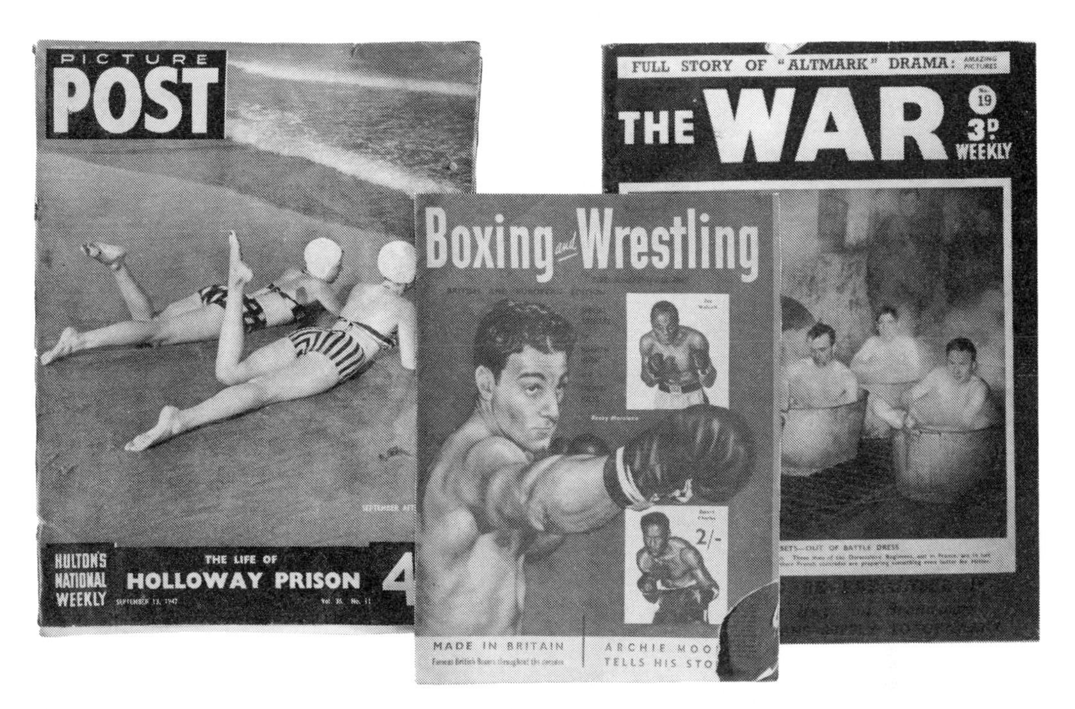

Picture Post, September 13th, 1947, The Life of Holloway Prison. £3

Boxing and Wrestling, March/April 1953. £3

The War, 1st March 1940, 'The Dorsets – Out of Battle Dress'. £4

Life, April 24th, 1950, Blouses under $5. £4

Le Cri de Paris, 3rd January, 1904. £4

Modern Wonder, December 2nd, 1939, Lifebelts and Warbirds. £6

(Yesterdays Paper)

Picture Post No. 1, October 1, 1938. **£10**

Country Life, Winter Days in Lakeland, January 23rd 1942. £2

The Sphere, Heralding the Coronation, May 8th 1937. £5

(Douglas Morgan)

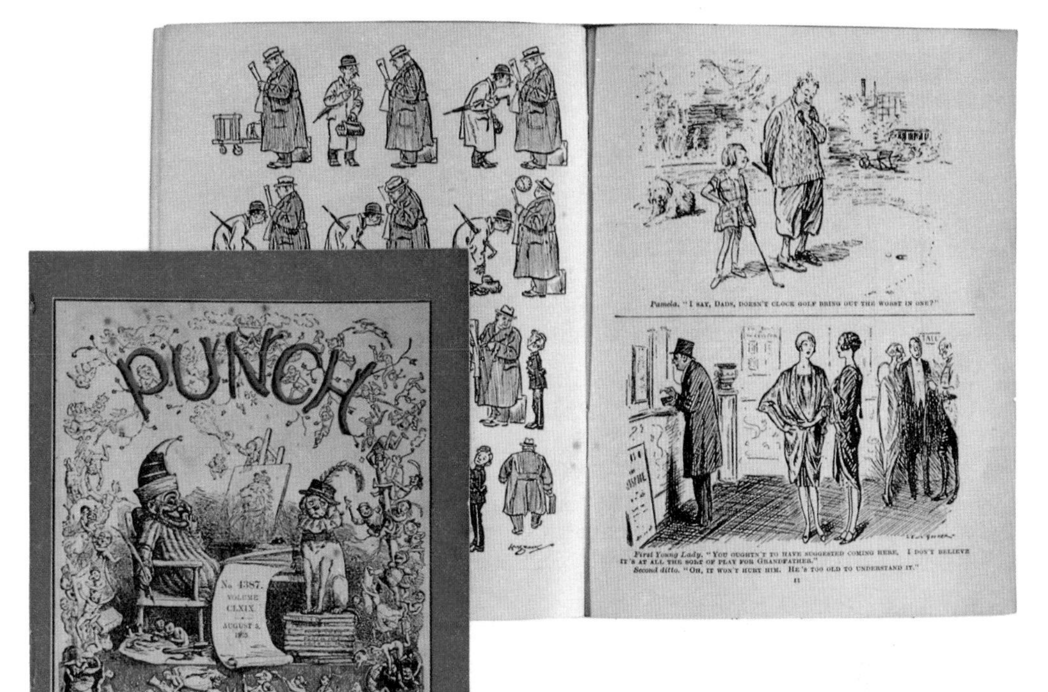

Punch No. 4387, August 5, 1925. £6

Peg's Paper No. 452, January 17, 1928, The Husband She Stole. £15

Play Pictorial No. 20 The Cricket on the Hearth. £12

(Spread Eagle Antiques)

Lilliput, February 1959, 'Mike Hawthorn's dice with fate'. £4

All the Year Round, March 1865, contains Dickens stories. £30

'Elvis in the Army', Fans Star Library. £12

World Radio, Christmas 1930. £3

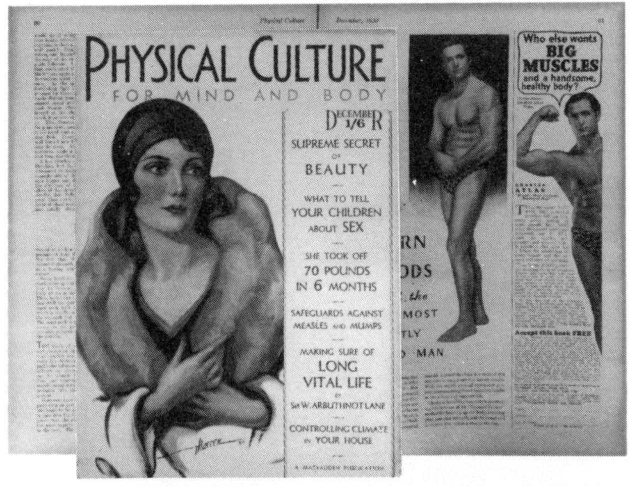

Physical Culture, For Mind and Body, December 1930. £3

Child's Companion and Juvenile Instructor 1890. £3

Canadian Colored Concert Co., 1890. £4

The Red Arrow Series 1932 No. 1 of the Swift Story Paper. £2

(Yesterdays Paper)

Football Favourites, 1952, Who's who in soccer. £7

Courier, Fact, Fiction, Art, Nature, March 1949. £4

Lilliput, April 1949, Charlie Chaplin Cover. £2

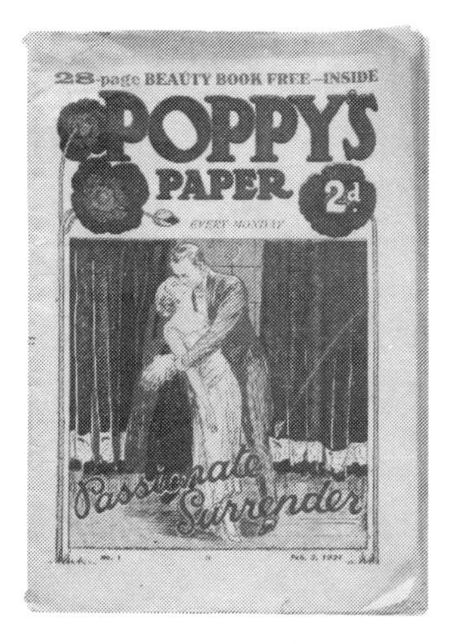

Poppy's Paper, February 2nd, 1924, 'Passionate Surrender'. £5

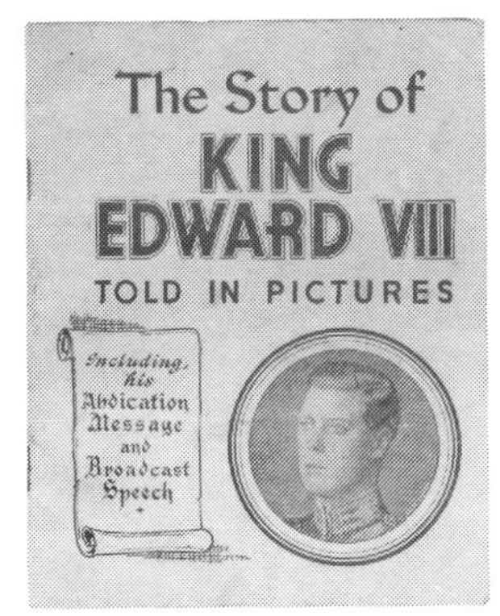

The Story of King Edward VIII told in pictures, 1937. £10

Uncensored, May 1957, 'Victor Mature, secret honeymoon without a bride'. £5

Cycling, the leading cycling journal of the world, June 1st, 1938. £5

Mad, Special Cop Out Issue, No. 152. £5

The Pele-Mele, Journal Humoristique Hebdomadaire, 23rd September, 1900. £8

(Yesterdays Paper)

Play Pictorial No. 26 The Chevaleer. £12

The Surprise, August 19, 1933, the Glass Room. £15

The London Pictorial, May 4 1932. £12

(Spread Eagle Antiques)

Home Companion No. 158, February 24, 1900. £12

The War Illustrated, On Top in Tunisia, February 5th 1943. £2

Picture Post, The Woman's Army, February 17th 1940. £2

(Spread Eagle Antiques)

HUMOROUS

A Basinful of Fun, No. 94, by F. Youngman Ltd. £1.50

You've Had It, No. 70, Service With A Smile. £1.50

This Is It, No. 55, Lots of Laffs. £1.50

Razzle, No. 61, Ritz Publishing Co. 1935. £3

You've Had It, Summer Special, Jasmit Publications. £1.50

Slick, No. 3, Jasmit Publications. £1.50

Humour Variety, No. 49, Louder and Funnier. £1.50

Fun, August 1945, Fireside Publications, Toronto. £1.50

Halt, No. 4, July 1945, Duchess Publishing. £2

(Yesterdays Paper)

Private Eye, Pressdram Ltd., 24th Oct. 1969. £1.50

Laff, America's Picture Humor Magazine, July 1965. £2

The Humorist, July 27th, 1935, Summer Number. £6

Humors of History by Arthur Moreland, 1905. £4

Punch, June 11th, 1859, with the original postal wrapper. £15

The Passing Show, April 14th, 1934, Four Pages of Humour. £4

(Yesterdays Paper)

Swedish, non phosphorus safety matches, Protection from Fire, Ignite Only on Box. 50p

Japanese Impregnated Safety Matches. 50p

The Three Monkeys impregnated Safety Matches, Swedish. 75p

Deutsch-West Afrikanische Safety Matches, Westküste Afrika, German West Africa. £1

Bryant & May's Brymay Special Safety Matches, British. 10p

Swedish Superior Impregnated Safety Matches. 30p

The Viking Ship Special Impregnated Safety Matches, Swedish. 50p

Cockfight Safety Matches, Swedish. 50p

The Bullock Paraffin Matches, Swedish. 40p

Durbar Safety Matches, Swedish. £1

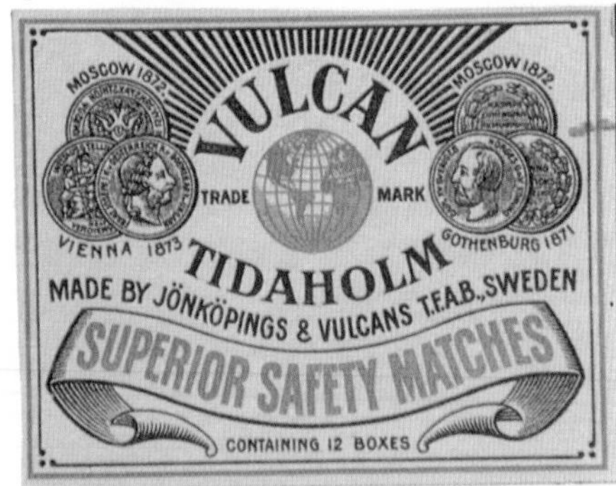

Vulcan Superior Safety Matches, Swedish. £3

Teikoku Boyeki Goshi Kaisha, Japanese matches. £2

Double Horse Safety Matches, Belgian. £1

Dragon & Pagoda Damp Proof Safety Matches, Swedish. 75p

Jönköping's Best Impregnated Safety Matches, Swedish. 50p

The Dancing Foxes Superior Quality Matches, Belgian. 50p

Wecker Handel MY Lianhien Superior Safety Matches, Batavia, Dutch East Indies. £1

The Lark Tandstickor matches, exported by Samuel Samuel & Co., Kobe, Japanese. 75p

Running Lion Safety Matches, Kerala Manufactory. 50p

Lidköping Safety Matches, Swedish. £2

Artillery Specially Safety Matches, Swedish. £2

Cock on Barrel Safety Matches, Swedish. £1

The Automobile Safety Matches, Swedish. £3

The Crown Safety Matches, Swedish. £1

Radja Hindostan Safety Matches, Swedish. £1

The Melatti Safety Matches, Swedish. £4

I Use Only Swedish Matches, Manufactured in Sweden. £1

Superior Safety Matches, Japanese. 75p

Farmhouse Safety Matches, Swedish. £1

The Airship Superior Safety Matches, Made in Japan by the Toyo Match Co., Kobe.

'Mammy' brand safety matches Made in Nigeria. £4

An interesting Japanese label with a host of spelling mistakes. £10

Russian label commemorating Yuri Gagarin, 1961. £1

Chinese match box label with 2000 contents. £3

Bryant & May's Pearl Matches, 1886. £4

'Fixed Stars' by R. Bell & Co., London, circa 1863. £30

Pegasus, Foreign Made, 1930. £2

One of Bryant & May's early labels, circa 1891. £10

The North Star, Belgium, 1925. £1

Polar Bear, Made in Belgium, 1925. £1

Assurance Safety Matches, 1961. 50p

Uran Safety Matches for Export to Britain, 1939. 75p

Pegasus, Foreign Made, 1930. £2

Bryant & May's Royal Wax Vestas. £1

The North Star, Belgium, 1925. £1

Polar Bear, Made in Belgium, 1925. £1

An old label from a British Company no longer in existence, early 1920's. £30

Wild Goose Chase, Made in Belgium, 1939. £1

'God Bless Edward VII', Made in Austria. 50p

'All Round The Box' label from a British Manufacturer no longer in existence, early 1900's. £15

Squirrel Brand matches made in India, 1923. £5

Phildale, Foreign Made, 1951. 75p

Angling, Made in England, 1982. 25p

Advertising Label, 1980. 15p

Emergoplast Flexible Plaster Dressing by Boots. **£3**

Boric Ointment, British Pharmacopoeia. **£3**

Zubes Cough Mixture, for quick relief. **£4**

Dr Wernet's Powder for holding dental plates. **£7**

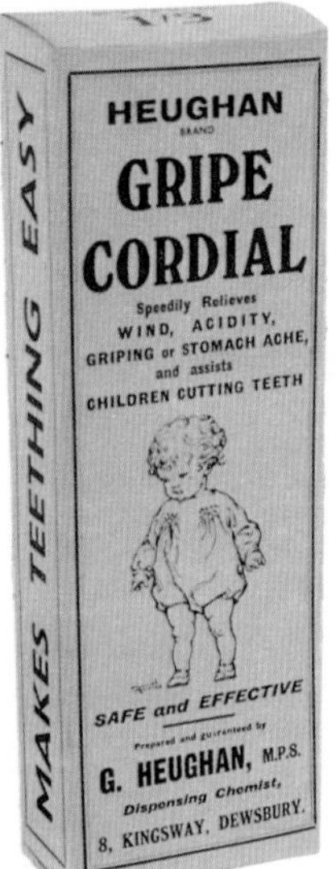

Heughan Gripe Cordial, Safe and Effective. **£2**

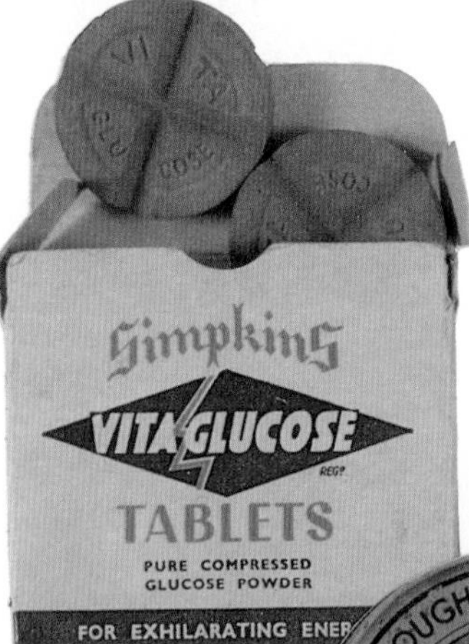

Simpkins Vita Glucose Tablets. **£4**

Fine white, open wove Bandage by Boots. **£2**

California Syrup of Figs. **£3**

Vaseline Petroleum Jelly. **£3**

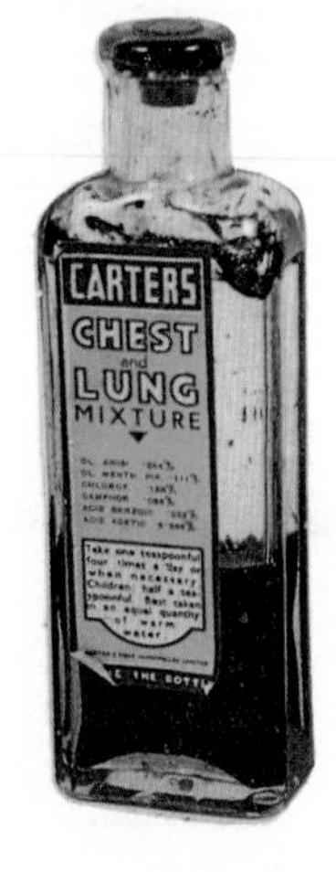

Carters Chest and Lung Mixture. **£5**

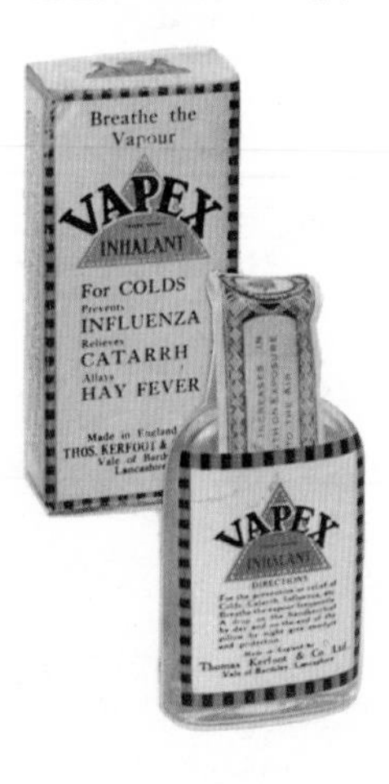

Vapex Inhaler bottle and box. **£12**

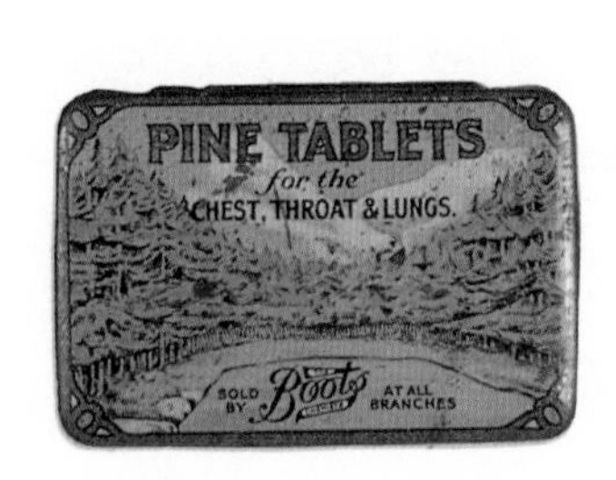

Pine Tablets by Boots. **£2**

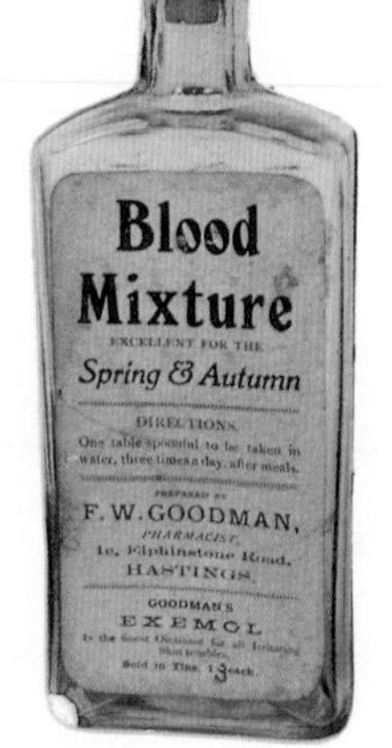

Blood Mixture by F. W. Goodman. **£6**

(Douglas Morgan)

Virol, amber glass bottle with lid. £6

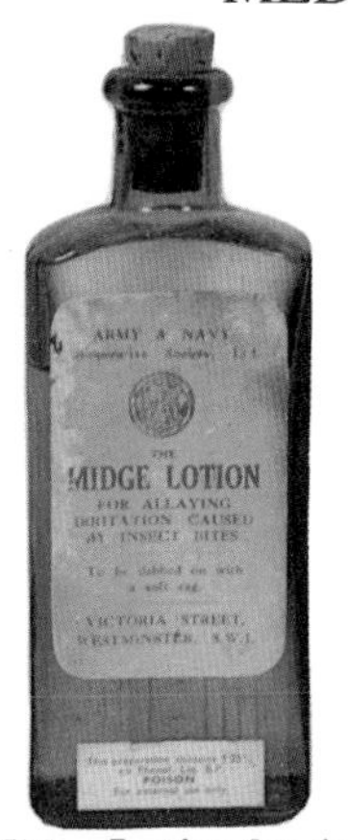

Midge Lotion by Army & Navy Co-operative Society Ltd. £3

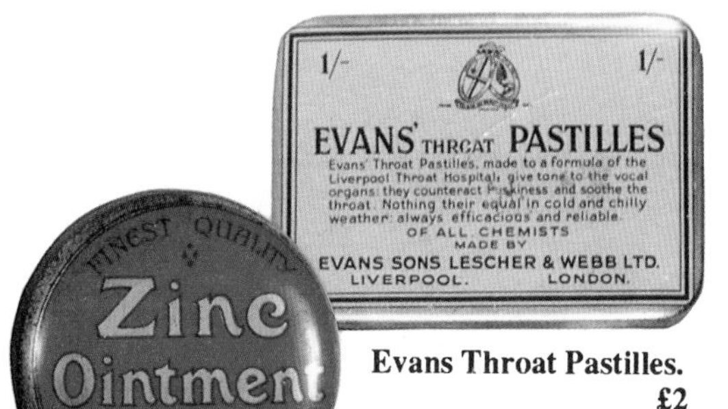

Zinc Ointment, Antiseptic, Soothing and Healing. £3

Evans Throat Pastilles. £2

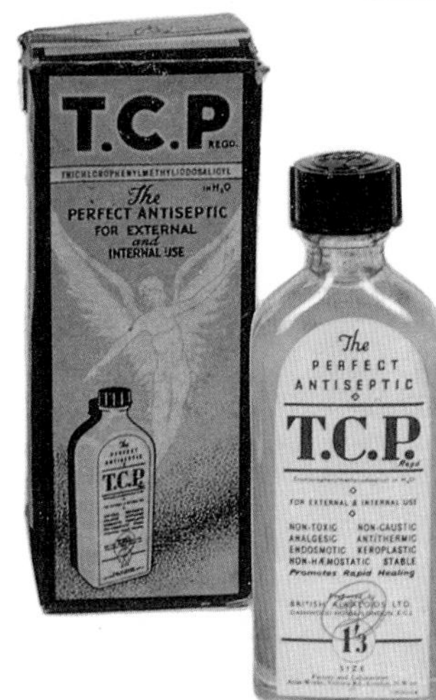

T.C.P. The Perfect Antiseptic, bottle & box. £10

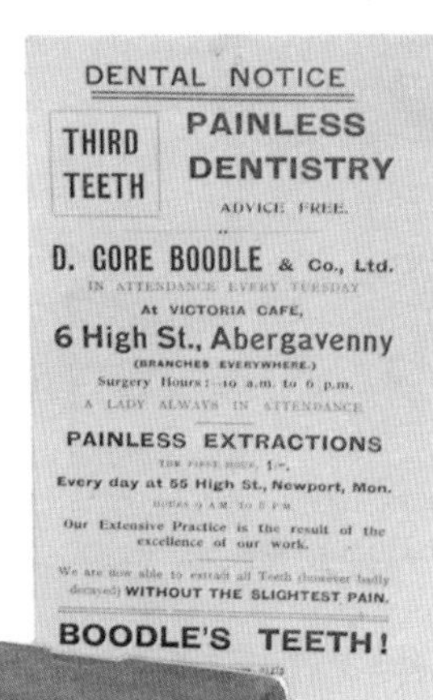
DENTAL NOTICE

THIRD TEETH

PAINLESS DENTISTRY

ADVICE FREE.

D. GORE BOODLE & Co., Ltd.

IN ATTENDANCE EVERY TUESDAY

At VICTORIA CAFE,

6 High St., Abergavenny

(BRANCHES EVERYWHERE.)

Surgery Hours:—10 a.m. to 6 p.m.

A LADY ALWAYS IN ATTENDANCE

PAINLESS EXTRACTIONS

Every day at 55 High St., Newport, Mon.

Our Extensive Practice is the result of the excellence of our work.

We are now able to extract all Teeth (however badly decayed) WITHOUT THE SLIGHTEST PAIN.

BOODLE'S TEETH!

Nelson's Improved Inhaler. £15

Boodle's Teeth together with box and Dental Notice. £12

Carters Bronchial Mixture. £4

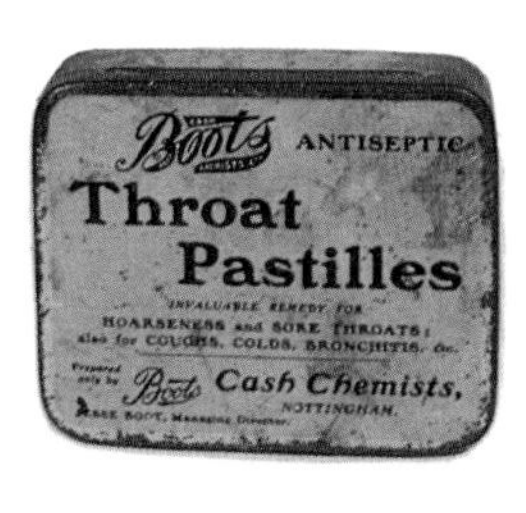

Boots antiseptic Throat Pastilles. £2

Green glass ribbed bottle, Plumbi Acet. £20

Cobalt blue Poison bottle from A. C. Olds & Co. £4

(Douglas Morgan)

Ointment containers.
50p each

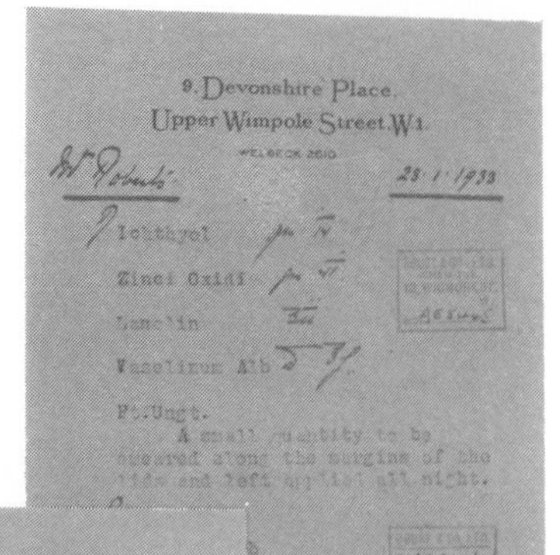

9, Devonshire Place,
Upper Wimpole Street, W1.
WELBECK 2610

28.1.1933

Ichthyol

Zinci Oxidi

Lanolin

Vaselinum Alb

Ft. Ungt.
A small quantity to be smeared along the margins of the lids and left applied all night.

dissolved in half a
warm water and used to
eyes as directed.

ROUSE & CO., LTD.,
Dispensing Chemists,
12, WIGMORE STREET,
(4 DOORS FROM HARLEY STREET),
LONDON, W. 1.

Prescription and envelope by Rouse & Co Ltd, Dispensing Chemists.
£2

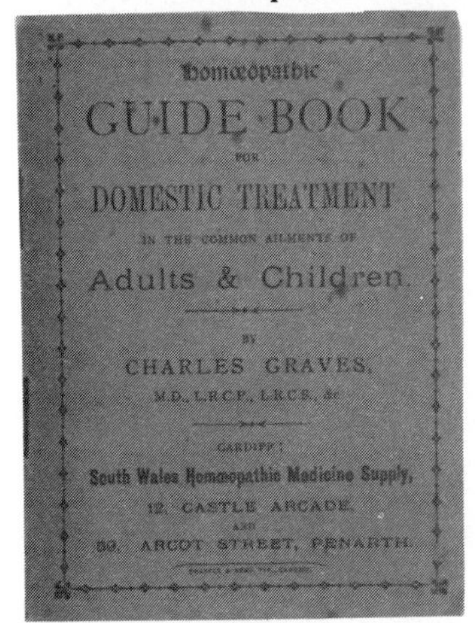

Homoeopathic
GUIDE BOOK
FOR
DOMESTIC TREATMENT
IN THE COMMON AILMENTS OF
Adults & Children.
BY
CHARLES GRAVES,
M.D., L.R.C.P., L.R.C.S., &c.
CARDIFF:
South Wales Homoeopathic Medicine Supply,
12, CASTLE ARCADE,
AND
89, ARCOT STREET, PENARTH.

Homoeopathic Guide Book for Domestic Treatment. £2

Zant Germicide by Evans Sons Lescher & Webb Ltd. £5

White glass chemists bottle Liq Calcis.
£15

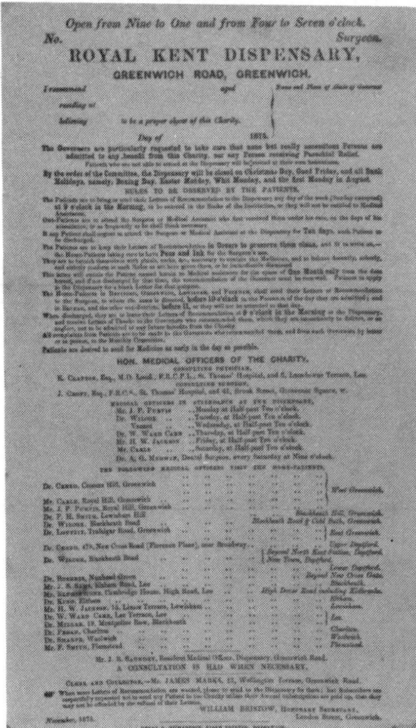

Open from Nine to One and from Four to Seven o'clock.
No. *Surgeon.*
ROYAL KENT DISPENSARY,
GREENWICH ROAD, GREENWICH.

Day of 1875.

By the order of the Committee, the Dispensary will be closed on Christmas Day, Good Friday, and all Bank Holidays, namely, Boxing Day, Easter Monday, Whit Monday, and the first Monday in August.

RULES TO BE OBSERVED BY THE PATIENTS.

Patients are desired to send for Medicine as early in the day as possible.

HON. MEDICAL OFFICERS OF THE CHARITY.

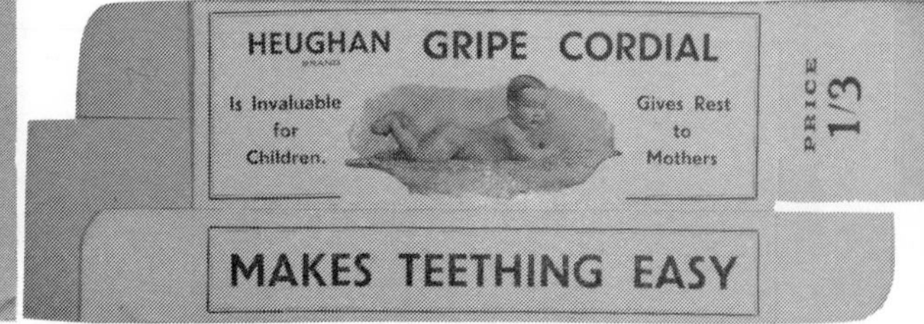

Royal Kent Dispensary Rules 1875. £15

Heughan Gripe Cordial. £3

(Douglas Morgan)

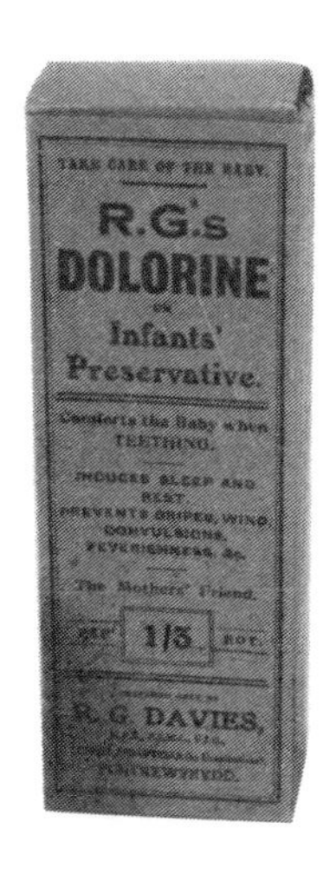

R.G's Dolorine or Infants Preservative. £6

Elastic Thread, for all types of smocking, shirring, knitting. £2

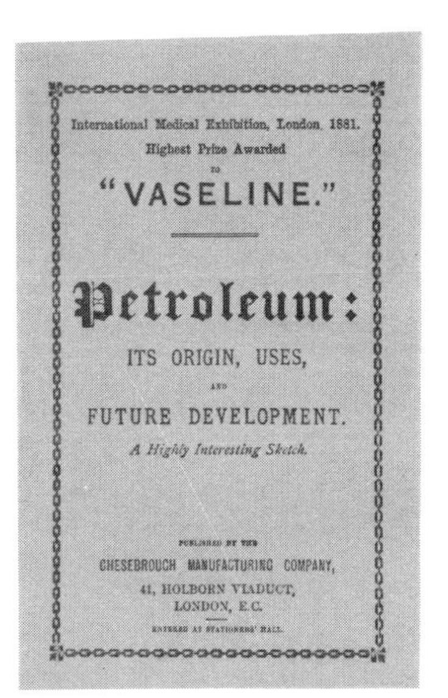
International Medical Exhibition, London, 1881.
Highest Prize Awarded
TO
"VASELINE."

Petroleum:
ITS ORIGIN, USES,
AND
FUTURE DEVELOPMENT.
A Highly Interesting Sketch.

PUBLISHED BY THE
CHESEBROUGH MANUFACTURING COMPANY,
41, HOLBORN VIADUCT,
LONDON, E.C.
ENTERED AT STATIONERS' HALL.

Sales literature for Vaseline Petroleum. £2

Camphorated oil by Wright, Layman & Umney Ltd. £4

Licoricine, Acts like magic for coughs, colds. £2

Glyco Thymoline eye bath complete with box. £6

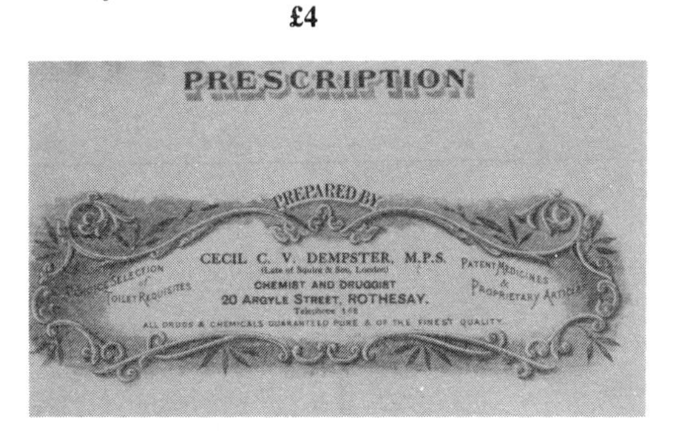

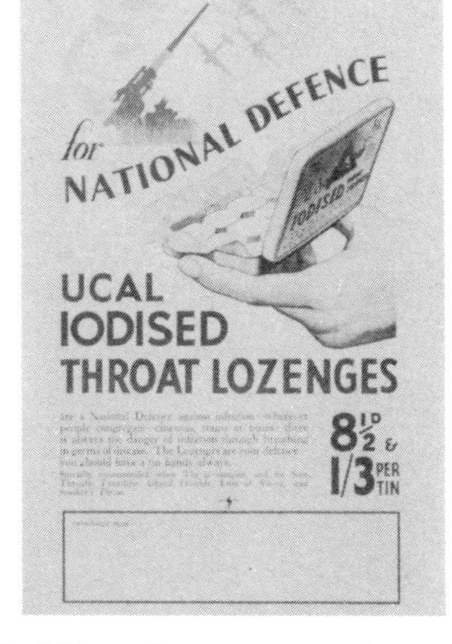

Prescription prepared by Cecil C. V. Dempster, Chemist and Druggist. £2

Ucal Iodised Throat Lozenges, magazine insert. £3

(Douglas Morgan)

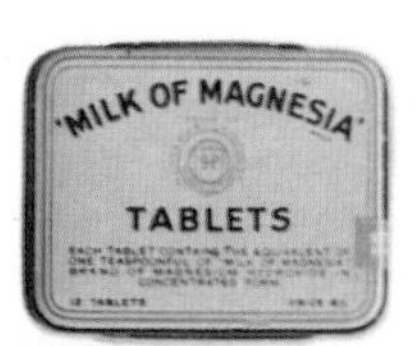

Milk of Magnesia Tablets. £3

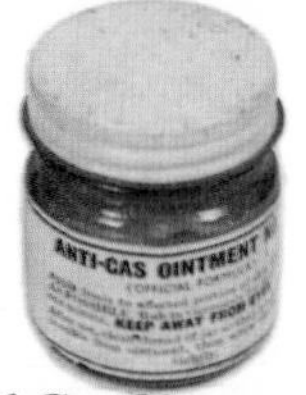

Anti-Gas Ointment, official Formula. £3

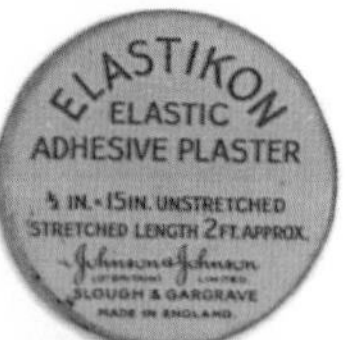

Elastikon, Elastic Adhesive Plaster. **£2**

Nigroids by Ferris & Co Ltd. £4

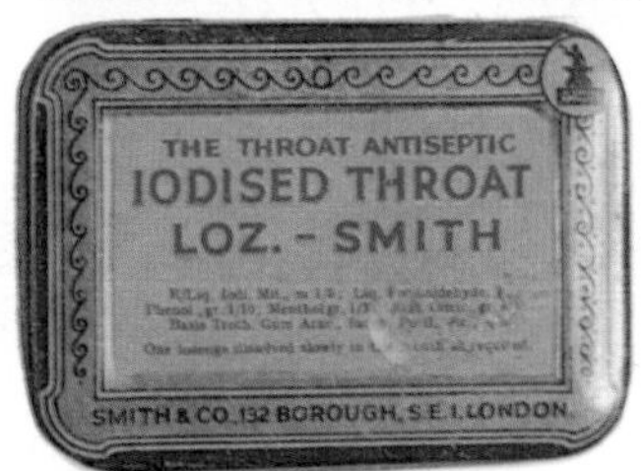

Iodised Throat Lozenges by Smith & Co. £3

The Zinc Ointment, The Elco Brand. £1

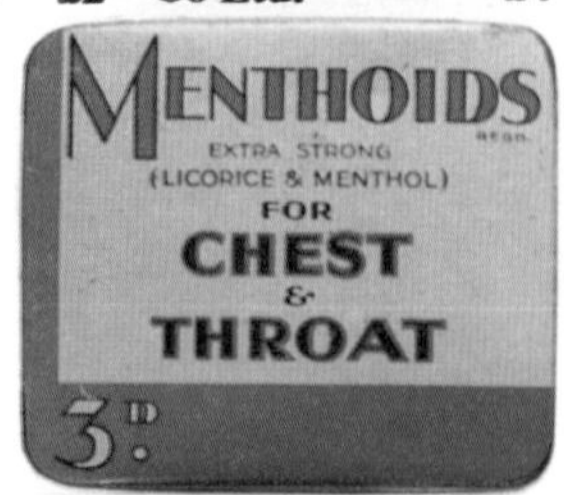

Menthoids for Chest and Throat. £6

Bottle of tablets dispensed by Geo Oxley. £2

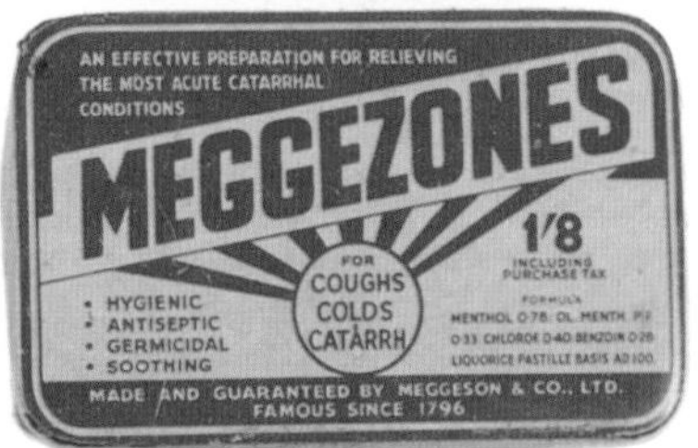

Meggezones for Coughs, Colds and Catarrh. £2

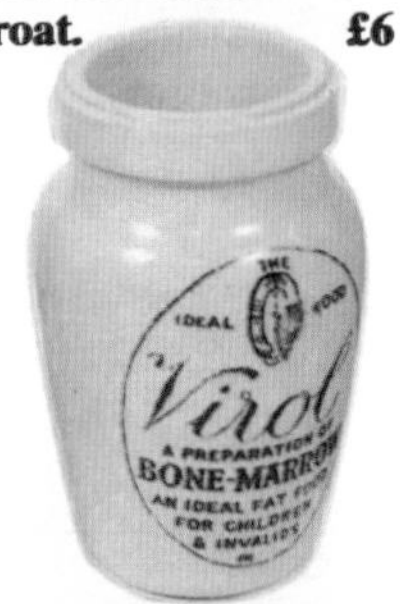

Virol, a preparation of bone marrow, 4" high. £5

Vigor Tonic will pick you up. £5

The 'Home' first aid case by Boots. £20

Diuromi blue glass bottle by Pharmax Ltd. £3

(Douglas Morgan)

Snowfire, for chapped hands, with contents. £3

Ayesha Poppies Toilet Powder with contents. £5

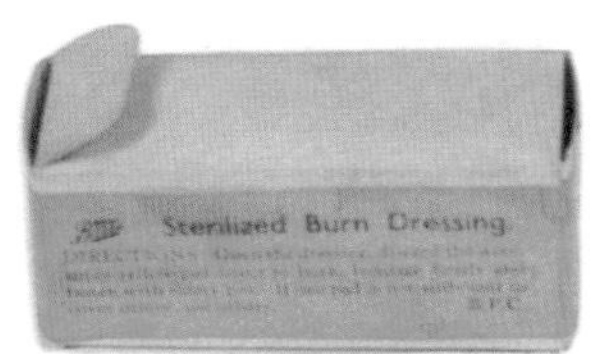

Sterilized Burn Dressing by Boots. £2

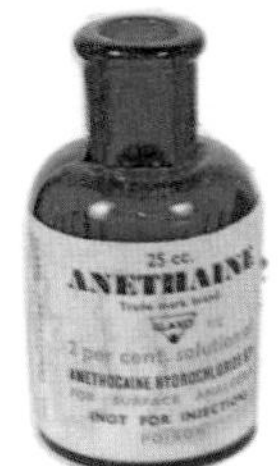

Anethaine blue glass bottle by Glaxo. £4

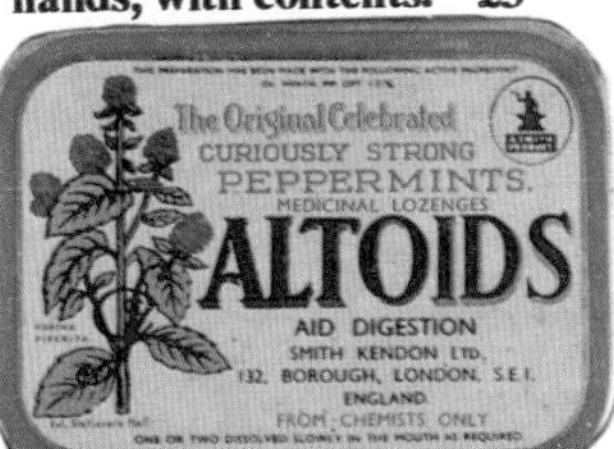

The Original Celebrated Altoids. £3

Zinc Ointment. £3

Meloids for a mellow voice. £5

Oil of Pine by Potter & Clark. £8

Finegans' Nip-a-Kofs. £6

Elastoplast, Elastic Adhesive Bandage. £2

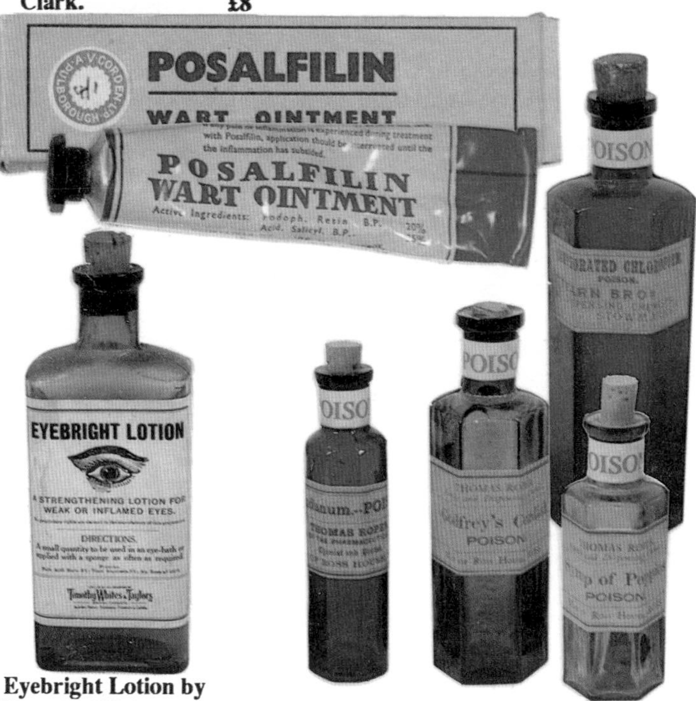

Eyebright Lotion by Timothy Whites & Taylors. £6

Poison bottles with original labels. £6 each

Green glass ribbed bottle Tinct Camph. Co. £15

(Douglas Morgan)

The Junior Imperial League, 1930. £1

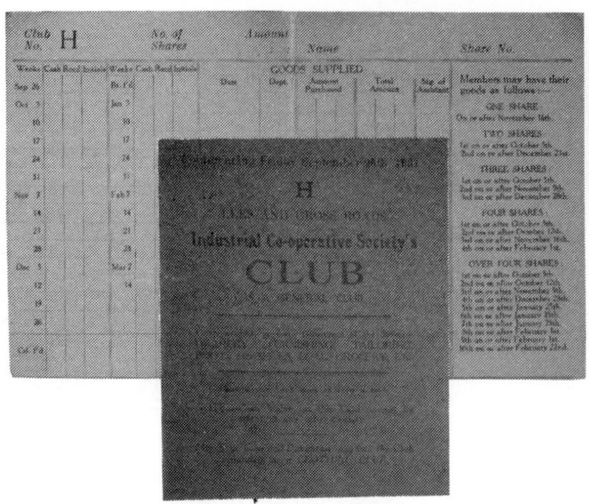

Industrial Co-operative Society's Club, 1931. £1

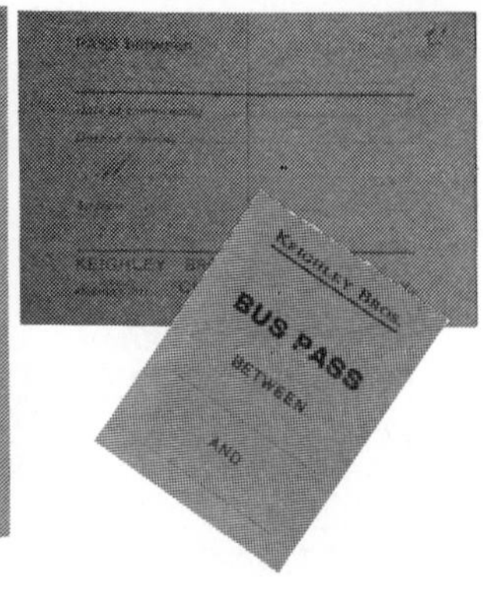

Bus Pass, Keighley Bros. £2

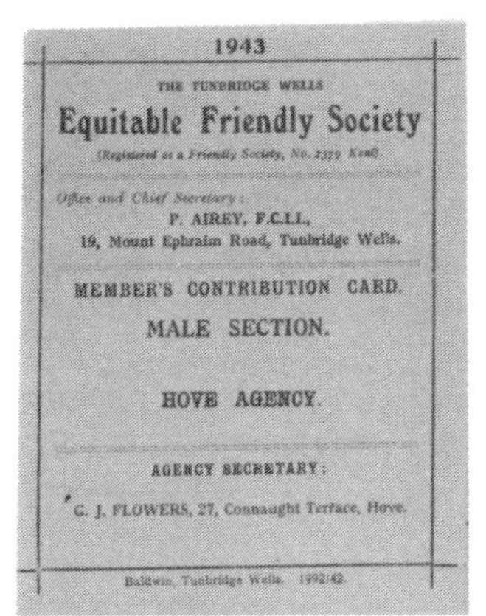

Equitable Friendly Society contribution card, 1943. £1

Membership certificate in The Society of The Cincinnati for Otho Holland Williams, signed by Washington and Henry Knox, New York, August 7, 1790.
(Eldred's) £8,062

Certificate for Joseph Chadwick to serve as Fireman in the City of New York, 1807, 14 x 10¼in.
(Skinner) £247

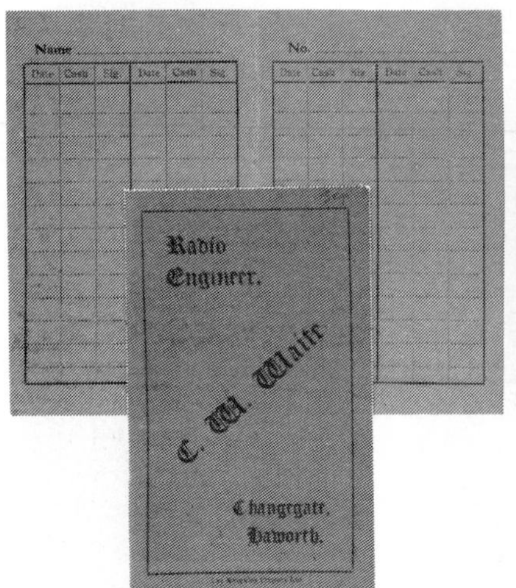

C.W. Waite, Radio Engineer. £1

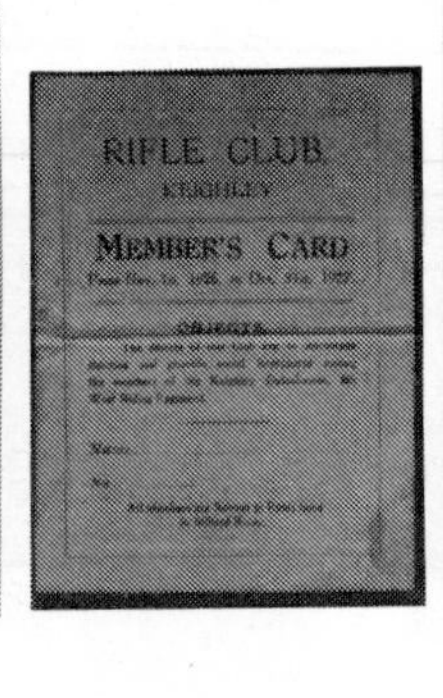

Rifle Club Member's Card, 1926/1927. £1

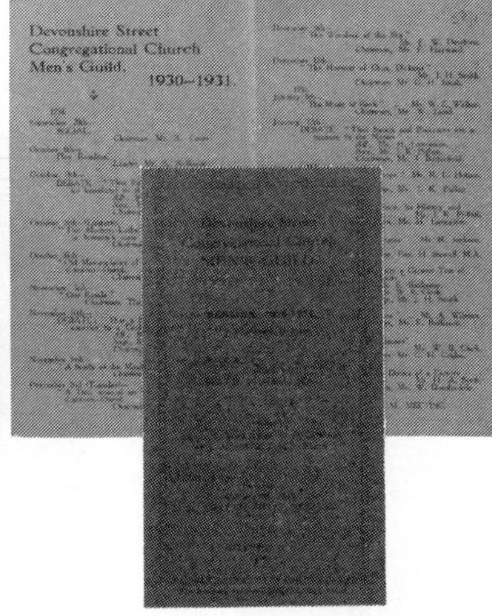

Devonshire Street Congregational Church Men's Guild, 1930/1931.

(Yesterdays Paper)

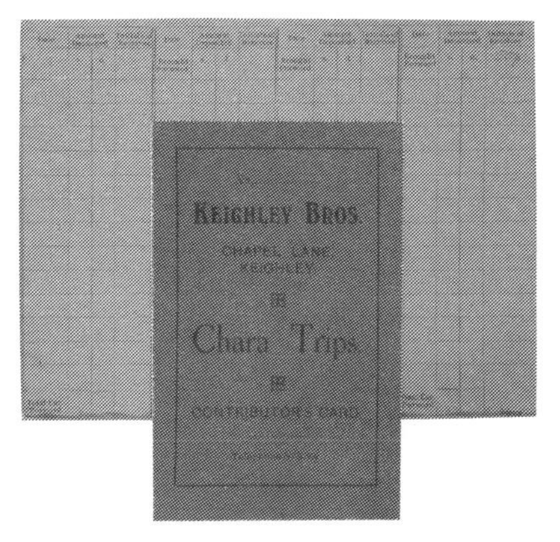

Chara Trips, Contributor's Card. £1

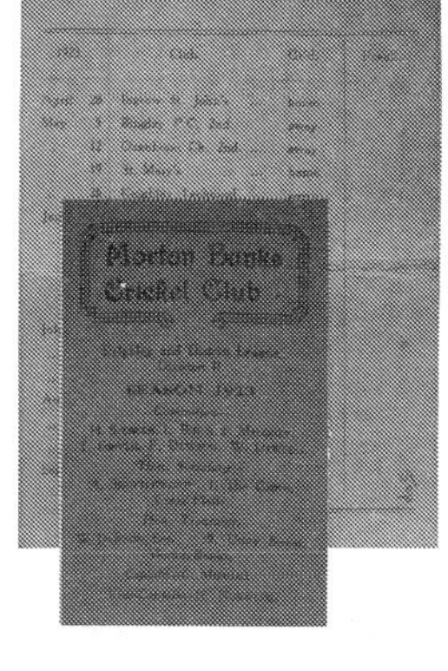

Morton Banks Cricket Club, 1923. £3

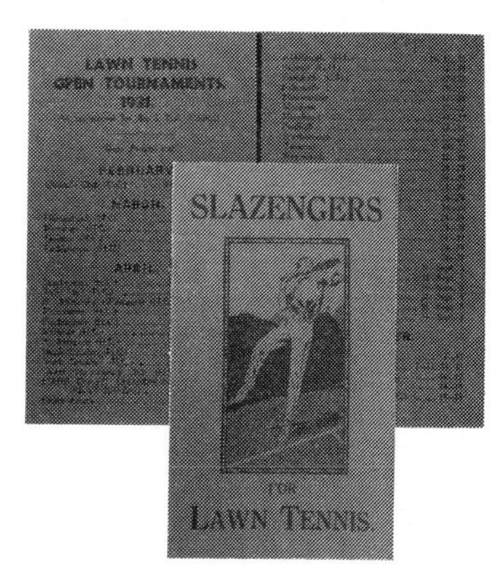

Slazengers Lawn Tennis Tournaments, 1931. £2

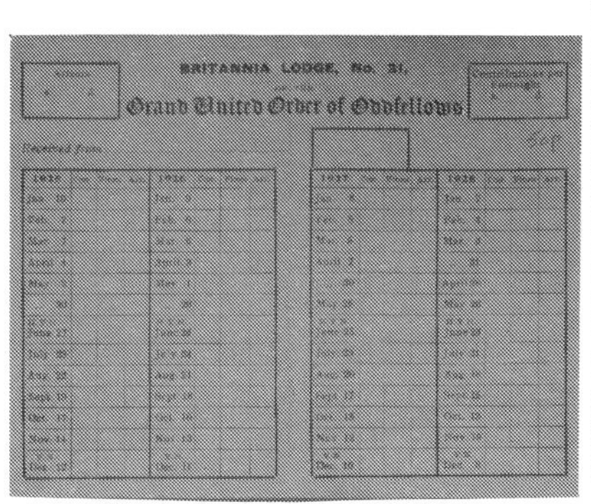

Grand United Order of Oddfellows, Britannia Lodge No. 31, 1925. £1

Poultry, Rabbit, Fruit and Vegetable Club, 1925. £1

Airedale Hockey Club. £1

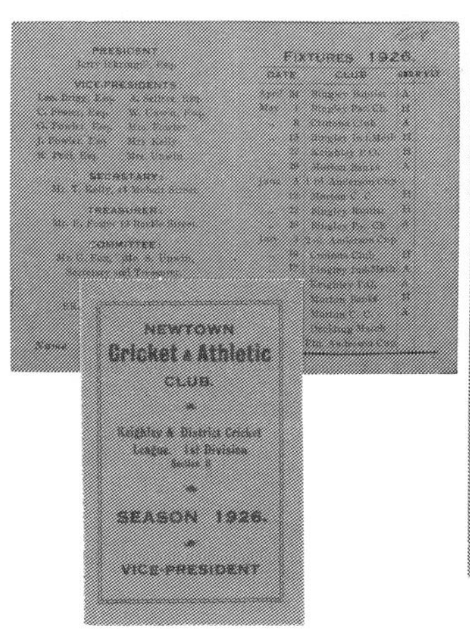

Newtown Cricket & Athletic Club, 1926. £1

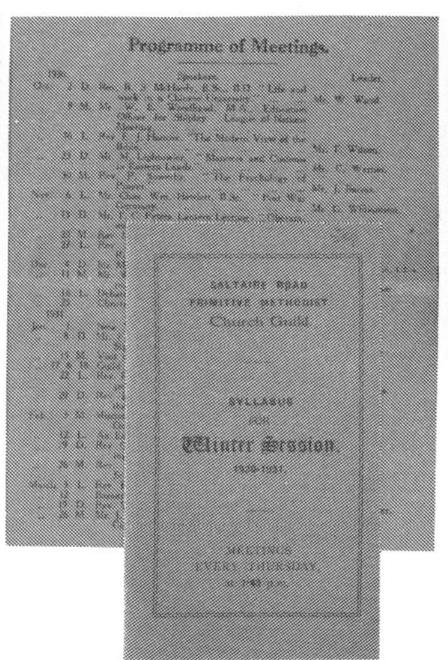

Church Guild, Winter Session 1930–1931. £1

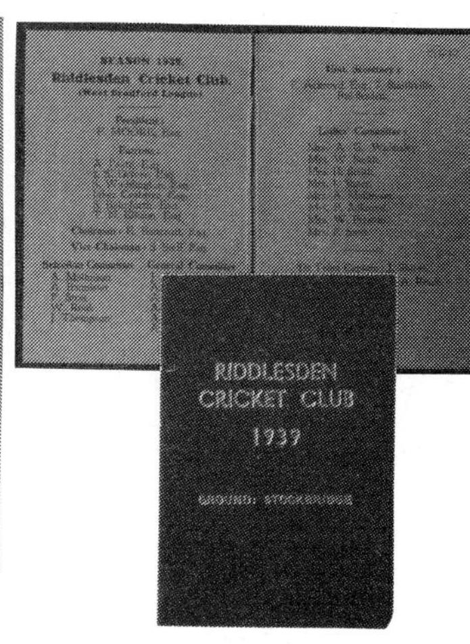

Riddlesden Cricket Club, 1939. £2

(Yesterdays Paper)

The Wassail Bowl. £12

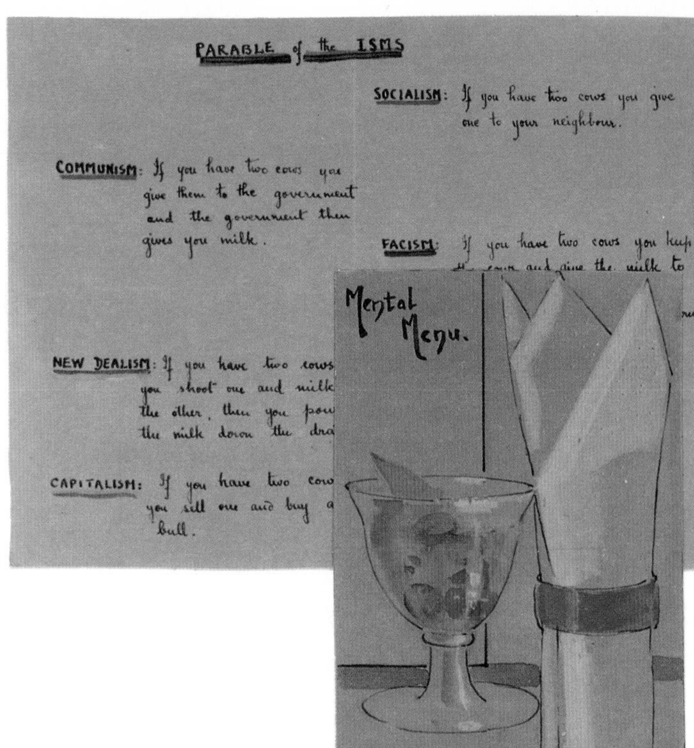

1893 menu, shaped as artists' palette. £12

Mental menu. £8

First Guards Club menu, 1st June 1931. £15

Menu for Piccadilly Hotel, New Years Eve 1916. £80

(Spread Eagle Antiques)

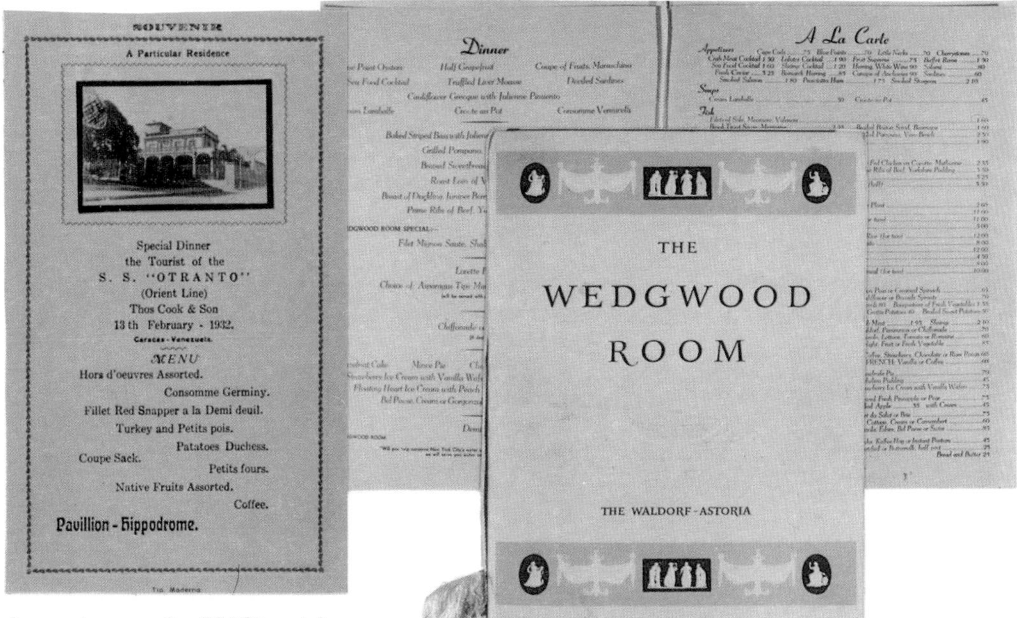

Souvenir menu for SS 'Otranto' 13 February 1932. £10

Wedgwood Room menu, Waldorf-Astoria, January 25 1950. £8

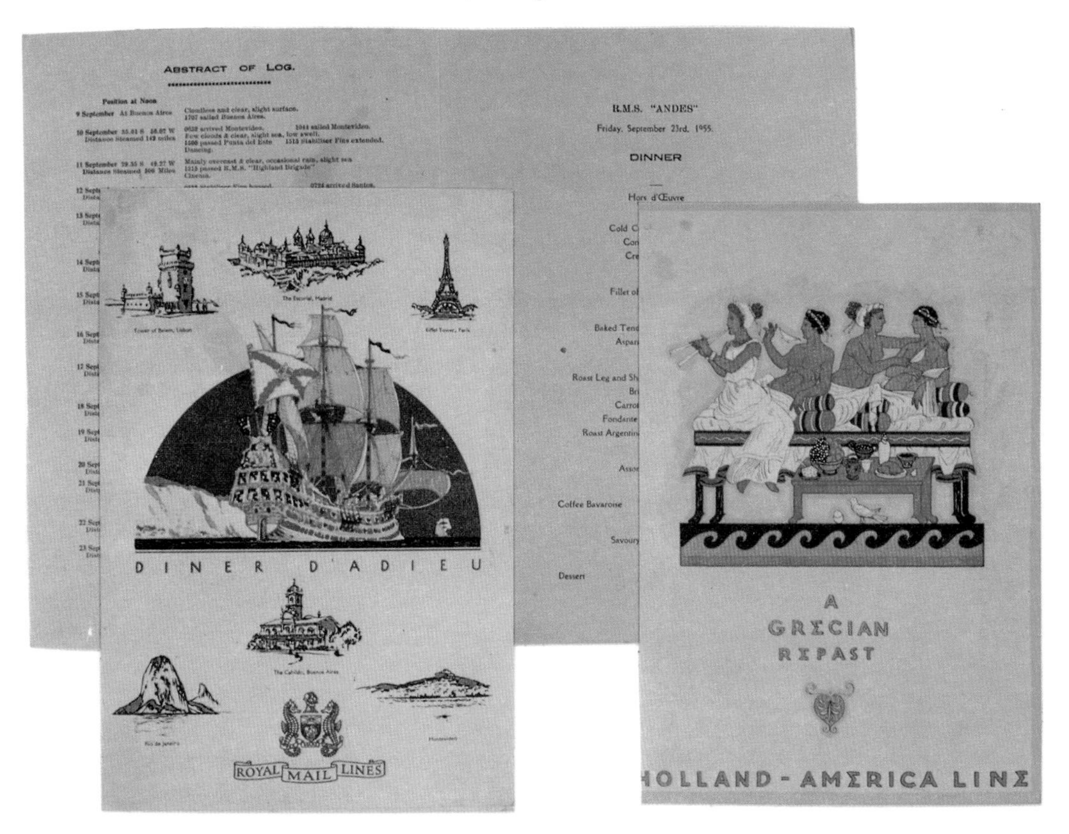

Royal Mail Line menu, September 23 1955. £15

Holland America Line menu covers 1915–16. £12

(Spread Eagle Antiques)

M.V. 'Reina Del Pacifico' Luncheon Menu, 13th August, 1932. £4

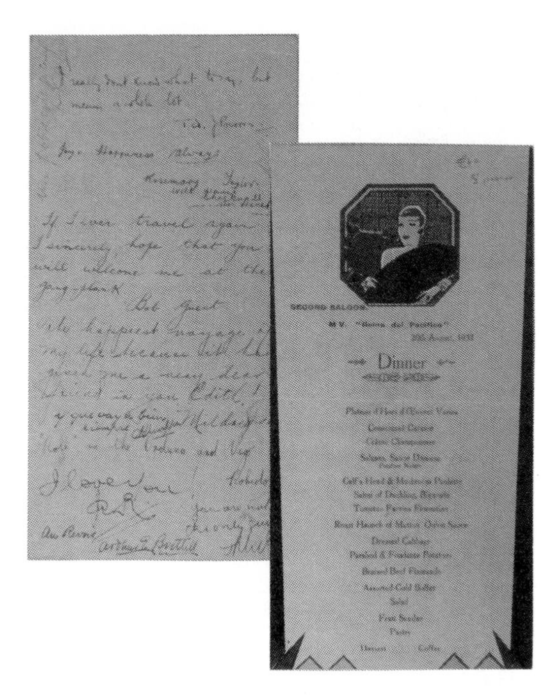

M.V. 'Reina Del Pacifico' Dinner Menu, 20th August, 1932. £4

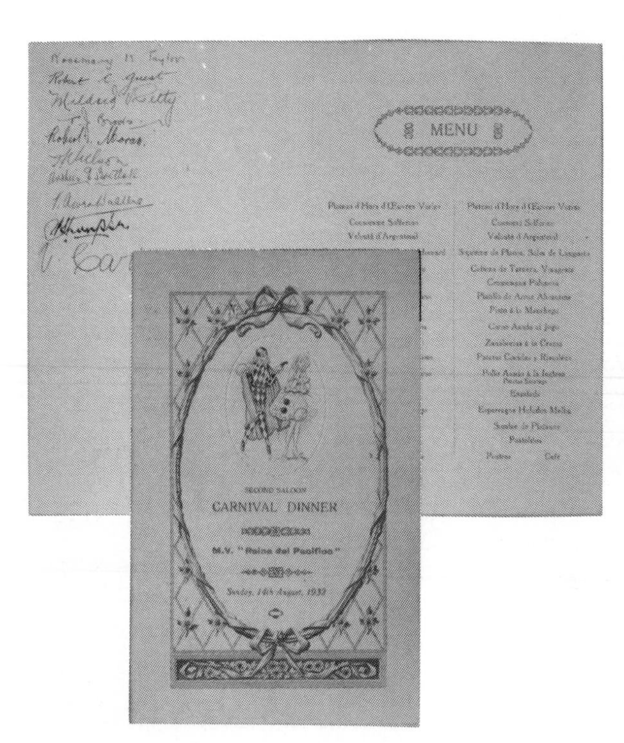

M.V. 'Reina Del Pacifico' Carnival Dinner, 14th August, 1932. £4

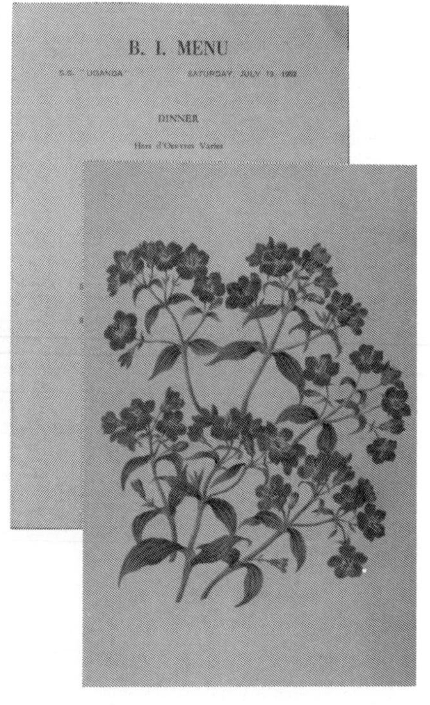

S.S. 'Uganda' Menu, July 19th, 1952. £2

(Yesterdays Paper)

R.N.S. 'Queen Elizabeth', April 28th, 1947. £3

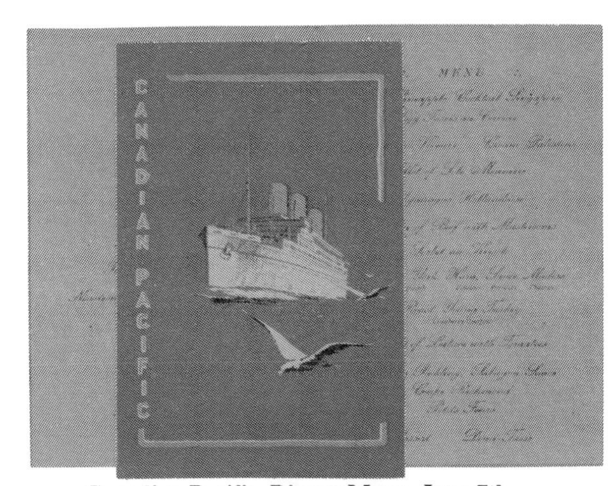

Canadian Pacific, Dinner Menu, June 7th, 1934. £4

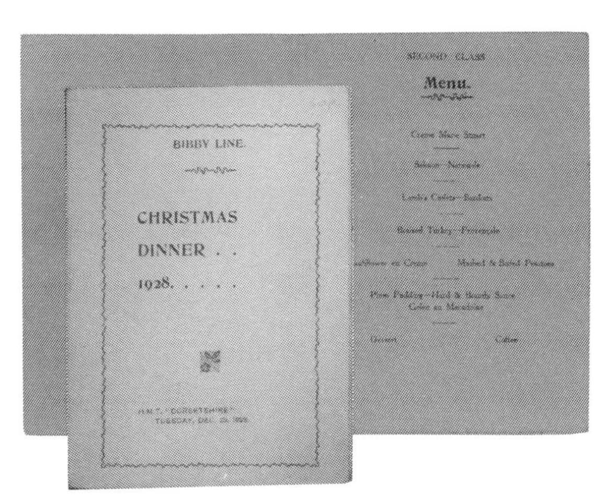

Bibby Line, Christmas Dinner 1928, H.M.T. 'Dorsetshire'. £2

R.M.S. 'Queen Elizabeth' Dinner Menu, May 1st, 1947. £3

Pacific Line, R.M.S. 'Orduna', Carnival Dinner, 18th October 1932. £2

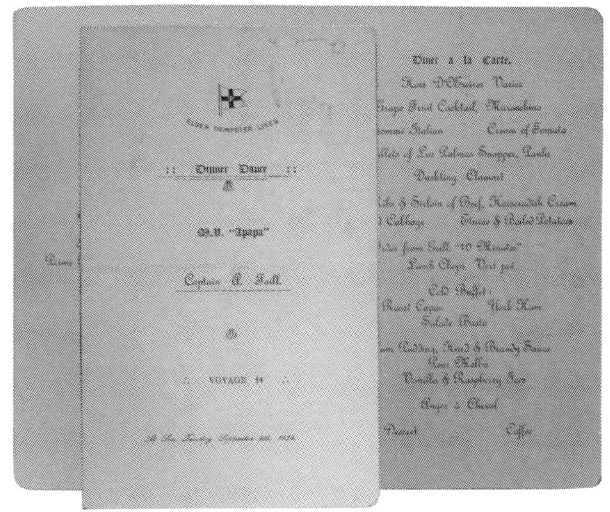

Elder Dempster Lines, Dinner Dance M.V. 'Apapa', Sept. 4th, 1934. £2

(Yesterdays Paper)

Menu for Piccadilly Hotel, New Years Eve 1915. **£80**

Puzzle menu. £12

THE MANSION HOUSE.

THE RT. HON. JAMES WHITEHEAD, LORD MAYOR.

BANQUET
TO THE
BANKERS & MERCHANTS OF THE CITY OF LONDON.
WEDNESDAY, 13th MARCH, 1889.

MENU.

SOUP.
TURTLE.
FISH.
FILLETS TURBOT À LA CHESTERFIELD.
BOILED SALMON WITH TARTARE SAUCE. WHITEBAIT.
ENTRÉES.
SALMI DE PLUVIERS À LA SEFTON.
RIS D'AGNEAU EN CAISSES À LA PRINTANIER.
REMOVES.
BOILED CHICKENS À LA ZINGARI. HAMS BRAISED.
SADDLE OF MUTTON.
GUINEA FOWLS. WIDGEON.
ENTREMETS.
GATEAUX ENDYMION. ORANGE JELLY.
BAVAROIS À LA MODERNE. BABA AU RHUM.
MERINGUES À LA FRANCAISE.
REMOVES.
ICED PUDDING. CROUTES À LA BERNE.

Mansion House Banquet 1889. £6

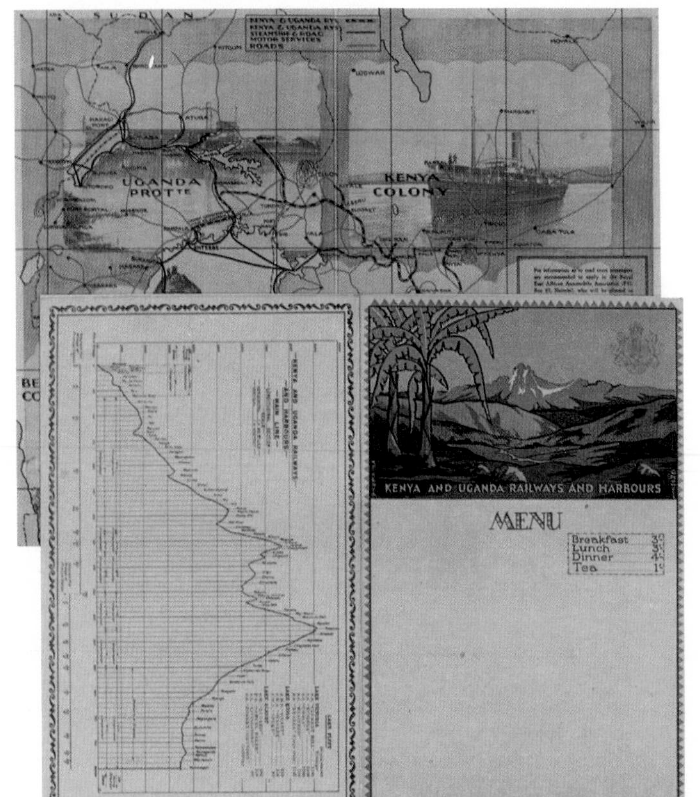

Kenya & Uganda Railways Menu. £18

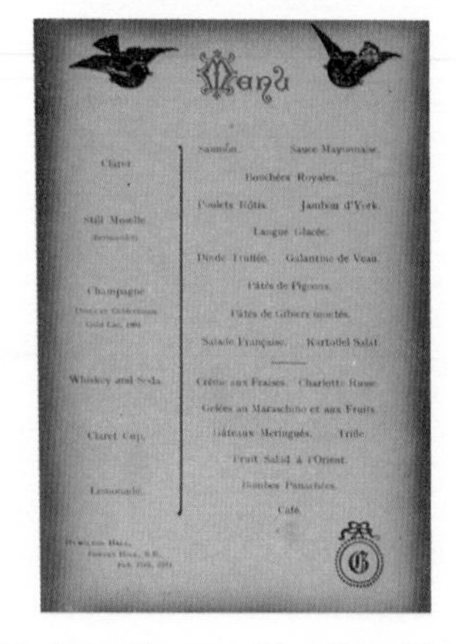

Embossed menu, Hamilton Hall 1911. £6

(Spread Eagle Antiques)

Fishmongers Hall menu, 16 June 1927. £15

Menu for Les Tuileries Restaurant, 16 September 1934. £20

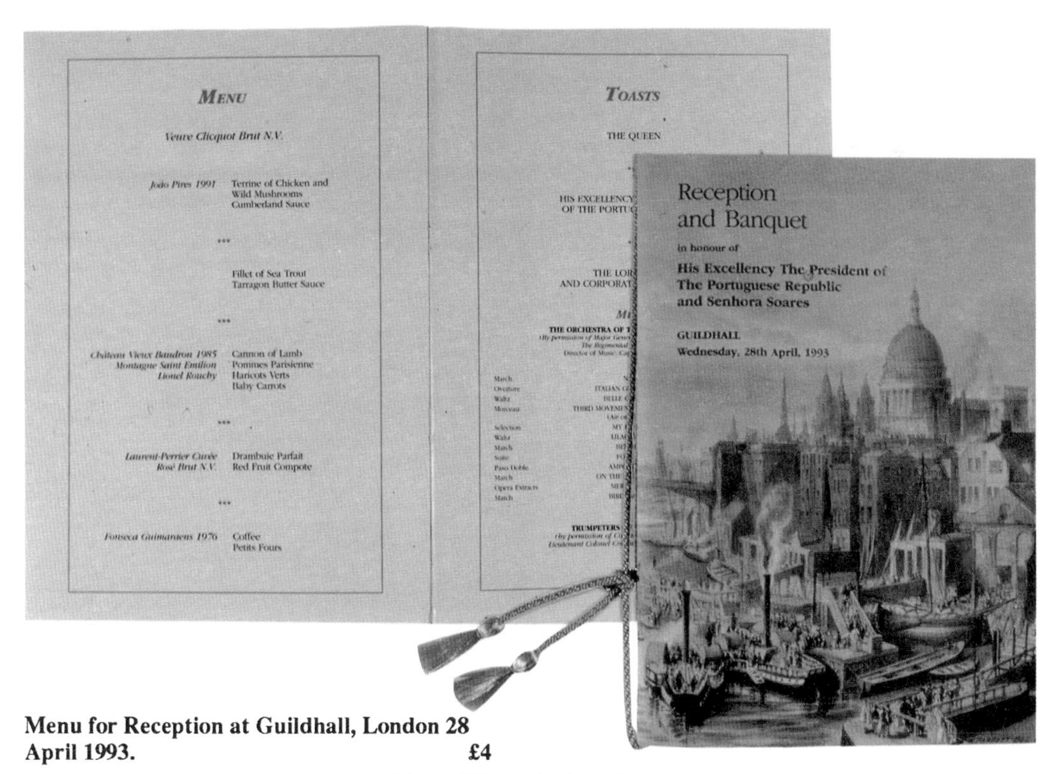

Menu for Reception at Guildhall, London 28 April 1993. £4

(Spread Eagle Antiques)

M.A.P. edited by T. P. O'Connor, September 19th, 1908. £4

Pretty Pets Weekly Magazine, Golden Locks and the Three Bears. £3

Pearson's Magazine, 1908, 3in. high. £6

A 17th century miniature Book of Psalms with embroidered cover, England, 2 x 3¼in. £1,400

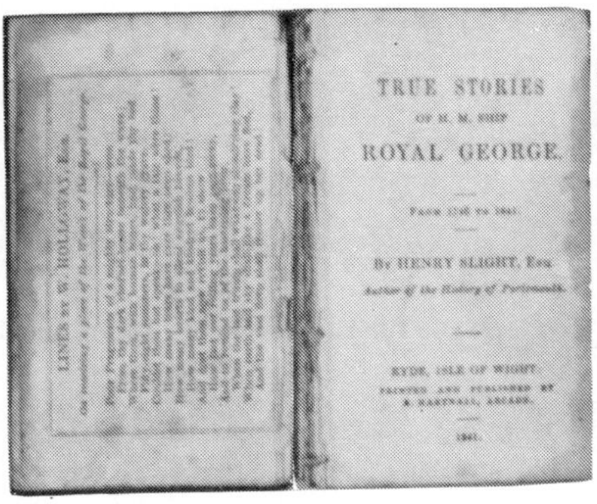

True stories of H.M. Ship Royal George, by Henry Slight, 1841. £35

Miniature Holy Bible, Oxford University Press, leather bound, 2in. high, 1919. £6

Tales for Tiny People, Cinderella and the Magic Slipper. £3

Home Notes, October 15th, 1908, Featuring Handkerchief Toys. £5

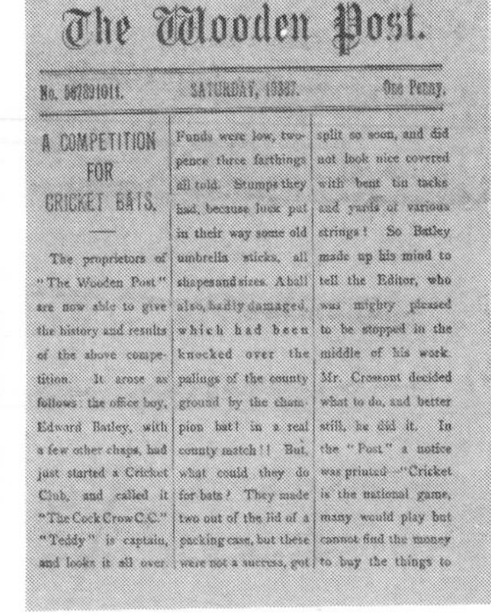

The Wooden Post.

No. [illegible] SATURDAY, [illegible] One Penny.

A COMPETITION FOR CRICKET BATS.

The proprietors of "The Wooden Post" are now able to give the history and results of the above competition. It arose as follows: the office boy, Edward Batley, with a few other chaps, had just started a Cricket Club, and called it "The Cock Crow C.C." "Teddy" is captain, and looks it all over. Funds were low, twopence three farthings all told. Stumps they had, because luck put in their way some old umbrella sticks, all shapes and sizes. A ball also, badly damaged, which had been knocked over the palings of the county ground by the champion bat! in a real county match!! But, what could they do for bats? They made two out of the lid of a packing case, but these were not a success, got split so soon, and did not look nice covered with bent tin tacks and yards of various strings! So Batley made up his mind to tell the Editor, who was mighty pleased to be stopped in the middle of his work. Mr. Crossont decided what to do, and better still, he did it. In the "Post" a notice was printed—"Cricket is the national game, many would play but cannot find the money to buy the things to

The Wooden Post, miniature magazine. £2

Phoenix Car Service Brochure, 1930. £2

Rowntree's 'Motoring Chocolate' wrapper. £2

Motor Fuel Ration Book for a motor cycle. £4

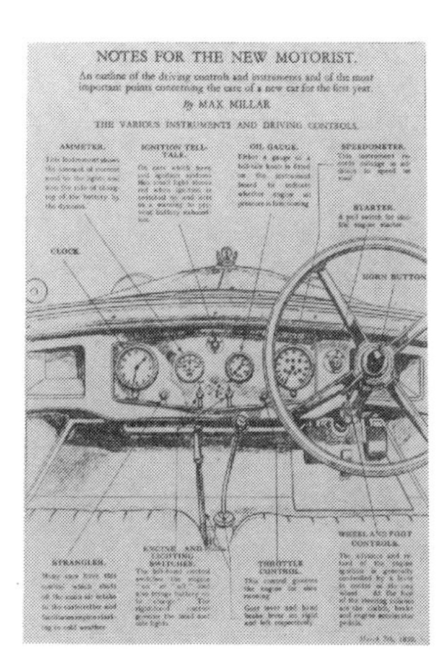

Autocar, March 7th 1930. £5

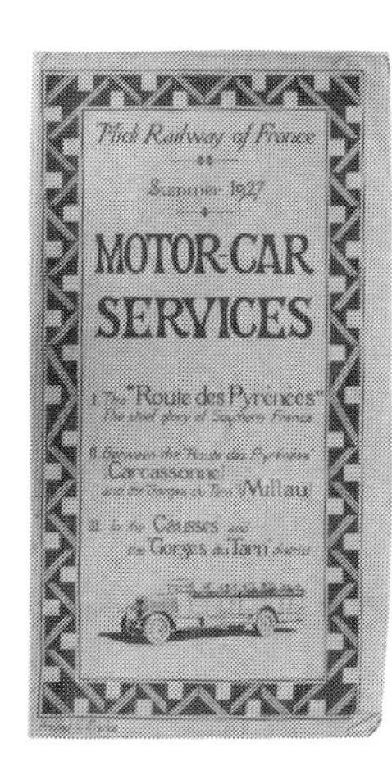

Motor Car Services, 1927, Route des Pyrenees. £3

The Autocar, January 1952. £2

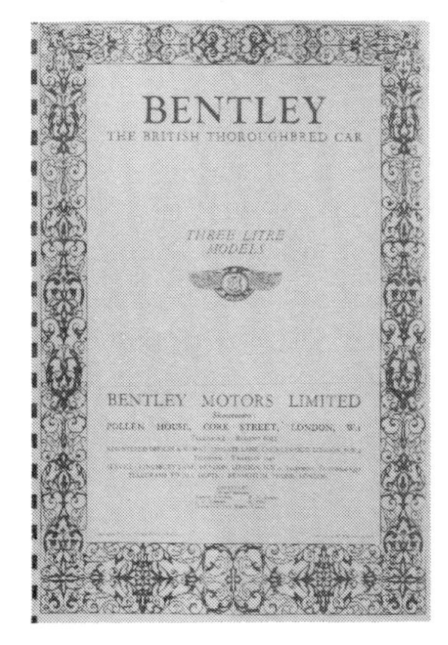

Bentley Sales Brochure, 1928. £60

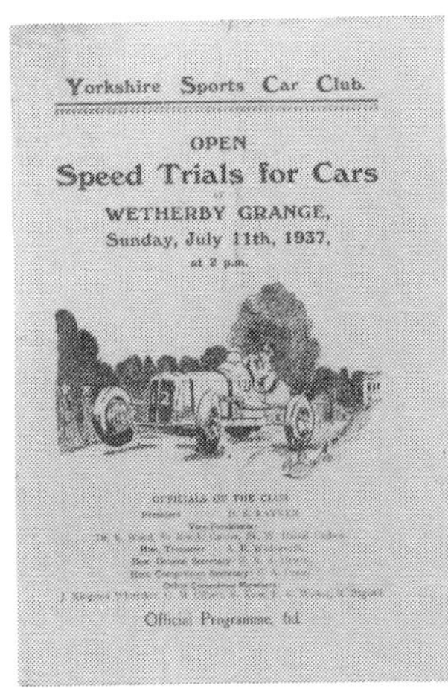

Yorkshire Sports Car Club, Speed Trials Programme, 1937. £10

Motor Cycling, June 1942. £4

(C.A. Winder)

A Mingozzi designed lithograph 'V^a Corsa in salita Vittoria Cansiglio, 1 July 1928, 36 x 45cm. (Finarte) £125

Abarth & C sign with scorpion and script in relief in wood on yellow, blue and red painted metal base, 1950s, 47 x 56 x 3.5cm. (Finarte) £580

A poster designed by Paolo Cassa for the XXIV Mille Miglia Brescia, 11–12 May 1957, 70 x 100cm. (Finarte) £2,768

Large illuminated 'Ferrari Service' sign in double sided flexiglas complete with electrics, 1970s, 77 x 178 x 17cm. (Finarte) £2,768

'How to buy oil-cheaper-cleaner-quicker' by Tom Purvis, published by Shell No. 117, 75 x 114cm., 1925. (Onslows) £1,400

Monaco, 1er et 2 juin 1952, lithograph in colours by B. Minne, 48 x 31in. (Christie's New York) £4,290

An Englebert advertising poster showing Tazio Nuvolari's Alfa Romeo B type P3, winner of the 1935 German Grand Prix, French text, 44 x 62cm. (Finarte) £536

A watercolour by Giovanni Alloisi, showing a red Cisitalia in competition, drawn for the XXI Italian Grand Prix at the Monza Autodrome on 3 September 1950, 52 x 70cm. (Finarte) £1,071

A Maserati poster with a Maserati valve in the foreground, designed by Adriani, 1941, 68 x 103cm. (Finarte) £1,161

Royal Automobile Club, Guide & Handbook 1927–8. £5

M.G. Sales Brochure, 1970's. £2

Fiat 509, Poster.  £20

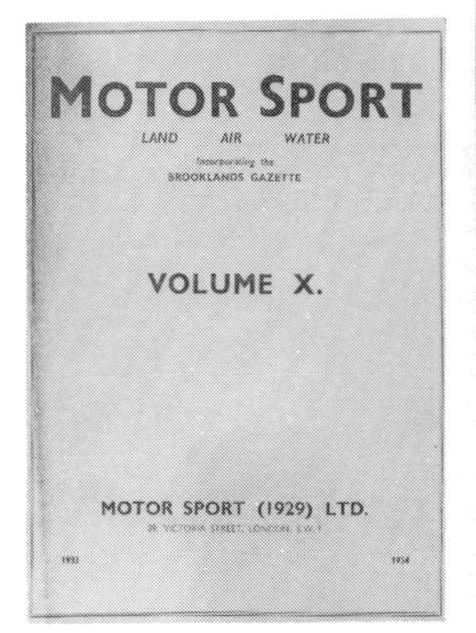

Motor Sport Magazine incorporating Brooklands Gazette. £5

Practical Motorist & Motor Cyclist, May 1954, no. 1. £7

The Story of Vauxhall by L. C. Darbyshire, 1946. £10

Grand Prix by Anthony Pritchard. £10

The Austin Magazine, October 1958. £2

Round The Bend with Brockbank. £8

(C.A. Winder)

A motorcycle racing poster by Gamy, France, 1913, 7.5/8 x 35¼in. £250

Palmares Juillet 1934 Shell, by Geo Ham, poster on linen, 79 x 60cm.
(Onslow's) £690

'Grand Prix de France Rheims 17th Juillet 1949', by Jean Des Gachons, poster on linen, 80 x 120cm.
(Onslow's) £2,000

Theodore Alexandre Steinlen: Motocycles Comiot, lithograph printed in colours, 1899, on two joined sheets of thin tan wove paper, 1,885 x 1,280mm.
(Christie's) £8,250

XXII Mille Miglia, Brescia 1 Maggio 1955, colour poster showing the Moss and Jenkinson Mercedes 300 SLR, signed and autographed by Stirling Moss, 23/300, 29 x 23½ in.
(Christie's) £682

Two of twenty-one R.A.C.I. dashboard plaques, late 1920's early 1930's, approx. 3 x 2in.
(Christie's) £700

'Montaut', Bayard "En Reconnaissance", poster on linen, 155 x 115cm.
(Onslow's) £1,400

1967 Le Mans Poster, 60 x 40cm.
(Onslow's) £650

Misti [Ferdinand Mifliez] Usines D'Automobiles G Brouhot, poster on linen, 158 x 121cm.
(Onslow's) £1,400

Red and white cotton Bugatti driver's armband for the 1924 Grand Prix D'Europe. (Onslow's) £500

Philippe Chapellier, 'Eclaireurs Bleriot', published by Philippe Chapellier, Paris, on linen, 38 x 48in. (Onslow's) £2,000

Aero Shell Lubricating Oil The Aristocrat of Lubricants, by E McKnight Kauffer, printed tin advertisement, 1932, 48 x 74cm. (Onslow's) £700

Moto MV Agusta Agenzia enamel shield, red base, 48 x 48cm., slightly worn. (Finarte) £201

5eme Grand Prix Automobile Monaco 23 Avril 1933, by G. Ham, colour lithograph, 47 x 31½in. (Onslow's) £2,000

Geo Ham, Side-Car Cross Et Motocross Montreuil, on linen, 123cm. x 119cm. (Onslow's) £180

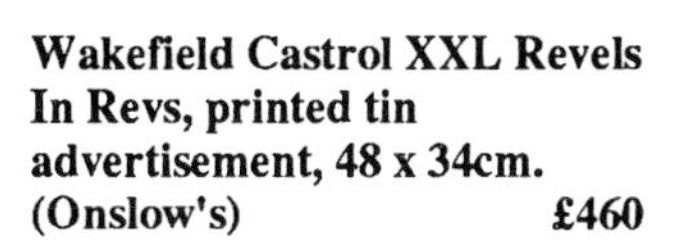

Wakefield Castrol XXL Revels In Revs, printed tin advertisement, 48 x 34cm. (Onslow's) £460

Leonnetto Cappiello, Peugeot poster, lithograph in colours, printed by Devambez, Paris, backed on linen, 59 x 46in. (Christie's) £550

Clincher Non-Skid Tyres, colour lithographic poster, on original board, 35 x 25cm. (Onslow's) £1,300

Souvenir of Brooklands, 1907. **£20**

Map by Librairie Hachette, 1920's. £6

Saab, Owner's Manual. £4

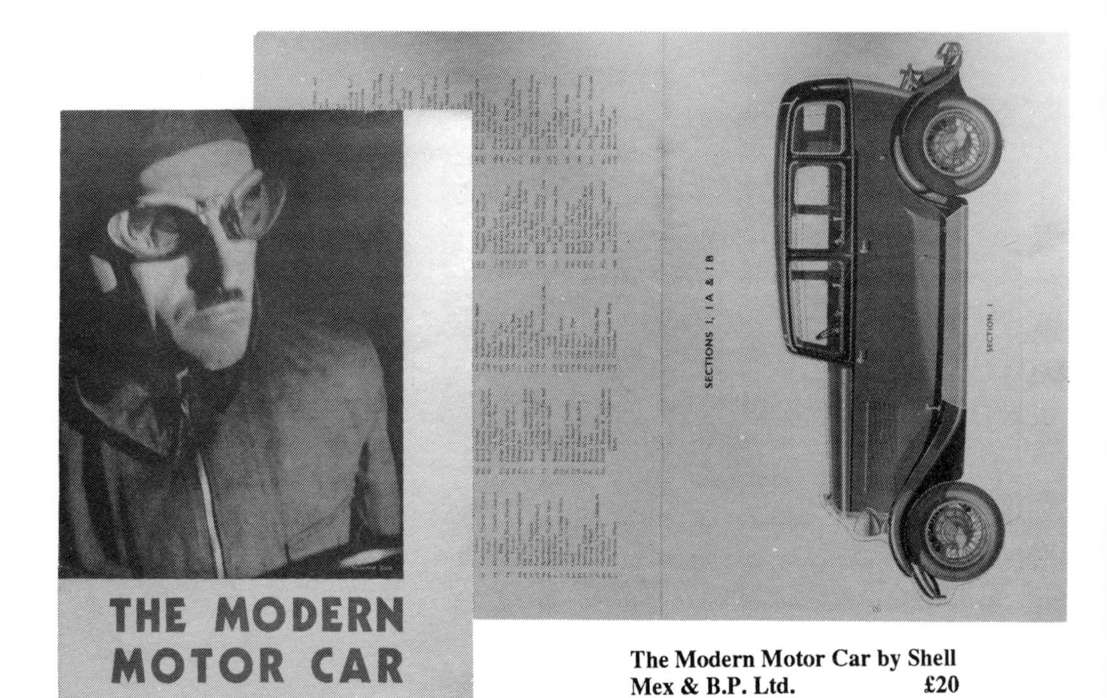

The Modern Motor Car by Shell Mex & B.P. Ltd. £20

Castrol, Achievements Book 1938. £10

The Bulletin, Vintage Sports Car Club, 1980. £3

Car Ticket for Ascot Races. £1

(C.A. Winder)

Delanite Spring Oil Brochure. **£2**

The New Vauxhall Victor, 1961. **£3**

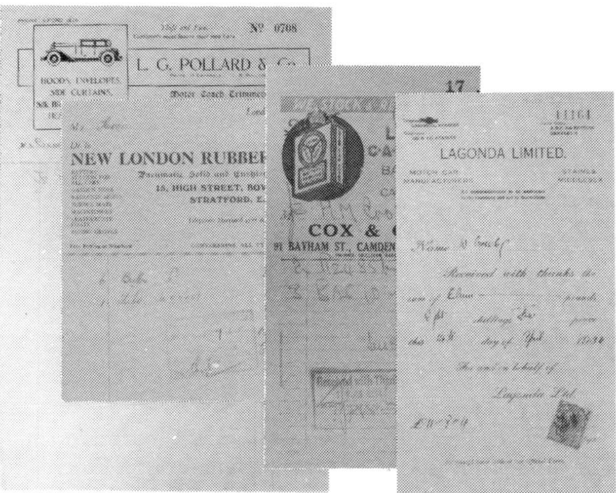

Various Motoring Invoices 1934/35. **£1 each**

Various Business Cards 1930. **50p each**

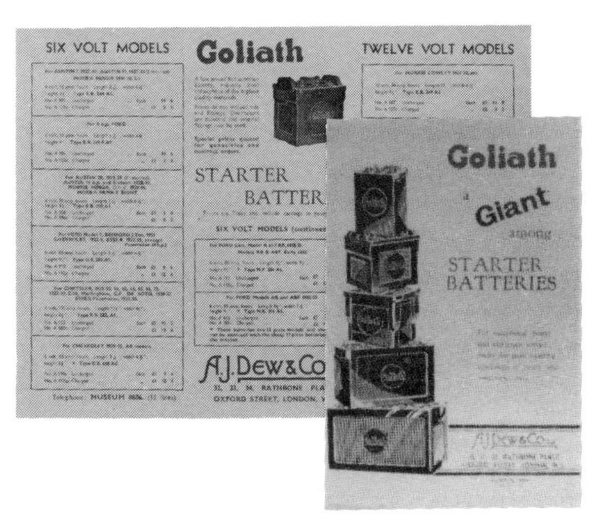

Goliath Starter Batteries Brochure. **£1**

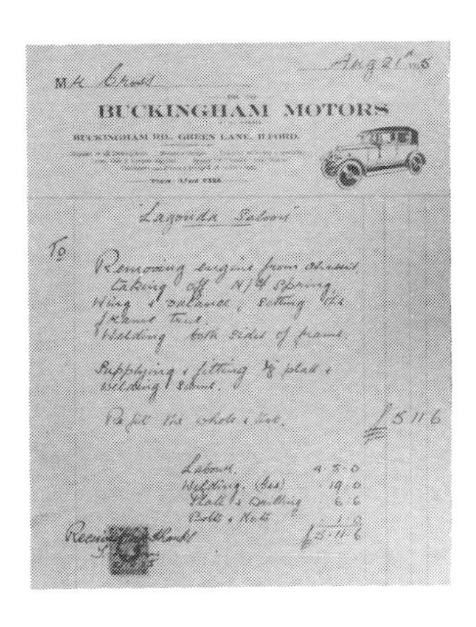

Invoice for Lagonda 1935. **£2**

(Yesterdays Paper)

Mercedes-Benz Model SS, loosely inserted technical data and price list of standard bodies, 1929.
(Onslow's) £750

The Years Automobile Sport 1906 with the compliments of the Michelin Tyre Company Ltd, pub. in England.
(Onslow's) £2,400

A sales brochure for Carrosserie Van Den Plas, colour plates by Rene Lelong, French text, hard bound, circa 1914.
(Onslow's) £400

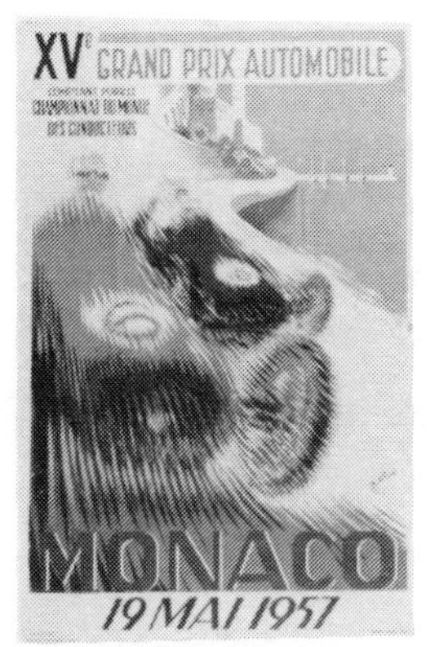

Monaco, 19 mai 1957, by B. Minne, lithograph in colours, printed by Imp Adia, Nice, fold marks, 47 x 31in.
(Christie's Monaco) £2,000

Charles Pascarel, Le Mans, 1980, the Porsche leading a BMW, colour lithograph poster, limited edition, signed, 25½ x 33½in. (Christie's) £154

Join The R.A.C., printed tin-plate hanging leaflet box, 11in. high, with some membership leaflets. (Onslow's) £75

A large framed poster of a French family beside a vintage car, removing a spare tyre from the belly of the "Michelin Man", 158 x 116cm.
(Phillips) £470

Lucas Lamps, We make Light of Our Labour, colour lithograph advertisement, 74 x 49cm.
(Onslow's) £2,000

German Grand Prix poster, Won On Texaco Brooklands Riley Model First in the 1100cc Class July 19th 1928, published by Texaco, 74 x 48cm.
(Onslow's) £240

Poster, Liege, Rome, Liege Rally, 1933, 73 x 53cm.
(Onslow's) £470

Rapiditas Rivista Universale D'Automobilismo, Vol 1 no 1, 1906, plates some colour, French, English and German text.
(Onslow's) £1,600

Nurburgring programme 'Grosser Preis von Deutschland 26th July 1936'.
(Onslow's) £793

Goodyear, double sided shaped pictorial enamel sign, 87 x 56cm.
(Onslow's) £160

Olympia, Motor Show, Oct. 12 1933, colour lithograph poster, after A. E. Marty, 10 x 12½in.
(Christie's) £160

Hispano-Suiza, one of two laminated showcards related to aero engines and vehicles, each 32cm. x 18cm.
(Onslow's) £240

Beligond – Reims Trophee France Amerique, 3 & 4 Juillet 1965, original poster, 60 x 40cm. (Christie's S. Ken)
£154

Poster by F. Hugo d'Alesi, for Automobiles Bayard, 117 x 158cm. (Onslow's)
£2,000

Schenkel, 'Course Automobiles Internationale Anvers 14 Heures 22 Mai 1938', published by Patria, Anvers, on linen, 47 x 34in. (Onslow's) £400

An automobile racing poster, France, circa 1906, entitled 'Circuit des Ardennes, Belges 1906-Duray, 6 Gagnant', by E. Montaut, 35¼in. wide. £250

Poster advertising the Grand Prix at the Nurburgring, 1947. £800

L D'H, Automobiles Peugeot, poster on linen, 115 x 110cm. (Onslow's) £600

Les 24 heures du Mans 1954, official programme, the front and back covers with illustrations by Geo Ham. (Christie's) £220

Peugeot, by Rene Vincent, lithograph in colours, printed by Draeger, 1170 x 1540mm. (Christie's) £800

Automobiles Peugeot La Petit Poucet Montait Une Peugeot, by Pierre Simmar, poster on linen, 200 x 140cm. (Onslow's) £2,200

XVI 1000 Miglia, Coppa Franco Mazzotti, Brescia 24 Aprile 1949, by P. Calla, lithograph in colours on card, 13 x 9½in. (Christie's New York) £629

Nick, Terrot Cycles Motorcycles, pub by Pertuy, Paris, on linen, 158cm. x 119cm. (Onslow's) £280

24 heures du Mans, 15 et 16 juin 1963, original colour poster by Guy Leygnac, unframed, 22½ x 15½in. (Christie's) £495

Alfa Romeo rules pamphlet 6C 2500 Gran Turismo, Italian, French, English and German text, circa 1948. (Christie's Monaco) £220

Ferrari Yearbook, 1950, Italian text. (Christie's Monaco) £4,999

One of twelve prints in colour of various coachwork designs by Carrosserie Van Den Plas, circa 1925, 9¼ x 11in. (Christie's) (Twelve) £880

Rene Lorenzi poster, XVIIIe Grand Prix Monaco 29 Mai 1960, 32 x 25cm. (Onslow's) £495

Peugeot Revue, no's 1–52, bound in three volumes with covers and advertisements, 1923–1927. (Onslow's) £2,400

J. Jacquelin, Delage 1939, colour poster showing an open two seater at speed, 32 x 23in. (Christie's) £510

Beligond – Rouen, Grand Prix de France, 10 Juillet 1966, original poster, 60 x 40cm. (Christie's S. Ken) £110

Nuvolari, L'Asso della Velocita, a single issue, Anno 1, No. 4, 1933. (Christie's Monaco) £800

Ferrari Yearbook, 1946-1966, signed and inscribed by Enzo Ferrari, Italian text. (Christie's Monaco) £1,700

Sun Bathing Review, Summer 1933. **£6**

Album Eldorado. **£4**

Health and Efficiency Naturist's Holiday Panorama, No. 29. **£6**

As Nature Intended, A Pictorial History of the Nudists. **£8**

Nudisme 57. **£3**

Sun Bathing Review, Autumn 1947. **£3**

(Yesterdays Paper)

Sunbathing Annual, 1957. **£5**

Sun Seeker, No. 187, 1960's. £5

The Naked Truth About Nudism, 1935. £10

It's Only Natural, 'The Philosophy of Nudism', 1936. £12

International Holiday Naturist, 1973. £5

Nude Living, Nudism and Sex In Marriage, Oct. 1966. £6

Naked and Unashamed by William Welby, 1934. £10

(Yesterdays Paper)

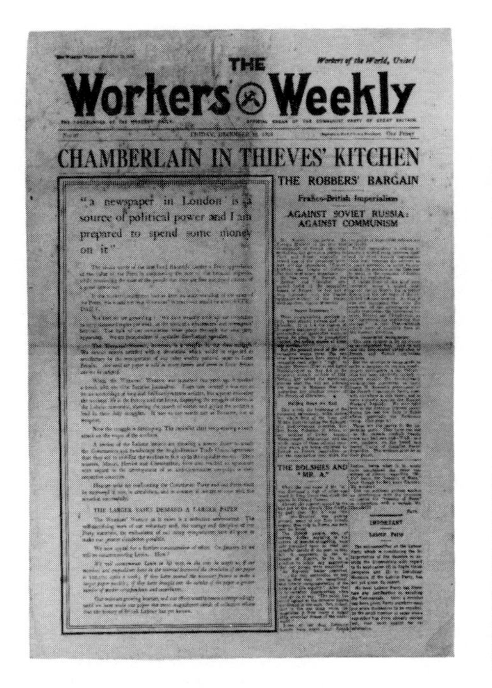
Workers of the World, Unite!

THE Workers' Weekly

CHAMBERLAIN IN THIEVES' KITCHEN

"a newspaper in London is a source of political power and I am prepared to spend some money on it"

THE LARGER TASKS DEMAND A LARGER PAPER

THE ROBBERS' BARGAIN

Franco-British Imperialism

AGAINST SOVIET RUSSIA: AGAINST COMMUNISM

THE BOLSHIES AND "MR. A."

IMPORTANT

The Workers' Weekly, Dec. 12th 1924. £2

THE GERMAN "BLONDE BEAST" MUST BE EXTERMINATED.

DAILY SKETCH.

'OLD BOYS' FOR THE (HOUSE) FIRING LINE.

Daily Sketch, Sept. 30th 1914. £3

THREE PAGES OF PICTURES OF OUR NORTH SEA SAILOR LADS.

DAILY SKETCH.

GERMAN OFFICERS GLORY IN THEIR ORGY

Daily Sketch, September 26th 1914. £3

Numb. 1898.

The London Gazette.

Published by Authority.

FRIDAY, MAY 20, 1898.

The London Gazette, May 20th 1898. £4

(Yesterdays Paper)

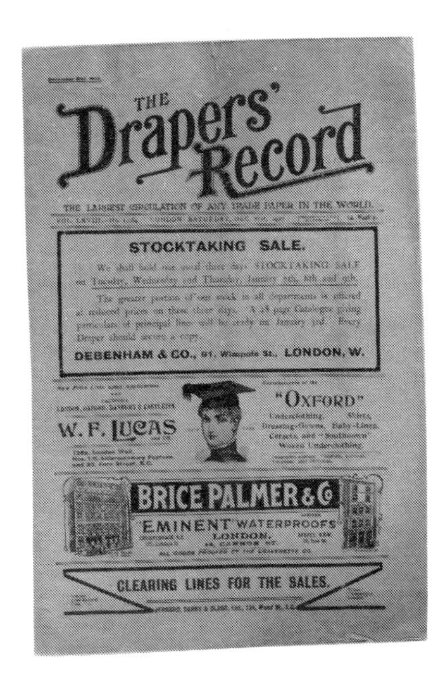

THE
Drapers' Record

THE LARGEST CIRCULATION OF ANY TRADE PAPER IN THE WORLD.

STOCKTAKING SALE.

DEBENHAM & CO., 91, Wimpole St., LONDON, W.

W. F. LUCAS

"OXFORD"

BRICE PALMER & Co

EMINENT WATERPROOFS
LONDON.

CLEARING LINES FOR THE SALES.

The Drapers' Record, Dec. 21st 1907. £5

The London Chronicle

Monday, Sept. 21.

The London Chronicle, September 1789. £6

No1
BRITAIN'S FIRST ALL-PICTURE POLITICAL PAPER!

THAT'LL BE THE DAY!

10p

SPECIAL REFERENDUM ISSUE

COMMON MARKET..?

If World V.I.P.'s welcomed our new magazine!

That'll Be The Day, Special Referendum Issue. £3

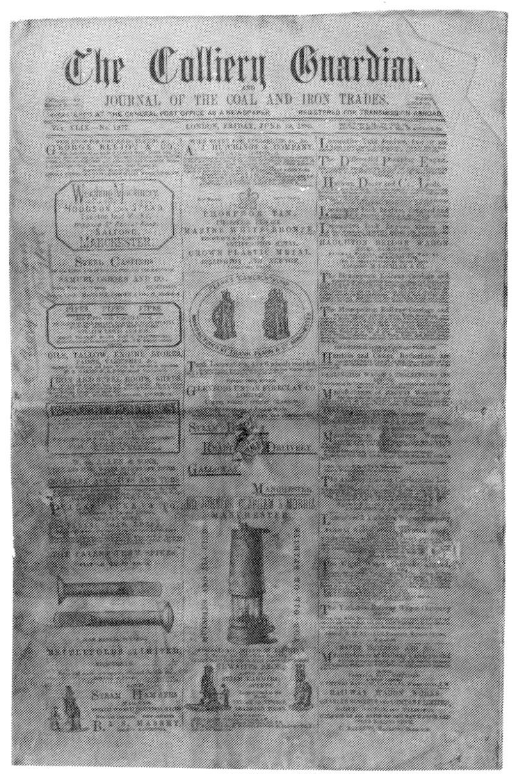

The Colliery Guardian
JOURNAL OF THE COAL AND IRON TRADES.

The Colliery Guardian, June 19th 1885. £4

(Yesterdays Paper)

DAS REICH

DEUTSCHE WOCHENZEITUNG

DIE NEUE SITUATION

Das große Wagnis

Walter Rohland

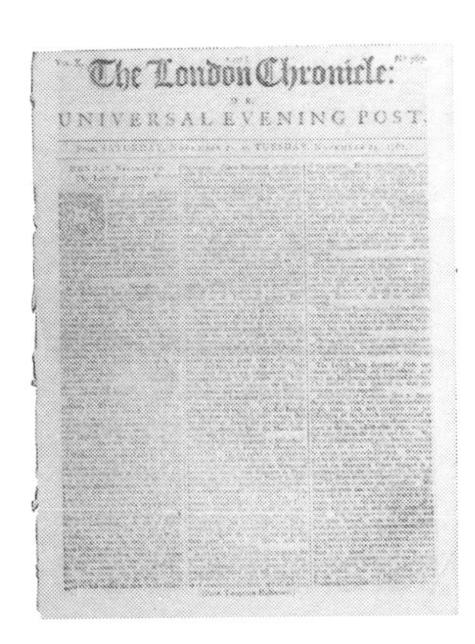
The London Chronicle:

UNIVERSAL EVENING POST.

Das Reich, 16th May 1943. **£12**

The London Chronicle or Universal Evening Post, November 21st, 1761. £60

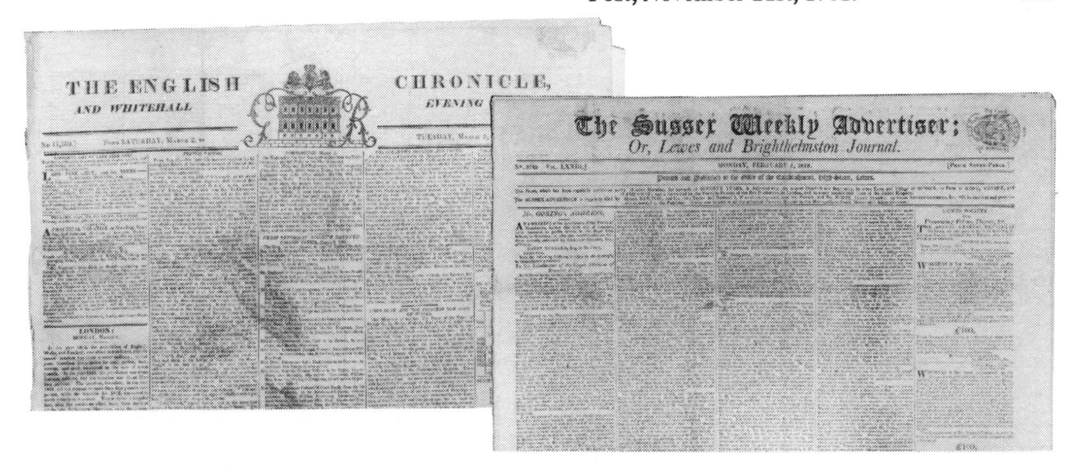
THE ENGLISH CHRONICLE,

AND WHITEHALL EVENING

The Sussex Weekly Advertiser;

Or, Lewes and Brighthelmston Journal.

The English Chronicle and Whitehall Evening Post, March 5th, 1822. £25

The Sussex Weekly Advertiser, February 1st, 1819. £30

Mark Lane Express,

Agricultural Journal &c.

London Markets.

Review of the British Corn Trade,

JACKSON'S OXFORD JOURNAL.

Mark Lane Express, Agricultural Journal, July 19th, 1847. £30

Jackson's Oxford Journal, April 29th, 1826. £30

(Yesterday's News)

DAILY EXPRESS

Berlin says Russians are throwing in more and more reserves: "They have vast superiority in men"

GERMANS ANNOUNCE BIG NEW RETREAT

Russians seize 30 places north of the Crimea

NEW COAL RATION:

Red Joan of Arc has been avenged

All will pay as they earn

DISCOVERY: THE SON—

KHERSON

The YORK COURANT And Original Advertiser.

The Daily Express, October 29th, 1943. £20

The York Courant and Original Advertiser, May 1st, 1832. £30

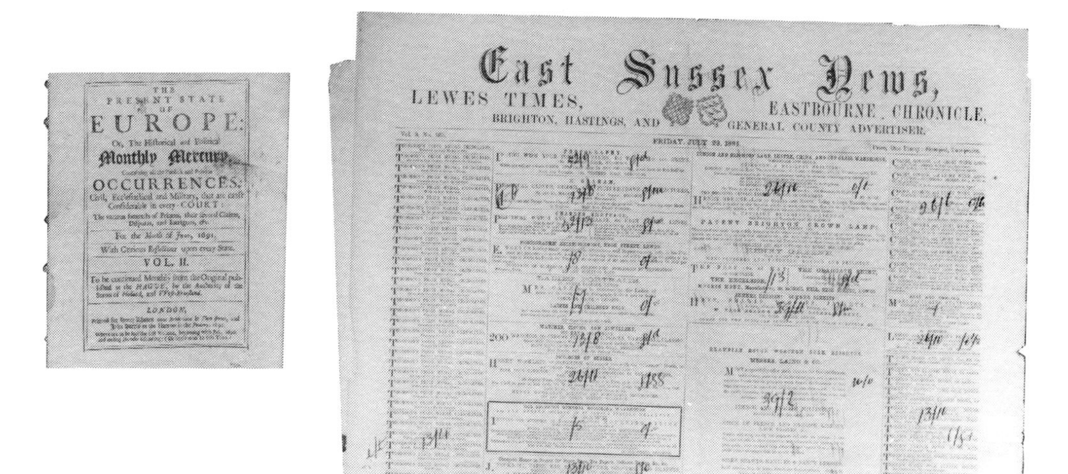
THE PRESENT STATE OF EUROPE: Or, The Historical and Political Monthly Mercury, Containing all the Publick and Private Occurrences, Civil, Ecclesiastical and Military, that are most Considerable in every Court.

For the Month of June, 1691.

VOL. II.

LONDON,

East Sussex News, LEWES TIMES, BRIGHTON, HASTINGS, AND EASTBOURNE CHRONICLE, GENERAL COUNTY ADVERTISER.

Monthly Mercury for June 1691. £150

East Sussex News, July 29th, 1864, with hand-written contemporary advertisement departments. £12

Münchener Ausgabe

VÖLKISCHER BEOBACHTER

Kampfblatt der nationalsozialistischen Bewegung Großdeutschlands

USA drängen auf Annahme des jüdischen Währungsplanes

Morgenthau möchte den Wallstreetspekulanten die absolute Kontrolle über die Weltwirtschaft zuspielen

Großraum und Weltstaat

The Guardian.

Volkischer Beobachter, 21st May 1944, the official Nazi Party daily. £20

The Guardian, April 6th, 1864, complete with used penny stamp. £80

(Yesterday's News)

Daily Mirror

FORWARD WITH THE PEOPLE

THE SMILES OF THE DAY

After the ceremony—hand in hand

Daily Mirror, 21st Nov. 1947, Wedding Issue. £2

Psychic News

THE SPIRITUALIST NEWSPAPER WITH THE WORLD'S LARGEST CIRCULATION

LONDON : SEPTEMBER 12, 1936 | Price TWOPENCE

Building A Home After "Death"

Sixteenth Century Mansion Duplicated

He Wrote His Own Funeral Oration

Etheric Replicas Of All Its Contents

"I Am More Alive Than Any Of You"

Psychic News, 12th Sept. 1936. £2

The National Police Gazette

The Leading Illustrated Sporting Journal of the World

LONDON, WEDNESDAY, MAY 26, 1897.

The "Police Gazette" is the World's Sporting Authority.

THE OLD MAN SPOILED THE FUN.

The National Police Gazette, May 26th, 1897. £5

The Guardian Journal

Evening Post NEWS

EMERGENCY EDITION | No. 24. | NOTTINGHAM | Saturday 18 July 1959. | TWOPENCE.

ANOTHER REBUKE FOR CITY COUNCIL

Minister's 'rocket' sent to the Town Clerk

Popkess Protest Meeting to be in Market Square

PODOLA STILL IN HOSPITAL

Mr. F. J. WILLATT DIES ON HOLIDAY

SHORT LIST FOR NEW POLICE CHIEF

ORDERED OUT

Evening Post News, 18th July 1959, Emergency Edition. £4

(Yesterdays Paper)

Daily Mirror
FORWARD WITH THE PEOPLE
Millions will hear the Princess say "I will"
PHILIP IS NOW THE DUKE OF EDINBURGH
21 M.P.s will consider King's offer
Royal Wedding
The Princess's Gown
Whiter teeth fresher mouth that's the gift of COLGATE'S

Daily Mirror, 20th November 1947, Duke Of Edinburgh. £2

LARGEST CIRCULATION OF ANY RELIGIOUS JOURNAL IN THE WORLD.
THE SUNDAY COMPANION
"I WAS SICK AND YE VISITED ME."

The Sunday Companion, 28th August, 1908. £2

The Pawnbrokers' Gazette
AND
Trade Circular.
SATURDAY, JUNE 27, 1896.
JOHN BEEVER,
Yorkshire Cloth Hearthrugs.
JOHN BEEVER,
ALFRED ST., HUDDERSFIELD.
ROBERT PRINGLE & Co.
Old Gold & Silver
NEWMARK Bros.
ALL PAWNBROKERS WHO DO THE SALE TRADE SHOULD SEE
S. ABRAHAMS & SONS'
LARGE & VARIED STOCK OF GOLD & SILVER JEWELLERY.
I. S. GREENBERG & Co.
Pawnbrokers' Supply Stores.
HOLD THE LARGEST STOCK IN ENGLAND
126, Gt. Hampton St.,
BIRMINGHAM.
MOULE & MEYER,
7, GOSWELL ROAD,
PIE LOTS, WATCHES, DIAMONDS, &c.,
SPECIAL NOTICE.
MASTERS & LEETE,
4, CLERKENWELL ROAD, LONDON, E.C.
PURCHASE for CASH TO ANY AMOUNT,
MASTERS & LEETE
DIAMOND JEWELLERY,
TO OUR COUNTRY SUBSCRIBERS.

The Pawnbroker's Gazette, June 27th, 1896. £5

The Sunderland Echo
County Final
and Shipping Gazette
AMID THE CHEERS

The Sunderland Echo, 2nd June, 1953, Coronation Issue. £2

(Yesterdays Paper)

The New York Times.

LATE CITY EDITION

1ST ARMY OPENS DRIVE AT TOP OF BELGIAN
3D GAINS BEYOND BASTOGNE, 7TH FORCED
U. S. FLIERS BOMB LUZON, FORMOSA AND

DEWEY ASKS STATE TO SPEND BILLION IN POST-WAR AIDS

Mayor Forecasts Increase In Realty Valuations Here

DIES GROUP IS PUT ON PERMANENT BASIS BY HOUSE, 207 TO 186

18-25 Farm Labor in Draft; Hershey Acts on Byrnes Plea

Commercial Chronicle.

LONDON TUESDAY, FEBRUARY 14, 1815.

The New York Times, January 4th, 1945. £20

The Commercial Chronicle, February 14th, 1815. £25

Münchner Illustrierte Presse

SUNDAY EXPRESS

The war has lasted exactly six years—six years to the day. Britain was at war with Germany at 11 a.m. on Sunday, September 3, 1939. Japan formally surrendered at 10.30 a.m. today, Sunday, September 2, 1945

MacARTHUR'S MOVING SPEECH AS THE JAPANESE SIGN SURRENDER

'The unshackled peoples are tasting the full sweetness of liberty and relief from fear'

Historic scene in battleship cabin in Tokyo Bay

JAPAN NOW UNDER FOREIGN CONTROL FOR FIRST TIME IN 2,000 YEARS

THE WORLD WAR IS OVER.

In the early hours of this morning, 10.30 Tokyo time, 2.30 a.m. British Summer Time, it came to a formal end with the signing of the "surrender instrument" by Japanese and Allied delegates.

President Truman in a broadcast immediately after the ceremony said: "This is a day we shall always remember. From this day we move forward to a new and better world."

The instrument of surrender (printed below) sets down in simple words for history the fact that the Japanese Empire was utterly defeated in war and surrendered unconditionally.

51 ALLIED GENERALS AND ONE SERGT. SAW THE JAPS SIGN

Big purge may follow ENSA row

'Airmen murder' charge against Goering

Munchner Illustrierte Dresse, 26th May 1929. £5

Sunday Express, September 2nd, 1945, 'The World War is Over'. £10

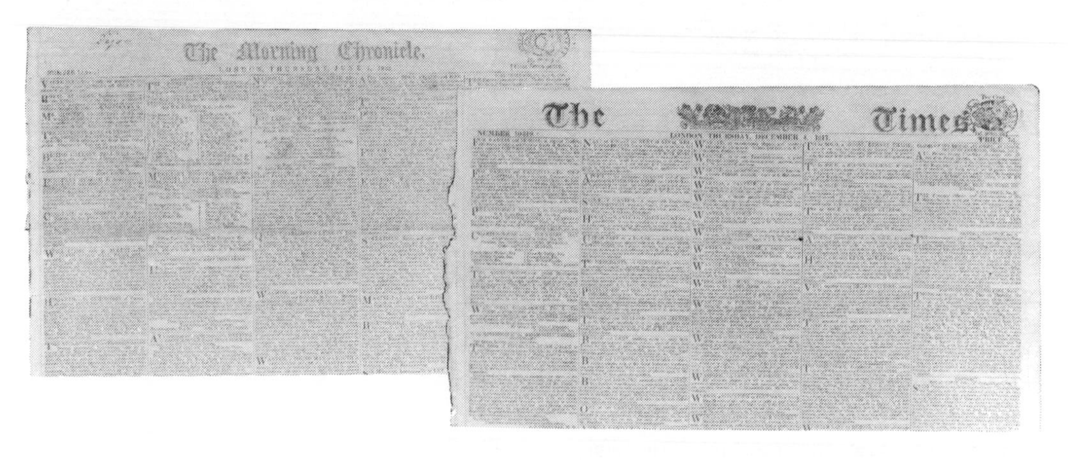

The Morning Chronicle.

The Times.

The Morning Chronicle, June 1st, 1820. £20

The Times, December 4th, 1817. £25

(Yesterday's News)

The Cambrian,
GENERAL WEEKLY ADVERTISER FOR THE PRINCIPALITY OF WALES.

The Edinburgh Gazette.

Published by Authority.

The Cambrian, February 12th, 1831, or General Weekly Advertiser for the Principality of Wales. £12

The Edinburgh Gazette, Published by Authority, March 8th, 1844. £15

The Edinburgh Evening Courant.

The English Chronicle,
AND UNIVERSAL EVENING POST.

The English Chronicle, January 12th, 1799. £12

The Edinburgh Evening Courant, March 25th, 1793. £35

The Star

COUNTER ATTACKS THROW BACK SOVIET FORMATIONS

Bitter Fighting Continues on all Fronts

YORKSHIRE GAZETTE.

SATURDAY, APRIL 13, 1850.

Wartime Channel Islands edition of The Star, January 31st, 1945, with German propaganda. £10

`Yorkshire Gazette, April 13th, 1850. £25

(Yesterday's News)

THE MAFEKING MAIL
SPECIAL SIEGE SLIP.

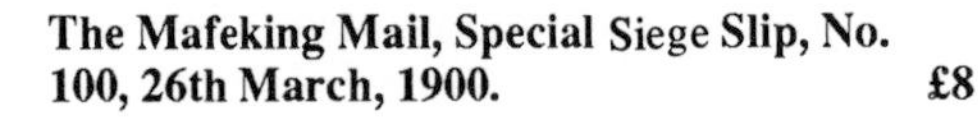

The Mafeking Mail, Special Siege Slip, No. 100, 26th March, 1900. £8

DAILY SKETCH AND DAILY GRAPHIC
Coronation Souvenir

Happy and Glorious!

THEIR HANDS UNITE

Daily Sketch, 3rd June, 1953, Coronation Issue. £2

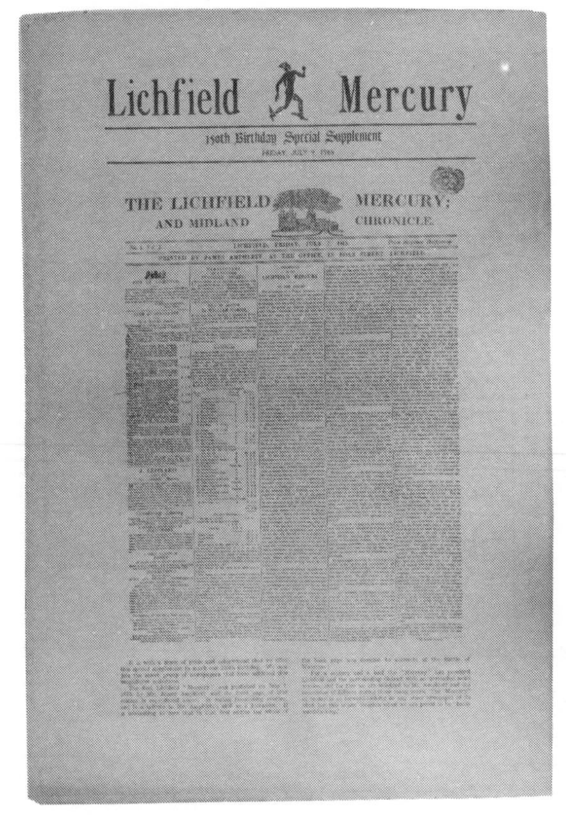

Lichfield Mercury
150th Birthday Special Supplement

THE LICHFIELD MERCURY; AND MIDLAND CHRONICLE.

Lichfield Mercury, 1965, 150th Birthday Issue. £3

IS EUROPE DRIFTING TO ANOTHER WAR?

CHRISTIAN HERALD AND SIGNS OF OUR TIMES

TRAGEDY OF THE WORLD'S BIGGEST AIRSHIP.

Christian Herald, 16th October, 1930, R. 101 Airship Disaster. £5

(Yesterdays Paper)

The Spectator

NEWS OF THE WEEK.

The Spectator, 7th August, 1915. £1

The Daily Mirror

TWO HOUNDSDITCH MURDERERS COMMIT SUICIDE IN A BURNING HOUSE IN MILE END AFTER FIGHTING WITH ARMED POLICE AND GUARDSMEN FOR OVER EIGHT HOURS

The Daily Mirror, January 4th, 1911, Sidney Street Siege. £5

HOW I FLEW ACROSS THE CHANNEL: BY M. BLERIOT.

THE DAILY GRAPHIC

ONE PENNY

BRAVO BLERIOT!

The Daily Graphic, Bleriot Channel Flight. £8

Padiham Advertiser.

DAWSON & SON,
TAILORS & OUTFITTERS,
NEW MATERIALS FOR SPRING WEAR.
Style and Durability,
Lowest Price possible,
Good Workmanship,
OUR AIM
High-Class Tailoring
53, Burnley Rd., Padiham.
Grand Show of New Spring Goods
W. H. MERCER'S,
Hatter, Hosier, & Outfitter,
18, BURNLEY ROAD, PADIHAM.
LADIES', GENT'S, & CHILDREN'S HOSIERY.
MERCER, THE CYCLIST OUTFITTER
W. H. MERCER, Outfitter, 18, Burnley Road, Padiham.

SPRING & SUMMER
ROWSON & SON,
Manchester House,
NEW & COMPLETE
Mantles,
Dresses,
Millinery,
Fancy Drapery
JACKETS & CAPES
HATS & BONNETS
UNDERCLOTHING
W. J. HELM

Miss WOOD
SCIENTIFIC DRESSMAKER,
8, Chapel Walk, Padiham.

Padiham Advertiser, May 4th 1897. £3

(Yesterdays Paper)

Canadian Pacific 'Duchess Of Richmond', 1934. £4

'Aeneas Fragments', Grand Concert Programme Nov. 2nd 1921. £2

Holland-America Line Information. £15

Elder Dempster Lines, Passenger List M. V. Apapa 1934. £3

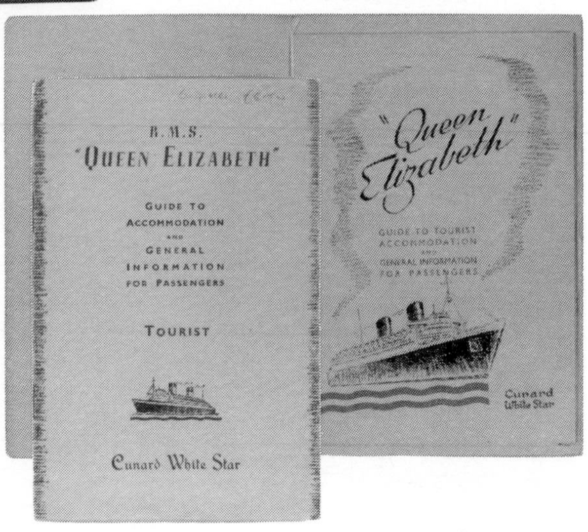

Queen Elizabeth Guide To Accommodation. £4

(Yesterdays Paper)

Northern Germany Services, 1930. £5

Royal Mail, List Of Passengers, 1933. £5

Cunard White Star, Passenger List 'Queen Elizabeth' 1947. £2

Nippon Yusen Kaisha Line Services. £5

Belgian Royal Mail Steamers Service Handbook 1932. £5

(Yesterdays Paper)

Gulliver's Travels, 1938, wood engravings by T. Naish. £4

The Carmelites by George Bernanos, Fontana Books. £3

The Diary Of A Nobody, Pan Books, 1945–47. £4

Young, by Miriam Colwell, Ballantine Books. £6

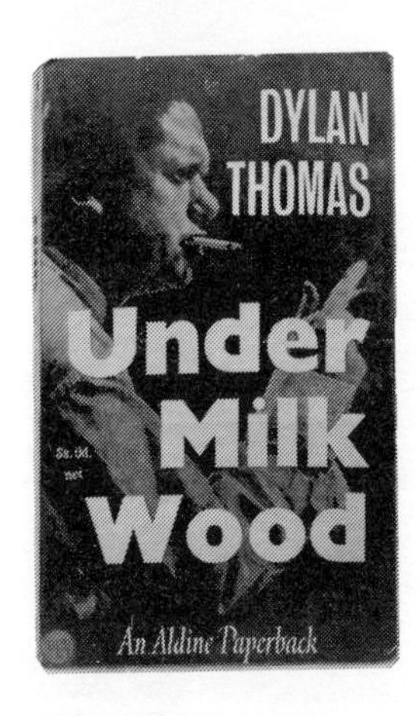

Under Milk Wood, by Dylan Thomas, an Aldine Paperback. £2

A Tangled Web by L. G. Moberly, Ward Lock, 1931. £3

Nigger Heaven, by Carl Van Vechten, Avon Books. £30

The Ides of Mad by William M. Gaines, New American Library. £4

Rumble, by Harlan Ellison, Pyramid, 1958. £20

(Yesterdays Paper)

Ariel, by Andre Maurois, No. 1, 1935. £100

Edgar Cayce on ESP, Paperback Library, New York. £6

The Terror of the Leopard Men, Avon, 1951. £5

Germany Puts The Clock Back, 1st Special 1937. £6

Up the Junction by Nell Dunn, Pan Books. £5

Reform School Girl, by Felice Swados, Diversey, 1948. £125

Marihuana, by William Irish, Dell, 1951. £75

LSD The Problem-Solving Psychedelic, a Tandem book. £8

(Yesterdays Paper)

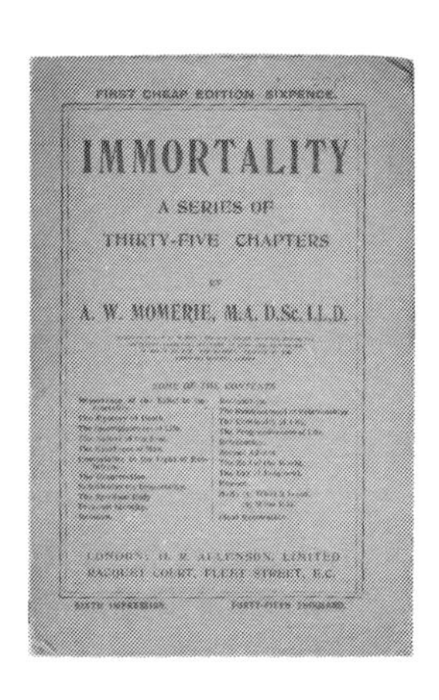

Immortality, 1919, 1st Cheap Edition. £3

Book on Swimming by Professor W. C. Pearson of York. £5

Five Years of Liberal Mis-Rule, printed and published by Jordison & Co. £8

The Gipsy King by J. Bosworth, Dick's Standard Plays. £1.50

Tam by Edgar Wallace. £5

Penny Book of Fun. £3

The Governor of Chi-Foo by Edgar Wallace. £5

Bus Stop, the Story of the 20th Century-Fox Film, starring Marilyn Monroe. £12

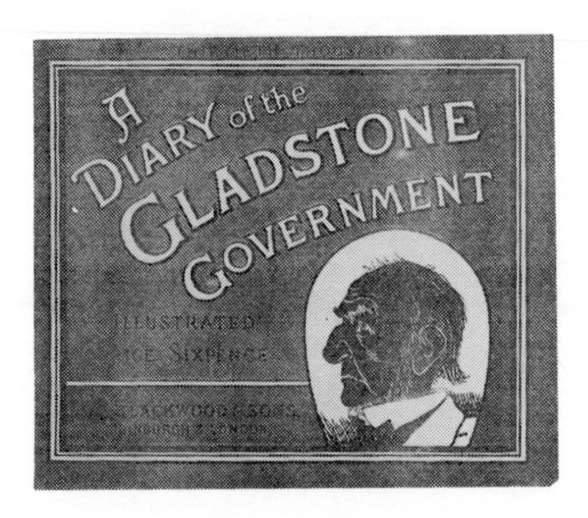

A Diary of the Gladstone Government, Blackwood and Sons. £8

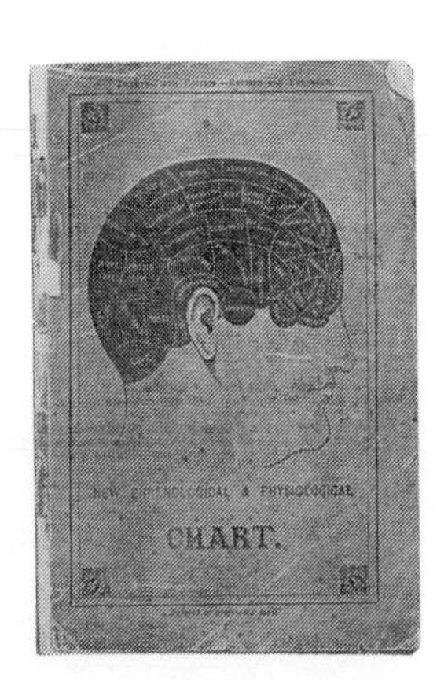

New Phrenological and Physiological Chart, pre 1940. £3.50

(Yesterdays Paper)

Strange Ritual, Compact '64' Series. **£4**

Mrs Miniver, by Jan Struther, Pocket Books. £4

Marijuana Girl, U.S. Publication.

£10

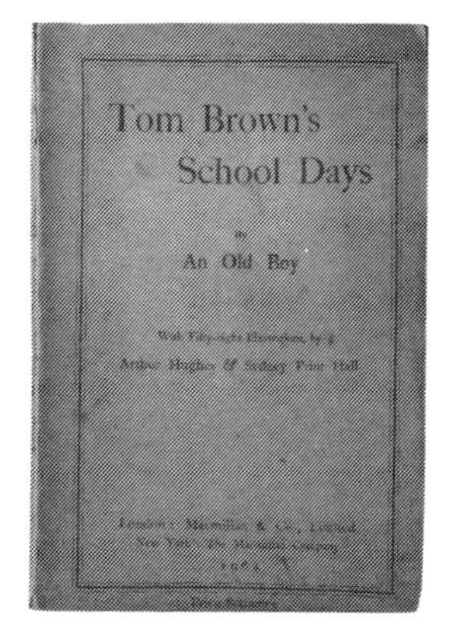

Tom Brown's School Days, Macmillan, 1904. £3

Naked On Roller Skates, by Maxwell Bodenheim, Diversey 1949. £30

Sweeney Todd, The Demon Barber, Hellifont Press, 1920's. £13

Tarzan and the Lost Empire, Dell, 1951. £3

The Bride Wore Weeds, Gaywood Press, Heade Cover. £4

All Over But The Shooting, Popular Library. £2

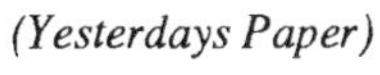
(Yesterdays Paper)

DETECTIVE

The Curse of the Bronze Lamp by Carter Dickson, Pan Books. £4

The High Window by Raymond Chandler, Pocket Books Inc. £4

The Bandaged Nude by Robert Finnegan, Boardman Books. £5

Situation Grave by Hank Janson. £6

Superintendent West, Murder, London-Australia by John Creasey, Pan Books. £4

Halo for Nobody by Henry Kane, Boardman Books. £5

The D'Arblay Mystery by Austin Freeman, Pan Books. £4

The Square Emerald by Edgar Wallace, Pan Books. £4

Inspector West Makes Haste by John Creasey, Pan Books. £4

(Yesterdays Paper)

DETECTIVE

Love Me To Death, Phantom Books, 1956. £3

Death Hitches A Ride, Tracked Down, Ace Double, 1954. £4

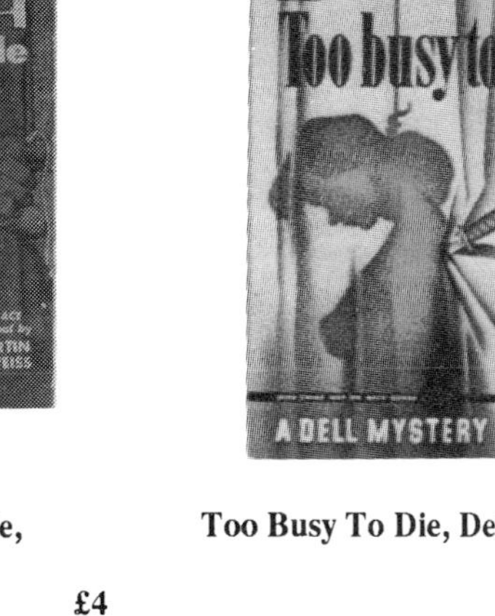

Too Busy To Die, Dell 1947. £6

The Postman Always Rings Twice, by James M. Cain, Pocket Books. £3

Verity, Corpse in Lovers Lane, Herrett Publications, 1940's. £3

Thin Edge of Violence, Phantom Books, 1956. £3

Six Nights Of Mystery, by William Irish, Popular Library. £5

The Four of Hearts, by Ellery Queen, Pocket books. £4

Tiger Standish Does His Stuff, Hodder & Stoughton, Yellow Back, 1952. £3

(Yesterdays Paper)

SCIENCE FICTION

Science Fiction, Formula 695, by Denis Hughes, Curtis Warren Ltd. £4

The Last Martian by Vargo Statten, Scion, 1952. £5

Before the Beginning by Marx Reisen, Titbits Library. £4

The New Satellite by Vargo Statten, Scion, 1951. £5

Reconnoitre Krellig II by Jon J. Deegan, Science Fiction Series. £4

The Sun Makers by Vargo Statten, Scion, 1950. £5

The Lonely Astronomer by Volsted Gridban, Scion, 1954. £5

Vanguard to Neptune by J. M. Walsh, Fantasy Books. £4

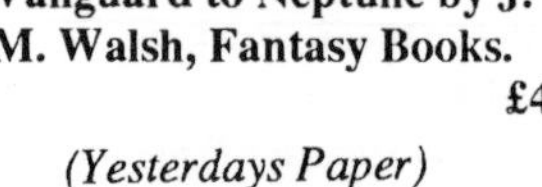

The 7th Dimension by Victor La Salle. £5

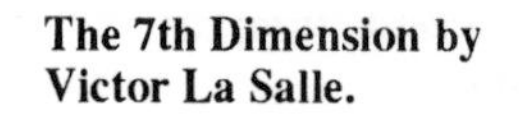

(*Yesterdays Paper*)

SCIENCE FICTION

Into The Alternate Universe, Coils Of Time, Ace Double, 1964. £4

The Time Traders, Ace Books, 1958. £4

I Am Legend, Corgi Books, 1956. £3

Freaks Against Supermen, Laywood Press, 1951. £5

Tales Of Tomorrow, Spencer Publications, 1940's. £4

The Weird Shadow Over Innsmouth, Bart House. £45

Into Plutonian Depths, Avon Books. £35

Fight For Life, Crestwood U.S.A. 1947, Murray Leinster, 1st Edition. £8

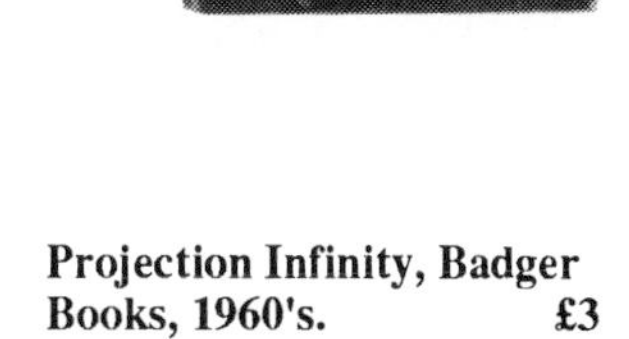

Projection Infinity, Badger Books, 1960's. £3

(Yesterdays Paper)

SENSATIONAL

Redhead Rhapsody by Bart Carson. **£5**

The White Slaves of London by W. N. Willis. **£6**

The Streets of Paris by Edwin Laforge, translated from the French. **£5**

Sin Street by Paul Reville, An Archer Book. **£5**

The Troubled Night by Ricky Drayton, Make sure its a Milestone. **£5**

Gertie Vesser by George Ryley Scott, 'Secrets of the Oldest Profession revealed'. **£5**

So Long – Sucker by Max Clinten, a 'Red' Miller story. **£5**

Passion's Plaything by Roland Vane. **£5**

She Who Hesitates by Paul Renin. **£5**

TEENAGE GANG

Cut and Run by Bill McGhee, Corgi Books. £4

The Little Caesars by Edward De Roo, Ace Books. £10

Cosh Boy by Bruce Walker, Ace Books. £7

Savage Delinquents by Alan Bennett. £5

Run Tough, Run Hard by Carson Bingham. £5

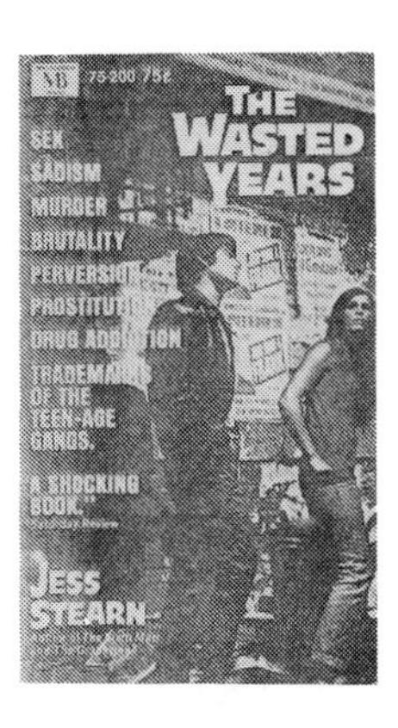

The Wasted Years by Jess Stearn, Macfadden Books. £5

Marijuana Girl by N. R. De-Mexico, Soft Cover Library. £10

Rock 'n Roll Gal by Ernie Weatherall. £8

The Gang Girls by Carson Bingham, Monarch Books. £8

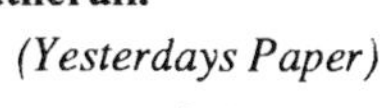
(Yesterdays Paper)

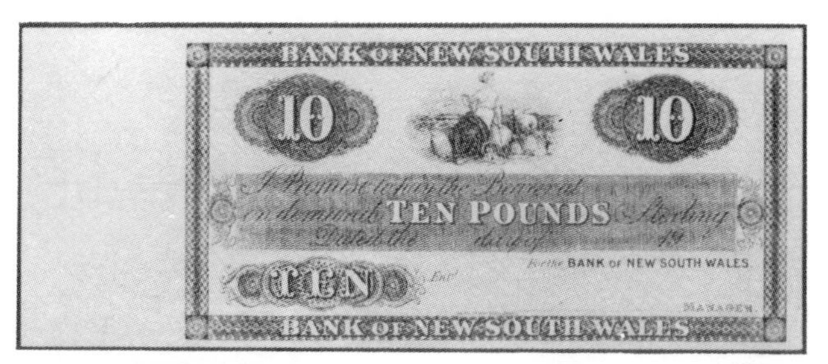

New Zealand: 1923–34 Bank of New South Wales £10 specimen.
(Phillips) £200

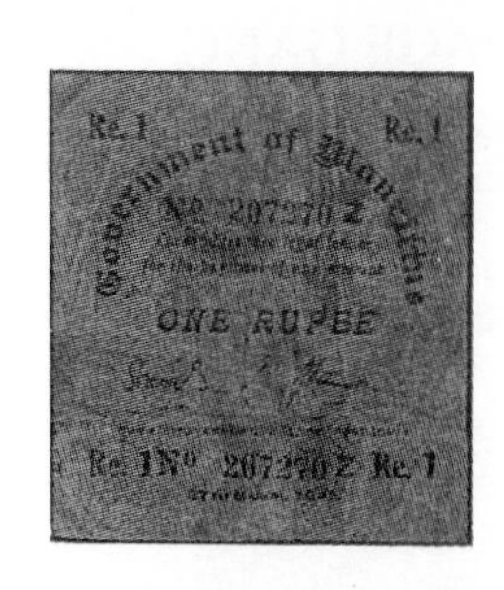

Mauritius: 1942 1 rupee emergency issue.
(Phillips) £580

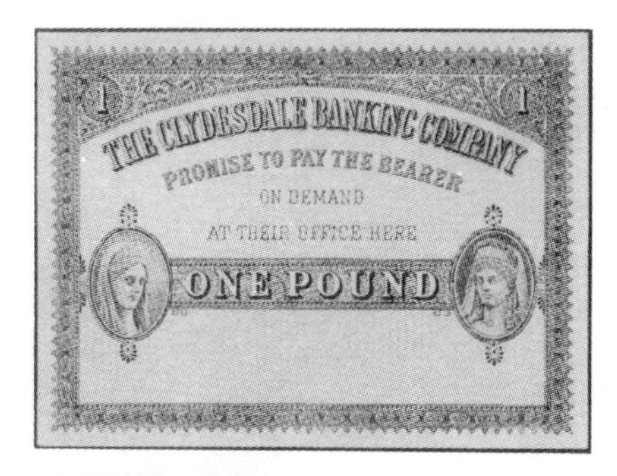

Clydesdale Banking Company: £1 proof/ artwork in green and purple.
(Phillips) £200

Bank of England Note, J.G. Nairne: £5 21 February 1910 issued at Plymouth.
(Phillips) £4,600

Great Britain: Bradbury Wilkinson advertising note in red and black for "Biglietti di Banca" with large allegorical vignette at left.
(Phillips) £95

Bank of Scotland: £1 February 1893 signed by J.F. Stormonth Darling.
(Phillips) £253

Great Britain, J. Bradbury: 10/- August 1914.
(Phillips) £450

Ulster Bank: £100 Specimen in black on white 1920.
(Phillips) £220

Djibouti: 1945 500 francs perforated "Paye" and with "Specimen" handwritten across face.
(Phillips) £400

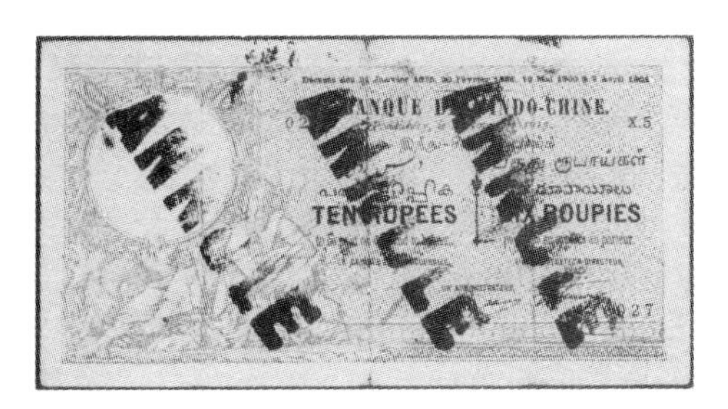

French India: 1919 10 roupies overstamped "Annule" three times.
(Phillips) £260

Great Britain, Bank of England Note, K.O. Peppiatt: £100 15 March 1937.
(Phillips) £340

Italy: 1867 100 lire handsigned by Garibaldi at right.
(Phillips) £200

Cape Verde: 1941 50 escudos.
(Phillips) £180

French Indo-China: 1925 Banque de L'Indochine 100 piastres Haiphong issue perforated "Specimen".
(Phillips) £680

Northern Bank Ltd: £100 1919.
(Phillips) £207

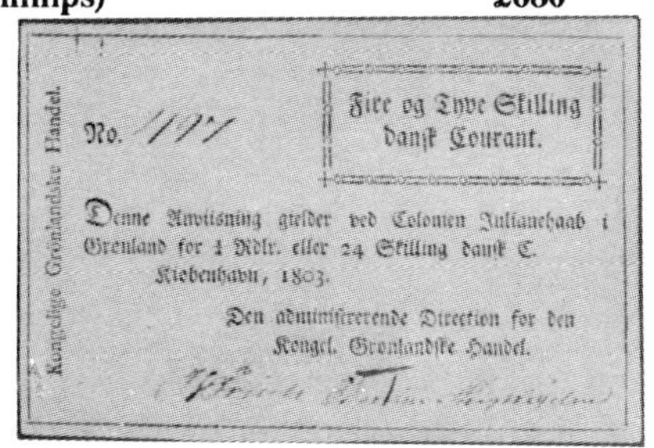

Greenland: 1803 24 skilling, early and rare.
(Phillips) £1,150

Canada: 1900 Dominion $4.
(Phillips) **£280**

Germany: 1924 20 billion marks.
(Phillips) **£150**

British West Africa: 1954 Currency Board £5, pinholes.
(Phillips) **£190**

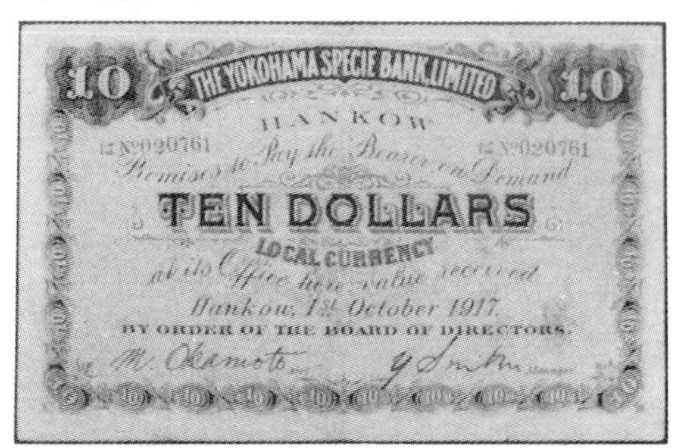

China: 1917 Yokohama Specie Bank $10 issued at Hankow.
(Phillips) **£780**

Bank of England Note, George Forbes: £5 24 May 1871, Forbes was the first Chief Cashier to have his printed signature on Bank of England notes, extremely rare.
(Phillips) **£4,800**

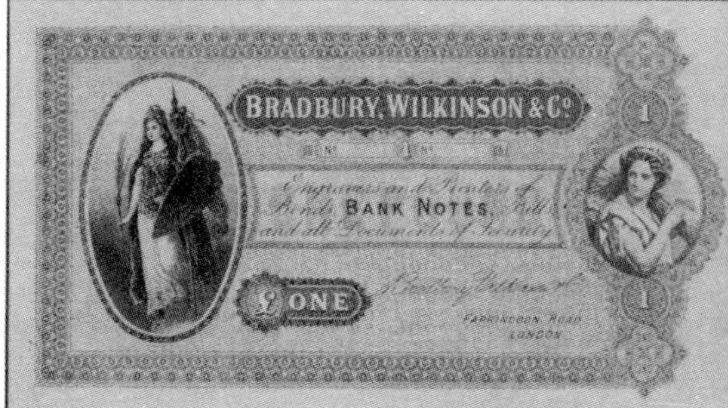

Great Britain: Bradbury Wilkinson & Co. advertising note 1880 (c.), uniface, brown and black on face with large vignette at left of allegorical woman.
(Phillips) **£110**

Carlisle City & District Banking Company: £20 proof by Lizars, small piece missing left side.
(Phillips) **£120**

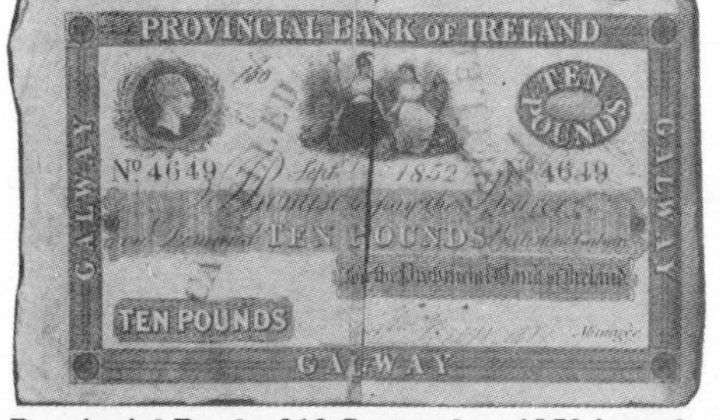

Provincial Bank: £10 September 1852 issued at Galway, split along middle and overstamped 'Cancelled'.
(Phillips) **£230**

Lebanon: 1939 25 livres.
(Phillips) **£460**

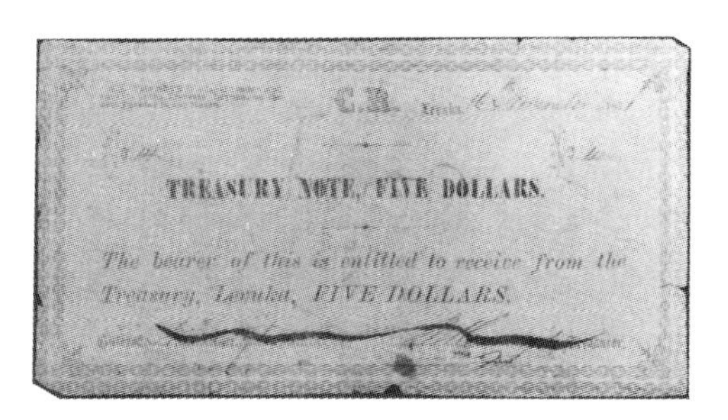

Fiji: 1871 $5 Treasury note.
(Phillips) **£480**

Bank of England Note, E.M. Harvey: £10 29 June 1920 issued at Manchester.
(Phillips) **£300**

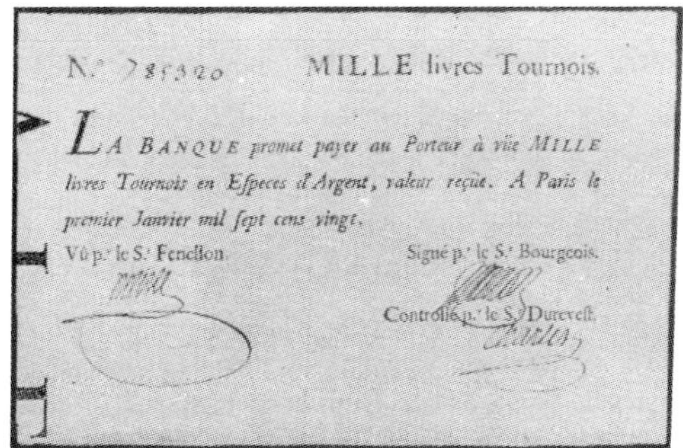

France: 1720 La Banque Royale 1,000 livres, 3mm nick top edge otherwise good.
(Phillips) **£210**

New Zealand: 1886 (?) National Bank of New Zealand £20 issued at Auckland, difficult to be precise with handwritten date but note very well preserved and extremely rare.
(Phillips) **£1,500**

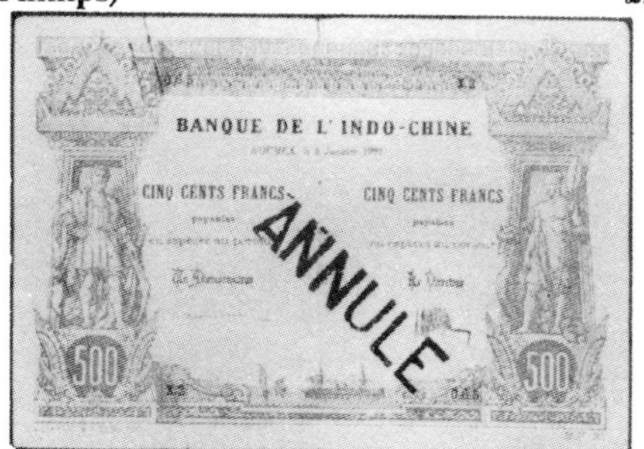

New Caledonia: 1921 500 francs, most attractive design with allegorical figures left and right, note overstamped "Annule" and with small tear top of centre crease.
(Phillips) **£900**

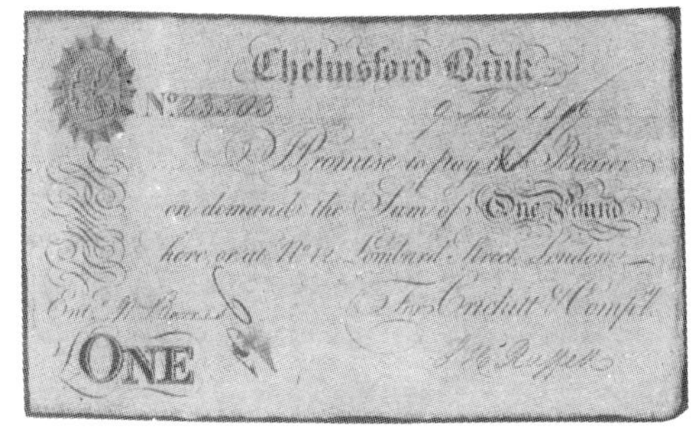

Chelmsford Bank: £1, 1819 Crickitt & Co. fully printed on back as 'Bank of Crickitt, Russell & Co., Chelmsford'.
(Phillips) **£110**

Mauritius: 1815 (c.) Colonial Bank of Mauritius Bourbon and Dependencies 5 crowns unissued.
(Phillips) **£350**

Great Britain, J. Bradbury: £1 August 1914, heavy centre crease.
(Phillips) £280

Djibouti: 1945 1,000 francs overstamped "Annule" and with four small punch-holes.
(Phillips) £700

Isles de France et de Bourbon: 1780 (c.) 6 livres tournois, officially rebacked and re-numbered.
(Phillips) £600

El Salvador: 1925, El Banco Salvadoreno 100 colones Waterlow colour trial in brown, orange and green, two punch-holes.
(Phillips) £85

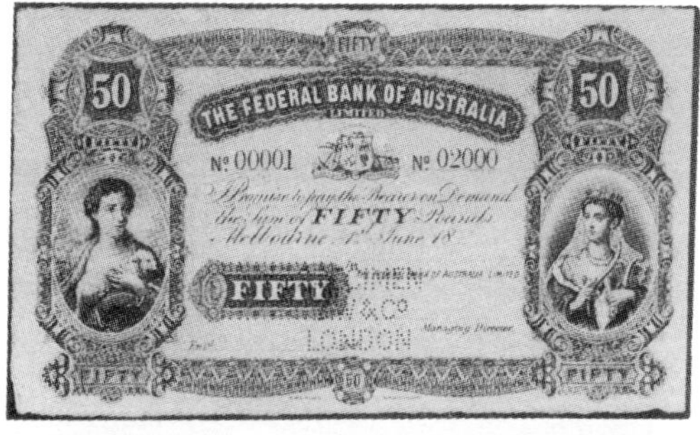

Australia: 1882 (c.) Federal Bank of Australia £1 (2), £5, £10, £20 and £50 "Specimen" notes of Bradbury Wilkinson & Co., one of the £1 notes is payable at Sydney with the others all at Melbourne.
(Phillips) £2,000

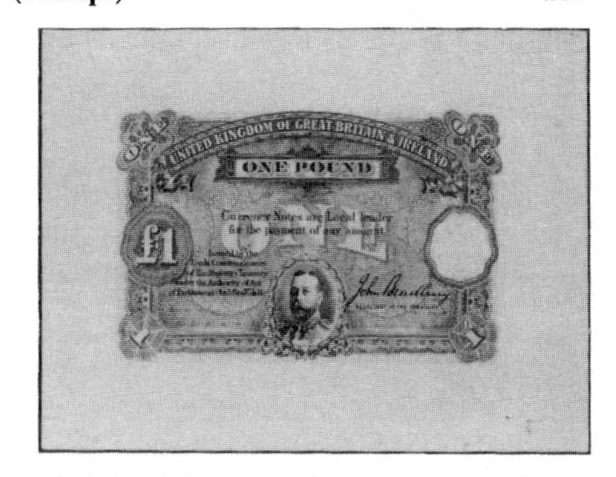

Great Britain: £1 trial in green, brown and blue on watermarked paper (210 x 155mm) with large white margin which has "Passed" pencilled in twice.
(Phillips) £805

Germany: 1907 Deutsch-Asiatische Bank $10 issued at Tientsin.
(Phillips) £820

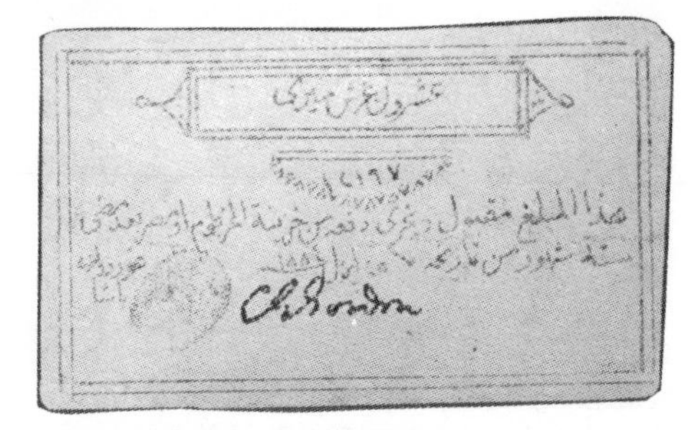

Sudan: 1884 20 piastres, Siege of Khartoum, hectographic signature.
(Phillips) £150

New Zealand: 1925 Bank of New South Wales **£20 perforated 'Specimen'.**
(Phillips) £240

Great Britain: Robert Owen 1 Hour 'Labour Exchange' note, handsigned and dated 17 September 1832, plus card token for 1/6 hour.
(Phillips) £220

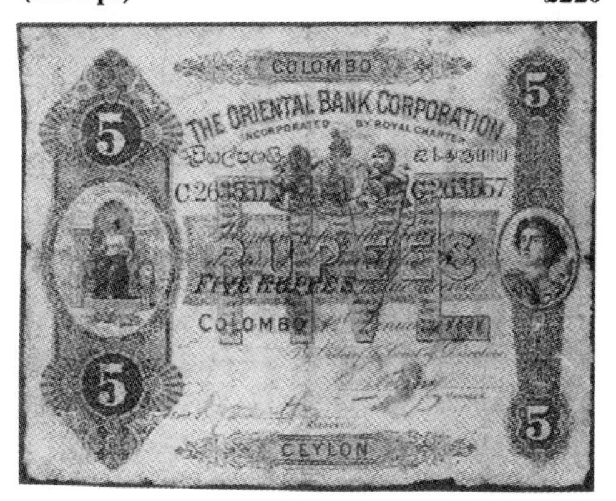

Ceylon: 1881 Oriental Bank Corporation 5 rupees issued at Colombo, attractive Bradbury Wilkinson engraving.
(Phillips) £340

U.S.A.: 1917 $10,000 Gold Certificate, payable to the 'Federal Reserve Board', uniface and perforated across portrait 'Payable only to The Treasurer of the US'.
(Phillips) £368

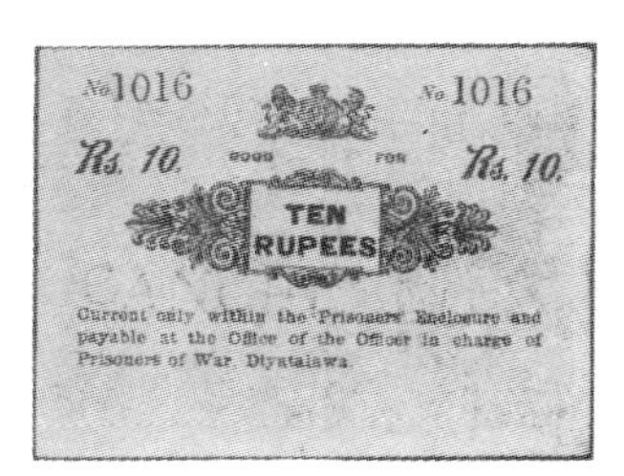

Ceylon: 1900 10 rupees issued at Diyatalawa Camp.
(Phillips) £300

Russia: 1919 Banque de L'Indochine 500 roubles **Specimen prepared for Allied Forces, brown with central vignette of Marianne.**
(Phillips) £800

Netherlands: 1888 Munt-Biljet for 10 gulden, few pinholes left side.
(Phillips) £1,495

Bank of England Note, E.M. Harvey: £20 28 May 1918 issued at Leeds.
(Phillips) £480

U.S.A., 1934 $500 Federal Reserve note.
(Phillips) £320

Ludlow Bank: £20 unissued 18.
(Phillips) £75

Bank of England note £1 Applegarth and Cowper essay in red and blue on black 1821.
(Phillips) £220

Bermuda, 1927 Government £1. (Phillips London) £130

Bank of England note £20 1985–89 with large piece of extra paper at bottom, including colour bars.
(Phillips) £500

Bank of England note £1 17 December 1825, piece missing upper left but not infringing on design.
(Phillips) £280

Paraguay: 1870 Lezica y Lanus (Argentine occupation) 5 pesos.
(Phillips) £100

Sri Lanka, 1900c Diyatalawa P.O.W. camp 5 rupees. (Phillips London) £80

Singapore: 1860 Chartered Bank $50 Post Bill, used as currency at the time. (Phillips) £160

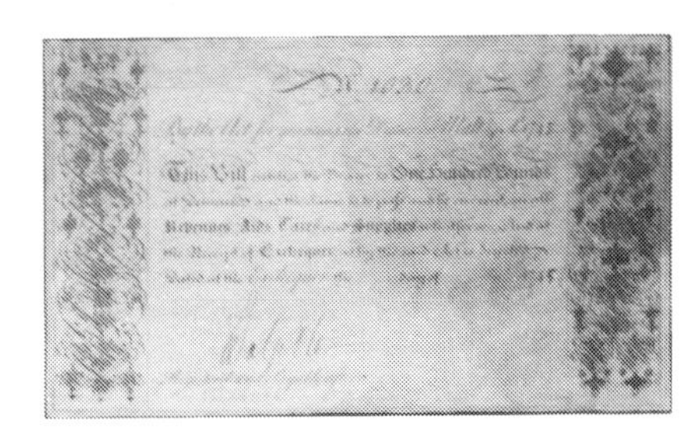

Great Britain, Exchequer Bill for £100 signed by Walpole and dated 1745. (Phillips London) £720

British Guiana 1928 Barclays Bank $5. (Phillips London) £190

Sri Lanka, 1865 Asiatic Banking Corporation £1, Colombo. (Phillips London) £260

Great Britain: Five francs 1914–18 P.O.W. note at 'Depot des Prisonniers de Guerre Anglais'. (Phillips) £80

Town and County of Southampton Bank: £1, 1810. (Phillips) £190

Sweden, 1921, 1,000 kronor. (Phillips London) £130

Sudan: 2,500 piastres Siege of Khartoum. (Phillips) £130

U.S.A., 1970 Military Payment Certificate $10 Series 692.
(Phillips) £160

Nicaragua, 1908 100 pesos, specimen.
(Phillips London) £200

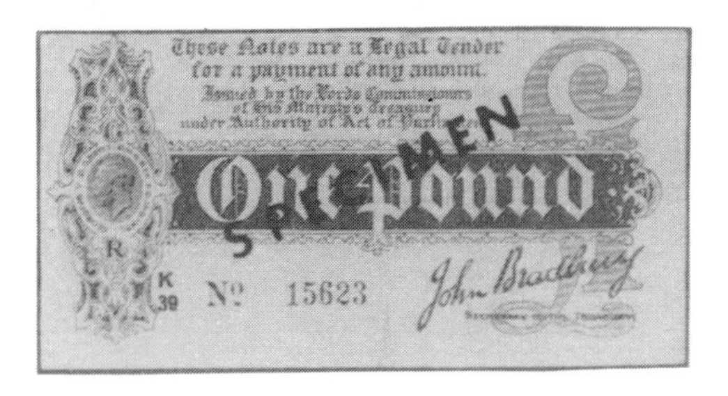

Great Britain treasury note, August 1914.
(Phillips) £400

£1 1915 overprinted for use in the Dardanelles.
(Phillips) £1,200

Bank of England Note, Abraham Newland, £1, 12 June 1804 (Dugg. B200), few small holes in body otherwise very well preserved for this issue. (Phillips London)
£1,600

Bank of England note £1 1940–48 error with extra paper.
(Phillips) £140

Egypt: 1916 £10 National Bank.
(Phillips) £220

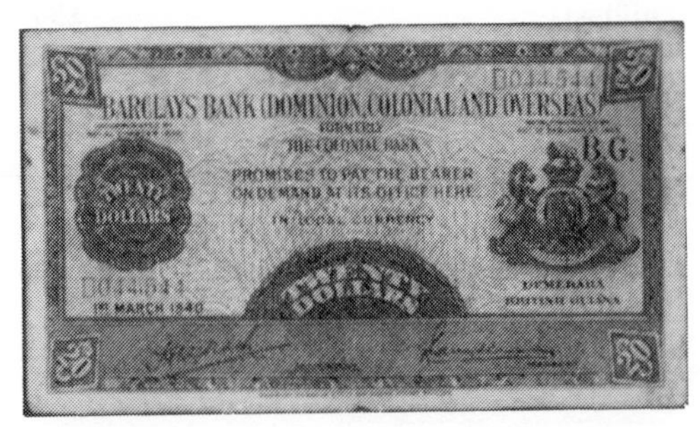

British Guiana, 1940 Barclays Bank $20.
(Phillips London) £180

Canada, 1897 Dominion of Canada $1.
(Phillips London) £400

U.S.A., Military Payment Certificate $20
Series 692.
(Phillips) £160

Zanzibar: 1916 20 rupees. (Phillips) £1,000

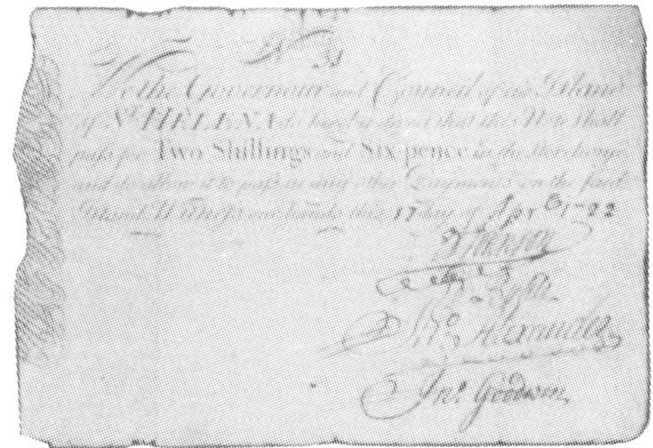

St Helena, 1722 2/6d issued by The Governor and council of the Island; the first paper currency of St Helena was produced in 1717 for a total issue of £400. This note is believed to be the only surviving paper money of that period. (Phillips London) £5,500

Zanzibar: 1928 (1st February) Government 10 rupees. (Phillips) £1,250

British Guiana, 1918 Government $2.
(Phillips London) £440

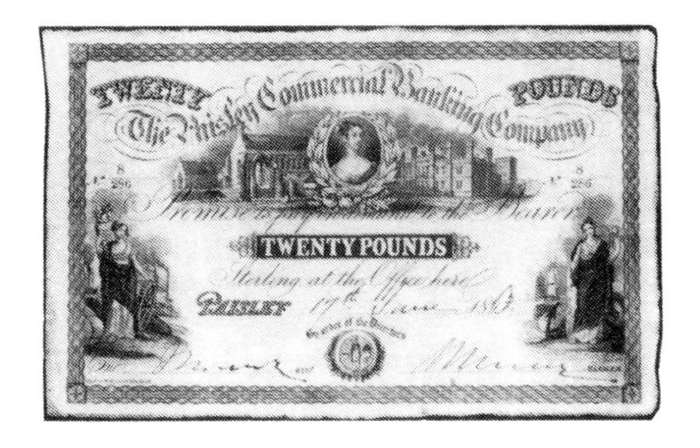

Paisley Commercial Banking Company, £20, 1843. (Phillips London) £820

French Equatorial Africa, 1941, 1,000 francs, Phoenix note. (Phillips London) £368

Barbados, 1922 Canadian Bank of Commerce $5. (Phillips London) £210

Canada, 1912 Molsons Bank $10 specimen colour trial in brown/black and light green with red back, two punch holes. (Phillips London) £200

Bank of England Note. 10 shilling note 1948 specimen, serial R00 000000 with metal thread. (Phillips London) £900

Bank of England, £1 error 1948, missing prefix and serial numbers. (Phillips) £100

Town & County Bank Ltd., £1, 1890. (Phillips London) £260

South Africa – 1900 Siege of Mafeking £1, no centre crease and therefore an unusually good example of this note. (Phillips) £550

Huddersfield Bank, £5, 18--, proof on card. (Phillips London) £140

Greece, 1870 National Bank 100 drachmai. (Phillips London) £360

Bank of England Note, J. S. Fforde, 10/-, 1966-68 error with large piece of extra paper at right. (Phillips London) £210

Canada, 184- La Banque du Peuple uniface proof of $10 printed by Toppan, Carpenter & Co. (as P. S907). Four small punch holes at bottom. (Phillips London) £320

Bank of England Note, Abraham Newland, £1, 2 March 1797, note number 4 (Dugg. B200), first date of issue for the first £1 notes ever produced by the Bank of England, (Phillips London) £17,000

States of Guernsey, £5 essay on thin paper produced in 1836 with a covering letter to Perkins, Bacon & Petch approving the general design and requesting delivery of 2,000 notes. (Phillips London) £4,200

Timor, 1924 5 patacas. (Phillips London) £110

Cyprus, 1949 George VI £5. (Phillips London) £160

Seychelles, 1919 Government 50 cents, emergency issue. (Phillips London) £580

Japan, 1885 1 yen. (Phillips London) £260

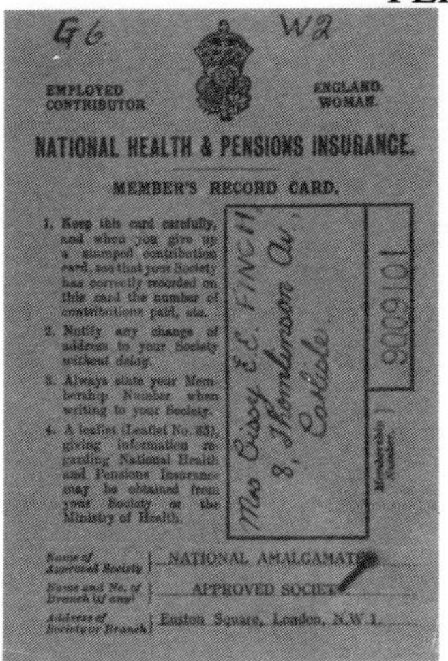

G6 W2

EMPLOYED CONTRIBUTOR ENGLAND. WOMAN.

NATIONAL HEALTH & PENSIONS INSURANCE.

MEMBER'S RECORD CARD.

1. Keep this card carefully, and when you give up a stamped contribution card, see that your Society has correctly recorded on this card the number of contributions paid, etc.
2. Notify any change of address to your Society without delay.
3. Always state your Membership Number when writing to your Society.
4. A leaflet (Leaflet No. 85), giving information regarding National Health and Pensions Insurance may be obtained from your Society or the Ministry of Health.

Mrs Cissy E.E. Finch
8, Thomlinson Av.
Carlisle

Membership Number. 1016009

Name of Approved Society: NATIONAL AMALGAMATED
Name and No. of Branch (if any): APPROVED SOCIETY
Address of Society or Branch: Euston Square, London, N.W.1.

National Health and Pensions Insurance card. £2

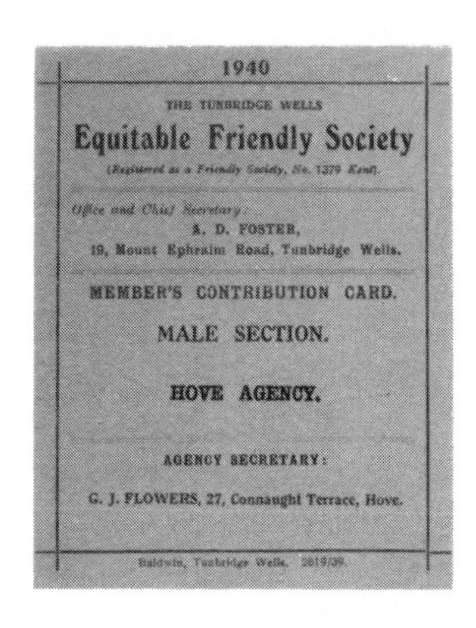

1940

THE TUNBRIDGE WELLS

Equitable Friendly Society

(Registered as a Friendly Society, No. 1379 Kent).

Office and Chief Secretary:
A. D. FOSTER,
19, Mount Ephraim Road, Tunbridge Wells.

MEMBER'S CONTRIBUTION CARD.

MALE SECTION.

HOVE AGENCY.

AGENCY SECRETARY:

G. J. FLOWERS, 27, Connaught Terrace, Hove.

Baldwin, Tunbridge Wells. 2019/39.

Equitable Friendly Society contribution card, 1940. £1

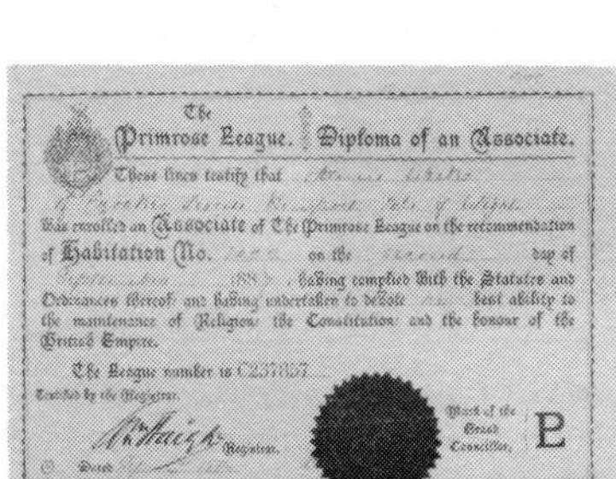

The Primrose League. Diploma of an Associate.

These lines testify that [illegible]
was enrolled an Associate of The Primrose League on the recommendation of Habitation (No. [illegible]) on the [illegible] day of September 1887, having complied with the Statutes and Ordinances thereof; and having undertaken to devote [illegible] best ability to the maintenance of Religion: the Constitution: and the honour of the United Empire.

The League number is C237857

Certified by the Registrar.

Registrar. Mark of the Grand Councillor. P

The Primrose League, Diploma of an Associate, 1887. £1.50

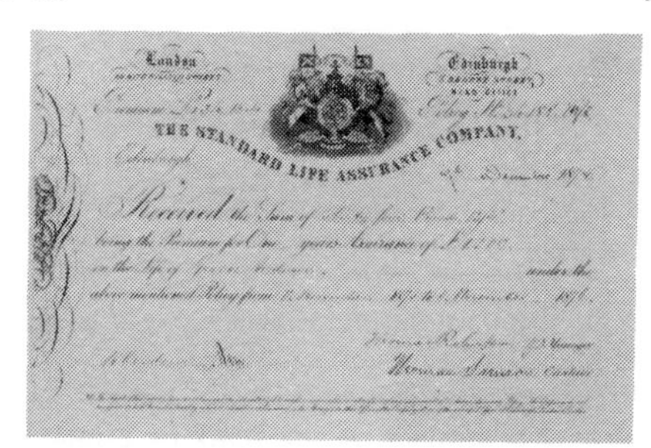

London Edinburgh

THE STANDARD LIFE ASSURANCE COMPANY.

Received the Sum of [illegible] being the Premium for [illegible] years Assurance of £ [illegible] on the Life of [illegible] under the above-mentioned Policy from [illegible] 1875 to [illegible] 1876.

Receipt from Standard Life Assurance Co., 1875. £2

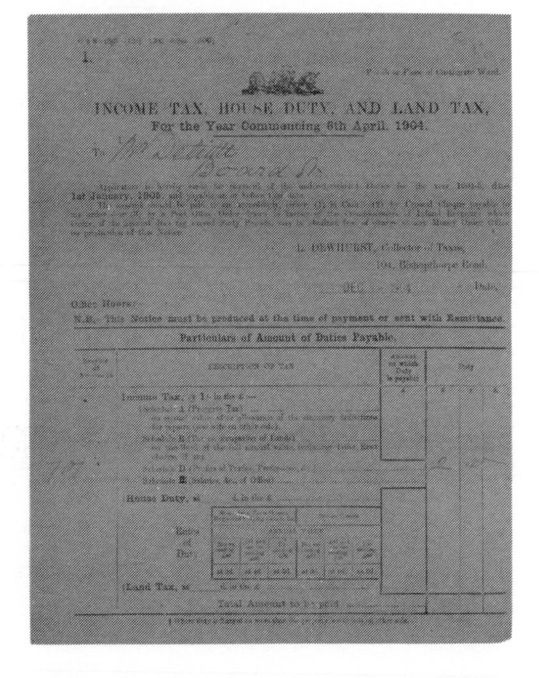

INCOME TAX, HOUSE DUTY, AND LAND TAX,
For the Year Commencing 6th April, 1904.

To Mr [illegible]

L. DEWHURST, Collector of Taxes,
104, Bishopthorpe Road.

DEC 1904

Office Hours:—
N.B.—This Notice must be produced at the time of payment or sent with Remittance.

Particulars of Amount of Duties Payable.

Income Tax, @ 1/- in the £ —
Schedule A (Property Tax)
Schedule B (Occupation of Lands)
Schedule D (Profits of Trades, Professions, &c.)
Schedule E (Salaries, &c. of Offices)

House Duty, at [illegible] in the £

Land Tax, at [illegible] in the £

Total Amount to be paid

Income Tax, House Duty and Land Tax, 1904. £2

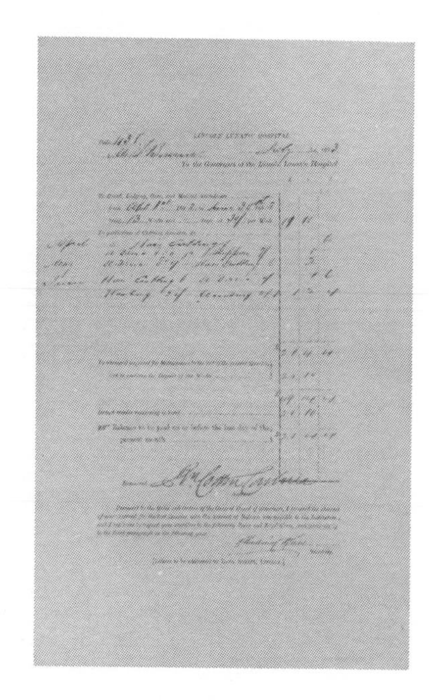

Statement of Account from Lincoln Lunatic Hospital, July 1893. £8

(Douglas Morgan)

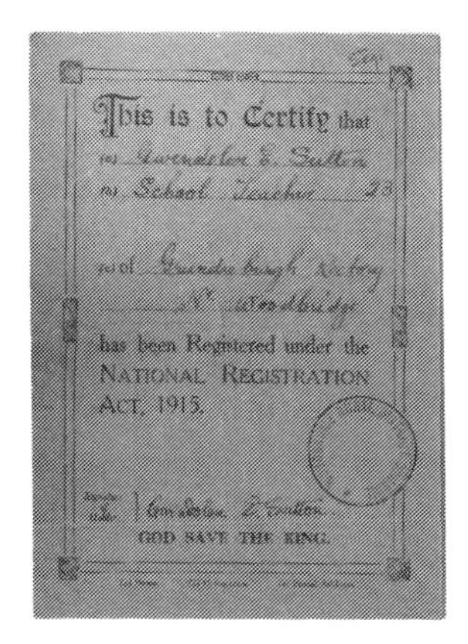
This is to Certify that
Gwendolen E. Sutton
School Teacher 23
of Grundisburgh Rectory
Nr Woodbridge
has been Registered under the NATIONAL REGISTRATION ACT, 1915.
Gwendolen E. Sutton
GOD SAVE THE KING.

National Registration Act, 1915. **£2**

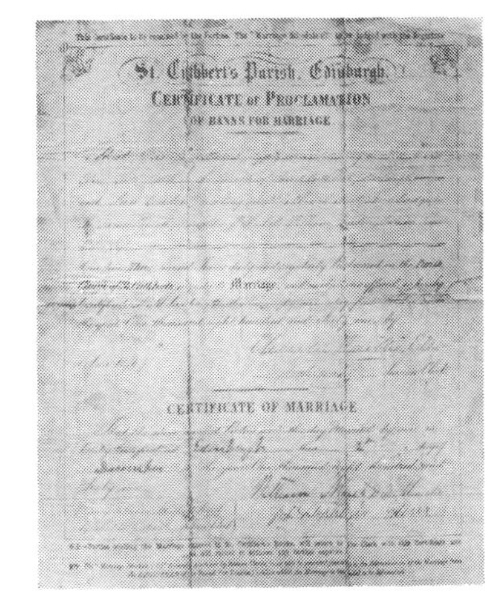
St. Cuthbert's Parish, Edinburgh.
CERTIFICATE OF PROCLAMATION OF BANNS FOR MARRIAGE
CERTIFICATE OF MARRIAGE

Certificate of Marriage, Edinburgh, 1861. **£4**

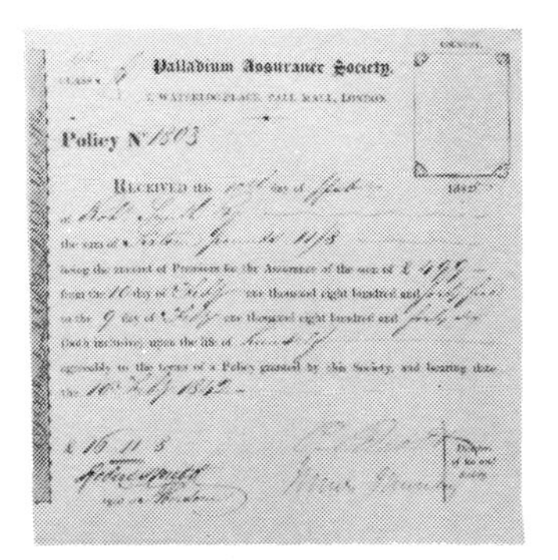
Palladium Assurance Society.
7, Waterloo Place, Pall Mall, London.
Policy No 1503

Receipt from Palladium Assurance Society, 1845. **£2**

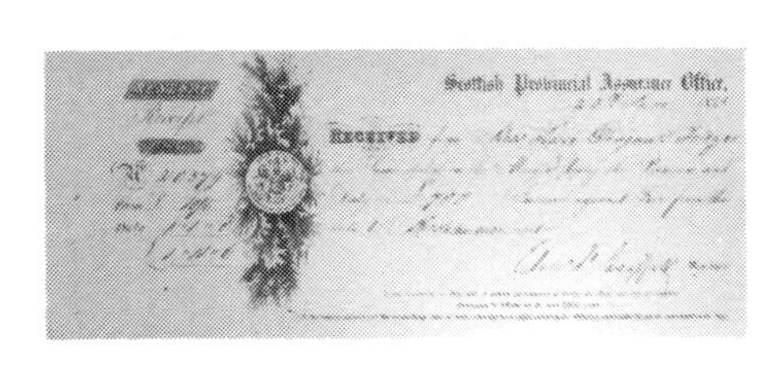
Scottish Provincial Assurance Office.
RECEIVED

Receipt from Scottish Provincial Assurance Office, 1853. **£2**

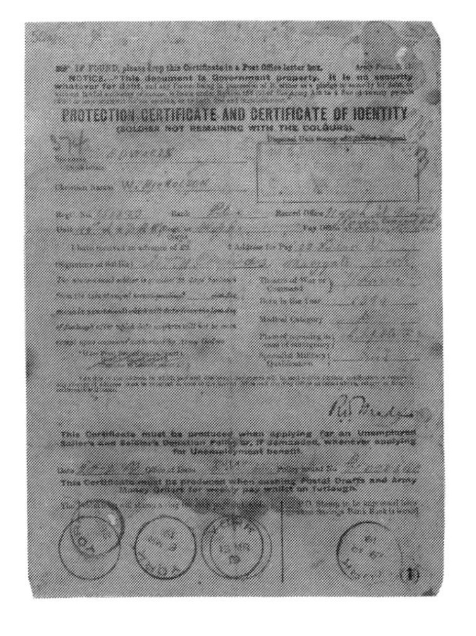
PROTECTION CERTIFICATE AND CERTIFICATE OF IDENTITY
(SOLDIER NOT REMAINING WITH THE COLOURS.)
This Certificate must be produced when applying for an Unemployed Sailors and Soldiers Donation Policy or, if demanded, whenever applying for Unemployment benefit.
This Certificate must be produced when cashing Postal Drafts and Army Money Orders for weekly pay whilst on furlough.

Protection Certificate for Soldier not Remaining with the Colours. **£3**

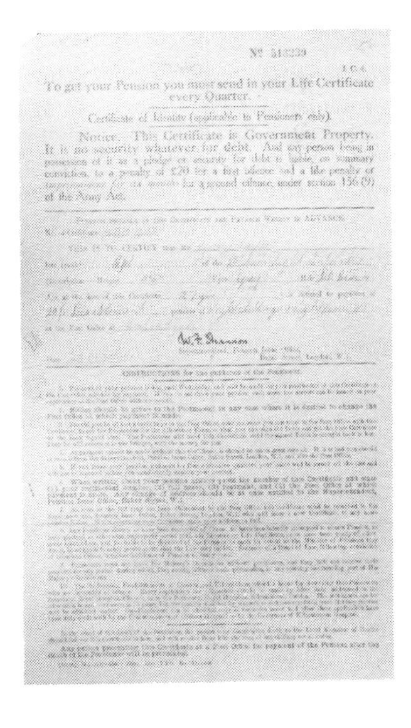
No 513239
To get your Pension you must send in your Life Certificate every Quarter.
Certificate of Identity (applicable to Pensioners only).
Notice. This Certificate is Government Property. It is no security whatever for debt. And any person being in possession of it as a pledge or security for debt is liable, on summary conviction, to a penalty of £20 for a first offence and a like penalty or imprisonment for six months for a second offence, under section 156 (9) of the Army Act.

Certificate of Identity, 1919. **£4**

(Yesterdays Paper)

David Octavius Hill and Robert Adamson, Three Newhaven Fisherwomen, mid 1840s, calotype, $7\frac{3}{4}$ x $5\frac{1}{2}$in.
(Christie's) £1,495

Bill Brandt, 'Religious Demonstration, Epsom Derby Day', 1930s, gelatin silver print, $6\frac{1}{2}$ x $8\frac{3}{8}$in.
(Christie's) £805

Herbert List (1903–1975), Headstand, London, 1936, printed circa 1950, gelatin silver print, $11\frac{1}{2}$ x 9in.
(Christie's) £1,380

Alexander Rodchenko, 'Solntsepoklonniki, 1933' [Sun Worshippers], gelatin silver print, $22\frac{3}{4}$ x $14\frac{7}{8}$in., signed, titled (twice) and dated in pencil.
(Christie's) £8,625

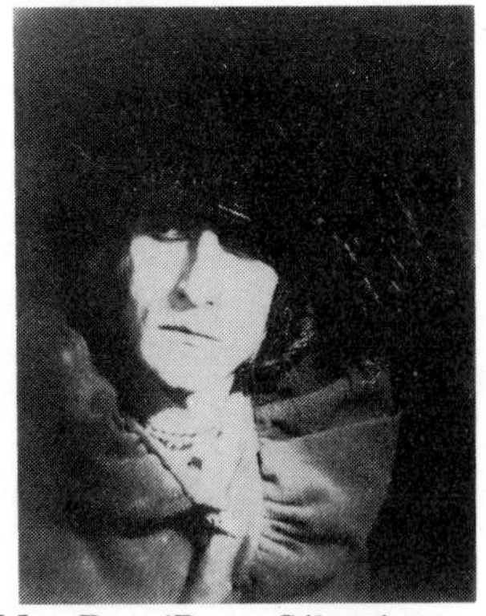

Man Ray, 'Rrose Sélavy' [Marcel Duchamp], 1921, printed circa 1936–40, gelatin silver print, $8\frac{3}{4}$ x 7in., photographer's ink credit stamp, *8 rue Val de Grâce*, on verso.
(Christie's) £6,820

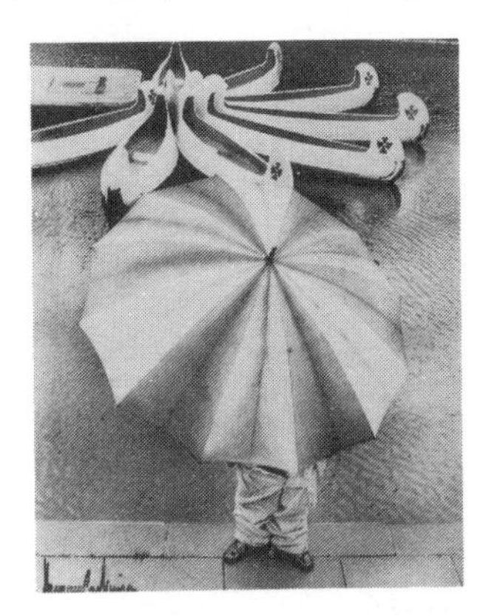

Norman Parkinson, 'Changing of the Guard', late 1970s, gelatin silver print, image size 14 x $11\frac{1}{2}$in., signed in ink on recto, mounted on card.
(Christie's) £880

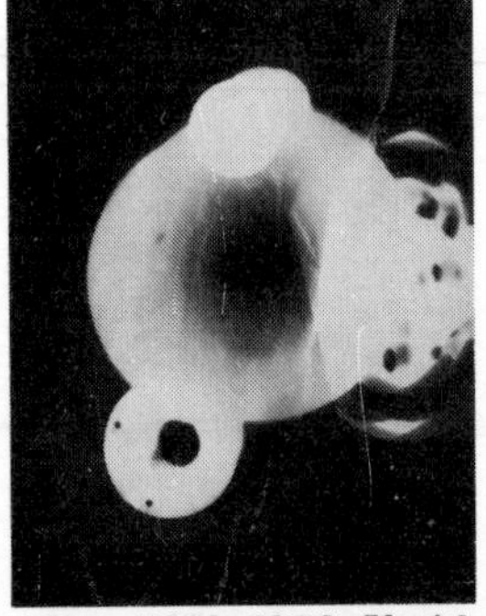

Man Ray (1890–1976), Untitled (spherical light objects), 1926, Rayograph, $9\frac{3}{4}$ x $7\frac{5}{8}$in., signed and dated *Man Ray '26* in pencil on image.
(Christie's) £24,200

David Octavius Hill and Robert Adamson, Mr Finlay the deer stalker, mid 1840s, calotype, 8 x $5\frac{3}{4}$in.
(Christie's) £3,220

Alexander Rodchenko, 'Kulaki, 1928' [Kulaks], gelatin silver print on textured paper, $11\frac{3}{8}$ x $9\frac{1}{16}$in., titled and dated in pencil.
(Christie's) £9,200

Ida Kar, Stanley Spencer, 1954, gloss gelatin silver print, 11¾ x 9in., signed in white crayon.
(Christie's) **£322**

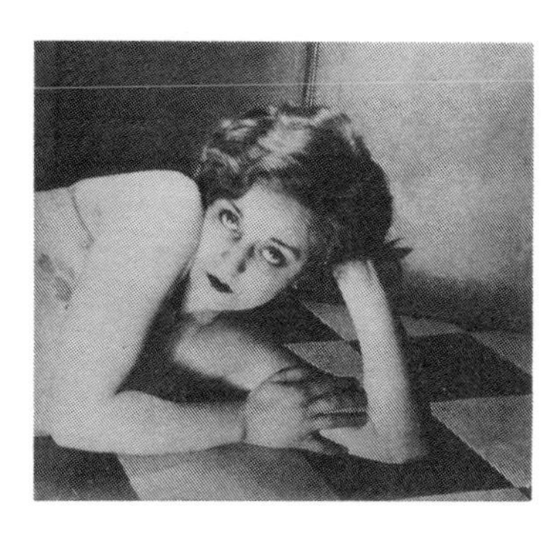

Cecil Beaton, 'Tallulah Bankhead', 1930 printed 1960s, gelatin silver print, 15 x 16¾in.
(Christie's) **£632**

Bill Brandt, 'Homes fit for Heroes', 1930s, gloss gelatin silver print, 9 x 7⅝in.
(Christie's) **£1,150**

Alexander Rodchenko, 'Pionerka, 1930' [Pioneer], possibly printed 1940s-early 50s, gelatin silver print, 17 7/16 x 13 9/16in., signed, titled and dated in pencil.
(Christie's) **£10,350**

Alexander Rodchenko, 'Otriad pionerov Akademii kom-vospitaniia, 1925', gloss gelatin silver print, 11 5/16 x 9 3/16in., photographer's ink credit stamp *Foto A. M. Rodchenko* with title and date in pencil on verso.
(Christie's) £1,045

Anon, Tintern Abbey detail, [1850s], salt print, 7⅝ x 6in., possibly an early view by Roger Fenton.
(Christie's) £345

Weegee (1899–1968), Arrest, 1940s, gelatin silver print, image size 13½ x 10⅝in., photographer's ink credit stamp.
(Christie's) £1,150

A ninth-plate daguerreotype, hand-tinted and gilt highlights, arched top gilt surround, in folding morocco case.
(Christie's) £72

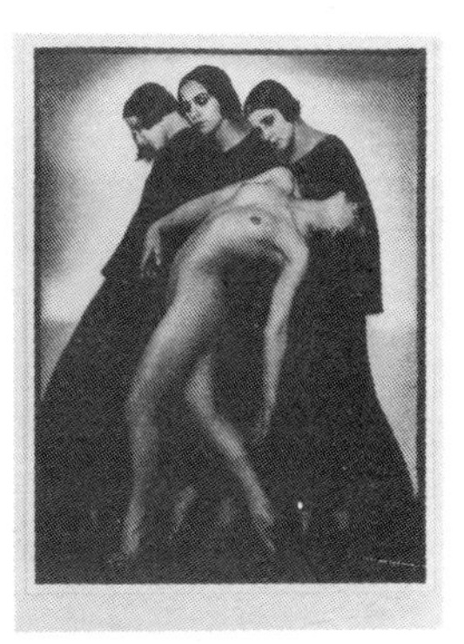

Rudolf Koppitz (1884–1936), Bewegungsstudie [study of movement], 1926, gelatin silver print, 10¾ x 8in., matted, signed in pencil on mount.
(Christie's) £19,550

Lewis Hine, 2 photographs: "Baltimore cannery", and Four schoolboys, both circa 1910, gelatin silver prints, the first $4\frac{3}{4}$ x $6\frac{5}{8}$in.
(Butterfield & Butterfield)
£325

Ansel Adams, "Dogwood, Yosemite National Park, California", 1938, printed 1970s, gelatin silver print, $13\frac{1}{2}$ x $9\frac{1}{2}$in., signed in pencil on mount.
(Butterfield & Butterfield)
£2,070

Ralph Steiner, "American baroque", 1929, printed 1949, gelatin silver print, $7\frac{7}{8}$ x $9\frac{7}{8}$in., signed and dated in pencil on verso.
(Butterfield & Butterfield)
£946

Peter Stackpole, "Minsky's dressing room", 1937, printed later, gelatin silver print, $9\frac{3}{8}$ x $7\frac{3}{8}$in., signed in pencil.
(Butterfield & Butterfield)
£296

Philippe Halsman, "Nixon jumping in the White House", 1955, printed 1969, gelatin silver print, 14 x 11in., signed, titled, and dated in pencil.
(Butterfield & Butterfield) £503

William Heick, "Woman on bus, Seattle", 1951, gelatin silver print, $9\frac{7}{8}$ x 8in., signed and dated in pencil on the mount.
(Butterfield & Butterfield)
£384

Arthur Dunn, 'Mark Twain and Family at Dollis Hill', 1900, carbon print, 6 x 8in., mounted on card.
(Christie's) £154

Nicholas Nixon, "MDC Park, Brighton, Massachusetts", 1979, printed later, gelatin silver print, $7\frac{1}{8}$ x $9\frac{5}{8}$in., signed.
(Butterfield & Butterfield)
£473

William Heick, "Hats, Seattle", 1952, gelatin silver print, $9\frac{1}{2}$ x $12\frac{1}{2}$in., signed and dated in pencil on the mount.
(Butterfield & Butterfield)
£325

Max Yavno, "Orson Wells", circa 1942, gelatin silver print, $7^{6}/_{8}$ x $9^{6}/_{8}$in., photographer's stamp in ink.
(Butterfield & Butterfield) £591

Max Yavno, "Muscle Beach Los Angeles", 1949, printed later, gelatin silver print, $7^{7}/_{8}$ x $13^{3}/_{8}$in.
(Butterfield & Butterfield)
£2,366

Ansel Adams, "Frozen lake and cliffs, Sierra Nevada, Sequoia National Park", 1932, printed later, approximately 8 x 10in.
(Butterfield & Butterfield)
£6,505

Photographer unknown, Portrait of a black woman with a white child, $^{1}/_{2}$ plate tintype, gilt preserver, leather case broken at hinges.
(Butterfield & Butterfield)
£207

Horst P. Horst, 'Lisa Fonssagrives, New York, 1940', printed 1980s, platinum-palladium print, image size $18^{3}/_{4}$ x 15in., signed in pencil in margin.
(Christie's) £2,200

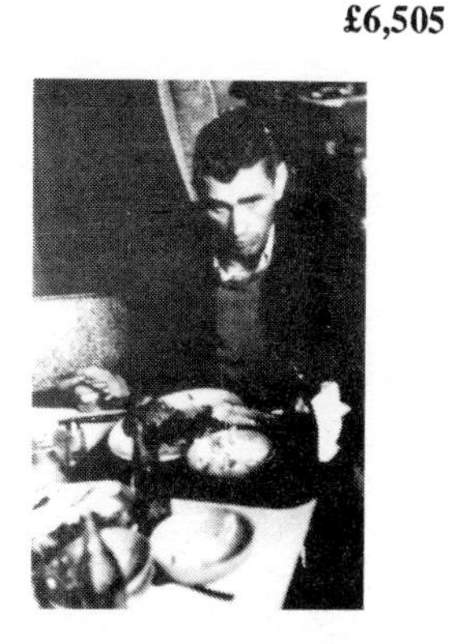

Robert Frank, 'San Francisco 1956', printed 1970s, gelatin silver print, $13^{1}/_{4}$ x 9in., signed and titled in ink in margin, matted, framed.
(Christie's) £605

Man Ray, Head of a woman, 1946, solarised gelatin silver print, 8 x $6^{1}/_{4}$in., includes signature and date.
(Butterfield & Butterfield)
£1,478

Nicholas Nixon, "Yazoo City, Mississippi", 1979, printed later, gelatin silver print, $7^{1}/_{8}$ x $9^{3}/_{4}$in., signed.
(Butterfield & Butterfield)
£503

Anne W. Brigman, 'Incantation', 1905, gelatin silver print, $11^{3}/_{8}$ x $6^{5}/_{8}$in., signed in ink on the image, titled in ink and annotated in pencil on verso.
(Butterfield & Butterfield)
£1,756

Ansel Adams, 'Moonrise, Hernandez, New Mexico', circa 1942, printed circa 1976, gelatin silver print, $15\frac{1}{4}$ x $19\frac{3}{8}$in., signed in pencil on the mount. (Butterfield & Butterfield) £4,788

Frantisek Drtikol, Fat boy posing, 1925, gelatin silver print, $8\frac{7}{8}$ x $6\frac{3}{4}$in., photographer's blindstamp with date on recto. (Christie's) £660

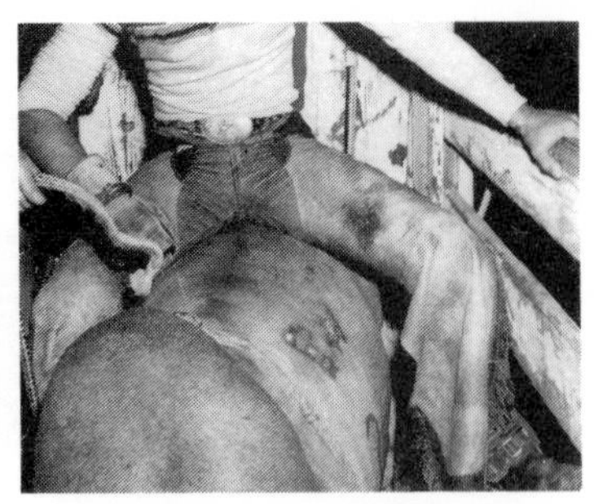

Susan Felter, 'Roy (red chaps) riding bull', 1978, Cibachrome, 13 x $16\frac{7}{8}$in., signed and dated in the margin, signed and dated in pencil on the reverse. (Butterfield & Butterfield) £303

Anon, Lady with large black dog, circa 1860, quarter-plate ambrotype, with gilt metal mount. (Christie's) £220

Henri Cartier-Bresson, 'Rue Mouffetard', 1954, printed later, 14 x $9\frac{3}{8}$in., signed in ink and the photographer's blindstamp in the margin. (Butterfield & Butterfield) £2,234

Willard Van Dyke, "Nehi", circa 1931, gelatin silver print, $9\frac{1}{2}$ x $7\frac{1}{2}$in., signed, titled, dated. (Butterfield & Butterfield) £651

Roger Mayne, Boy with gun, 1956, gelatin silver print, $9\frac{7}{8}$ x $7\frac{1}{4}$in., photographer's ink copyright stamp on verso. (Christie's) £330

Photographer unknown, Album containing 24 photographs of The Paris Exposition Universelle, 1889, albumen prints, each measuring approximately $8\frac{3}{4}$ x $11\frac{3}{4}$in. (Butterfield & Butterfield) £266

W. Eugene Smith, "Spanish spinner", 1951, printed 1977, gelatin silver print, $12\frac{3}{4}$ x 9in., signed on the mount in ink. (Butterfield & Butterfield) £887

Duane Michals, "Magritte's room", 1965, printed later, gelatin silver print, 6¾ x 9⅞in., signed.
(Butterfield & Butterfield)
£251

Andre Kertesz, "Circus", 1920, printed for "A Hungarian Memory" portfolio, gelatin silver print, 9¾ x 7¾in.
(Butterfield & Butterfield)
£710

Jacques Henri Lartigue, "Horse races at Montreuil", 1911, printed 1972, 6½ x 9in., signed in ink on the mount.
(Butterfield & Butterfield)
£766

R. Lowe (Cheltenham), Caroline Georgina Colledge and her brother John, circa 1855, a 5 x 4in. daguerreotype.
(Christie's) £440

Andre Kertesz, "Wandering violinist", 1921, printed 1980 for "A Hungarian Memory" portfolio, gelatin silver print, 9¾ x 7½in., signed in pencil on verso.
(Butterfield & Butterfield) £710

Frank Meadow Sutcliffe, 'His Son's Son', late 19th century, carbon print, image size 7⅛ x 6in., numbered *31* with photographer's initials in the negative, matted.
(Christie's) £308

Edward Steichen (1879–1973), Noel Coward, 1932, gelatin silver contact print, 10 x 8in.
(Christie's) £825

Photographer unknown, 2 albums containing 133 photographs: Chinese landscapes, portraits and genre scenes, 1880s, albumen prints.
(Butterfield & Butterfield)
£1,183

Man Ray, 'Mrs Simpson', 1936, double exposure silver print, 8⅜ x 6¼in., matted, framed.
(Christie's) £1,485

Anon, Family group portrait, circa 1895–97, mammoth carbon print, 29½ x 39½in., finely hand-tinted, contemporary gilt frame.
(Christie's) £418

Gustave Le Gray (1820–82), The Great Wave, Sète, 1856–59, albumen print from two negatives, 12⅜ x 15½in.
(Christie's) £18,700

Jacques Henri Lartigue, Woman and dog, 1920s, printed 1972, 6½ x 9in., signed in ink on the mount.
(Butterfield & Butterfield) £355

Edouard-Denis Baldus, 'Paris Saint-Eustache', circa 1860, albumen print, 16⅜ x 13in., signed in the negative, mounted on card.
(Christie's) £4,400

Auguste Belloc, Reclining nude, 1852–54, coated (possibly waxed) salt print, 6 x 7⅞in., corners trimmed, mounted on card.
(Christie's) £4,400

Bert Hardy (b. 1913), 'Maidens in Waiting, Blackpool', 1951, printed later, gelatin silver print, image size 13 x 10in., signed in ink in margin, framed.
(Christie's) £440

Lotte Jacobi (1896–1990), 'Peter Lorre', 'Grock' and other portraits, (1940s–50s), printed late 1950s, six gelatin silver prints, 6½ x 4¾in., to 9½ x 7½in.
(Christie's) £352

Robert Howlett (1831–1858), Attempted launch of the "Great Eastern", November 28, 1857, printed early 1900s, gelatin silver print, 10 x 8½in., arched top, mounted on card.
(Christie's) £308

Yousuf Karsh (b. 1908), Pablo Picasso, 1954, printed later, gelatin silver print, 23½ x 19½in., mounted on card, signed in ink on mount, matted, framed.
(Christie's) £1,210

Berenice Abbott, "Portrait of Orozco", early 1930s, gelatin silver print, 13¾ x 11⅝in, signed in pencil on mount. (Butterfield & Butterfield) £444

Irving Penn (b. 1917), Pablo Picasso, Cannes, 1957, probably printed early 1960s, gelatin silver print, 22⅞ x 22⅞in., flush mounted on plywood. (Christie's) £1,320

Frederick Evans, Portrait of Aubrey Beardsley, circa 1894, photogravure, 5 x 4⅛in., credit printed in the margin. (Butterfield & Butterfield) £118

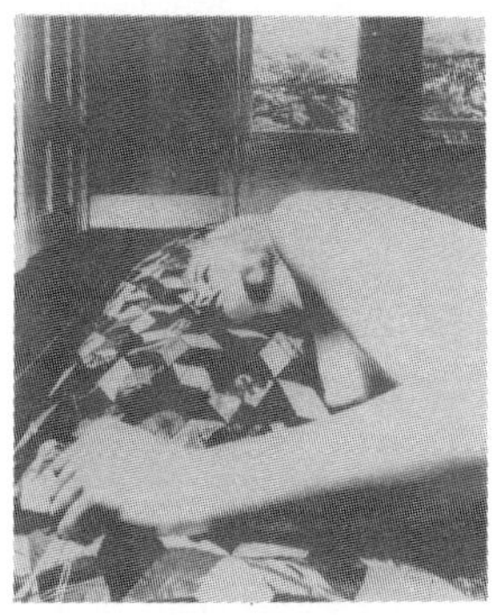

Bill Brandt (1906–1984), 'Hampstead, London 1953', printed later, gelatin silver print, 12⅜ x 10⅜in., singed in ink on verso, matted, framed. (Christie's) £462

Judy Dater, "Nehemiah", 1975, gelatin silver print, 10⅜ x 13⅜in., signed in pencil on the mount, framed. (Butterfield & Butterfield) £384

Gisèle Freund, 'Samuel Beckett', n.d., gelatin silver print, image size 12 x 7⅞in., photographer's blindstamp on image, signed in ink in margin. (Christie's) £418

Philippe Halsman, "Marc Chagall", 1946, printed later, gelatin silver print, 13⅝ x 10¾in., signed, titled, and dated in pencil. (Butterfield & Butterfield) £503

Irving Penn (b. 1917), Igor Stravinsky, 1948, printed 1970, multiple-printed and hand-coated platinum-palladium print, 19 x 13¾in., with aluminium backing, signed. (Christie's) £2,640

(?) Herman, Toulouse Lautrec seated at his easel, 1894, gelatin silver print, 7¾ x 6¼in., mounted on card, signed and dated by the photographer, matted and framed. (Christie's) £880

Ivan Shagin, 'Final Fashizma 1945', [The End of Fascism], gloss gelatin silver print, 16¾ x 20¾in., titled, signed and dated in pencil and with other annotations in ink on verso.
(Christie's) £1,320

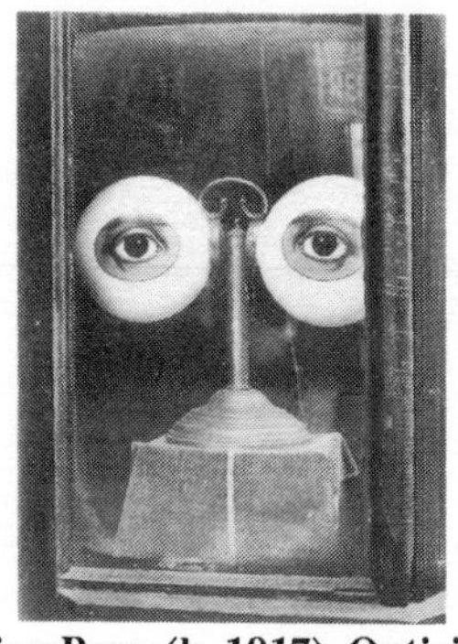

Irving Penn (b. 1917), Opticians window, New York, 1939 printed later, gelatin silver print, 13 x 9½in., signed, stamped, matted, framed.
(Christie's) £2,420

Norman Parkinson (1913–90), British Airways Electra, n.d. circa 1937, gelatin silver print, 12 x 16½in., matted, framed.
(Christie's) £1,760

Alexander Rodchenko, 'Pozharnaia lestnista, 1927' [Fire Escape], gelatin silver print, 11 7/16 x 9⅛in., signed, titled, dated and inscribed *niz* [bottom] in pencil with collection stamp of Rodchenko and Stepanova on verso.
(Christie's) £49,500

Diane Arbus (1923–1971), Teenage couple on Hudson Street, N.Y.C., 1963 printed later, gelatin silver print, image size 15 x 14¾in., stamped *A Diane Arbus Photograph*, signed *Doon Arbus*.
(Christie's) £880

Alexander Rodchenko, 'E. I. Shub. (kinorezhisser) 1928' [E. I. Shub (film director)], gelatin silver print, 15⅜ x 11 11/16in., signed, titled and dated in pencil and with collection stamp of Rodchenko and Stepanova on verso.
(Christie's) £8,250

Ivan Shagin, 'I. V. Stalin, 1935', gelatin silver print, 23 x 16⅜in., signed, titled, dated in pencil and with Novosty press agency stamp on verso.
(Christie's) £660

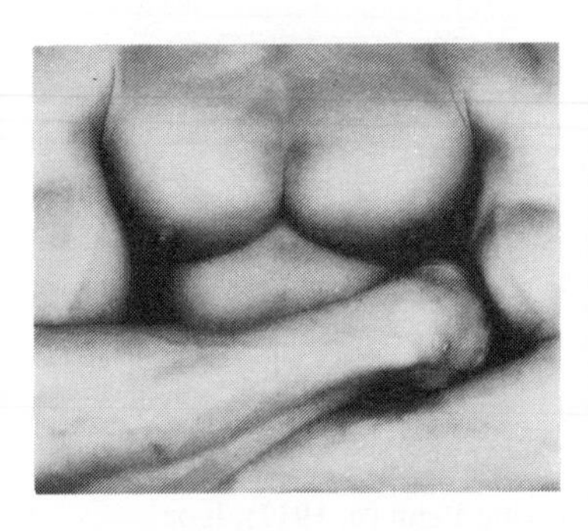

Robert Mapplethorpe (1946–89), Chest, 1987, selenium-toned gelatin silver print, 19½ x 23¼in., signed, stamped and numbered on verso.
(Christie's) £3,520

Cecil Beaton (1904–80), Nancy Cunard, 1927 printed 1960s, gelatin silver print, 17⅞ x 14¼in., mounted on card, signed in pencil on mount.
(Christie's) £682

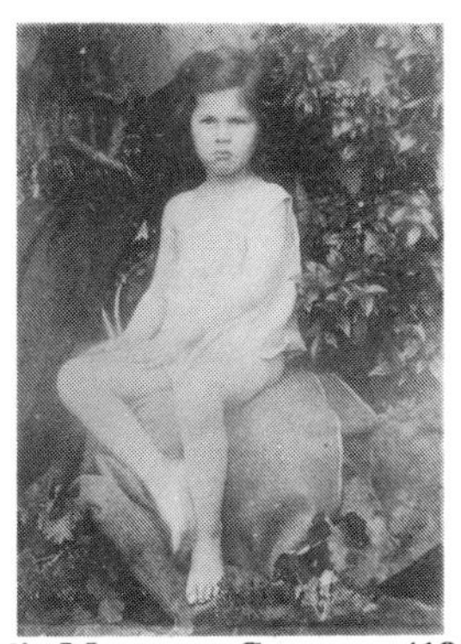

Julia Margaret Cameron (1815–79), 'The Passing of Arthur', 1874 and 'Childhood of St. John the Baptist', 1872, two albumen prints, $13\frac{3}{4}$ x 10in. and $14\frac{1}{4}$ x $10\frac{1}{2}$in.
(Christie's) **£770**

Alexander Rodchenko, 'Kolonna Dinamo, 1928' [Dynamo's Formation], gelatin silver print, 11 x $16\frac{1}{16}$in., signed, titled and dated in pencil and with collection stamp of Rodchenko and Stepanova on verso.
(Christie's) **£13,200**

Alexander Rodchenko, 'V. V. Maiakovskii, 1926', gelatin silver print, $16\frac{1}{2}$ x $11\frac{1}{2}$in., signed, titled and dated in pencil and with collection stamp of Rodchenko and Stepanova on verso.
(Christie's) **£12,100**

Anon, Turkoman gentleman with tall hat, circa 1850, quarter-plate daguerreotype, black and tortoiseshell-effect octagonal glass surround with gilt edges, paper-taped.
(Christie's) **£880**

Alexander Rodchenko, 'Pioner', [Pioneer], n.d. [circa 1930–31], gloss gelatin silver print, $4\frac{7}{8}$ x 5in., photographer's ink credit stamp *Foto A. M. Rodchenko* with title in pencil and collection stamp of Rodchenko and Stepanova on verso.
(Christie's) **£17,600**

Alexander Rodchenko, 'Devushka leikoi, 1934' [Girl with Leica], warm-toned gelatin silver print, $15\frac{3}{4}$ x $11\frac{7}{16}$in., signed, titled and dated (1932 changed to 1934).
(Christie's) **£115,500**

Frank A. Reinhart, 'Blackhorse', 'Three Fingers', 'Yellow Feather' and 'Bony tela and Hattie Tom', 1898–1900, four platinum prints, each approx. $9\frac{1}{8}$ x $7\frac{1}{8}$in., signed.
(Christie's) **£1,100**

Alexander Rodchenko, 'Na Krasnoi Ploshchadi Zariadiia, 1938' [In line on Red Square], warm-toned gelatin silver print, $11\frac{1}{2}$ x $14\frac{7}{8}$in., contemporary retouching, photographer's monogram on recto.
(Christie's) **£3,080**

Alvin Langdon Coburn (1882–1966), 'Vortograph', 1917, gelatin silver print, $10\frac{7}{8}$ x 8in., mounted on card, signed in pencil on recto.
(Christie's) **£74,800**

Choumoff (Paris), Autographed portrait of Claude Monet, circa 1910, warm-toned platinum print, 6³/₈ x 8¹/₄in., signed in red ink.
(Christie's) £1,540

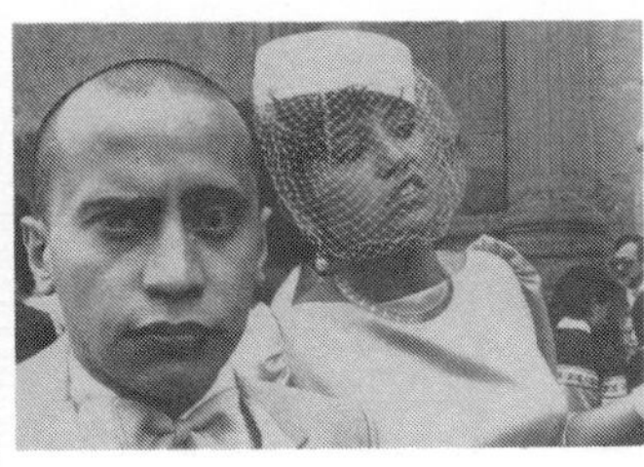

Pedro Meyer, "Boda en Coyoacan" (Wedding in Coyoacan, 1983, gelatin silver print, 8 x 12in., signed and titled in pencil on verso, framed.
(Butterfield & Butterfield) £251

Yousuf Karsh, "Jascha Heifetz", 1950s, gelatin silver print, 9⁶/₈ x 11³/₄in., signed in ink in the margin, framed.
(Butterfield & Butterfield) £444

Julia Margaret Cameron, "Sappho", circa 1866, albumen print, 14¹/₂ x 11¹/₂in., signed and annotated *from life not enlarged* in ink.
(Butterfield & Butterfield) £1,065

Roger Mayne, 'Ladbroke Grove – group watching car crash', 1958, printed circa 1960, gelatin silver print, 7¹/₄ x 9¹/₈in., photographer's ink copyright stamp and title on verso.
(Christie's) £275

Dorothy Wilding, HRH Princess Margaret, 1947, gelatin silver print, 18 x 14⁵/₈in., pencil border, mounted on tissue with photographer's printed signature.
(Christie's) £110

Alfred Ellis, two photographs: 'Mr. Oscar Wilde' and Oscar Wilde and friend, circa 1880s, albumen cabinet cards.
(Butterfield & Butterfield) £319

Brassaï, 'Salvador Dali', 1932, printed later, gelatin silver print, 11³/₄ x 8¹/₂in., signed and numbered *11/30* in red ink in the margin.
(Butterfield & Butterfield) £638

Julia Margaret Cameron, 'Paul & Virginia', 1867–70, albumen print, 10¹/₂ x 8¹/₂in., mounted on card.
(Christie's) £2,860

Anon, Sleeping dog, mid 1850s, sixth-plate daguerreotype, gilt metal mount.
(Christie's) £264

Lewis Carroll, 'Irene at Elm Lodge', July 1863, oval albumen print, $6\frac{7}{8}$ x $8\frac{7}{8}$in.
(Christie's) £7,700

Alice Boughton, portrait of Robert Louis Stevenson, circa 1900, platinum print 6 x 8in.
(Butterfield & Butterfield) £1,774

Edouard-Denis Baldus, Pavillon Turgot, Louvre, circa 1855, salt print, $17\frac{5}{8}$ x $13\frac{5}{8}$in., signed and numbered *E. Baldus No. 47* in the negative, mounted on card.
(Christie's) £1,210

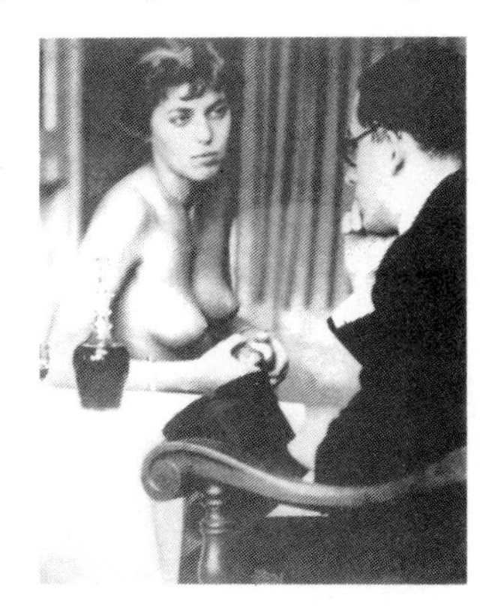

Josef Britenbach, 'Dr. Riegler and J. Geno', 1933, printed later, photogravure, 12 x $9\frac{1}{2}$in., the photographer's estate blindstamp.
(Butterfield & Butterfield) £383

Dorothy Wilding, The Duke and Duchess of Windsor, autographed portrait, 1944, gelatin silver print, $9\frac{1}{8}$ x $6\frac{1}{2}$in., mounted on tissue, signed by sitters and dated in ink.
(Christie's) £1,045

Alexander Rodchenko, "Portrait of Majakowski", 1924, printed 1989, gelatin silver print, 12 x $9\frac{3}{8}$in., titled and dated in pencil.
(Butterfield & Butterfield) £591

George Bernard Shaw (1856–1950), Alvin Langdon Coburn, July 1906, photogravure, $8\frac{3}{8}$ x $6\frac{3}{8}$in., on tissue, then card, matted.
(Christie's) £528

Cecil Beaton, "Lily Langtry, Lady de Bathe", gelatin silver print, $10\frac{7}{8}$ x 8in., titled in white ink on image, signed in orange watercolour on mount.
(Butterfield & Butterfield) £296

Howard Coster (1885–1959), T.E. Lawrence on his Brough Superior motorbike, 1925–26, gelatin silver print on textured card, 7³/₈ x 9¹/₄in.
(Christie's) £308

Lewis Carroll, 'Irene', July 1863, oval albumen print, 8³/₄ x 7in.
(Christie's) £9,900

Roger Mayne (b. 1929), Brenda Sheakey (screaming child), Southam Street, 1956, printed mid/late 1960s, gelatin silver print, 7¹/₄ x 9¹/₄in.
(Christie's) £990

Herb Ritts, 'Man holding shell', Australia 1986, gelatin silver print, image size 18⁵/₈ x 15¹/₄in., photographer's copyright blindstamp in margin.
(Christie's) £682

Irving Penn (b. 1917), 'Two Thin New Guinea Women', New Guinea, 1970, printed 1984, multiple-printed and hand-coated platinum-palladium print, 13¹/₄ x 13¹/₈in.
(Christie's) £1,650

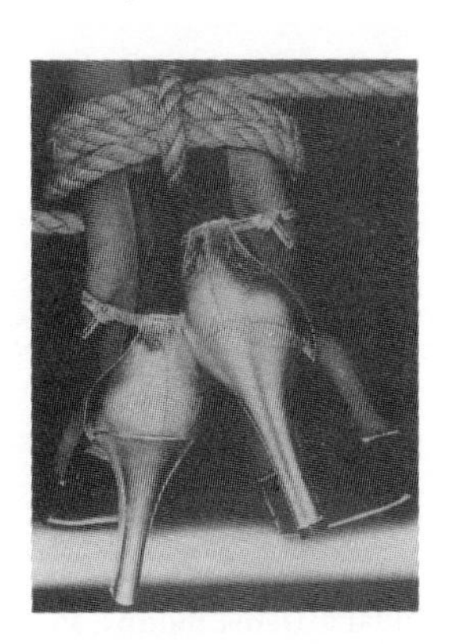

Albert Watson (b. 1942), Untitled, (1970s), gelatin silver print, 39¹/₂ x 29¹/₂in., mounted on board, signed and numbered *34/35* in ink on verso, framed.
(Christie's) £220

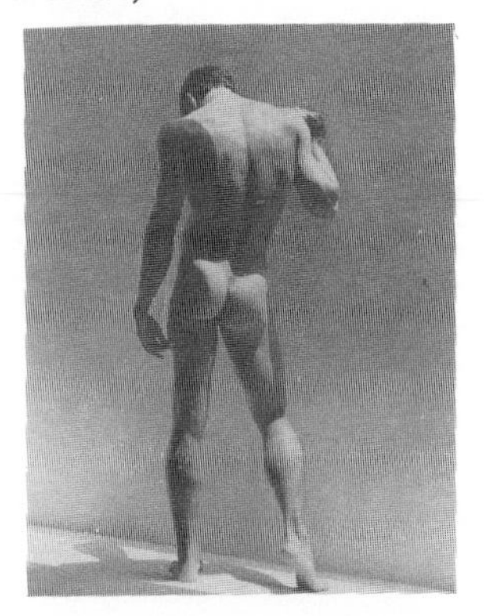

Greg Gorman, Dave Michelak, 1987, gelatin silver print, 30¹/₄ x 24³/₄in., signed and dated in ink with the photographer's copyright stamp.
(Butterfield & Butterfield) £770

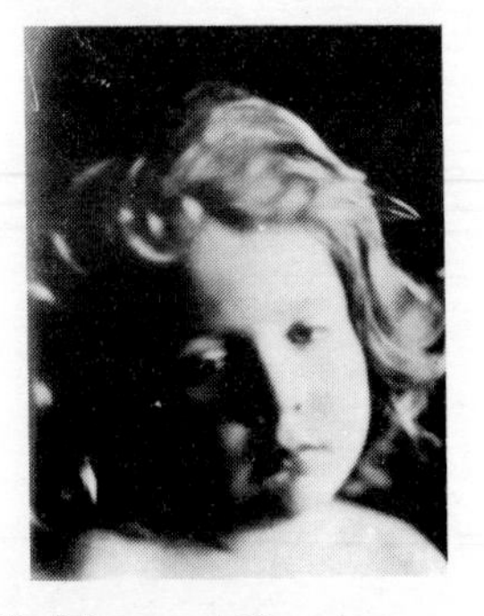

Julia Margaret Cameron, Untitled, child portrait, circa 1864–65, albumen print, 11¹/₂ x 9¹/₄in., mounted on card, ink manuscript credit and caption *From Life not Enlarged*, on mount.
(Christie's) £12,100

Izis (1911–1980), 'Jardin des Tuileries', Paris 1950, gelatin silver print, image size 11¹/₈ x 8⁵/₈in., titled and dated with photographer's credit stamp on verso.
(Christie's) £605

Algerine Woman, early 1850's, calotype, 22.6 x 18.1cm., titled in ink on mount, possibly Charles Marville.
(Christie's) £15,400

Lewis Carroll, 'Irene [MacDonald], Flo Rankin, Mary [MacDonald] at Elm Lodge', July 1863.
(Christie's) £8,250

David Octavius Hill & Robert Adamson, John Henning, mid 1840s, calotype, 8 x 6in., matted and framed.
(Christie's) £825

Man Ray (1890–1976), Robert Winthrop Chanler, 1929, toned gelatin silver print, $10\frac{7}{8}$ x $8\frac{1}{8}$in., signed *Man Ray Paris* in red crayon.
(Christie's) £385

Edward Weston, "White Sands, New Mexico", 1940, gelatin silver print, $7\frac{5}{8}$ x $9\frac{5}{8}$in., initialled **and dated.**
(Butterfield & Butterfield) £6,505

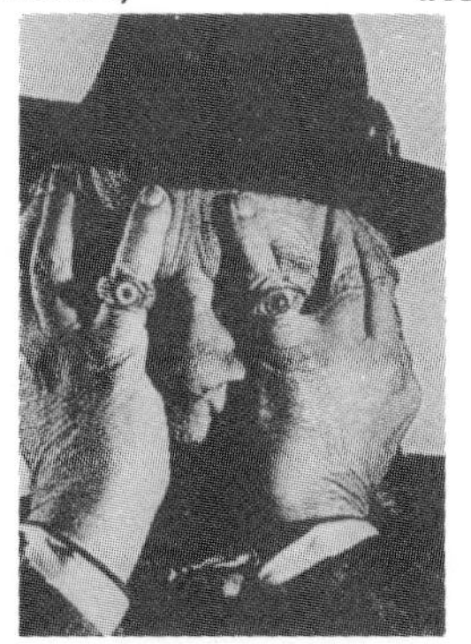

Brian Griffin (b. 1948), George Melly', 1990, printed later, gelatin silver print, image size 14 x 14in., signed and dated in pencil on verso, framed.
(Christie's) £330

Yousuf Karsh, "Nikita Khrushchev", 1963, printed later, $19\frac{3}{4}$ x $15\frac{3}{4}$in., gelatin silver print, signed in ink on the mount.
(Butterfield & Butterfield) £532

Julia Margaret Cameron — Mrs Herbert Duckworth, 1867, albumen print, $13\frac{1}{2}$ x $9\frac{3}{4}$in., mounted on grey card in original oak frame,
(Christie's) £14,300

Galerie Contemporaine series: Valery, "Victor Hugo", circa 1880, Woodbury type, 9 x $7\frac{1}{2}$in., on the original letterpress mount.
(Butterfield & Butterfield) £222

S.L. Carleton, 'Young girl with King Charles spaniel', circa 1848, sixth-plate daguerreotype, folding morocco case.
(Christie's) £176

Jacques-Henri Lartigue, 'Avenue du Bois de Boulogne', 1911, printed later, gelatin silver print, image size 9⅝ x 13⅞in., signed in ink.
(Christie's) £1,320

Lewis Carroll (Charles Lutwidge Dodgson) (1832–98), Xie Kitchin, circa 1873, cabinet card, albumen print 5½ x 4in., numbered *2223* in ink in Carroll's hand on verso.
(Christie's) £1,320

Thomas Annan (1829–87), 'Close, No. 28 Saltmarket', 1868–77, carbon print, 11 x 9in., mounted on card, printed title and number *26* on mount.
(Christie's) £330

Herb Ritts, 'Men with Kelp', Paradise Cove, 1987, gelatin silver print, image size 19⅛ x 15¼in., photographer's copyright blindstamp in margin, signed.
(Christie's) £330

G. Riebicke, 'Archer with borzoi', circa 1930, gelatin silver print, 6½ x 4¾in., photographer's ink credit stamp on verso, matted.
(Christie's) £440

Robert Doisneau, Pablo Picasso, 1952 printed 1989, gelatin silver print, image size 10⅜ x 8⅛in., signed in ink in margin.
(Christie's) £660

Anon, Little girl holding puppy, mid 1850s, sixth-plate daguerreotype, lightly hand-tinted, gilt metal mount.
(Christie's) £187

Don McCullin (b. 1935), Melanesian portrait, 1983, gelatin silver print, image size 17 x 12in., matted, signed and dated in ink on mount.
(Christie's) £330

Robert Frank, "Paris, 1950", printed later, gelatin silver print, 8¾ x 13⅜in., signed, titled, and dated in ink in margin. (Butterfield & Butterfield) £1,331

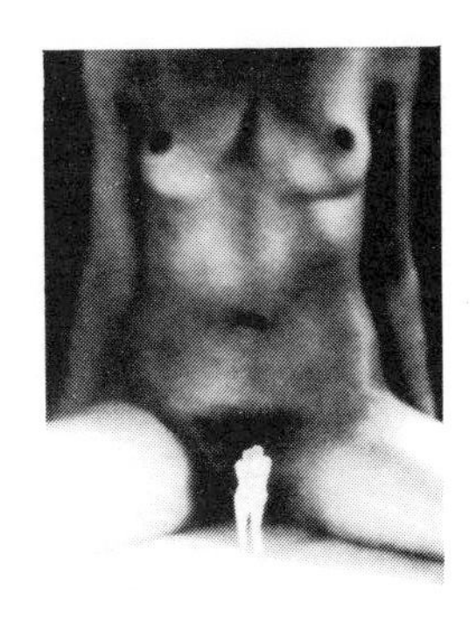

Frantisek Drtikol (1883–1961), Nude, 1933, toned gelatin silver print, 11½ x 9in. (Christie's) £1,760

Aleksandr Rodchenko (1891–1956), Red Square (early 1930s), gelatin silver print, 7 x 9⅜in., indistinct inscription in ink and pencil on verso. (Christie's) £3,300

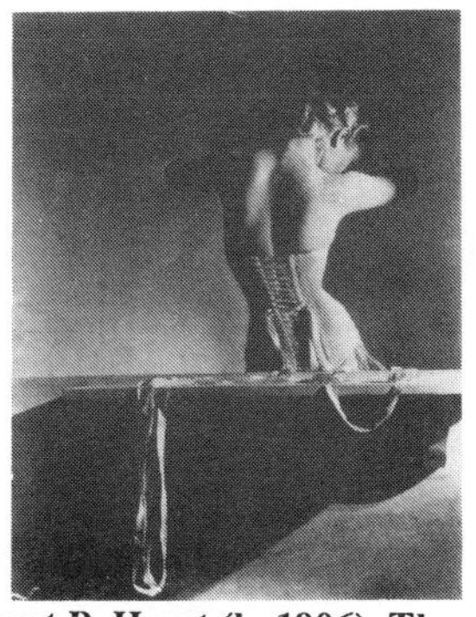

Horst P. Horst (b. 1906), The Mainbocher corset, Paris 1939 printed 1986–87, gelatin silver print, image size 16¼ x 13in., signed in pencil in margin, matted, framed. (Christie's) £2,640

Julia Margaret Cameron, Alfred, Lord Tennyson, 1860s printed 1875, carbon print, 13½ x 10in., printed by the Autotype Company, mounted on card. (Christie's) £330

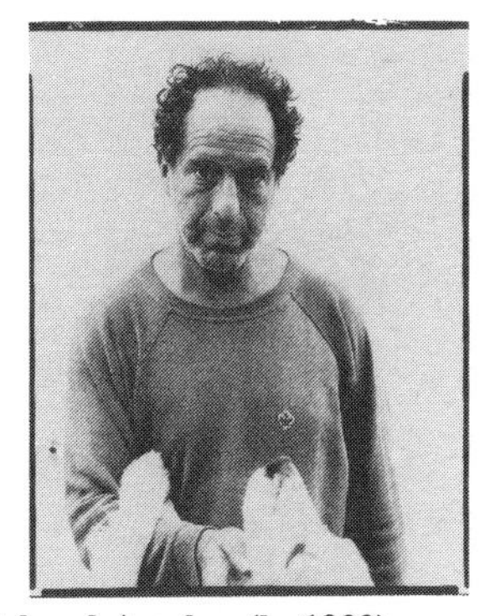

Richard Avedon (b. 1923), 'Robert Frank, photographer Mabou Mines, Nova Scotia', 1975, gelatin silver contact print, 10 x 8in., no. 29 of an edition of 50, signed in ink. (Christie's) £1,430

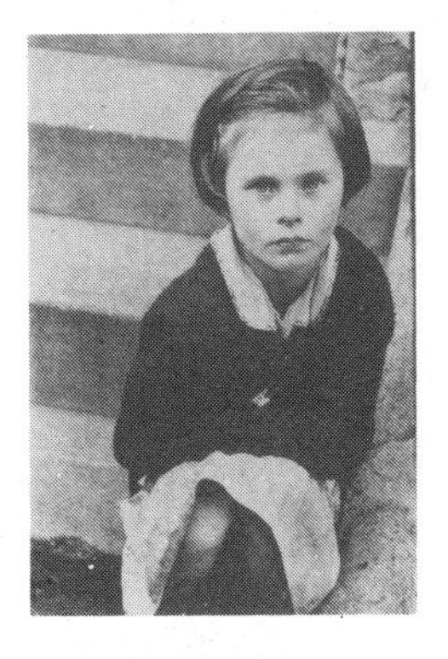

Roger Mayne (b. 1929), Girl seated on steps, Southam Street, late 1950s, gelatin silver print, 14⅞ x 10½in., mounted on card. (Christie's) £825

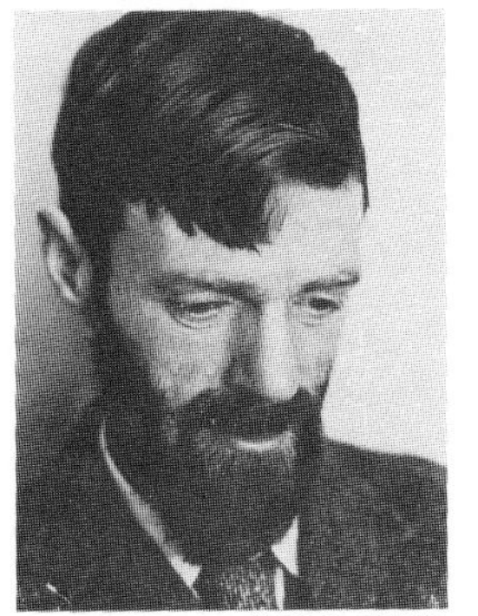

Edward Weston (1886–1958), D.H. Lawrence, 1924, gelatin silver print, 9½ x 7½in., ink credit stamp *The Carmelite* and various pencil annotations on verso. (Christie's) £330

Frank Meadow Sutcliffe (1853–1941), Portrait of a fisherman, 1880s, printed later, toned gelatin silver print, image size 8½ x 6in. (Christie's) £198

The Toff at Butlin's, All in Pictures, 1950's. £5

Buck Jones, All in Pictures, No. 230, 1957. £3

Lucky Lannagan, Cowboy Comics No. 118, 1954. £3

The Man from U.N.C.L.E., World Adventure Library, 1966. £3

Violent Destiny, War Picture Library, No. 100. £2

Robin Hood, Adventure Library. £3

The Ghost Battalion, Battle Picture Library. £2

The Victim, Top Secret Picture Library, 1975. £2

Rick Random and the Invaders from the Ocean Planet, All in Pictures. £5

The Picture of Dorian Gray, Told in Pictures. £5

Circus Riddle, All in Pictures, No. 56, 1950s. £4

Rick Random and Knights of Space, All in Pictures, No. 139. £4

(Yesterdays Paper)

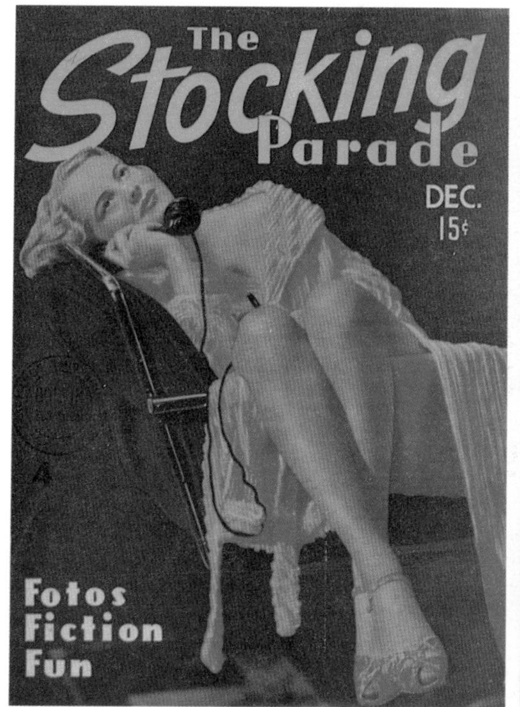

The Stocking Parade, Fotos, Fiction, Fun, December 1938. £12

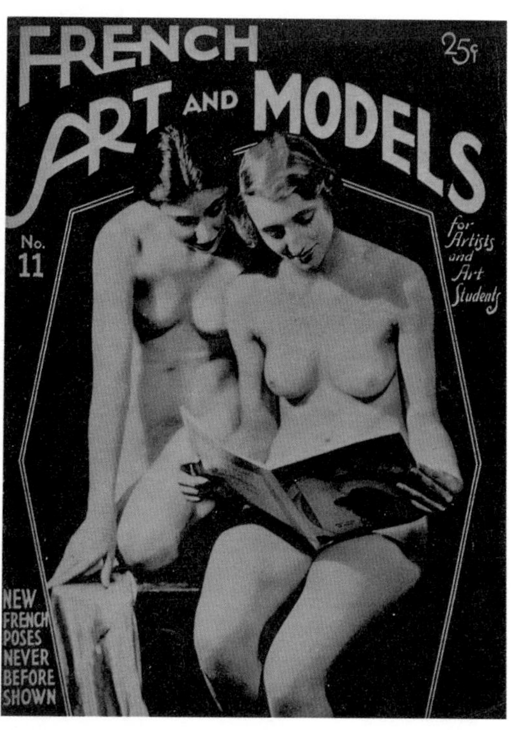

French Art and Models, New French Poses Never Before Shown, 1930s. £10

Paris Music Hall, Trois Mangan Tillerettes, December 1932. £12

(Yesterdays Paper)

Silk Stocking Stories, November 1937, Dryben Cover. £12

Movie Merry-Go-Round, July 1937. £12

High Heel Magazine, November 1937, Dryben Cover. £12

Breezy Stories, July 1936. £10

The Winning Post, 1919, Cover by Rene Bull. £8

Breezy Stories, Feb. 1937, Fire of Spring. £8

Bits of Fun and Fashion, Fads & Fancies, 1920. £12

Midi Paname, 1950's. £4

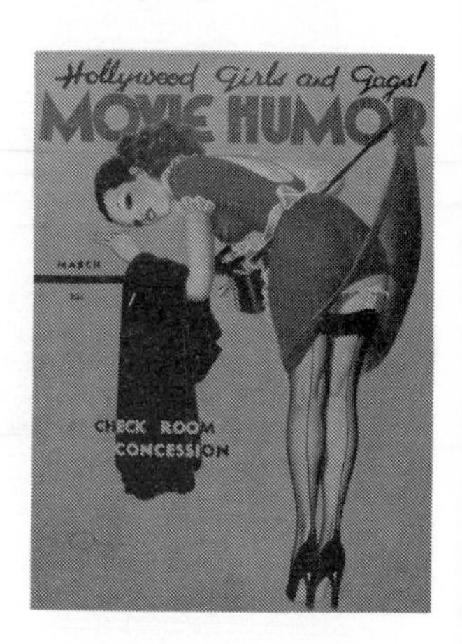

Movie Humor, Hollywood Girls and Gags, March 1938. £12

(Yesterdays Paper)

Gay French Nights, 1940's.
£4

The Kirchner Album, Sketch Publications London. £35

French Frolics, Spicy Story Magazine, 1940's. £3

Paris Sex-Appeal, August 1935. £6

Life, 1910. £10

Paris Magazine, February 1932. £7

Flirty, Daring, Thrilling, Exciting, 1940's. £6

l'Amour, August 1902, French. £8

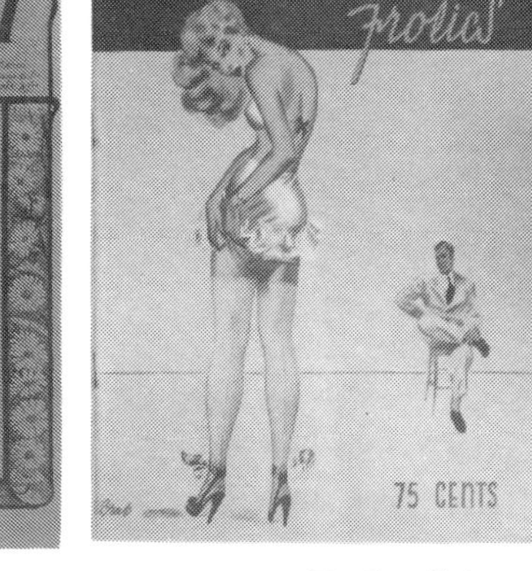

Hollywood Frolics, Spicy Stories, American, 1940's.
£3

(Yesterdays Paper)

Bas de Soie et Pantalon de Femme, circa 1920. £20

Der Orchideen Garten, Vol 16/17. £25

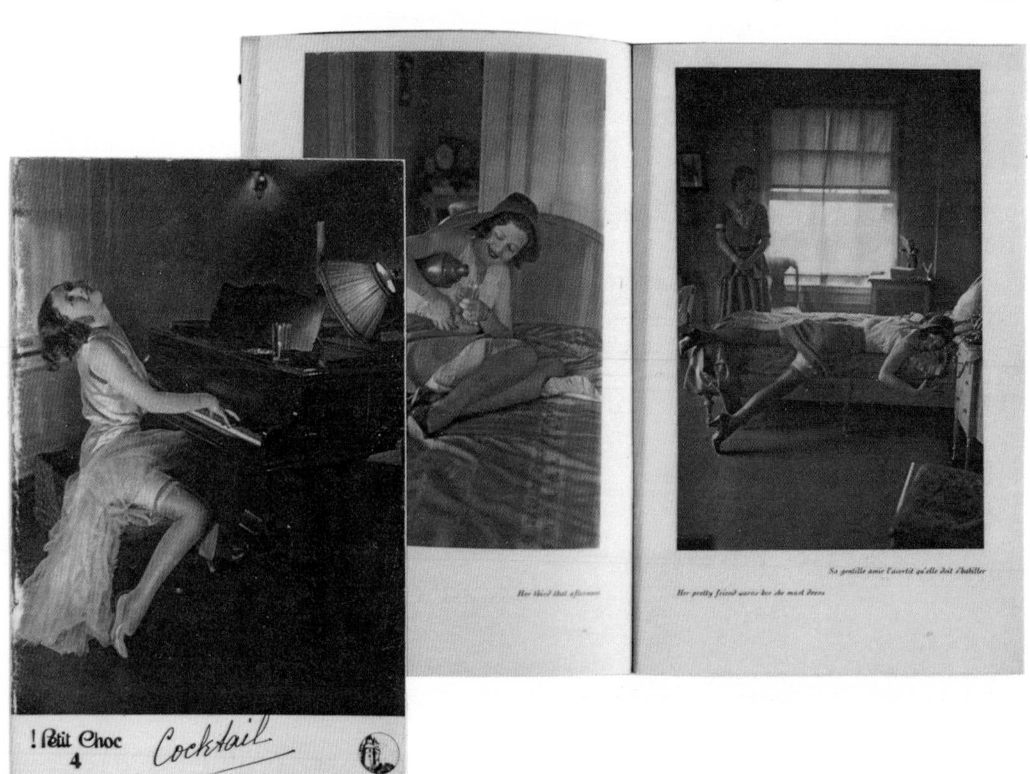

Petit Choc! Cocktail. £25

(Spread Eagle Antiques)

Der Orchideen Garten, Vol 15, fantastic love stories. £25

Les Jambes Savantes. £15

Intimités. £10

Paris Plaisirs, No. 117 featuring Marjorie King. £20

(Spread Eagle Antiques)

Gay Book Magazine, November 1937. £6

Health and Efficiency — The World's Leading Naturist Journal, March 1960. £3

The Naturist — Nudism, Physical Culture, Health, February 1947. £3

Pamela Green in 3-D, including spectacles. £8

Charm — The Magazine for Students and Photographers. £3

Continental Keyholes, No. 6, Joyart Photographs. £5

Spick, June 1956, 'A New Star is Shining'. £6

Fiesta, Volume 6, No. 8, published by Galaxy Publications. £3

Beaute Magazine — A Paris Cocktail, Adele Jergens cover. £5

Showgirls — The Body Beautiful, 'Burlesk Queens in Action'. £8

(Yesterdays Paper)

Solo, No. 44 by Harrison Marks, presenting Ann Wilson. £6

Existentialist, a Capital Publication. £5

Leslie Carol, photographed by Roye for the Camera Studios Club. £3

Mentor, 'Pussycat Tina with the Big Game'. £3

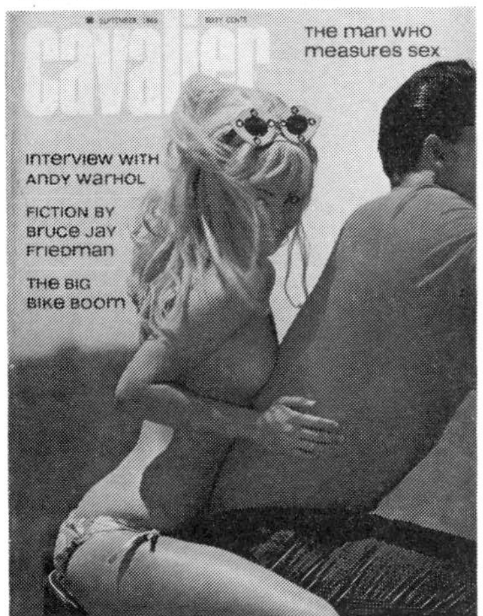

Cavalier, September 1966, cover photograph by Ron Vogel. £4

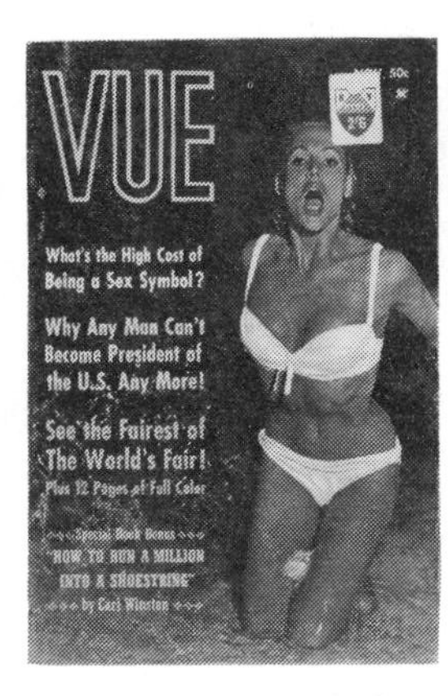

Vue, November 1964, 'Special Book Bonus'. £3

Wink – A Whirl of Girl, 'Silk Stockings and High Heels'. £8

Paris Frou Frou – Magazine Parisien, Froufroutant et Honnete. £5

Lovelies, published by Universal Publicity. £4

Art and Models Magazine – For Artists and Art Students, No. 1. £10

(Yesterdays Paper)

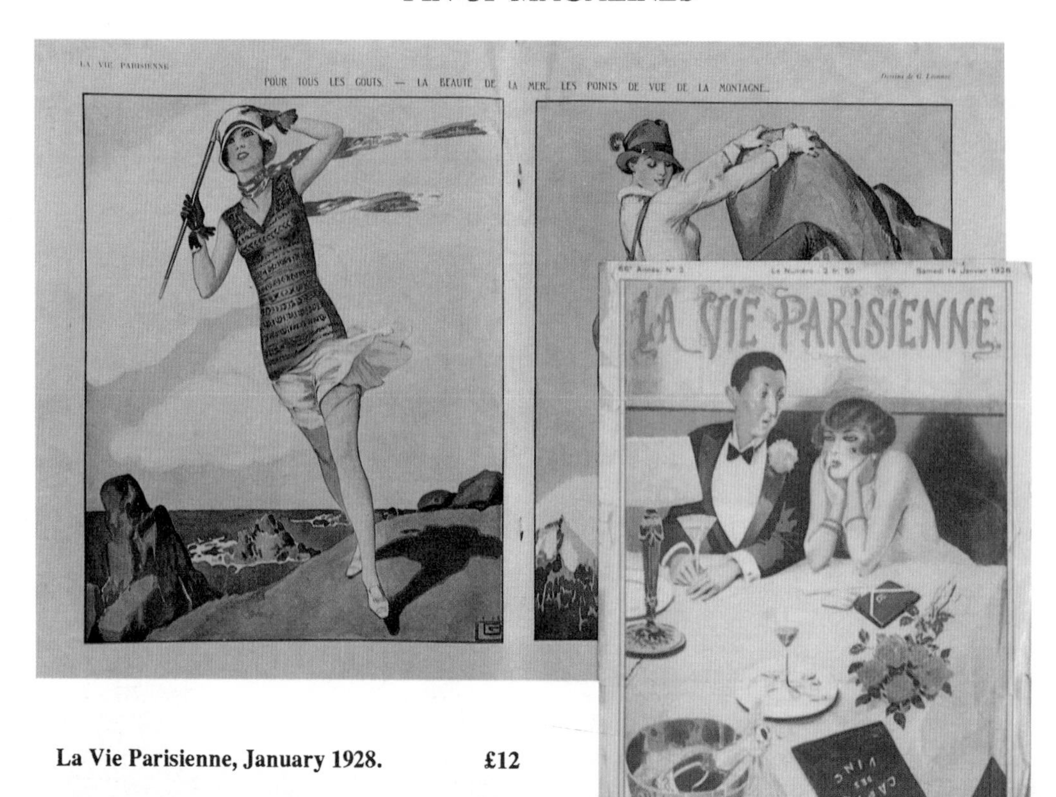

La Vie Parisienne, January 1928. £12

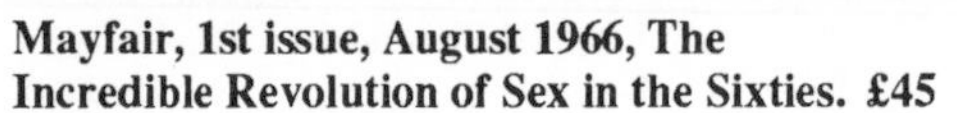

Mayfair, 1st issue, August 1966, The Incredible Revolution of Sex in the Sixties. £45

Film Fun, November 1936, Special 16 extra page Show Girl section. £12

(Yesterdays Paper)

ADVERTISING

Georgia, The Singer Manufacturing Co. £5

Biscuits Pernot, Chemin de Fer à Crémaillère 20. £5

Raphael Tuck advertising postcard, The Write Way Series. £50

Biscuits Pernot, Transatlantique 24. £5

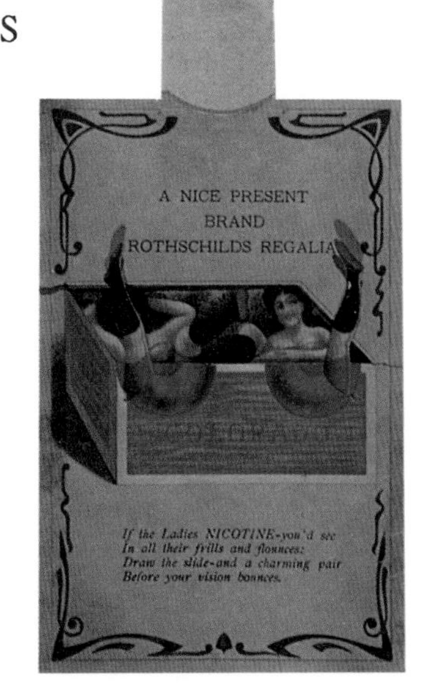

Rothschild's Mechanical cigarette advertising postcard. £60

National Savings Certificates & London Housing Bonds – Working class cottages. £5

Epp's Cocoa, Grateful & Comforting, advertising postcard. £30

(Spread Eagle Antiques)

GLAMOUR

Paris Series postcard No. 1519, lingerie study. £5

Les P'tites Femmes, by F. Fabiano, No. 42. £10

German Bathing Beauties 1903, S. Hildesheimer. £10

Olive Ann Alcorn, French Art Study. £4

Gestes Frivoles, by Suzanne Meunier. £15

French Bathing Beauty, Fabrication Francaise £5

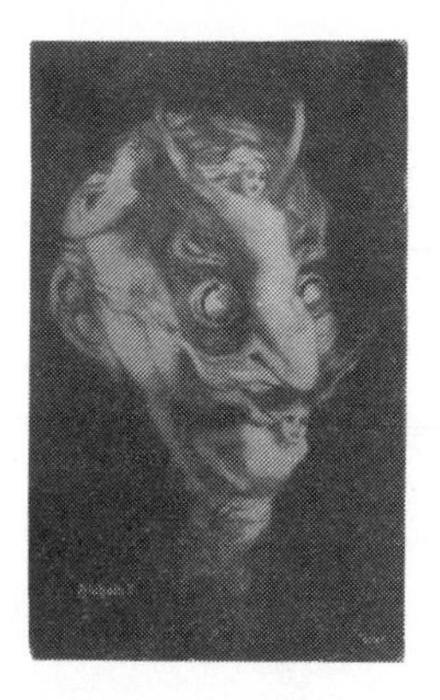

Diabolo?, Fantasy Head, Printed in Prussia. £10

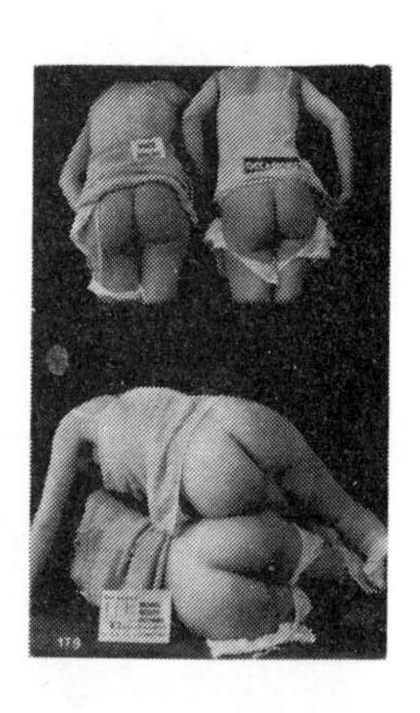

Whatever your desires, tastes or means, here you will find what you seek, 1920's, French. £12

French 'Bathing' Glamour, hand-tinted photo type. £5

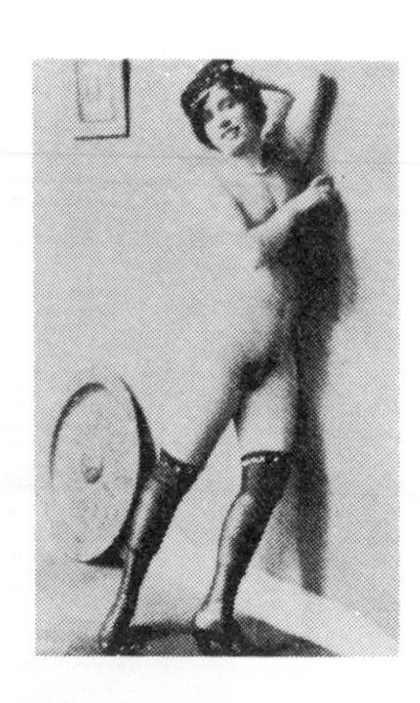

French Studio Model, 1920's. £6

French Bondage Study, 1920's. £8

Le Bain De La Parisienne by Suzanne Meunier. £15

GLAMOUR

1920's Fetishist photo-card, French. £12

French Bathing Beauty, Fabrication Francaise. £5

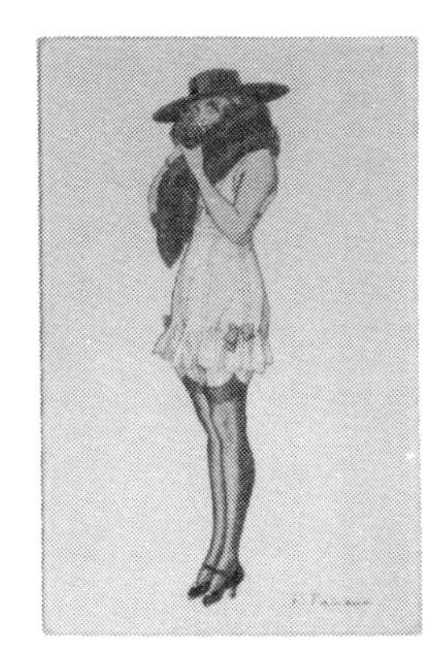

Les P'tites Femmes, by F. Fabiano, No. 39. £10

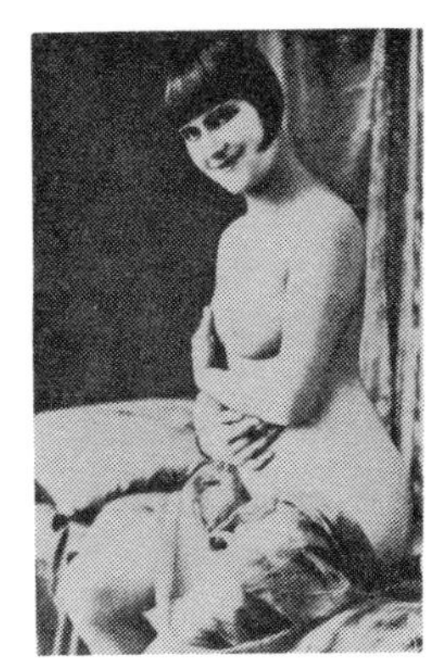

1930's French Nude Study. £5

Paris Series postcard No. 1831, a temptatious study in silk. £6

Glamour/Fantasy, Girl in Bubble, NPG Series. £12

Paris Series postcard No. 1445, silk stockings and frilly knickerbockers, partially dressed study. £4

Art Deco Glamour, by Marte Graf, 'Falto' Series, 'The Monkey and the Hopp. £10

'Bloomers', French Saucy postcard. £5

'A fair crack of the whip', 1920's, French postcard. £10

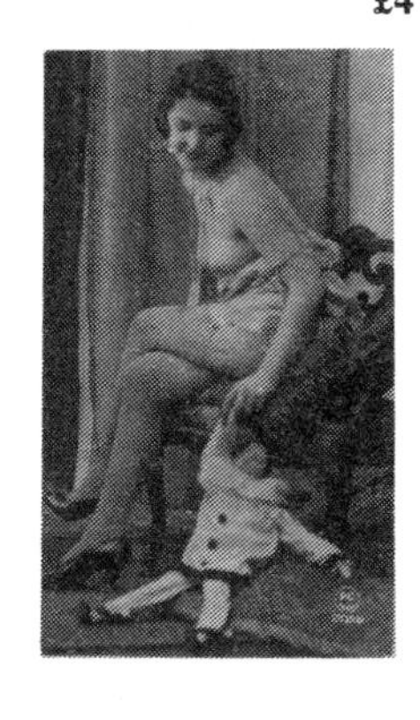

Parisienne Stocking Study with Pierrot doll. £6

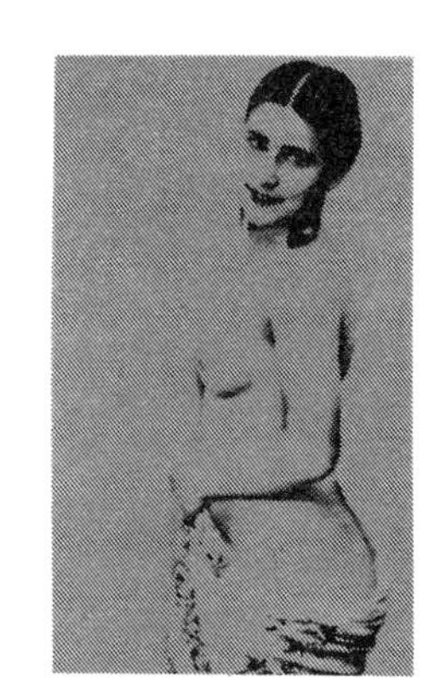

1930's French Studio Model. £4

HUMAN CURIOSITIES

Bearded Lady, three quarter length. £20

Double jointed native, seated. £20

Midget boy by Wendt, Boonton, NJ. £20

The Bohemian Twins. £12

Armless Woman. £20

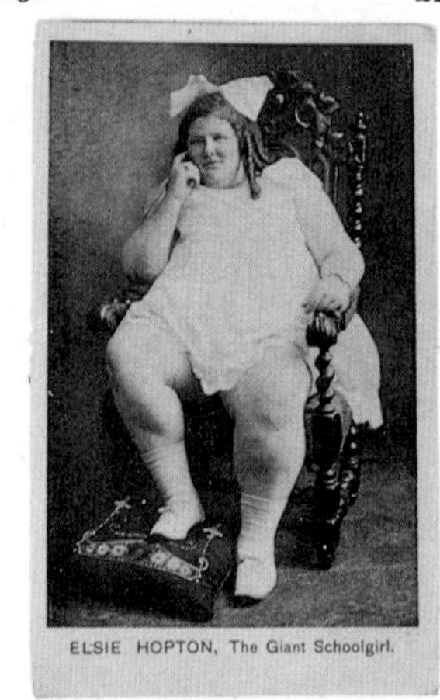

Elsie Hopton, the Giant Schoolgirl. £8

Female Siamese twins, by Obermuller NY. £20

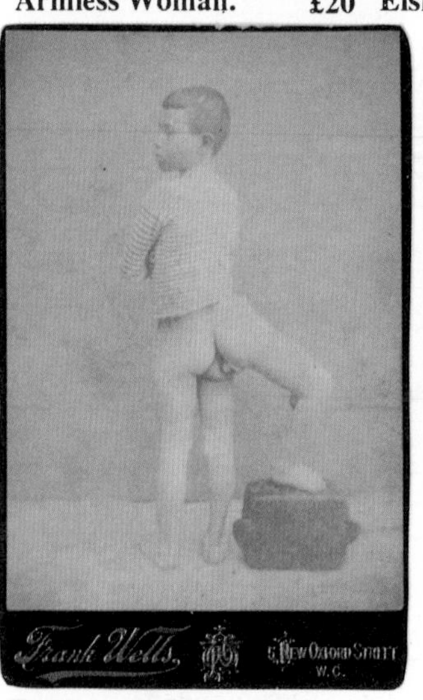

Three-legged boy. £20

(Spread Eagle Antiques)

Siamese twin boys & family. £20

My Photograph, 'Eye Hath Not Seen It'. £5

Coon Kids by Raphael Tuck, 'We'se Out Sportin'. £4

His Only Means of Support. £5

Try to Keep Smiling, Bonzo by G.E. Studdy. £4

National Insurance Art postcard. £6

Oh! What a Night it Must Have Been. £4

German card, 'Devil, Is That All' Series 163. £8

'The Voyage Was Glorious – But', 1930s postcard. £8

German chromo litho humorous card, S.B. Series. £15

(Yesterdays Paper)

HUMOROUS

'I saw you first' , German embossed chromo lithograph, 1905. £4

'I didn't want to do it', Valentines Series, 1914. £2

'Patriots', from Raphael Tuck's 'Some' Clothes Series. £4

'How can we play 'Husbands and wives' when we're both girls? Women are doing all the men's jobs nowadays!', Donald McGill card published by Inter-Art Comique Series No. 2703. £4

'Summer girls and some are not' by J. L. Biggar, published by E.T.W. Dennis & Sons Ltd. £3

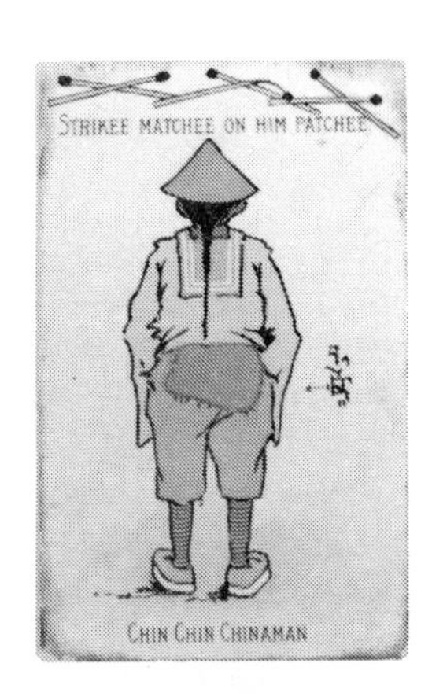

'Chin Chin Chinaman, Strikee Matchee on him Patchee'. £8

'You're No Bee Fool, by W. Stocker Shaw, 1916. £5

Lifeboat Saturday, a card delivered by air from Manchester to Haslingden on Sept. 20th 1902. £1,675

'For tampering with His Majesty's Males', from the 'Witty' Series by Bamforth. £15

HUMOROUS

'Things aren't what they used to be' by G. E. Studdy, 'Bonzo' Series card by Valentines. £5

Leslie Lester Ltd., 1950's comic card, 'Now all Henry wants to do is stay home every night and play with my pussy'. £1

'A trifle bald perhaps but Oh! Boy! I'm strong with the hens' Alpha Series, 'Smile Messengers'. £2

'Another puzzle for the Post Office. Bill: But I dunno the bloke's address. 'Arry: Can't yer write and arsk him for it?' The Humour of Life as seen by Phil May Series 6075. £5

'I'm frightened of nothing – but this put the wind up me at Wembley!!' 'Felix' the film cat comic card No. 4889. £6

Unusual comic card with Transvestite interest, 'It must be nice to be a girl, my heart it beats like mad, the feeling I've got through wearing these, is the nicest I ever had'. £10

'I'm the new housemaid, won't the Master be pleased!', comic card printed in Saxony. £2

'Everybody's doing it! This is what a sailor did!' comic card circa 1905. £4

'Oh, lor! Fancy 'avin' a pain in that!' 'Early' Donald McGill card (1907), published by E. S. card No. 2085. £6

(Paul Sheppard)

When You Are Single, Married, 1930s. £5

'Oh Emil Your Kisses Are So Wet Today, German. £10

Pre-historic Courtship by Lawson Wood. £4

Pretty Little Pansy Faces by Bamforth & Co. £6

Post From Barnstable with fold out views. £15

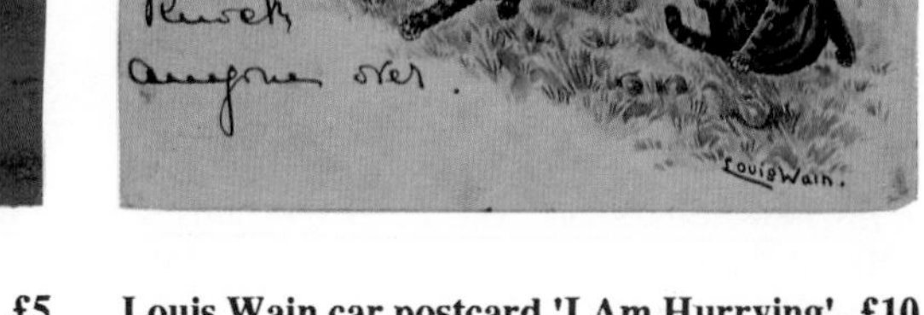

Home Rule, 1930s, humorous card. £5

Louis Wain car postcard 'I Am Hurrying'. £10

(Paul Sheppard)

An amusing German postcard, circa 1905. £8

A Leap Year Proposal 'Love One Another'. £5

Tender thoughts hereby expressed, with fold out views. £15

Skating is a very em-bracing pastime. £5

National Insurance Act, 'This is better than working'. £6

'They all love Jack' by G.M. Payne. £5

After 7 years. £6

(Paul Sheppard)

SILK

'Hands Across The Sea', woven card R.M.S. Franconia. £30

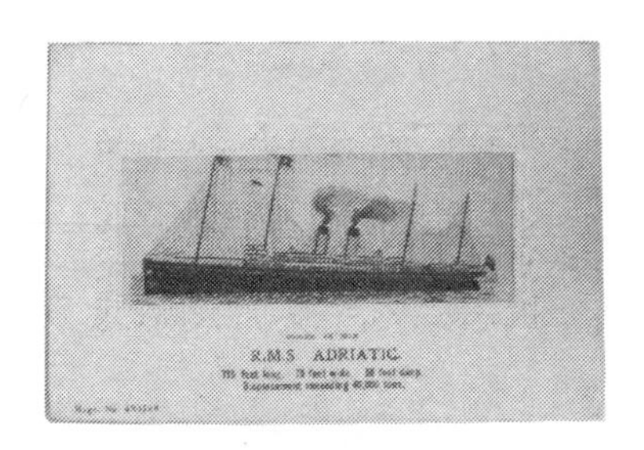

R.M.S. Adriatic, woven card. £40

Envelope type with patriotic flags by T.M.T., with insert card 'I'm thinking of you'. £10

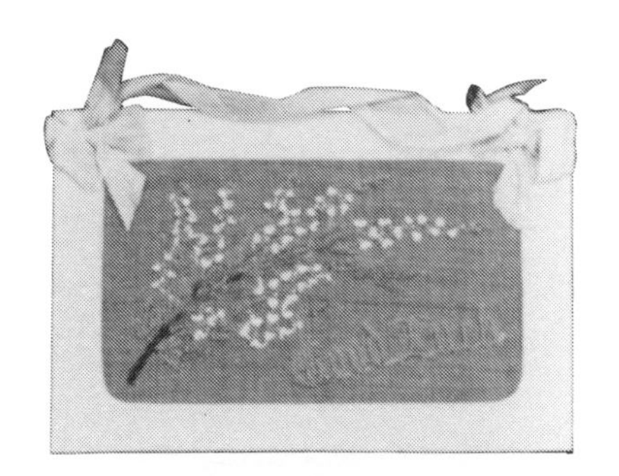

Embroidered silk card 'Good Luck', with silk ribbon. £8

'Home Sweet Home', by W. H. Grant, Coventry, postally used in 1915. £30

'United we stand', French envelope type, by Fabrication Francaise, Paris. £8

Woven silk card, 'Flames', Albert, 1914, by E. Deffrene. £20

'Good Luck' card with a felt cat and applied scrap. £5

'To my dear sister', envelope type with patriotic flag by H. S. £8

(Paul Sheppard)

SILK

'To my dear mother from your loving son', by J. S., Paris, 1915. £8

'To my dear wife', envelope type by Visa, Paris. £5

Nieuport 1914, 'Flames', woven. £20

'A Kiss From France', embroidered. £5

'Bonne Annee', silk greeting card by La Rosa. £5

Embroidered silk card 'Yours for ever', with enclosed card 'Tell her that I love her', by Fabrication Francaise. £5

'Cartel de Toros', by Alcana, Madrid. £5

A.S.C. (Army Service Corps) with Regimental badge by J. J. Saint. £12

'From your soldier boy', with woven butterfly, envelope type by M. M., Paris. £8

(Paul Sheppard)

George V, large size, 1919. £60

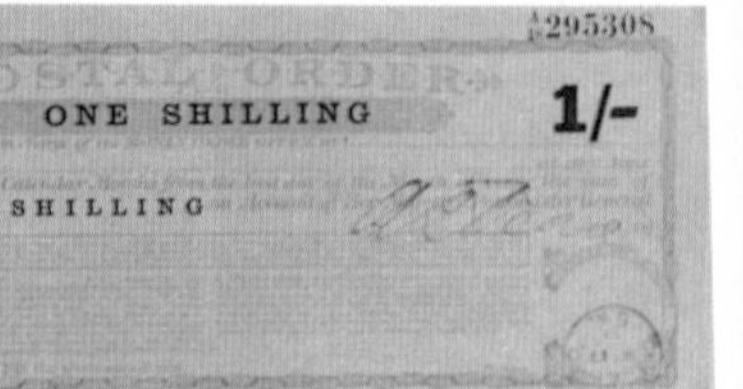

Victoria, second issue, 1891. £40

France, Bon de Poste, fourth issue and highest value, 1899. £500

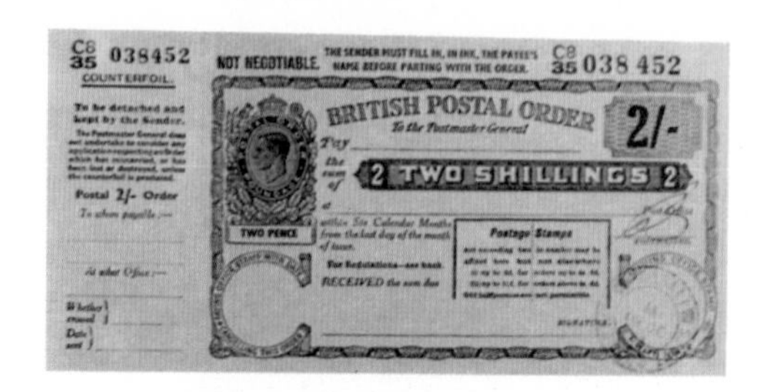

George VI, not easy to find. £5

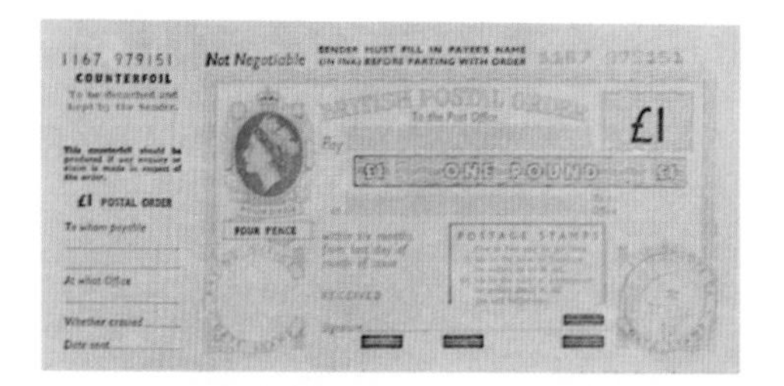

Elizabeth II, 1970, predecimal green, scarce. £35

George V, small size. £30

Elizabeth II, last guinea order, 1970, recent but very scarce. £40

Promotional order, Kleenex, 1988. £4

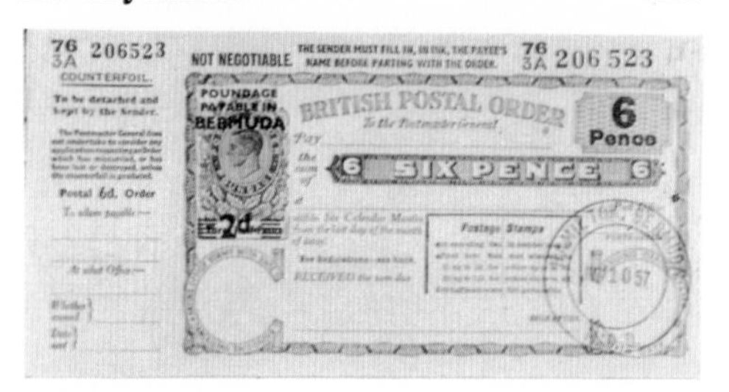

George VI, overprinted for issue in Bermuda, 1957. £40

George V, Silver Jubilee, the only commemorative issue, 1935. £30

(Richard Solly)

Victoria, first issue, specimen, 1881. £30

George V, overprinted for use in the Irish Free State, 1926. £150

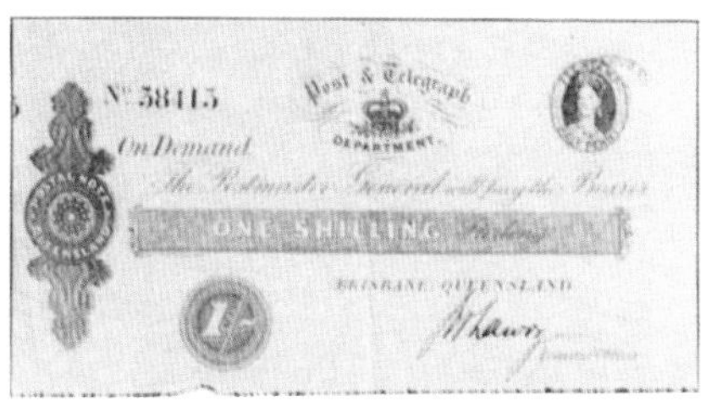

Queensland Postal Note, first type with Chalon portrait of Victoria, the 1/– also doubled as a telegram form, 1887. £100

Elizabeth II, with extensive overprinting for issue in the Republic of South Africa, 1970. £30

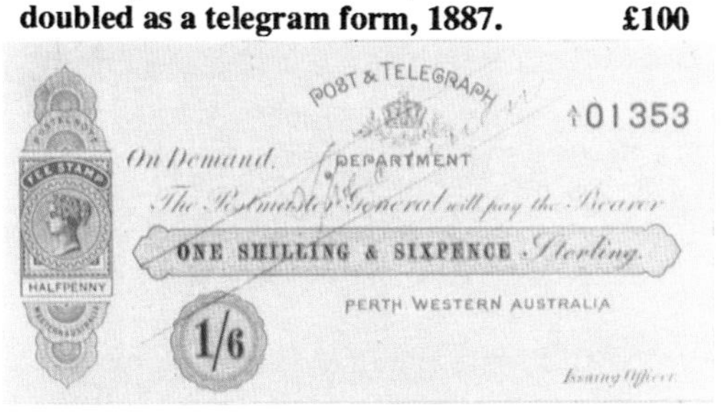

Western Australia, specimen Postal Note, circa 1896. £190

Promotional order, Tango, 1993, no value at present.

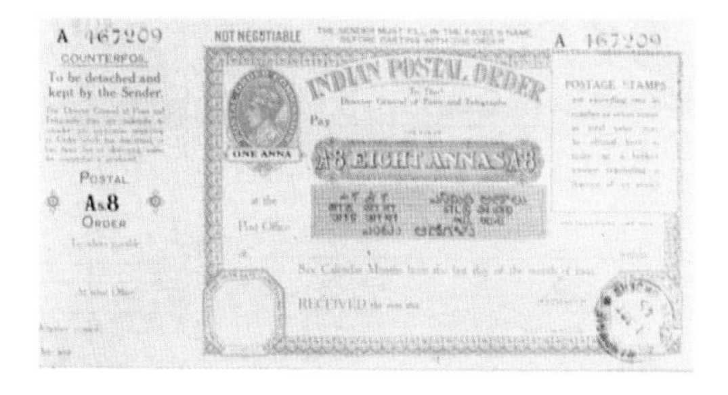

India, George VI, 1945. £75

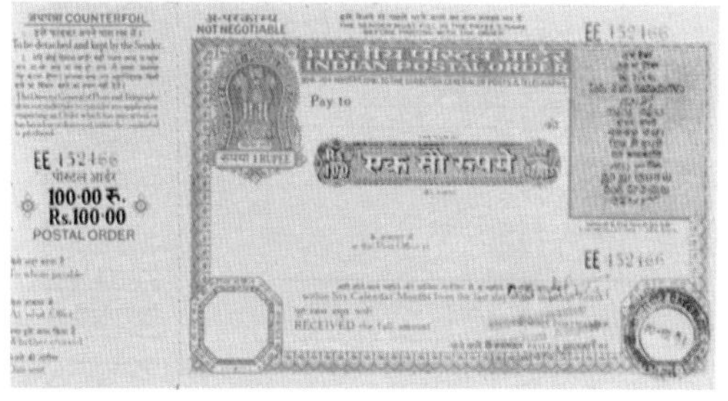

India, 1991 probably no longer available over the counter. £5

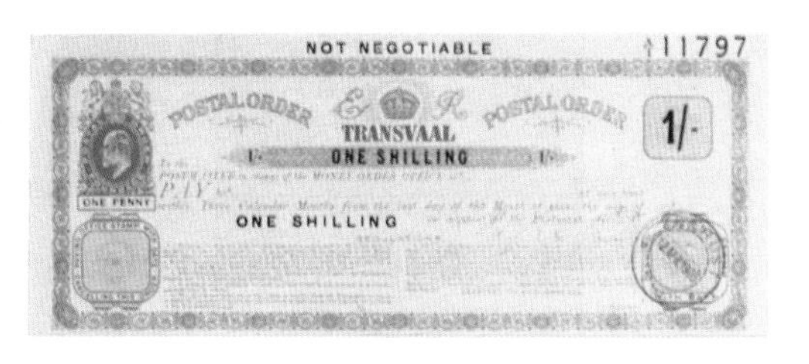

Transvaal, postwar Edward VII, 1905. £250

Elizabeth II, overprinted both value and poundage for issue in New Zealand, 1970. £30

(Richard Solly)

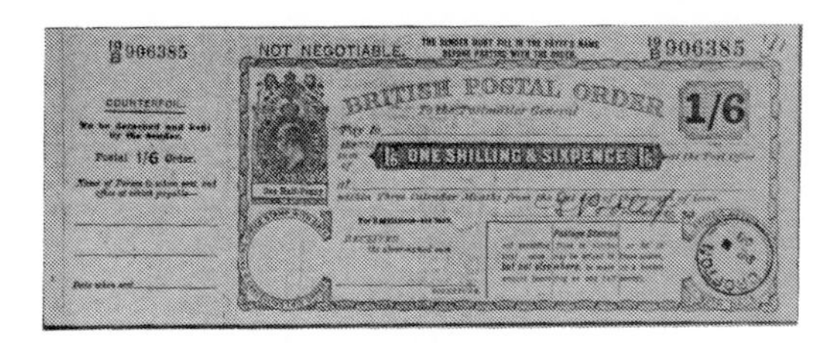

Edward VII, 1908, with counterfoil, blue. £75

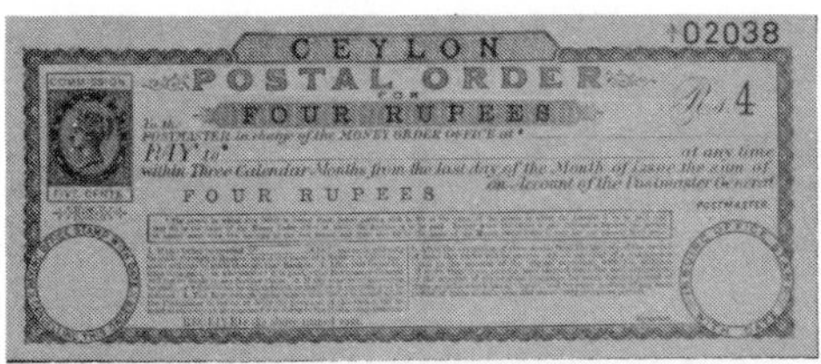

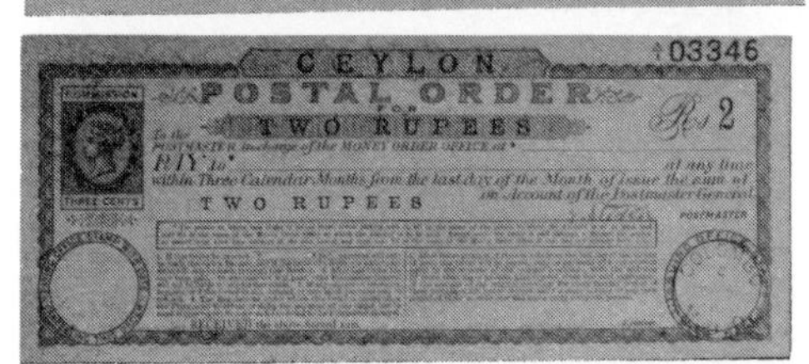

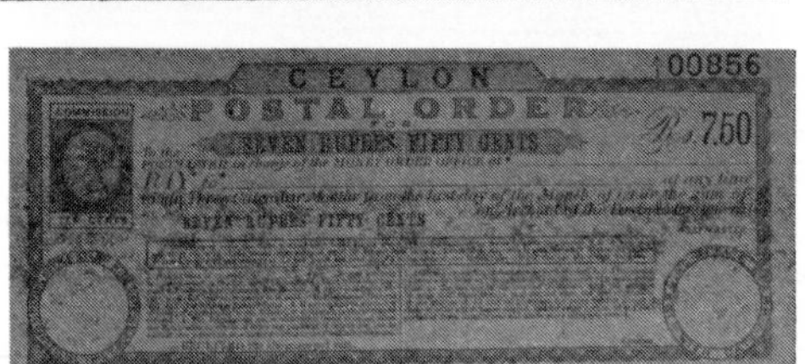

Ceylon, first type of Victorian order, finely printed with different colours for each denomination, circa 1888. £250

George V, 1925, with counterfoil, blue. £50

George VI, machine dispensed, with counterfoil, brown, very scarce. £150

Victoria, issued in the first year, 1881, scarce. £180

Western Australia postal note for four shillings, 1935. £40

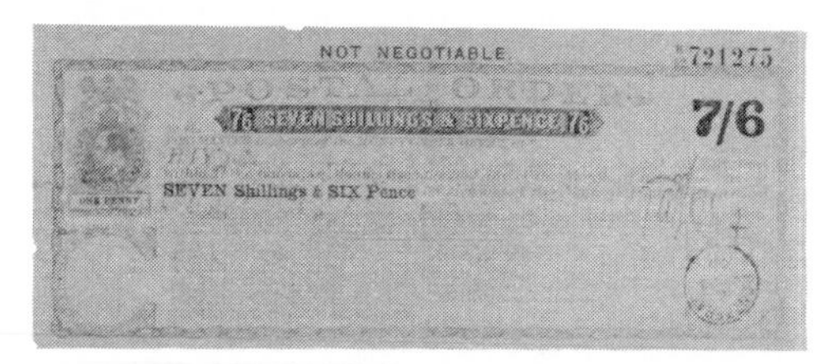

Edward VII, before the introduction of a counterfoil, 1903, scarce. £150

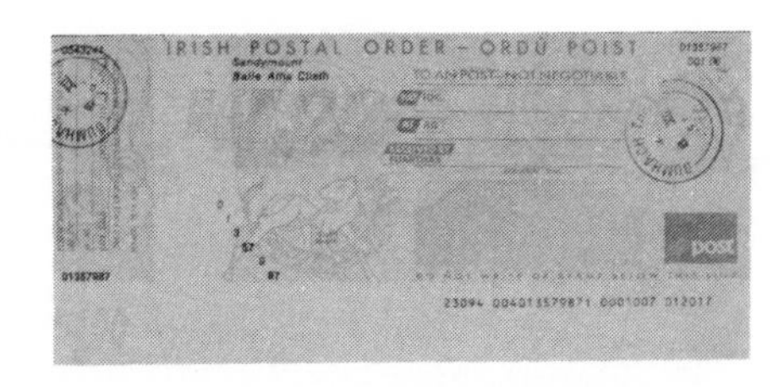

Irish Republic, 1993, this variety with the white stripe to the right of the counterfoil. £2

(Richard Solly)

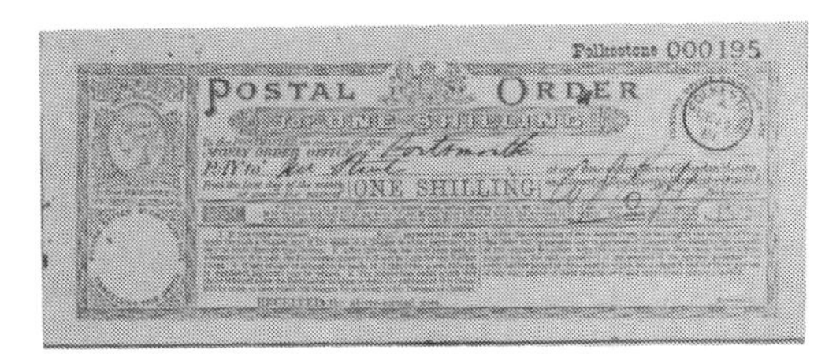

Victoria, 1881, first year of issue, blue. £150

George V, Silver Jubilee 1935, the only commemorative issue, blue. £30

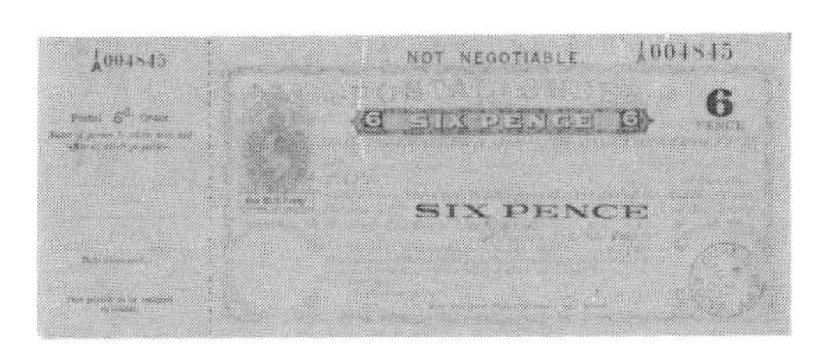

Edward VII, first type with counterfoil, 1904, scarce. £150

George VI, special printing for machine issue, one of the most unusual and desirable items. £150

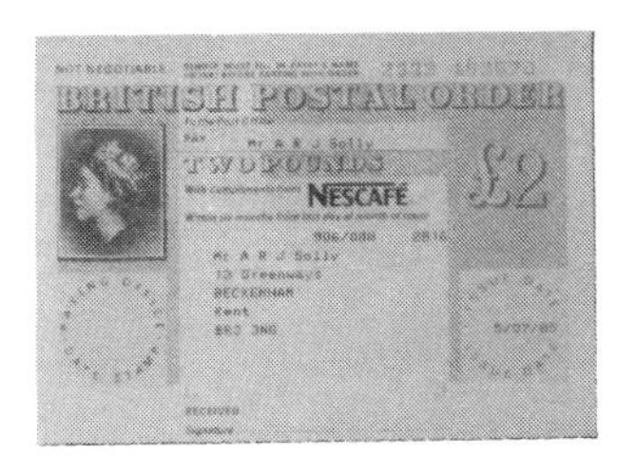

Promotional order, Nescafe, 1985. £10

George V, overprinted in green for use in Irish Free State, 1925. £75

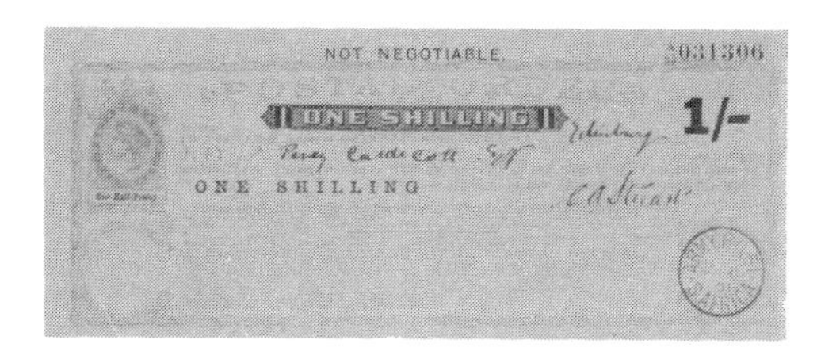

Victoria, third issue, no scarcer than second issue, but this one was issued to British Forces in South Africa, 1901. £150

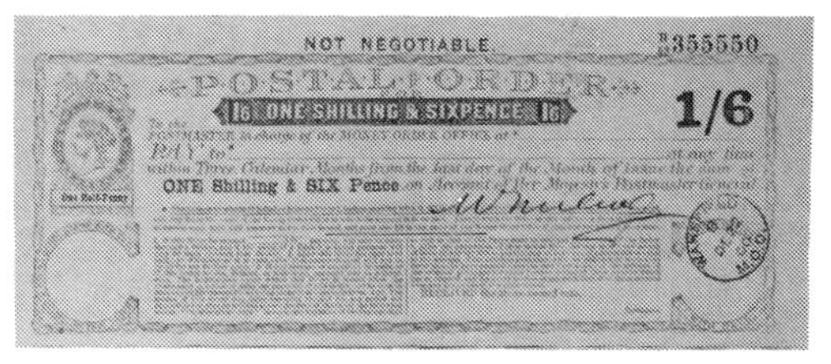

Victoria, type 3, 1900, blue. £60

Edward VII, first red, 1905, rare. £300

Namibia, overprinted on South West Africa, difficult to obtain, 1993. £5

(Richard Solly)

London Public Mail Service (PO authorised) Apollo 14 Commemorative philatelic cover, service operated between 20.1.71–8.3.71 by Gerald Rosen. £3

Brighton Private Postal Service philatelic cover, PO authorised, organised by D. Wilkinson & M. Hawkes between 20.1.71–8.3.71. £2

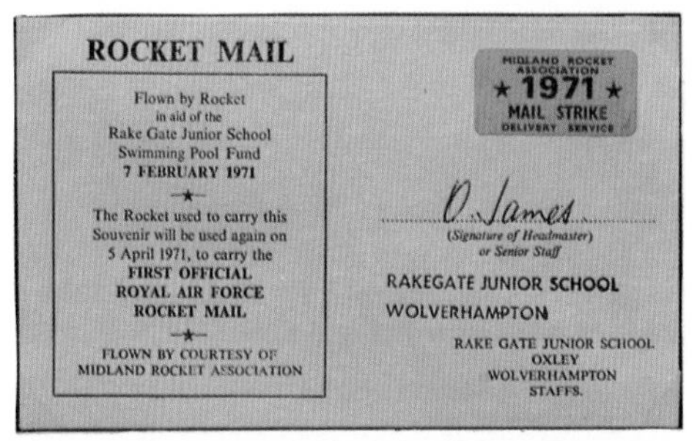

Midland Rocket Association, Wolverhampton, Rocket Mail philatelic cover, organised mainly for Association members. £12

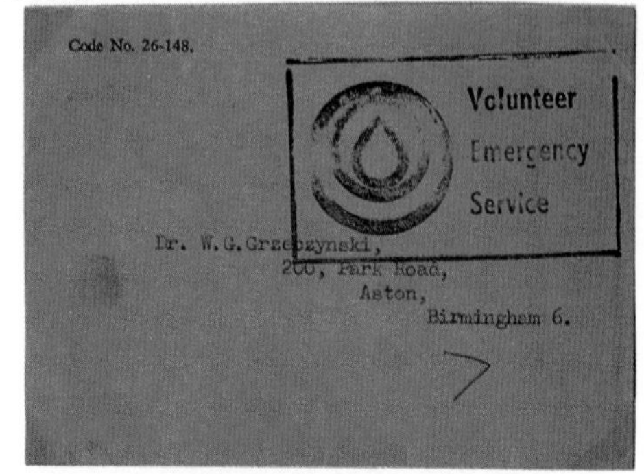

Birmingham Volunteer Emergency Service commercial cover for hospital mail. £15

London Bicycle Post newspaper wrapper and label, very rare if genuine, appeared in specialist auction in 1993. £300

Beaulieu Post philatelic cover, unauthorised private service organised by Lord Montagu between 20.1.71–8.3.71. £9

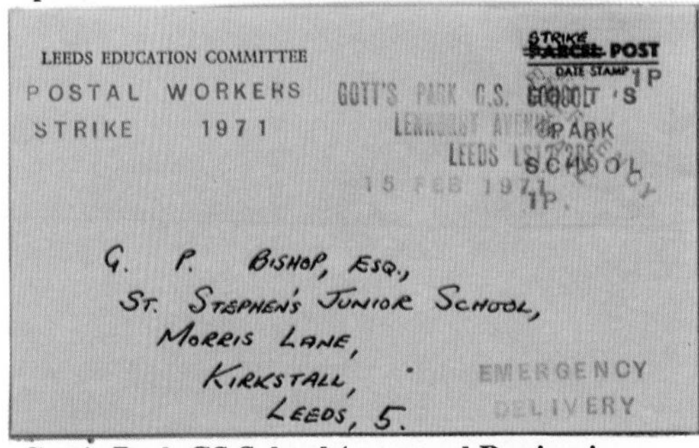

Gott's Park CS School (renamed Benjamin Gott School 5.2.71) Emergency Delivery Service commercial cover, organised by Alan Oliver and schoolboys who made deliveries from 26.1.71 until long after end of strike. £12

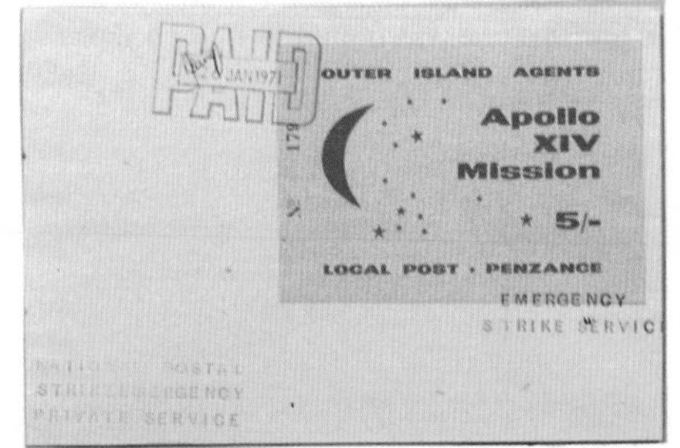

Cornwall – Outer Island Agents Local Postal Service philatelic cover with numbered label commemorating Apollo 14, signed by one of the organisers R. Barry and W. Mitchell, operated 20.1.71–8.3.71. £10

(Danny Widuch)

Biggin Hill Free Post commercial cover, organised between 20.1.71–8.3.71 by Gilbert Smith, with usual label, unsigned and undated. £12

Midland Rocket Association with handstamp only and modified rocket label. £12

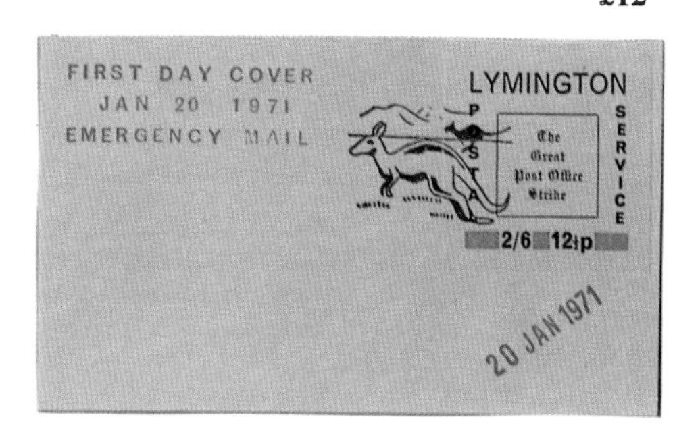

Lymington Hampshire Postal Service philatelic cover, PO authorised, organised by D. F. Marsh between 20.1.71–8.3.71. £3

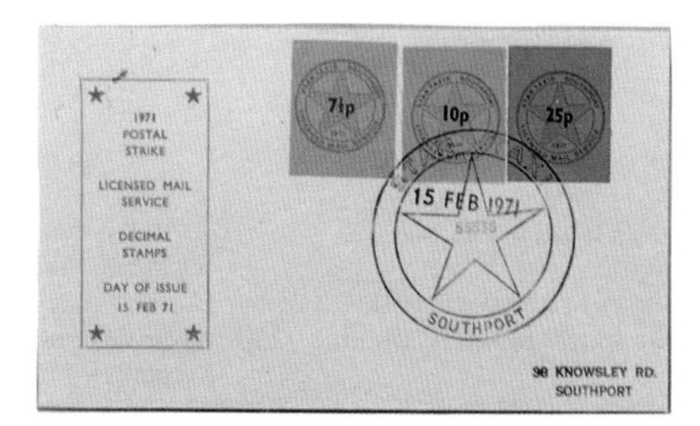

Star Taxis Southport philatelic cover, PO authorised service operated between 20.1.71–8.3.71. £3

Kingston Young Conservatives Post commercial cover, operated between 1.2.71–8.3.71, and begun to keep the Kingston MP J. Boyd-Carpenter in touch with his constituents, before developing into a public service, very scarce. £18

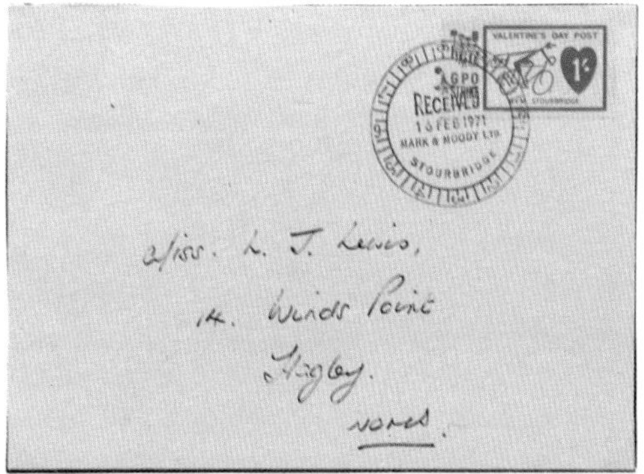

Mark & Moody Ltd Stourbridge, stationer's private Valentine's Day service commercial cover, delivered with help of boys from King Edward VI Grammar School, and extended beyond 14.2.71. £20

Dromoderry Emergency Postal Service, Decimal Day First Day Philatelic Cover, 15 February 1971; Dromoderry, derived from the names of its organisers, operated between 19.1.71 and 9.3.71. Scarce. **£10**

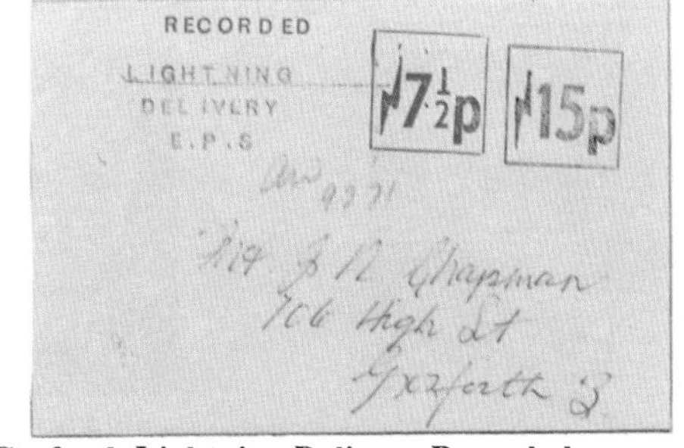

Gosforth Lightning Delivery Recorded Delivery cover, (unauthorised) organised by Alice Wake, then a student at Newcastle, very scarce. **£20**

(Danny Widuch)

Mayflower Mail Service (USA, Canada & South America) showing the 'Mayflower', 50p red, 15 February 1971. 25p

Special Courier Mail (overseas) with flags, 20np USA, 29 January 1971. £1

Europa Mail Delivery, Railway engine and map of Europe, 2/6 blue, January 30 1971. 50p

Stevenage Service, with Church, 10p black, printed Hitchin. 25p

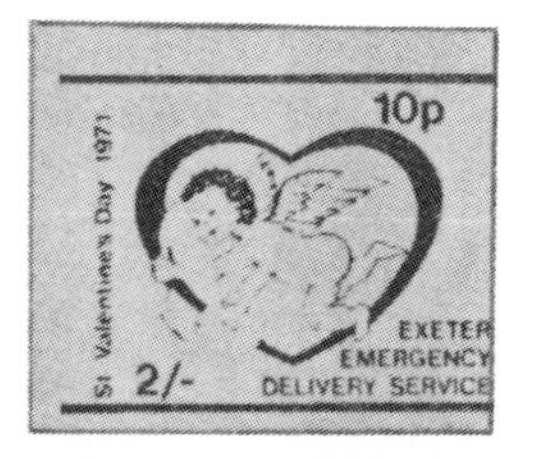

Exeter Emergency Delivery Services, (West Country, London & UK) Valentine's Day issue, 2/– mauve on pink, 10 February 1971. 25p

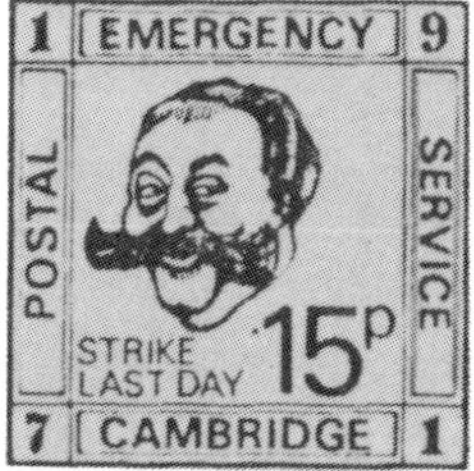

Cambridge Emergency Service (Cambridge UK & abroad) with head of Tom Jackson, 15p black on white. £3

Valentine card and cover by the Exeter Emergency Delivery Service (PO authorised) organised between 20.1.71–8.3.71 by Douglas Watson, card also with cancelled label. £3 each

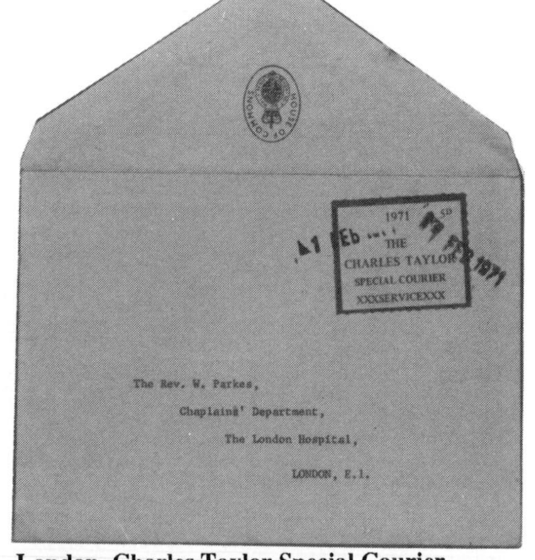

London, Charles Taylor Special Courier Service commercial cover, private service for the MP for Eastbourne, very scarce. £20

Public Mail, Apollo 14 Flight to the Moon, First Step on the Moon, 6d stamp. 50p

Pirate Post (Exeter, Bristol & London) 17½p black with skull and crossbones, February 1971. 50p

Pegasus (London & Home Counties), 15p black and red, January 21 1971. 50p

(Danny Widuch)

Emergency Strike Post, (overseas), Jethou Island, with puffin, overprinted Strike Mail and Europa 1961, Jan-Feb 1971. 25p

City of London Delivery (City of London) with City Arms, 5p mauve on yellow or pink, triangular, February 15 1971. 25p

Exeter Emergency Delivery Services (West Country, London and UK) with ship, £1 black, January 10 1971. 50p

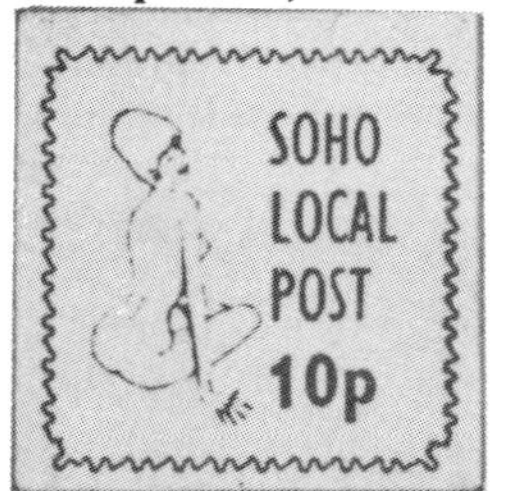

Soho Local Post (Soho and some mail to USA), nude girl, 10p black on yellow, February 15 1971. £3

Hadlow-Tonbridge Area Postal Service, (local and overseas), 1/– blue with vintage car, 3 February 1971. 25p

Rutland Postal Service, (County of Rutland) Rutland Horseshoe, 15p black, March 1 1971. 50p

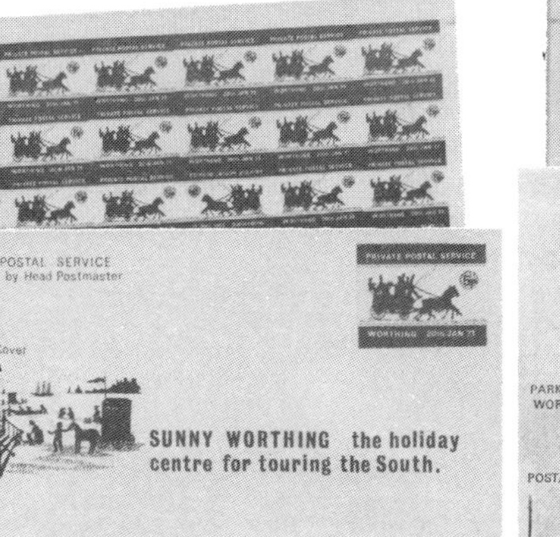

Worthing Private Postal Service, First Day Cover, (Sussex, UK and abroad), 20th January 1971. £10

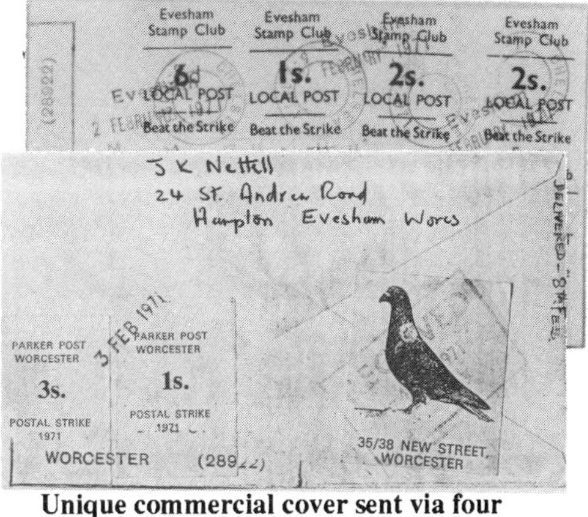

Unique commercial cover sent via four services, Evesham Stamp Club, Parker post Worcester, 'Pigeon Post' and Randall's Central London Delivery Service, and delivered 6 days after posting on 8.2.71. £100

Mayflower Mail Service, to the USA, Canada and South America, First man on the Moon, grey-blue Airmail to USA, February 3 1971. 50p

Channel Islands and Isle of Man Mail Delivery (Channel Is. and Isle of Man), stamp of Guernsey Alderney showing William the Conqueror overprinted British Postal Strike 1971, 1/–, January 20 1971. 50p

Public Mail, four penny Blacks overprinted 1971 Postal Strike Mail Delivery, 2/6 black, January 29 1971. 50p

(Danny Widuch)

Eros Post Cambridge Valentine Postal Service philatelic cover, unauthorised private service organised by Ms Coubaristra, a Spanish medical student with fellow students, rare numbered cover. £10

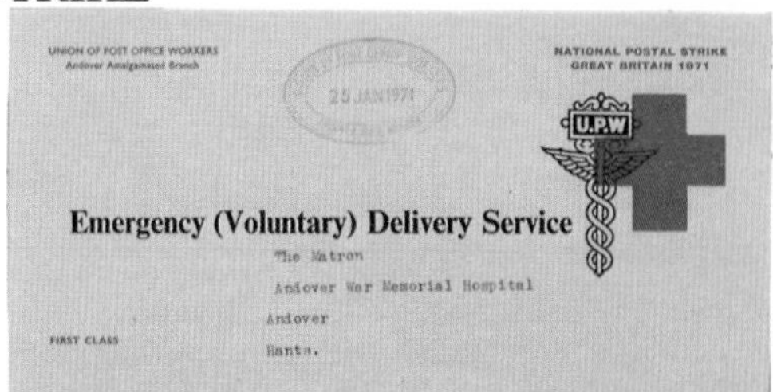

Emergency (Voluntary) Delivery Service Commercial Cover, free service organised by the Union of Post Office Workers (Andover Branch), mainly for the carriage of hospital mail, scarce. £15

British European Airway Letter Service numbered philatelic cover, Decimal Day Service, flown by BEA helicopter from Penzance to the Scillies, scarce. £12

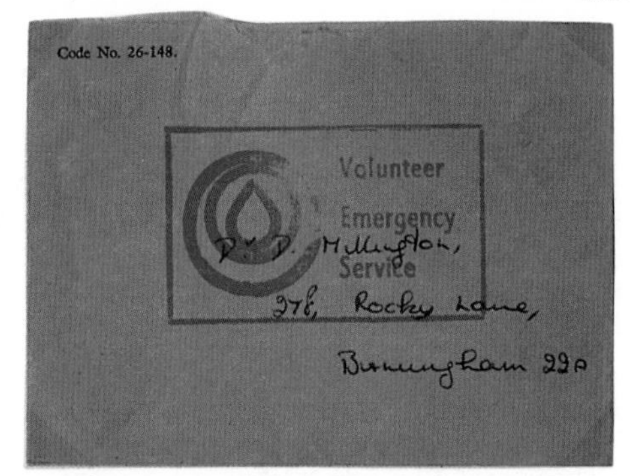

Birmingham Volunteer Emergency Service commercial cover for hospital mail, very scarce. £15

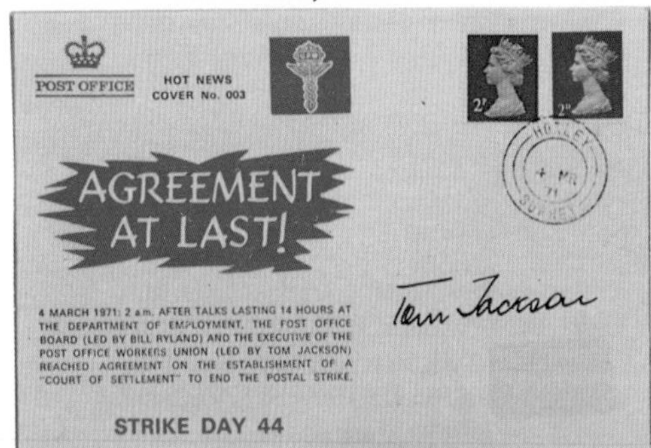

UPW Agreement at Last! philatelic cover signed by Tom Jackson, 4 March 1971, lacking self adhesive address label, scarce. £12

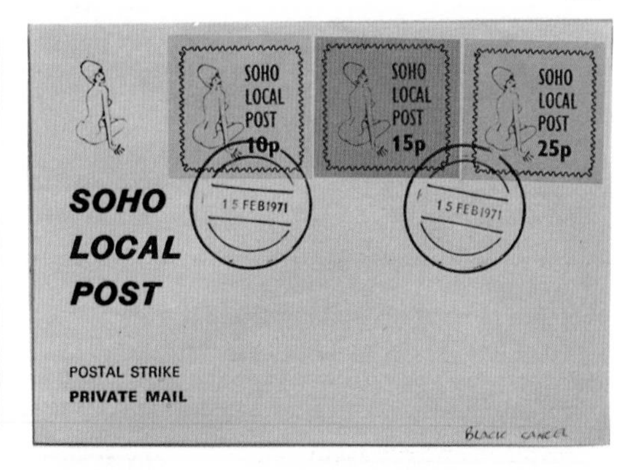

Soho Local Post philatelic cover organised between 5.2.71–8.3.71 by E. Melville. £4

Bexhill Delivery Service, Bicycle delivery commercial cover, operated between 21.1.71–8.3.71 by law student Simon Allen, PO authorised. £12

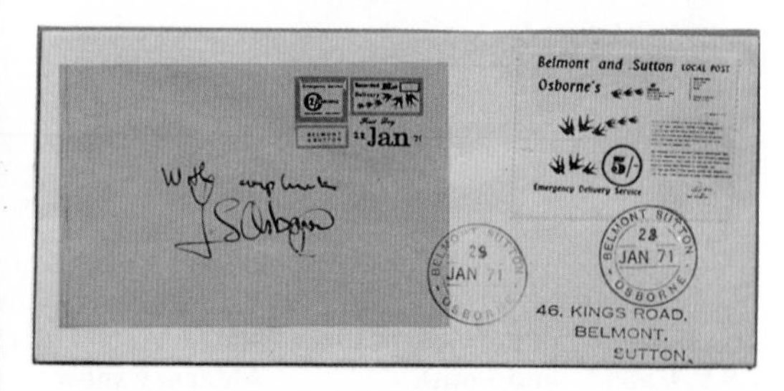

Osborne Emergency Delivery Service specimen cover, signed by the organiser L. S. Osborne, operating from 22.1.71, very scarce. £20

(Danny Widuch)

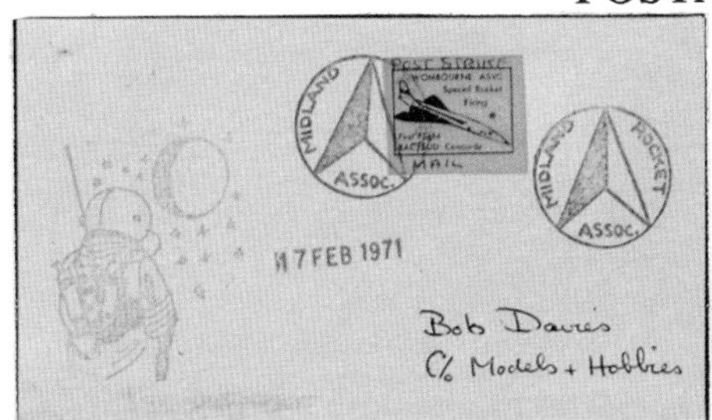

Midland Rocket Association, local delivery philatelic cover, with manuscript altered rocket label used previously in a firing, and decorative handstamp featuring a space shot. £10

World Courier's Authorised Service, London philatelic cover, organised from 19.2.71 by G. Thirlwell. £1 million label Moon Post claimed to be unique in Daily Mail of October 1 1973, but several examples exist. £100

Paisley Penny Post philatelic cover, Decimal Currency Day, cover addressed to operator, Peter Westwood, and initialled by him, scarce. £8

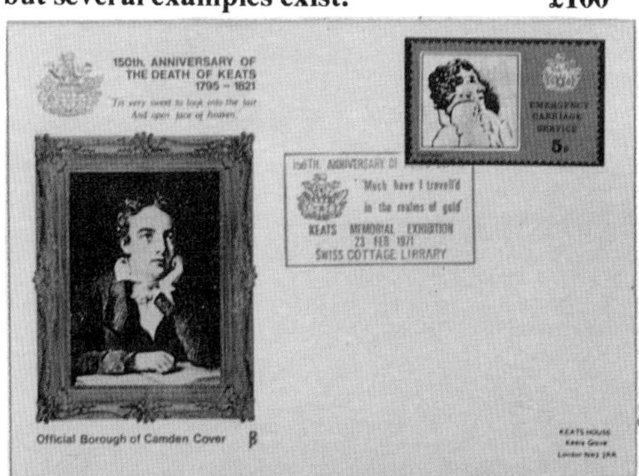

Camden Emergency Carriage philatelic cover organised by D. Picton-Phillips for London Borough of Camden, one day service only, 23 February 1971. £3

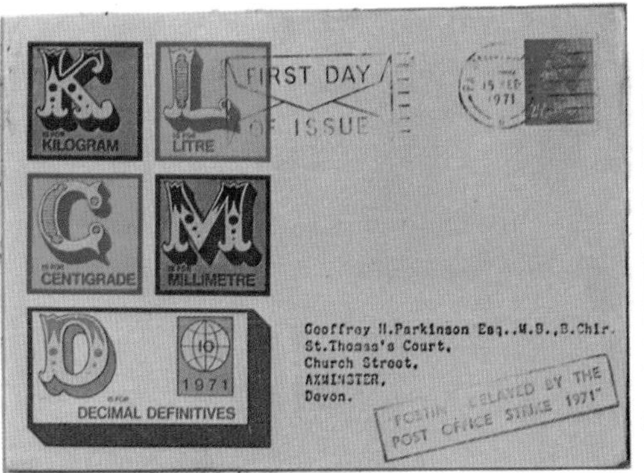

Decimal Day First Day cover with $2^1/_2$p stamp, stamped 'Posting delayed by the Post Office Strike 1971! £1

Southport Local Scooter Post organised by Derek Mills between 20. .71–8.3.71, using in this case a Swiss Railway Stamp. £10

Special Courier Mail philatelic cover, authorised by the Post Office, operated between 27.1.71–8.3.71 by Bridger & Kay Ltd. £3

Exeter Pirate Post philatelic cover, PO authorised, organised by Bellerby-Palmer from 29.1.71. £3

(Danny Widuch)

C.W.S. Alono string tin. £40

Salmon & Gluckstein's 'Dandy Fifth' cigarettes pictorial tin. **£15**

Remy's Pudding Powder counter display box. **£12**

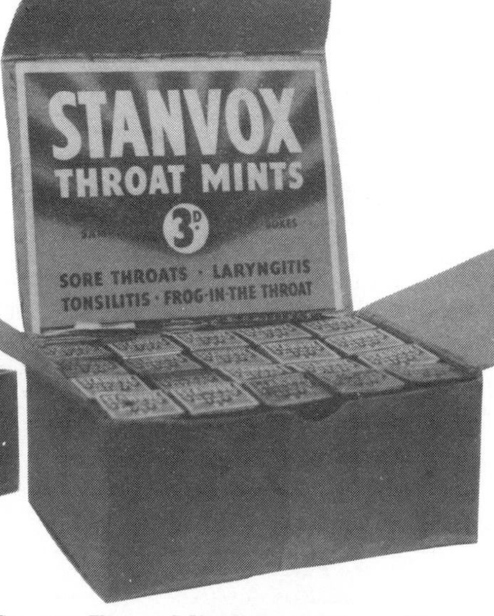

Stanvox Throat Mints counter box with contents. **£15**

Imp Soap, shop counter display sign, 1940's. **£40**

Robin Starch string tin showing various Reckitts products. **£75**

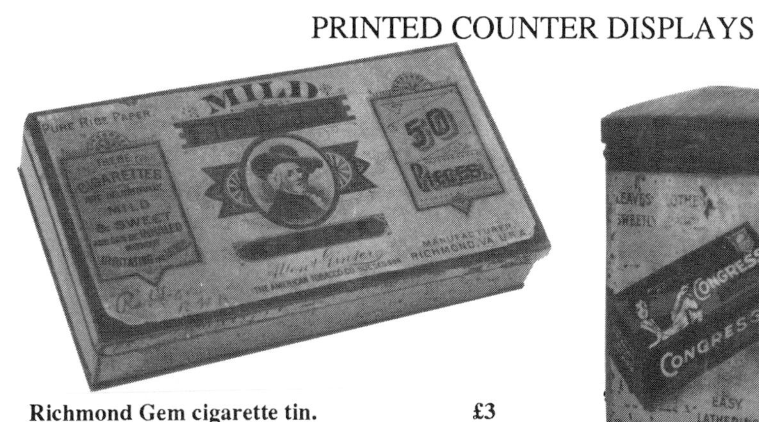

Richmond Gem cigarette tin. £3

C.W.S. string tin featuring Congress soap and Naptha Soap. £50

Cadbury's Turkish Delight counter box. £8

Flako, for fine fabrics, magazine insert, 1912. £8

Satinex Safety Bleach, display sign, 1960's. £70

INO Margarine display sign, 10" high. £15

Printed silk advertisement for 1st Bohemian Smoking Concert, September 29, 1907. £15

Changing face novelty 'Unhappy Moments'. £60

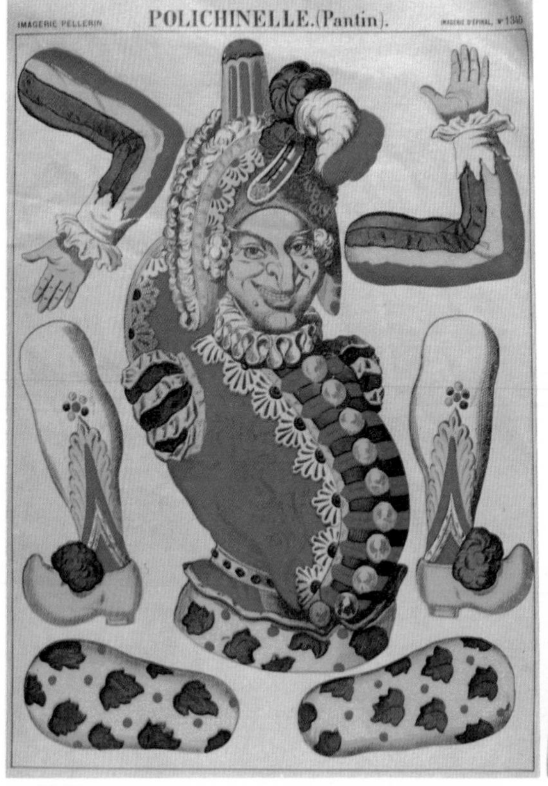

Paper puppet cut out sheet 'Polichinelle'. £18

Changing heads novelty figure. £16

(Spread Eagle Antiques)

'Prince Albert Driving His Favourites'. £20

The Baby Show, with ten alternate faces. £25

'If I could only get the door down, I should see them all for nothing'. £35

'No doubt my wife has something nice and warm for me this cold night'. £35

Changing picture novelty 'March winds & April showers'. £15

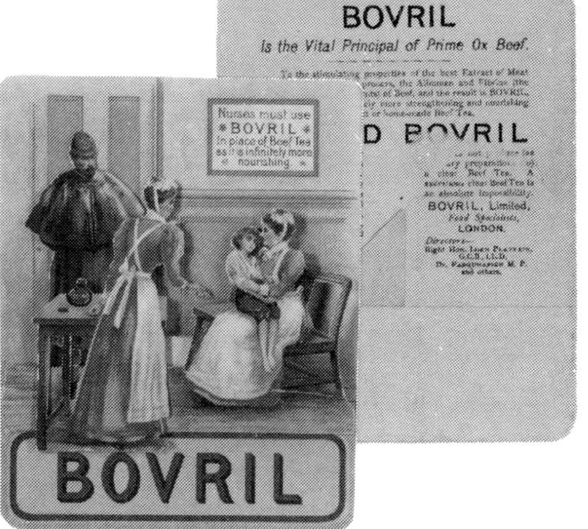

Bovril 'Pop-Up' advertising novelty. £25

(Spread Eagle Antiques)

N. Currier (Publisher), 'The road, – winter', hand coloured lithograph, a fine, fresh impression, with touches of gum arabic, on stone by Otto Knirsch, 1853, $17\frac{1}{2}$ x $26\frac{1}{4}$in.
(Sotheby's) £22,697

Currier and Ives (Publishers), 'A midnight race on the Mississippi', hand coloured lithograph, after the sketch by H. D. Manning, on stone by Frances F. Palmer, 1860, 18 x $27\frac{7}{8}$in.
(Sotheby's) £3,026

George Caleb Bingham (after), 'Stump speaking', engraving, mezzotint and roulette, by Louis-Adolphe Gautier, published by Fishel, Adler & Schwartz, New York, 1856, $22\frac{1}{4}$ x $30\frac{1}{8}$in.
(Sotheby's) £2,459

Henry A. Papprill, 'New York, taken from the north west angle of Fort Columbus, Governor's Island', hand coloured aquatint, 1844, published by Henry J. Megarey, New York, image $16\frac{5}{8}$ x $26\frac{3}{4}$in.
(Sotheby's) £3,405

William Sharp, 'Opening bud; Opening flower; Intermediate state of bloom; and Complete bloom', four chromolithographs, from John Frisk Allen's Victoria Regia, or The Great Water Lily of America, Boston, Dutton and Wentworth, 1854, $14\frac{5}{8}$ x $20\frac{5}{8}$in. (Sotheby's) £3,405

Sigismond Himely, 'New York', hand coloured engraving, after the painting by Heine, published by Goupil & Co., New York, Paris, London, Berlin, and W. Schaus, New York, 1851, plate $28\frac{7}{8}$ x 43in.
(Sotheby's) £4,539

John James Audubon (after), 'Polar bear', hand coloured lithograph, with touches of gum arabic, a fine, fresh impression by J. T. Bowen, Philadelphia, 1846, 21½ x 27⅛in.
(Sotheby's) **£2,572**

Currier and Ives (Publishers), 'The champion pacer Johnson', chromolithograph, with gum arabic, J. Cameron in the stone, 1884, 18⅛ x 27in.
(Sotheby's) **£908**

Currier and Ives (Publishers), 'The life of a hunter, 'A tight fix', hand coloured lithograph, a very fine impression of this rare lithograph, with touches of gum arabic, after the painting by A. F. Tait, 1861, 18½ x 27in.
(Sotheby's) **£41,447**

N. Currier (Publisher), 'Catching a trout, 'We hab you now, sar', hand coloured lithograph with touches of gum arabic, after the painting by A. F. Tait, lith. by N. Currier, 1854, 18⅛ x 25⅝in.
(Sotheby's) **£4,918**

E. Walker, 'Sleigh scene, Toronto Bay, Canada West', lithograph, printed with tint stone and with touches of hand colouring, after the painting by J. T. Downman, printed by Day & Son, published by Ackermann & Co., London 1853, 20⅝ x 30½in. (Sotheby's) **£4,161**

Sigismond Himely, 'Vue de New York, Prise de Weahawk, a view of New York taken from Veahawk', hand coloured aquatint, with touches of gum arabic, circa 1834, image 12¾ x 17½in.
(Sotheby's) **£5,296**

'The Great Fire at Boston', published by Currier & Ives, 1872, small folio.
(Skinner Inc.) £500

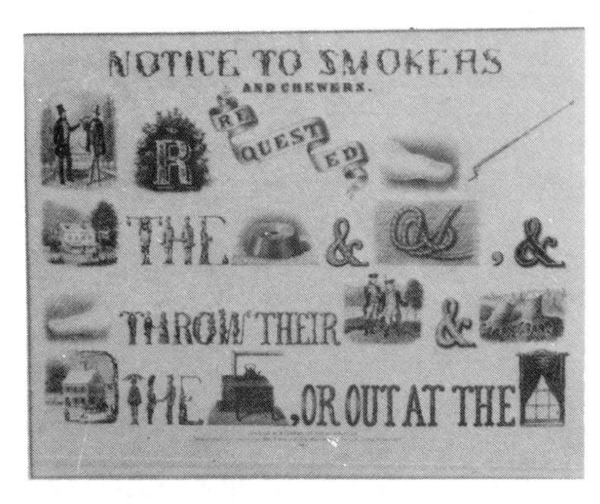

'Notice To Smokers And Chewers', published by N. Currier, 1854, small folio.
(Skinner Inc.) £700

Nathaniel Currier, publisher (active 1835–1907), Across the Continent, "Westward the Course of Empire Takes Its Way", by F.F. Palmer (Conningham 33; Peterz 2085), lithograph with hand-colouring, 1868, on wove paper, $17\frac{3}{4}$ x $27\frac{1}{4}$in.
(Christie's) £8,000

Currier and Ives, Publishers, The American National Game of Base Ball, Grand Match for the Championship at the Elysian Fields, Hoboken, N.J., lithograph with hand-colouring, 1866, on wove paper, $19\frac{3}{4}$ x $29\frac{3}{4}$in.
(Christie's) £9,700

'The Celebrated Horse Lexington (5 years old), by 'Boston' out of 'Alice Carneal'', published by N. Currier, 1855, large folio.
(Skinner Inc.) £500

'Maple Sugaring', published by Currier & Ives, 1872, small folio.
(Skinner Inc.) £700

'The Champion in Luck', published by Currier & Ives, 1882, small folio.
(Skinner Inc.) £100

'The Accommodation Train', published by Currier & Ives, 1876, small folio.
(Skinner Inc.) £300

Charles H. Crosby & Co., Boston, lithographer, (American, 1819–1896), *Built by the Amoskeag Manufacturing Company*/early fire engines, identified in the matrix, chromolithograph on paper, sheet size 24 x 31$^{7}/_{8}$in.
(Skinner Inc.) £2,500

Superb framed coloured lithograph after a painting by W.L. Walton, *The International Contest of Heenan and Sayer at Farnsborough on the 17th of April, 1860*, by Bufford Sons, Boston, 31$^{1}/_{2}$ x 40$^{1}/_{2}$in.
(Eldred's) £1,279

'The Celebrated Horse Dexter, 'The King Of The World' Driven By Budd Doble'', published by Currier & Ives, 1867, large folio.
(Skinner Inc.) £1,750

'Rysdyk's Hambletonian', published by Currier & Ives, 1876, large folio.
(Skinner Inc.) £1,250

KIRKVILLE GRASS.

The above Grass Parks

WILL BE LET

ON

WEDNESDAY, 25th APRIL,

At TWO o'clock p.m.

JAMES FARQUHAR, Auctioneer.

Kirkville Grass, Will Be Let. £4

Water is scarce at present.

Do not use more than is absolutely necessary. Turn off tap after use.

Water Is Scarce, 1930. £3

REGULATIONS.

1. The Front Entrance Door to be kept shut.
2. The Tenants on the ground floor, week about, are to keep the lobbies and front steps clean, washing them out every Wednesday and sweeping them out every morning.
3. The Tenants on the first floor, week about, are to keep clean their own landings and staircase, washing the stairs twice a week, and dusting them down every morning.
4. The same to be observed by the tenants on the attic floor, down to the first floor landing.
5. The whole Tenants are, week about, to wash out the lobbies every Saturday.
6. The W.C. is for the use of the whole tenants, and it will be the duty of them, week about, to keep it in order, washing and cleaning it out at least once a week; and no smoking or spitting allowed in the closet.
7. The W.C. is not to be used for any other purpose than that for which it is intended. The door is to be kept shut, and children are not to be allowed to play about it or on the stairs or lobbies.
8. The Tenants on the ground floor are entitled to the use of the wash-house and green every alternate Monday, the Tenants on the first floor every alternate Tuesday, and those on the attic floor every alternate Wednesday. Children are not to be allowed to play on the green.
9. The washing-house floor, with tubs, to be cleaned, and the boiler carefully dried out, before handing over the key the same evening of the day of using it to the party next entitled to receive it.
10. Parties receiving coals are to clean up and sweep out the lobbies, &c., immediately after the coals have been delivered.
11. As these Regulations are intended for the general good of all, it is requested that, as far as practicable, they may be observed.

Tenants Regulations. £8

NOTICE IS HEREBY GIVEN

That on Thursday, the 4th day of July next, application will be made to His Majesty's Justices of the Peace assembled at Quarter Sessions in and for the North Riding of the County of York at the Court House in Northallerton, in the said Riding, for an Order for diverting a certain footpath or highway on land belonging to Rachel Ayre and Mary Jane Moss lying between the road leading from Goathland Station to Goathland Village, in the township of Goathland, in the parish of Pickering, in the North Riding of the County of York, to the road leading from Goathland Village aforesaid to Beckhole, in the said township; and also for entirely stopping up such part of the said highway or footpath as will be rendered unnecessary by such diversion. And that the Certificate of two Justices having viewed the same on the day of the date hereof upon the application of the Rural District Council of Whitby, with the Plan of the old and proposed new highway or footpath, will be lodged with the Clerk of the Peace of the said Riding at his office at Northallerton aforesaid on or before the 4th day of June next.

Dated this 4th day of April, 1901.

Clerk to the Rural District Council of Whitby.

FORTH & SON, PRINTERS, FLOWERGATE, WHITBY.

Diverting A Footpath Notice, 1901. £6

NOTICE.

Any person or persons trespassing upon, interfering with, damaging, or destroying the occupation road or Bed of the River Calder at or within Pendle Hall Farm, situate in the Township of Higham, in the County of Lancaster, on both sides of the said River, the property of Col. Starkie, in the occupation of Messrs. Todd and Whittaker, or the gates, fences, or land on either side of the River there, will be treated as wilful trespassers after notice and dealt with according to law.

Daniel Howsin,

Agent for Colonel Starkie.

Huntroyde, 29th May, 1895.

Geo. W. Whewell, Printer, Castle Street, Clitheroe.

Notice to Trespassers, 1895. £8

Aberdeen Royal Infirmary.

NURSES' HOME.

RULES FOR NURSES AND PROBATIONERS

Aberdeen Royal Infirmary, Rules for Nurses, 1900. £8

(Yesterdays Paper)

Cheap Sale, Campbell's Stores, 1890. £8

VALUABLE FREEHOLD
FARM AND BUILDINGS,
TO BE SOLD BY AUCTION BY
MR. W. LAWSON,
AT THE
STARKIES ARMS HOTEL, CLITHEROE,
ON MONDAY, OCTOBER 19, 1903,
ALL THAT FREEHOLD
FARM
FARM HOUSE, BARN, SHIPPON, STABLE AND PIGGERIES
MR. E. L. PHILLIPS,

Farm and Buildings Auction, 1903. £10

Football Semi-Final, Moss Lane v. Highfield. £8

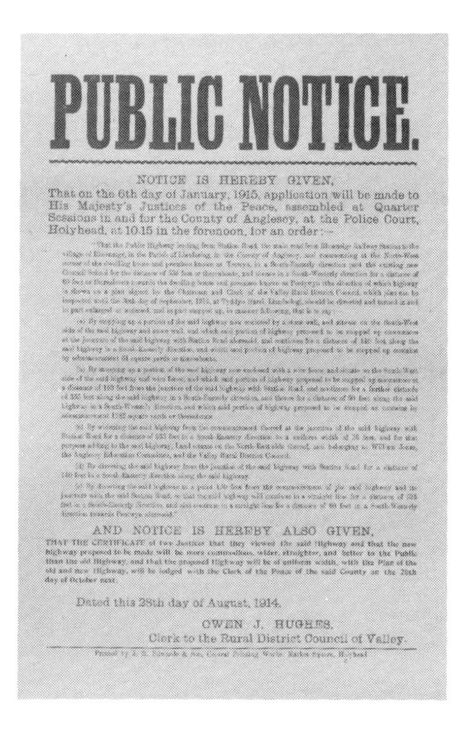

PUBLIC NOTICE.

NOTICE IS HEREBY GIVEN,
That on the 6th day of January, 1915, application will be made to His Majesty's Justices of the Peace, assembled at Quarter Sessions in and for the County of Anglesey, at the Police Court, Holyhead, at 10.15 in the forenoon, for an order:—

AND NOTICE IS HEREBY ALSO GIVEN,

Dated this 28th day of August, 1914.

OWEN J. HUGHES.
Clerk to the Rural District Council of Valley.

Notice of Proposed Highway, 1914. £6

(Yesterdays Paper)

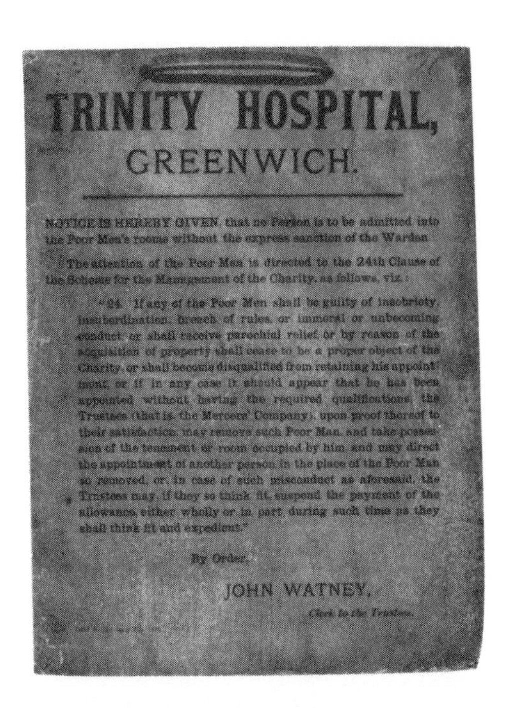

TRINITY HOSPITAL,
GREENWICH.

NOTICE IS HEREBY GIVEN, that no Person is to be admitted into the Poor Men's rooms without the express sanction of the Warden.

The attention of the Poor Men is directed to the 24th Clause of the Scheme for the Management of the Charity, as follows, viz.:

"24. If any of the Poor Men shall be guilty of insobriety, insubordination, breach of rules, or immoral or unbecoming conduct, or shall receive parochial relief, or by reason of the acquisition of property shall cease to be a proper object of the Charity, or shall become disqualified from retaining his appointment, or if in any case it should appear that he has been appointed without having the required qualifications, the Trustees (that is, the Mercers' Company), upon proof thereof to their satisfaction, may remove such Poor Man, and take possession of the tenement or room occupied by him, and may direct the appointment of another person in the place of the Poor Man so removed, or, in case of such misconduct as aforesaid, the Trustees may, if they so think fit, suspend the payment of the allowance, either wholly or in part, during such time as they shall think fit and expedient."

By Order,

JOHN WATNEY,

Clerk to the Trustees.

Trinity Hospital Greenwich notice, 1891. £25

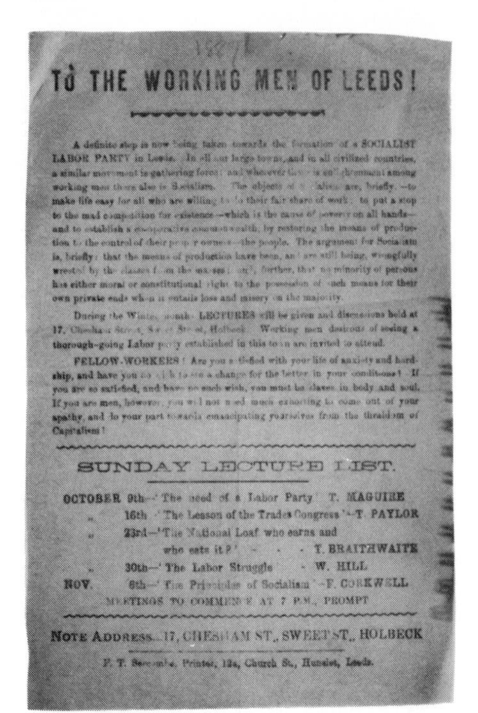

TO THE WORKING MEN OF LEEDS!

A definite step is now being taken towards the formation of a SOCIALIST LABOR PARTY in Leeds. In all our large towns, and in all civilized countries, a similar movement is gathering force; and wherever there is enlightenment among working men there also is Socialism. The objects of Socialism are, briefly,—to make life easy for all who are willing to do their fair share of work; to put a stop to the mad competition for existence—which is the cause of poverty on all hands—and to establish a co-operative commonwealth, by restoring the means of production to the control of their proper owners—the people. The argument for Socialism is, briefly: that the means of production have been, and are still being, wrongfully wrested by the classes from the masses; and, further, that no minority of persons has either moral or constitutional right to the possession of such means for their own private ends when it entails loss and misery on the majority.

During the Winter months LECTURES will be given and discussions held at 17, Chesham Street, Sweet Street, Holbeck. Working men desirous of seeing a thorough-going Labor party established in this town are invited to attend.

FELLOW-WORKERS! Are you satisfied with your life of anxiety and hardship, and have you no wish to see a change for the better in your conditions? If you are so satisfied, and have no such wish, you must be slaves in body and soul. If you are men, however, you will not need much exhorting to come out of your apathy, and do your part towards emancipating yourselves from the thraldom of Capitalism!

SUNDAY LECTURE LIST.

OCTOBER 9th—'The need of a Labor Party' T. MAGUIRE
" 16th—'The Lesson of the Trades Congress'—T. PAYLOR
" 23rd—'The National Loaf who earns and who eats it?' - - - T. BRAITHWAITE
" 30th—'The Labor Struggle' - W. HILL
NOV. 6th—'The Principles of Socialism'—F. CORKWELL

MEETINGS TO COMMENCE AT 7 P.M., PROMPT

NOTE ADDRESS—17, CHESHAM ST., SWEET ST., HOLBECK

F. T. Seccombe, Printer, 12a, Church St., Hunslet, Leeds.

'To the Working Men of Leeds' political pamphlet, 1887. £5

BY ORDER of the Executors of the late MISS M. A. DEWHURST

CLITHEROE.

MR. J. E. SMITHIES

will Sell by Public Auction, at No. 32, Eshton Terrace, Clitheroe, on

SATURDAY, MAY 11th, 1929

THE HOUSEHOLD GOODS

FURNITURE

AND EFFECTS

Consisting of mahogany Hat and Umbrella Stand; oval fronted mahogany double door Corner Cupboard; gilt Console Table and Mirror to match; Couch in red velvet; 3 rosewood Single Chairs; 1 Arm Chair in rosewood and Couch to match; Window Stool in rosewood frame; Needle Work Cover; octagon shaped Lady's Work Table; Pier Glass in gilt frame; Table Piano; mahogany Leaf Table; 5 mahogany balloon back Chairs; Piano Stool; Rocking Chair; Overmantel in gilt frame; Sewing Machine; double door mahogany Corner Cupboard; Sheraton chest of mahogany Drawers; valuable serpentine shaped mahogany Chest (antique) in fine condition; 4 mahogany Single Chairs; large mahogany Chest of Drawers; pair painted Toilet Tables; mahogany Bedstead; 2 rosewood Stools with needle work covers; 4 Single Chairs covered in red damask; pair birch Toilets; large painted Wardrobe; Kneeling Stool; useful mahogany Chest; large Rocking Chair; 1 comfortable Easy Chair; oblong Window Table; large Pier Glass in gilt frame; Feather Beds; rosewood Table with oval top; fine old Tea Service, gilt and blue decoration; part old Wedgwood Tea Service; another old fashioned Tea Service; set of 3 valuable Vases; some Lustre Ware; 3 Parian Marble Busts including one of Wellington; pair of plated Candlesticks; pair of brass Candlesticks; some blue and white Willow Pottery; Decanters; Wine Glasses; Tumblers, &c.; fine old moulded Glass Dish; Lacquer Workbox in good condition; Carpets; Pictures, including several prints after Birket Foster. The usual Pots and Pans and some good Knives, Forks and Spoons.

Sale of Furniture to commence at 1-30 p.m., prompt.

MR. SMITHIES will also sell by Public Auction on the premises, subject to conditions to be then produced (which may be inspected at the Office of the Vendors' Solicitors during Office hours on any week day in the week preceding the sale) the

DWELLINGHOUSE & PREMISES

No. 32, ESHTON TERRACE, CLITHEROE

which are Freehold and free from Ground Rent.

VACANT POSSESSION will be given on Completion.

Sale of House at 3 p.m. prompt.

BALDWIN, WEEKS & BALDWIN

VENDORS' SOLICITORS

4, DUCK STREET, CLITHEROE

Furniture Sale, Clitheroe, 1929. £8

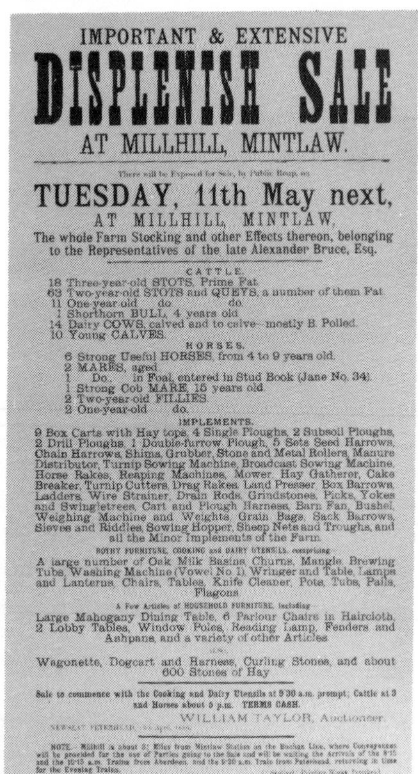

IMPORTANT & EXTENSIVE

DISPLENISH SALE

AT MILLHILL, MINTLAW.

There will be Exposed for Sale, by Public Roup, on

TUESDAY, 11th May next,

AT MILLHILL, MINTLAW,

The whole Farm Stocking and other Effects thereon, belonging to the Representatives of the late Alexander Bruce, Esq.

CATTLE.

18 Three-year-old STOTS, Prime Fat
63 Two-year-old STOTS and QUEYS, a number of them Fat
11 One-year-old do. do.
1 Shorthorn BULL, 4 years old
14 Dairy COWS, calved and to calve—mostly B. Polled
10 Young CALVES

HORSES.

6 Strong Useful HORSES, from 4 to 9 years old
2 MARES, aged
1 Do. in Foal, entered in Stud Book (Jane No. 34)
1 Strong Cob MARE, 15 years old
2 Two-year-old FILLIES
2 One-year-old do.

IMPLEMENTS.

9 Box Carts with Hay tops, 4 Single Ploughs, 2 Subsoil Ploughs, 2 Drill Ploughs, 1 Double-furrow Plough, 5 Sets Seed Harrows, Chain Harrows, Shims, Grubber, Stone and Metal Rollers, Manure Distributor, Turnip Sowing Machine, Broadcast Sowing Machine, Horse Rakes, Reaping Machines, Mower, Hay Gatherer, Cake Breaker, Turnip Cutters, Drag Rakes, Land Presser, Box Barrows, Ladders, Wire Strainer, Drain Rods, Grindstones, Picks, Yokes and Swingletrees, Cart and Plough Harness, Barn Fan, Bushel Weighing Machine and Weights, Grain Bags, Sack Barrows, Sieves and Riddles, Sowing Hopper, Sheep Nets and Troughs, and all the Minor Implements of the Farm.

BOTHY FURNITURE, COOKING and DAIRY UTENSILS, comprising—

A large number of Oak Milk Basins, Churns, Mangle, Brewing Tubs, Washing Machine (Vowel No. 1), Wringer and Table, Lamps and Lanterns, Chairs, Tables, Knife Cleaner, Pots, Tubs, Pails, Flagons.

A Few Articles of HOUSEHOLD FURNITURE, including—

Large Mahogany Dining Table, 6 Parlour Chairs in Haircloth, 2 Lobby Tables, Window Poles, Reading Lamp, Fenders and Ashpans, and a variety of other Articles.

Wagonette, Dogcart and Harness, Curling Stones, and about 600 Stones of Hay.

Sale to commence with the Cooking and Dairy Utensils at 9.30 a.m. prompt; Cattle at 3 and Horses about 5 p.m. TERMS CASH.

WILLIAM TAYLOR, Auctioneer.

Displenish Sale, Mintlaw, 1886. £10

(Yesterdays Paper)

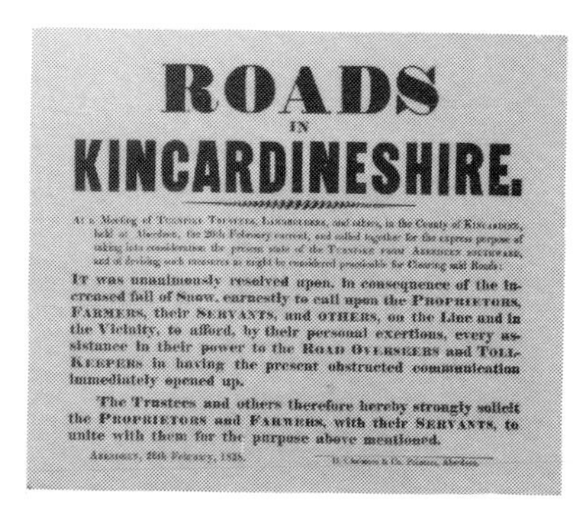

Roads In Kincardineshire, 1838. £12

Valuable Prescriptions That May Be Of Use To You. £4

Sunday Pictorial, Spies. £8

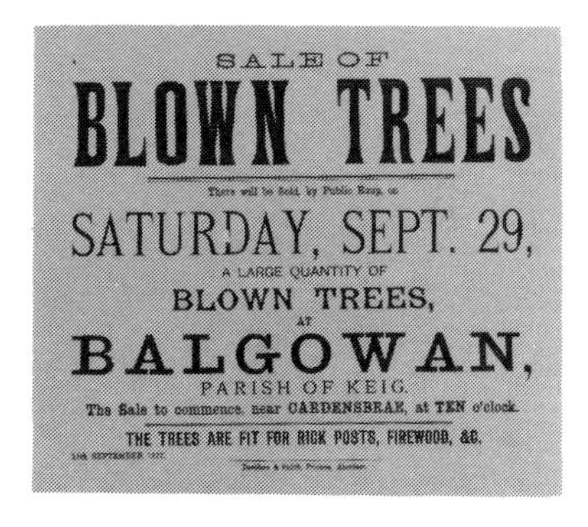

Sale of Blown Trees, 1877. £6

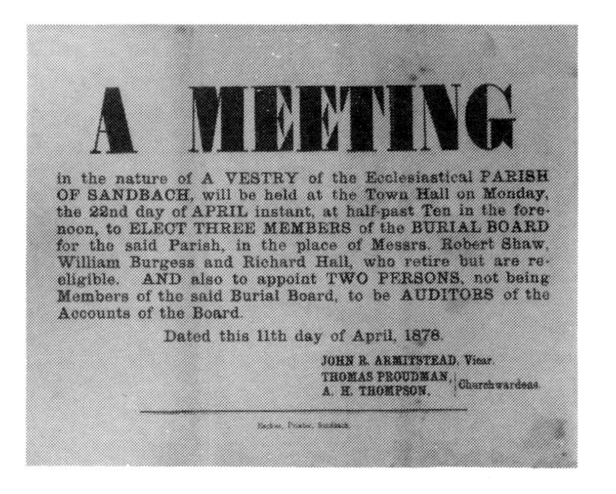

A Meeting At The Town Hall, 1878. £6

House Sale, 1913. £8

(Yesterdays Paper)

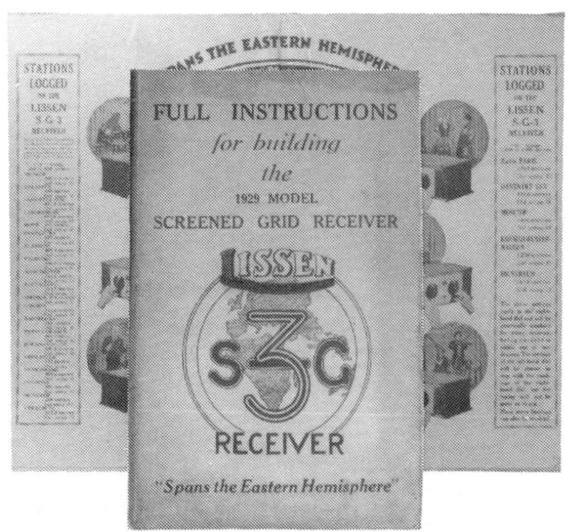

The Lissen S-G-3 Receiver, 1929 Model. £2

The Philco Battery Portable, A Musical Instrument of Quality. £2

Marconiphone, The World's Finest Radio Gramophone. £6

Practical Wireless, December 2nd, 1933. £3

Modern Wireless, October 1933. £4

(Yesterdays Paper)

Philco Mystery Control, The Greatest Radio Discovery Since Radio Itself. £2

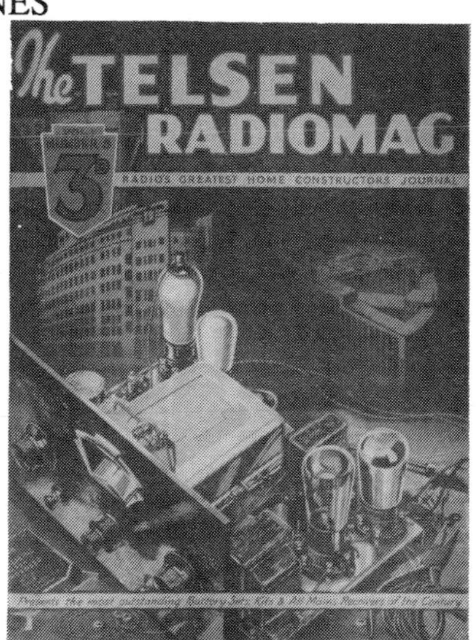

The Telsen Radiomag, Vol. 1 Number 5. £4

Radio For The Million, September 1927, Vol. 1 No. 4. £4

Mullard 'The Master Three', Built with 20 wires. £2

Practical Wireless, May 1957. £2

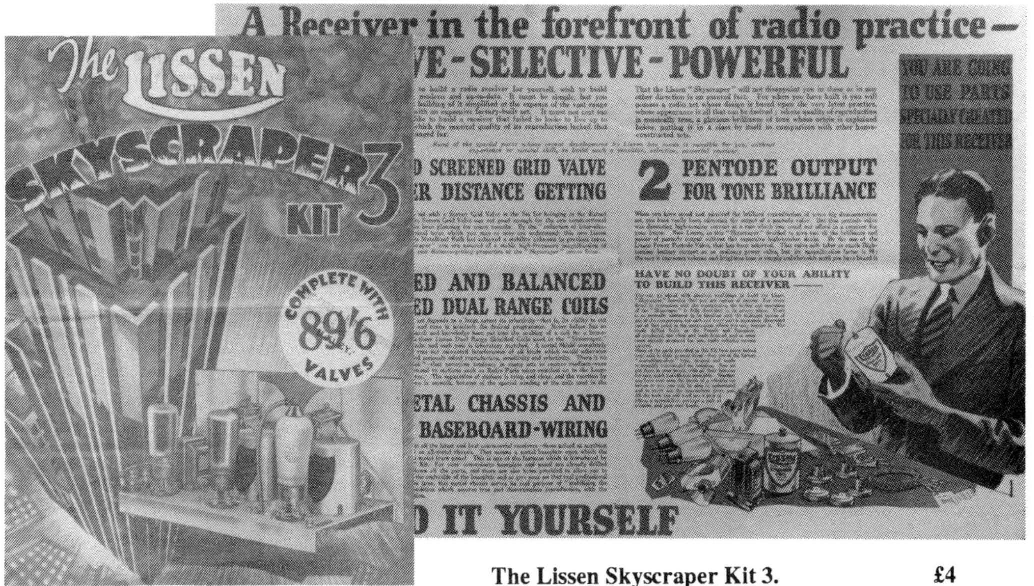

The Lissen Skyscraper Kit 3. £4

(Yesterdays Paper)

The Radio Times Radiolympia Number, August 10th 1934. £10

Radio Times, Coronation edition, May 7, 1937. £25

The Radio Times, June 8th, 1934, 'First Test Match'. £6

The Radio Times, Friday April 6th 1934, Charles Laughton plays Macbeth. £6

Radiolympia, Second Week, 17th August 1934. £7

(Yesterdays Paper)

Royal Command Variety Performance, 16th May 1930. £7

The Radio Times, September 16th–22nd 1934. £8

Ulster Tourist Trophy Motor Race, 24th August 1934. £8

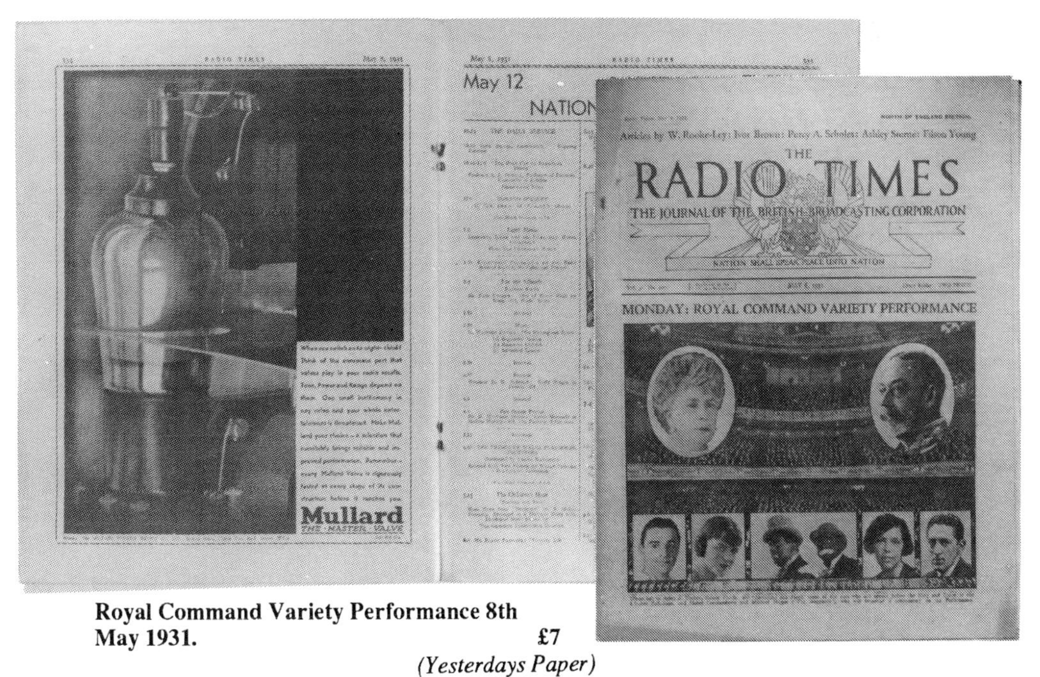

Royal Command Variety Performance 8th May 1931. £7

(Yesterdays Paper)

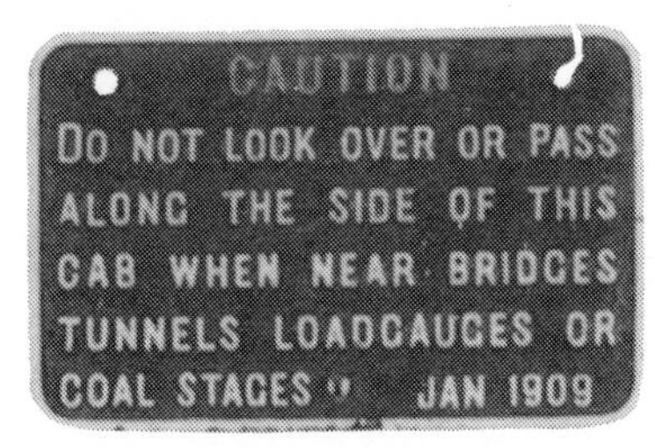

'Caution Do Not Look Over or Pass Along the Side of this Cab . . . ' cast iron Great Western locomotive sign, dated *Jan. 1909,* 19 x 30cm. (Onslow's) £65

Southern Railway Staff Magazine. £2

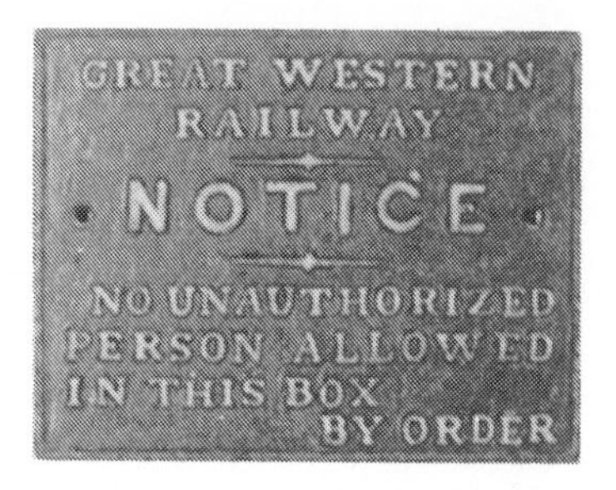

Great Western Railway 'No Unauthorised Person Allowed in this Box', cast iron sign, 21 x 28cm. (Onslow's) £60

Kerr, 'If You Must Travel Travel Light I Can't You Can', double crown. (Onslow's) £40

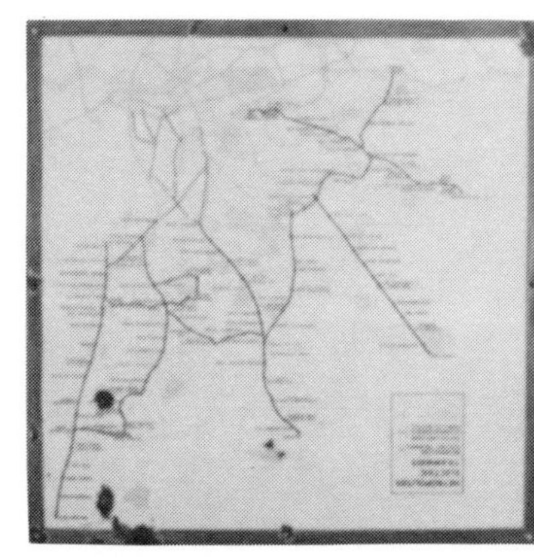

Metropolitan Electric Tramways, enamel map of the system, 74cm. square. (Onslow's) £60

'You May Have A Friend Here He's In Your Usual Train', published by Railway Executive Committee, double royal. (Onslow's) £35

Locomotive Post May 1949. £3

British Railways Western Region Excursions 1955. £3

Railway Ribaldry by Heath Robinson, GWR Publication. £50

'On Early Shift Greenwood Signalbox New Barnet', by Terence Cuneo, published by BR, quad royal on linen.
(Onslow's) £250

1955 British Railways Timetable. £5

South Eastern & Chatham Railway poster, 'Fashionable Folkestone Kent', on
South Eastern & Chatham Railway poster, 'Fashionable Folkestone Kent', on linen.
(Onslow's) £1,020

A Stevengraph *The Present Time 60 miles an Hour*, woven in silk by Thomas Stevens, Inventor and Manufacturer, Coventry and London (Registered), in original Oxford frame.
(Christie's S. Ken) £44

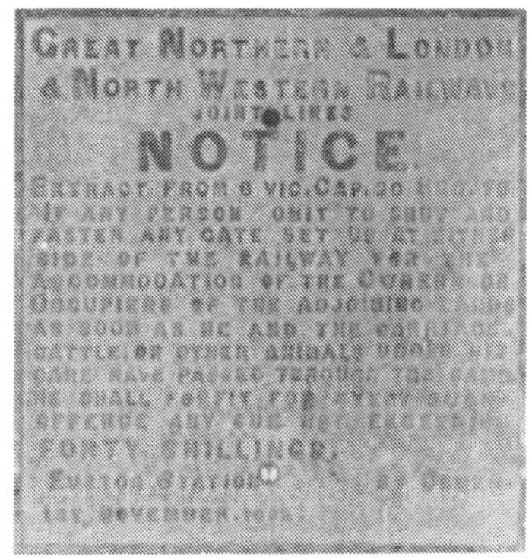

Great Northern & London & North West Railway Joint, cast iron gate warning sign, dated 1st November 1883, 47 x 46cm.
(Onslow's) £580

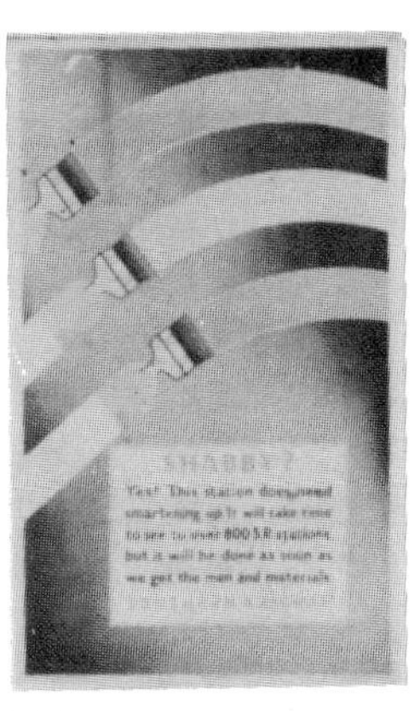

L. A. Webb, 'Shabby? Yes this station does need smartening up', published by SR, double royal, 1945.
(Onslow's) £75

Great Northern North Eastern and North British Railway, Glasgow International Exhibition 1901, on linen.
(Onslow's) £300

Furness Railway, blue and white enamel warning sign, 46cm. square, ex Grange-over-Sands. (Onslow's) £55

Irish Tourist Ticket, issued Euston Station London, 26th July 1853 First Class valid for one month price £6.10.0.
(Onslow's) £100

Bradshaw's Railway Manual 1903. £40

Railway Stamps have been issued by most companies but have limited appeal to collectors. £3 each

Buffet Car Price List. 50p

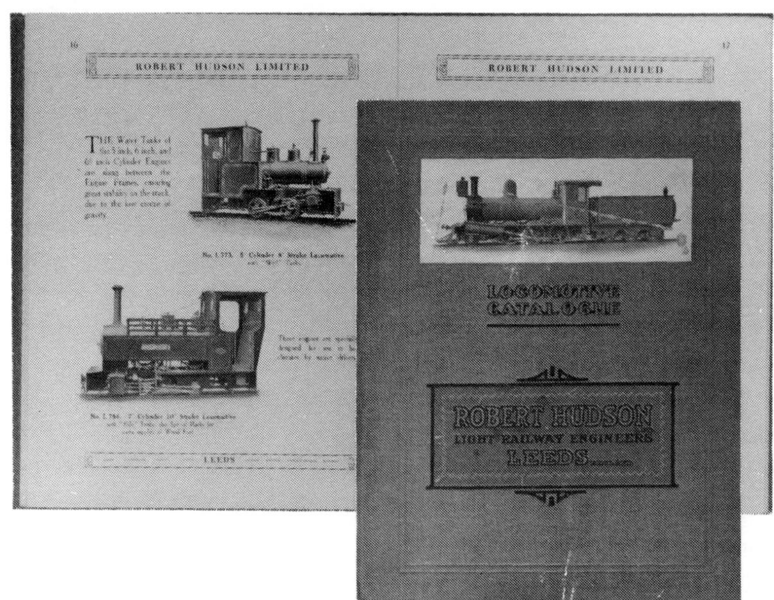

Locomotive Catalogue 1917, Robert Hudson Ltd. Leeds. £50

Pleasant Paths for Ramblers, published by L.S.W.R. 1915. £8

The Official Guide to the South Eastern Railway. £50

1,000 8/31

CHESHIRE LINES. 189

PACKED MANURE-URGENT

Date 1/4/ 1936

From LIVERPOOL (Huskisson Station)

To ______ N.E.

Via Stockport, Godley, Swinton Knottingley & Milford.

TOTAL NUMBER OF SHEETS

IN or ON Wagon

Owner and No. of Wagon

Consignee

Cheshire Lines wagon label, 'Packed manure – urgent', from Liverpool, Huskisson Station. £7

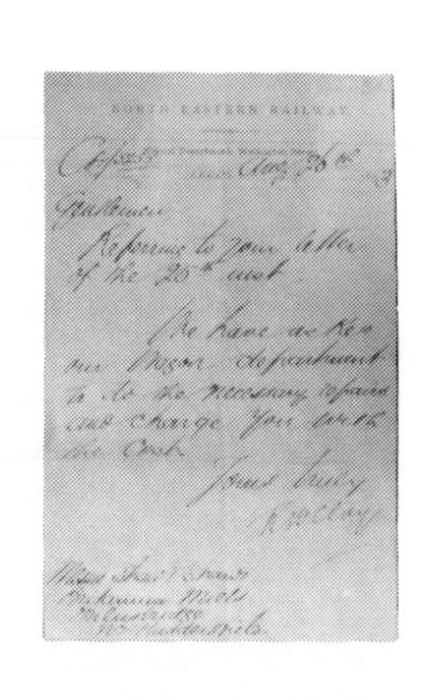

North Eastern Railway Notepaper Aug. 26th 1893. £1

(John F. Bradshaw)

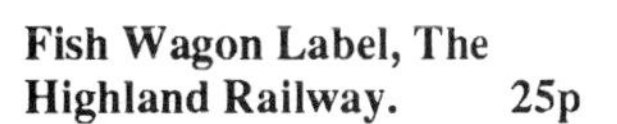
Fish Wagon Label, The Highland Railway. 25p

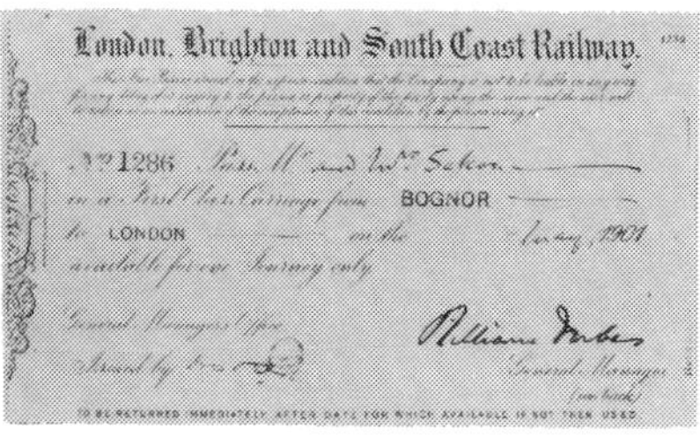
London, Brighton and South Coast Railway.
BOGNOR
LONDON

This Free Pass was issued to the editor of The Railway Magazine and his wife. £35

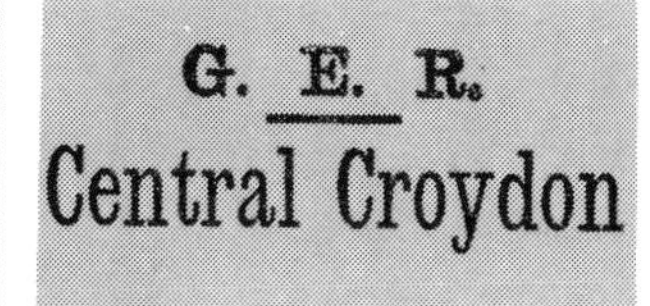

Luggage Label, Central Croydon, closed in 1890. £2

South Eastern Railway – Timetable and Popular Guide to Paris 1867. This early timetable was published privately. £80

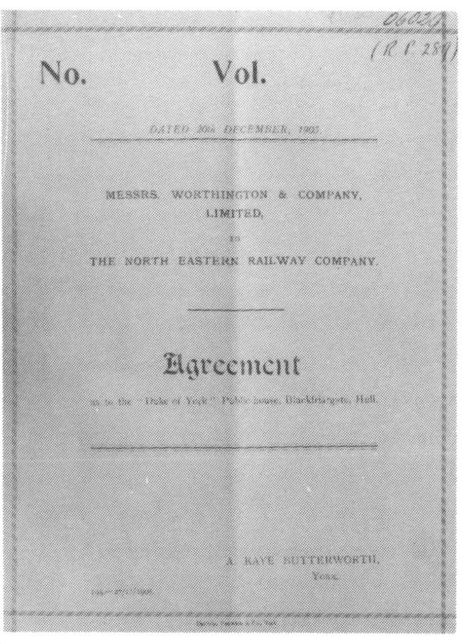
No. Vol.

MESSRS. WORTHINGTON & COMPANY, LIMITED,

TO

THE NORTH EASTERN RAILWAY COMPANY.

Agreement

A. KAYE BUTTERWORTH, YORK.

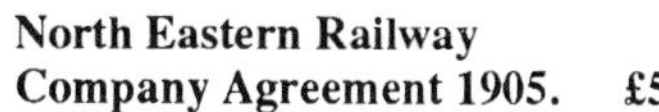
North Eastern Railway Company Agreement 1905. £5

Railway Clearing House, Official Map of England & Wales. £50

1932 Brighton Line Electrification Publicity and Timetable. £7

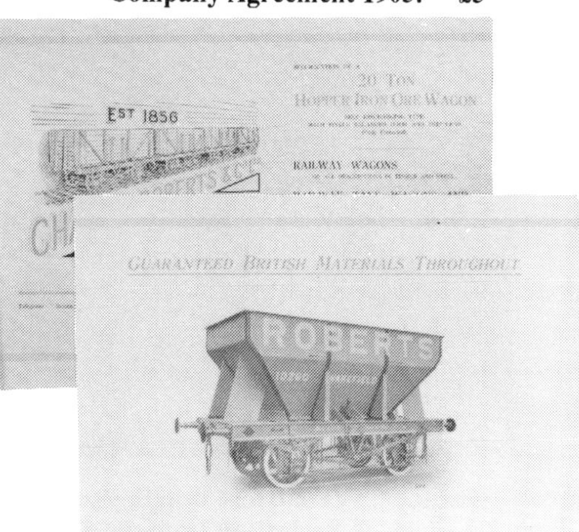

Charles Robert & Co., Wakefield, Wagon Leaflet. £2
(John F. Bradshaw)

Forces Leave Week-End Tickets, handbill. £1

Drawings of the London & Birmingham Railway, by J. C. Bourne, London, 1939. (Onslow's) £4,000

L.N.E.R. poster North Berwick, by Frank Newbould. (Onslow's) £470

L.N.E.R. poster Then and Now, 'The Flying Scotsman', The World's Most Famous Train, by A. R. Thomson. (Onslow's) £330

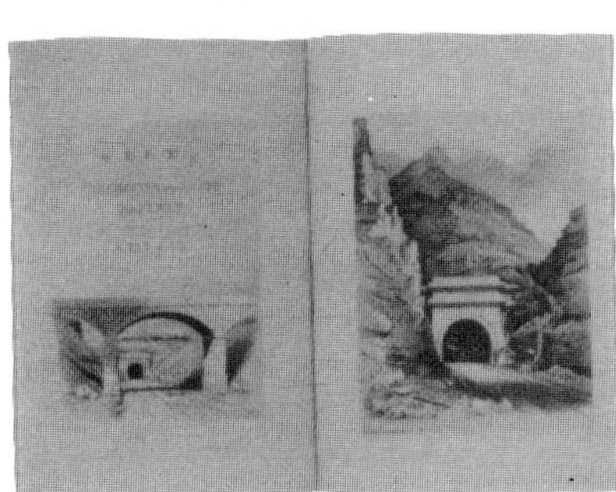

Views on the Manchester and Leeds Railway, a book by A. F. Tait, published by Bradshaw & Blacklock, London, 1845. (Onslow's) £1,600

Bert Thomas, 'Smaller Parcels Quicker Service', published by The Railway Executive Committee, 64 x 51cm. (Onslow's) £32

Great Western Railway, original painted cast iron sign, 8½ x 11in. (Onslow's) £35

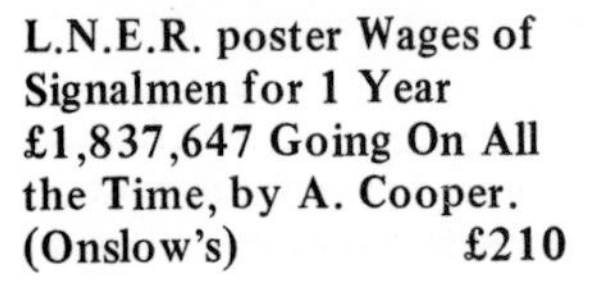

L.N.E.R. poster Wages of Signalmen for 1 Year £1,837,647 Going On All the Time, by A. Cooper. (Onslow's) £210

The Railways in Great Britain also the Line of Navigation from the Principal Sea Ports, printed cotton handkerchief, 24in. square. (Onslow's) £300

George Stephenson Standing on Chat Moss, engraving by T. L. Atkinson, after John Lucas, 32 x 21in. (Onslow's) £130

L.N.E.R. poster Then and Now 600 Golf Courses on the L.N.E.R. Including St. Andrews, by A. R. Thomson. (Onslow's) £280

L.M.S. poster The Irish Mails, by Bryan de Grineau. (Onslow's) £180

L.M.S. poster Luggage In Advance. (Onslow's) £260

An enamel sign, *G.W. and L.M.S. Railway Tickets Issued Here,* red on white ground, 24in. wide. (Christie's S. Ken) £418

Excavation of Olive Mount 4 miles from Liverpool, by T. T. Bury, H. Pyall and S. G. Hughes, hand-coloured aquatint, 10¼ x 13in. (Onslow's) £100

Moorish Arch looking from the Tunnel, by T. T. Bury, H. Pyall and S. G. Hughes, hand-coloured aquatint, 10¼ x 13in. (Onslow's) £100

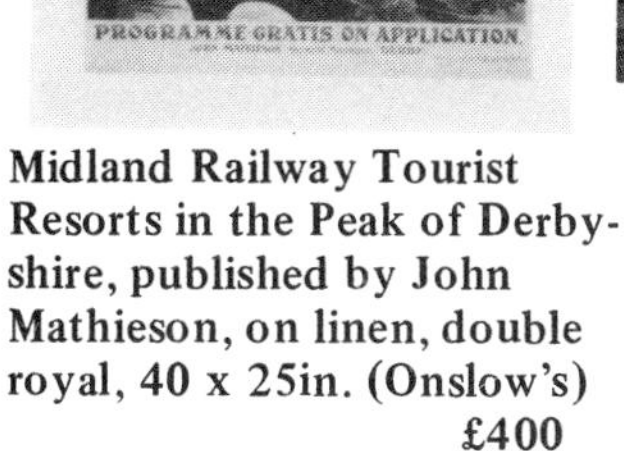

Midland Railway Tourist Resorts in the Peak of Derbyshire, published by John Mathieson, on linen, double royal, 40 x 25in. (Onslow's) £400

L.M.S. Pacific, Sir Wm. Stanier FRS ascending Shap Incline, by Vic Welch, signed, gouache, on board, 13½ x 18½in. (Onslow's) £170

Poster, Factories on L.N.E.R. Lines Are On The Right Lines, by A. Cooper. (Onslow's) £360

Platform Ticket for Ludgate Hill, closed in 1929. £340

Newington Road to Dalston Junction, second class, 1867. (Onslow's) £290

Southern Railway, Coffin Ticket, Waterloo to Brookwood. £25

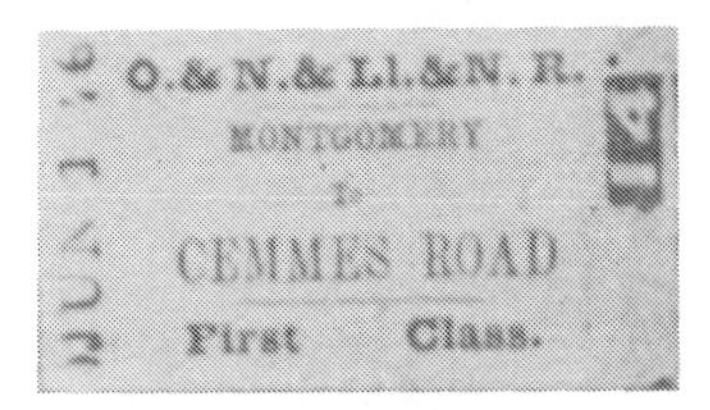

O. & N. & L.1. & N.R. Montgomery to Cemmes Road, first class 1876. (Onslow's) £130

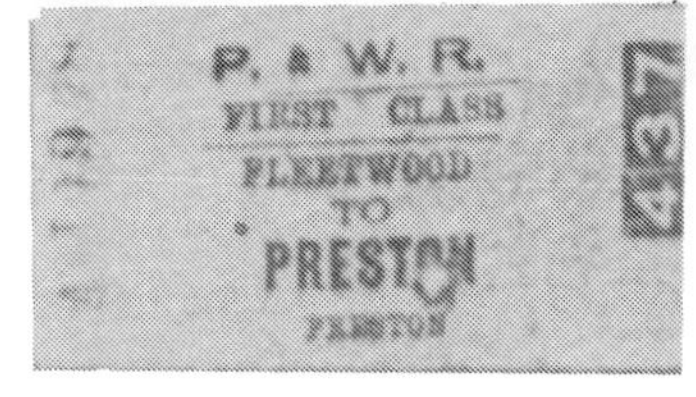

P. & W. R. Fleetwood to Preston, first class 1878. (Onslow's) £70

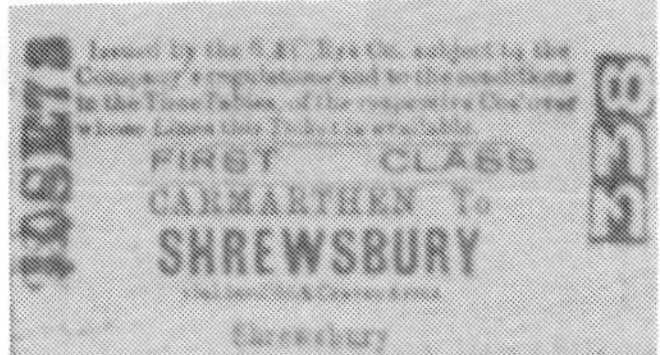

S. & C. R. Carmarthen to Shrewsbury, first class 1878. (Onslow's) £60

L. M. & S. Railway ticket from Stromeferry to Kyle of Lochalsh. £30

New Cross to Blackfriars, second class 1866, overprinted with the letter B. (Onslow's) £100

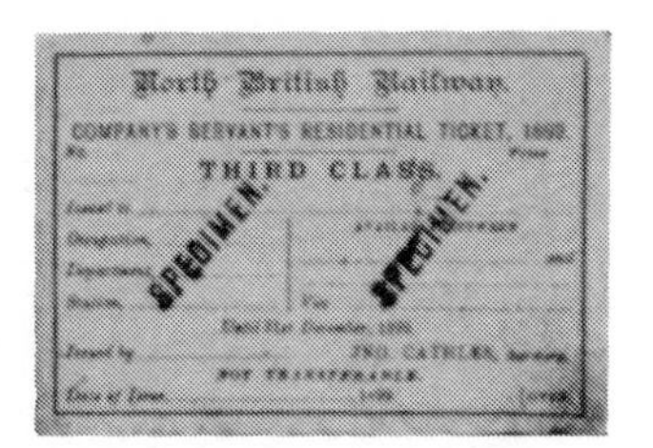

A Staff Season Ticket, printed on thick card. £10

St Austell to Bodmin Road, Express Train, second class, reverse overprinted C.R. Express. (Onslow's) £130

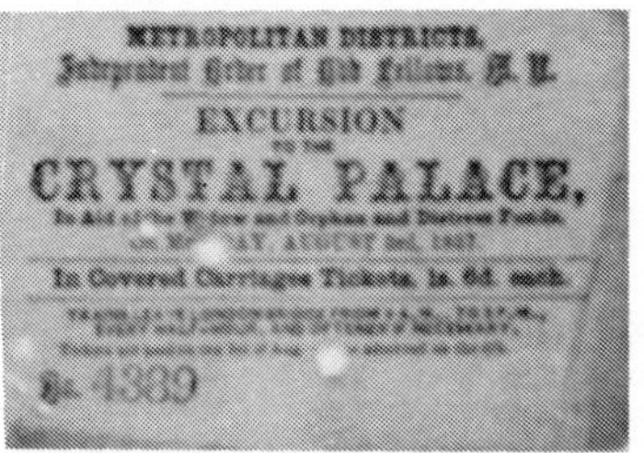

Metropolitan Districts, Independent Order of Odd Fellows Excursion to the Crystal Palace Monday August 3rd 1857 covered carriage ticket 1/6d. (Onslow's) £50

M. R. Blackwell to Barnt Green, second class 1874. (Onslow's) £70

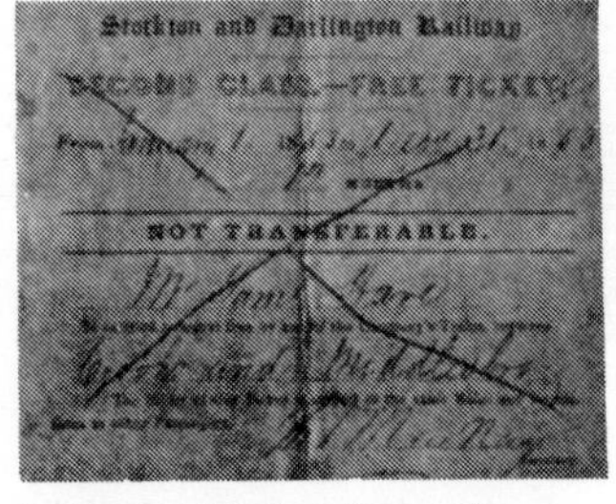

A Season Ticket from the pioneering Stockton and Darlington Railway, issued in 1853. £70

W & SC Joint Line, punch ticket No. 7033. (Onslow's) £32

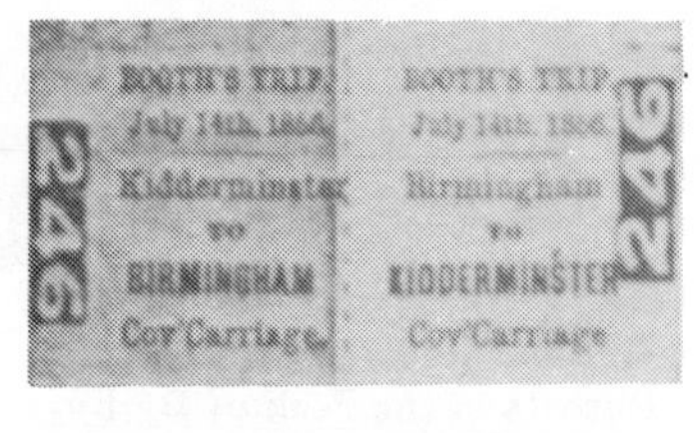

Booth's Trip, July 14th, 1856, Kidderminster to Birmingham Cov' Carriage. (Onslow's) £35

Gold Keg, British De Luxe Safety Razor Blade. 50p

Standard Gillette Blade, Made in England. 50p

Minora Blade, Made in England. £1

Laurel, Made in Sheffield. 75p

Thin Gillette Blade, Made in U.S.A. 50p

St. Leger, The 'Wonder' Safety Razor Blade. 50p

The 'Wonder' Blade, Tested & Guaranteed. 50p

Standard, British Made. 50p

Standard Gillette Thin Blade. 50p

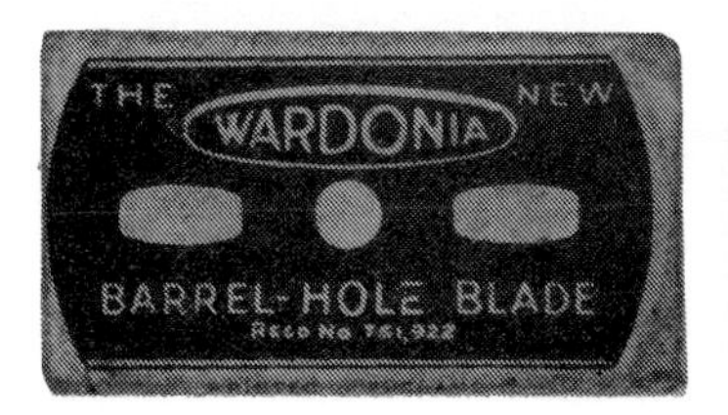

The Wardonia Barrel-Hole Blade. 50p

Paragon Safety Razor Blades, Sheffield. £1

Laurel Blades, The Shaving Edge With The Longest Life. 75p

The Kleen Razor Blade, by W. R. Swann & Co. Ltd., Sheffield. 50p

'Eclipse' Super Razor Blade, by James Neill & Co., Sheffield. 75p

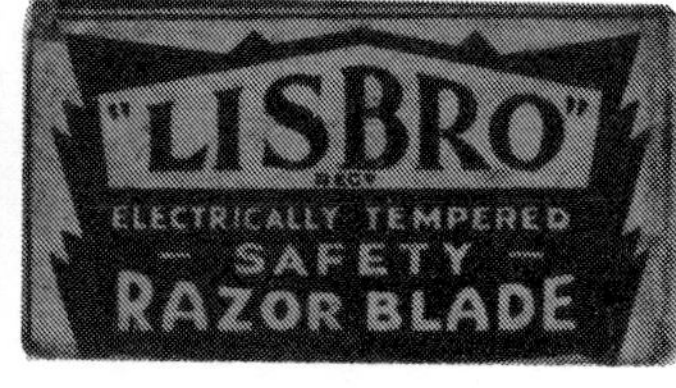

'Lisbro', Electrically Tempered Safety Razor Blade. 75p

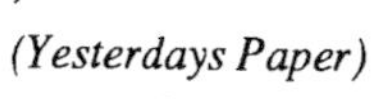

(Yesterdays Paper)

Rowntree's Orange Fruit Creams, $8\frac{1}{2}$ x 6in.
£8

Rowntree's Chocolate Nougatine, $6\frac{1}{2}$ x 10in.
£6

Rowntree's Windsor Mixture, 9 x 14in. £15

Rowntree's Swiss Milk Chocolate, 6 x $7\frac{1}{2}$in. £8

Rowntree's Finest Chocolate Almonds, $8\frac{1}{2}$ x $6\frac{1}{2}$in.
£5

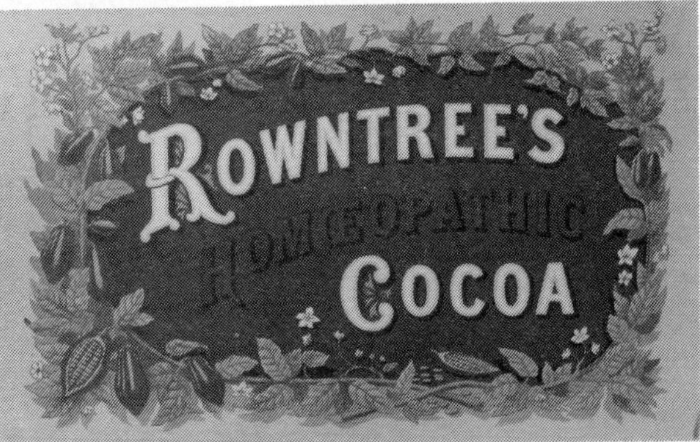

Rowntree's Homeopathic Cocoa, 8 x $13\frac{1}{2}$in.
£12

Rowntree's Pine Sticks, $7\frac{1}{2}$ x 10in. £10

Rowntree's Chocolate Cream, $7\frac{1}{2}$ x 11in. £8

(Yesterdays Paper)

Rowntree's Coker Nut Creams, 7 x 10in. £6

Rowntree's Cokernut Creams, 7 x 10in. £8

Rowntree's King Chocolate, 9 x 13in. £8

Rowntree's Chocolates, Christmas 1903, $6^1/_2$ x $9^1/_2$in. £8

Rowntree's Heliotrope Creams, $6^1/_2$ x 9in. £6

Rowntree's Cokernut Chocolate, 8 x $12^1/_2$in. £8

Rowntree's Ping Pong Biscuits, 7 x 13in. £25

Rowntree's Chocolate Mixture, $7^1/_2$ x 10in. £10

(Yesterdays Paper)

Edward the Eighth – Our King. £10

Edward VIII, Souvenir Book. £3

Souvenir programme of the Coronation of King George VI and Queen Elizabeth, 1937. £2

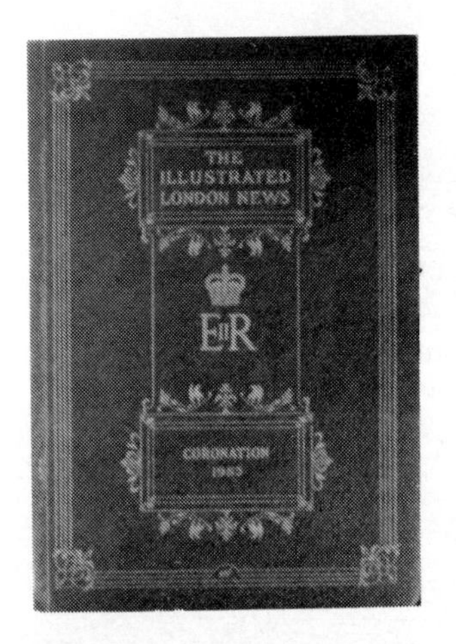

The Illustrated London News, Elizabeth II's Coronation, 1953. £4

King George's Jubilee Trust, Official Programme of the Jubilee Procession. £3

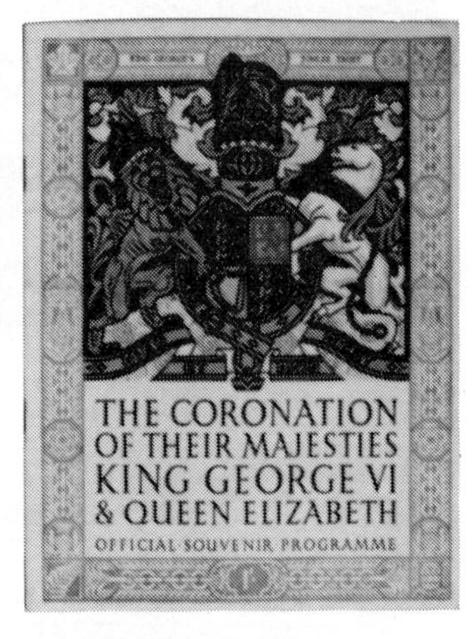

The Coronation of King George VI and Queen Elizabeth, published by Associated Newspapers, £5

The Story of Twenty-Five Years, Silver Jubilee Book, 1935. £6

Queen Victoria – A Personal Sketch by Mrs Oliphant, 1900. £6

Edward VII, His Life and Times, edited by Sir Richard Holmes, two volumes. £20

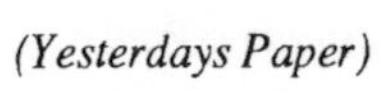
(Yesterdays Paper)

Daily Mirror Coronation Souvenir 1953. £6

Country Life Coronation Number 1953. £3

Picture Post, Special Coronation Souvenir Number 1953. £4

The Sphere, 'The Crowning of the Queen' 1953. £3

Everybody's Coronation Number 1953. £2

Picture Post 1953, 'God Save The Queen'. £2

(Yesterdays Paper)

The Queen's Christmas Carol, 1905, published on behalf of Queen Alexandra's Fund for the Unemployed. £15

Silver Wedding of George VI and Queen Elizabeth. £6

Princess Mary's Gift Book, in aid of the Queen's Work for Women Fund. £20

The Queen, The Coronation 1953. £4

Approved souvenir programme of the wedding of The Princess Margaret and Mr Antony Armstrong-Jones. £4

Our King and Queen and the Royal Princesses, published by Odhams. £6

The First Family, a diary of the Royal Year by L. A. Nickolls, 1950. £6

(Yesterdays Paper)

The Coronation of Her Majesty Queen Elizabeth II approved souvenir programme. £4

His Majesty The King 1910–1935, published by Associated Newspapers Ltd. £15

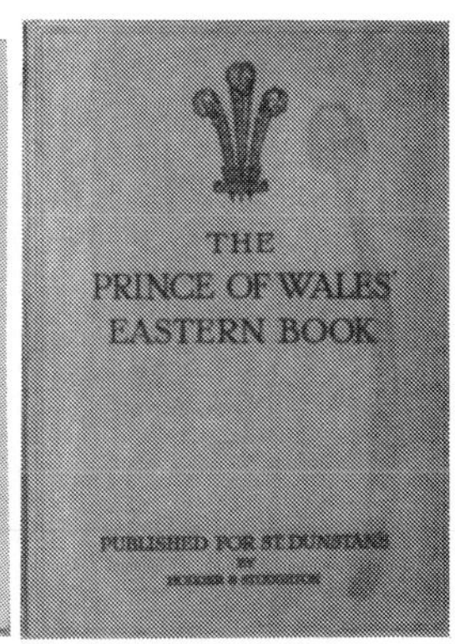

The Prince of Wales Eastern Book published by Hodder & Stoughton, 1922. £15

The Family Life of King George and Queen Mary. £2

Coronation Programme 1953. £2

Prince Charles of Edinburgh 1948. £2

The Silver Jubilee Book 1935. £4

(Yesterdays Paper)

The Illustrated London News, The Funeral Procession of King Edward VII, 1910. £7

Souvenir of the Royal Jubilee, April 1935. £4

Weekly Illustrated Annual, 'An Eventful Year In Pictures', 1936. £5

(Yesterdays Paper)

The Illustrated London News 1961. **£4**

The Illustrated London News 1952. **£4**

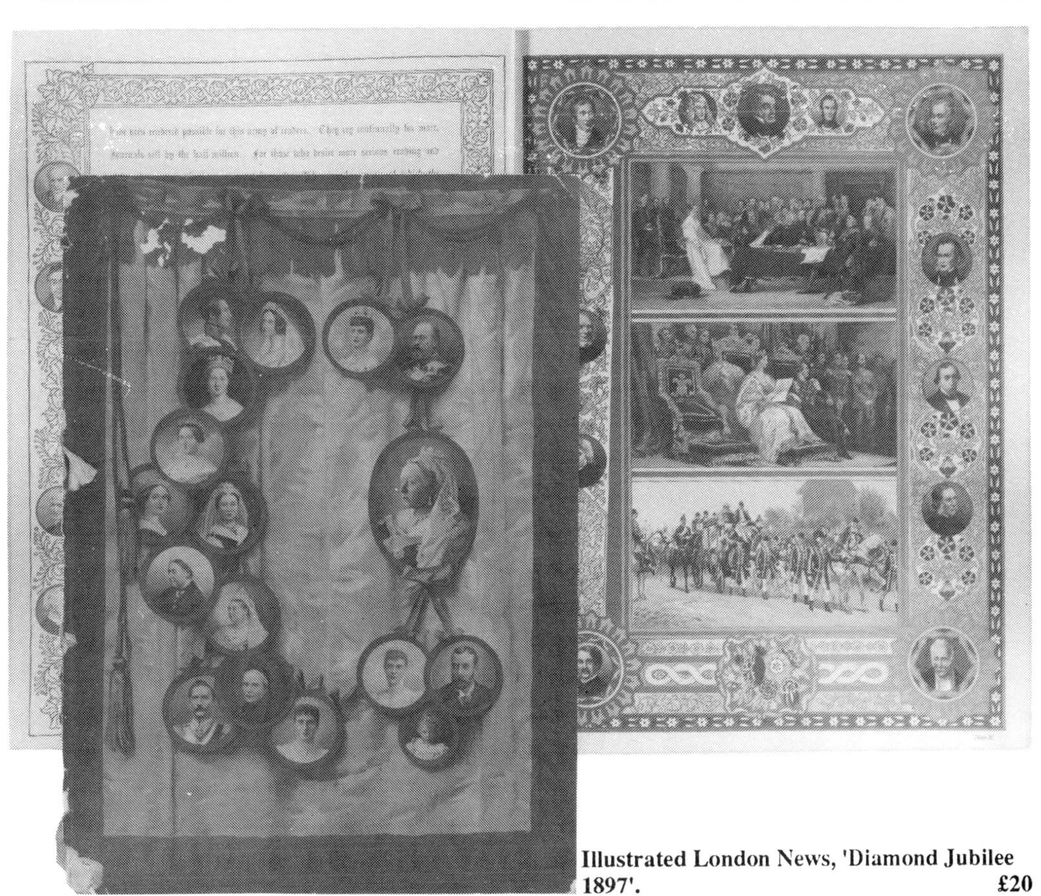

Illustrated London News, 'Diamond Jubilee 1897'. **£20**

(Yesterdays Paper)

The King and the Lady. £3

Coronation Pictures 1953. £3

The Queen's Book of the Red Cross, 1939. £8

The Coronation of the Queen, Pop-Up Book, 1953. £8

The Shell Magazine Coronation Issue 1953. £3

(Yesterdays Paper)

King Albert's Book, 1914, published for the Daily Telegraph Belgian Fund. £20

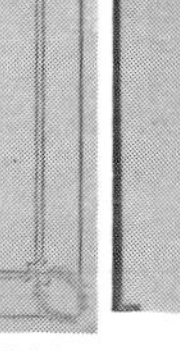

The Prince of Wales Book published for St. Dunstans, 1920. £8

The Coronation of King George VI and Queen Elizabeth by George Newnes Ltd. £10

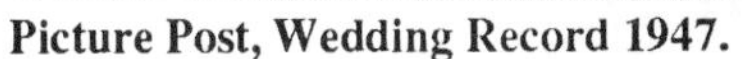
Picture Post, Wedding Record 1947. £4

The Daily Telegraph, Royal Tour 1953. £3

The Queen's Gift Book, in aid of the Queen Mary Convalescent Auxiliary Hospitals. £20

V.R.I. Her Life and Empire, published 1904. £12

The Princess Elizabeth Gift Book, in aid of the Princess Elizabeth of York Hospital for Children. £15

(Yesterdays Paper)

The 7th Dimension by Victor La Salle. £3

Astounding Science Fiction, 'The Big Front Yard', by Clifford Simak. £3.50

'Before the Beginning', by Marx Reisen, Tit Bits Science Fiction Library. £3

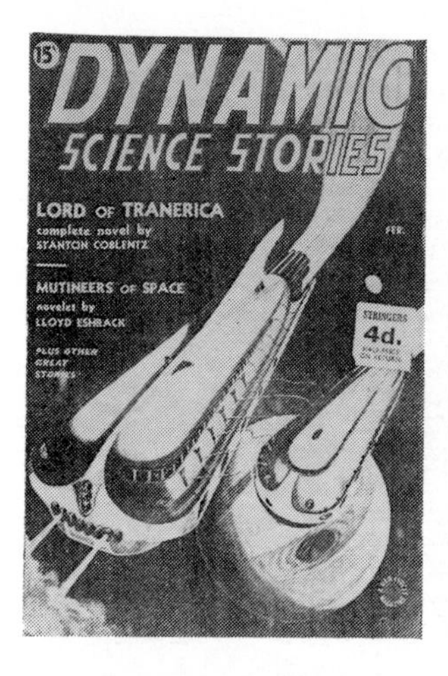

Dynamic Science Stories, 'Lord of Tranerica', a complete novel by Stanton Coblentz. £5

Amazing Stories Annual, featuring the new 'Master Mind of Mars' by Edgar Rice-Burroughs. £45

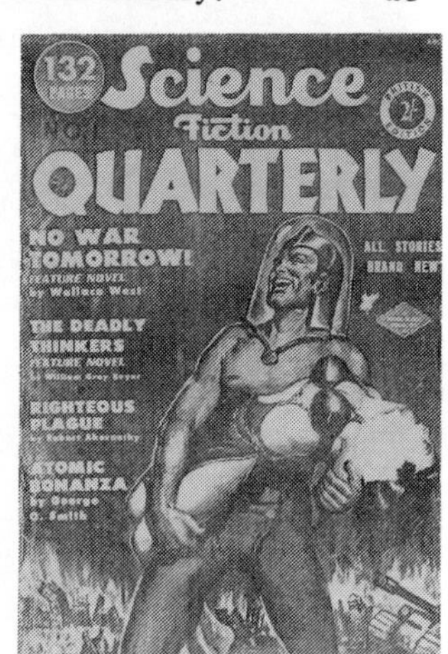

Science Fiction Quarterly, No. 1 – A Double Action Magazine. £4

Fantasy and Science Fiction, including Isaac Asimov, 1960's. £2

Science Fantasy, No. 30, Volume 10, 'Destiny Incorporated', by John Kippax. £2

Dark Andromeda by A. J. Merak, Panther Books. £3

(Yesterdays Paper)

Flash Gordon, Follow the Thrilling Adventures of the Fabulous Space Hero in the Satellite Prison, No. 1, 1962. £3

Tops in Science Fiction with features by Ray Bradbury, Ross Rocklynne and Isaac Asimov, Spring 1953, first issue. £30

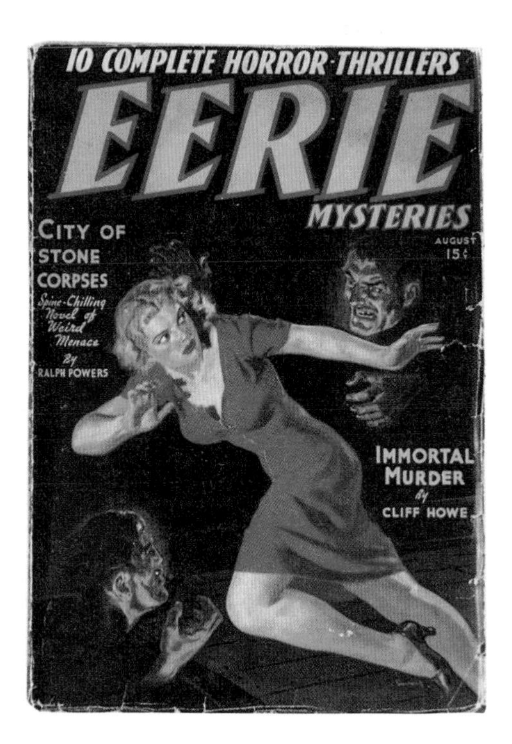

Eerie Mysteries, August 1938, featuring City of Stone Corpses by Ralph Powers, first issue. £90

Two Complete Science-Adventure Books featuring Pebble in the Sky by Isaac Asimov, Spring 1953, first issue. £25

(Denis Gifford)

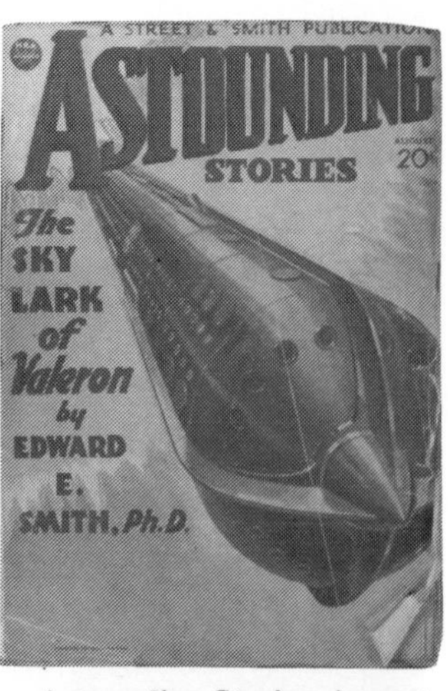

Astounding Stories, August 1934. £25

Amazing Stories, Volume 1, No. 1, April 1926, Hugo Gernsback, Editor. **£75**

Galaxy, 'Science Fiction', No. 27. £4

Fantastic, Vol. 1, No. 7, 1954. £4

Super Science Stories, No. 14. £5

Unknown, 'Fantasy Fiction', July 1940. £7

Thrilling Wonder Stories, October 1938. £18

(Yesterdays Paper)

Thrilling Wonder Stories, 'When Time Went Mad', by Dirk Wylie, a Thrilling Publication. £7

Venture Science Fiction Monthly, Zenna Henderson, Alfred Bester, 1960's. £4

Astounding Stories, November 1936, 'The Eternal Wanderer', by Nat Schachner. £12

Startling Stories, July 1939. £18

Yankee Science Fiction, No. 3, 1940's. £8

Marvel Science Stories, November 1938. £20

Wonder Stories, 'The Best In Science Fiction', August 1935. £18

Science Fiction, Vol. 1, Number 1, March 1939. £40

(Yesterdays Paper)

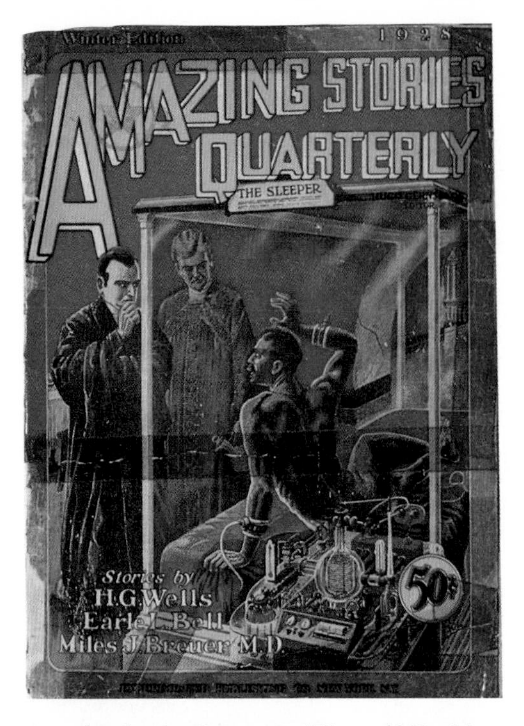

Amazing Stories Quarterly, Winter 1928 with stories by H. G. Wells, first issue. £100

Fantastic Adventures, May 1939 featuring The Invisible Robin Hood by Eando Binder, first issue. £75

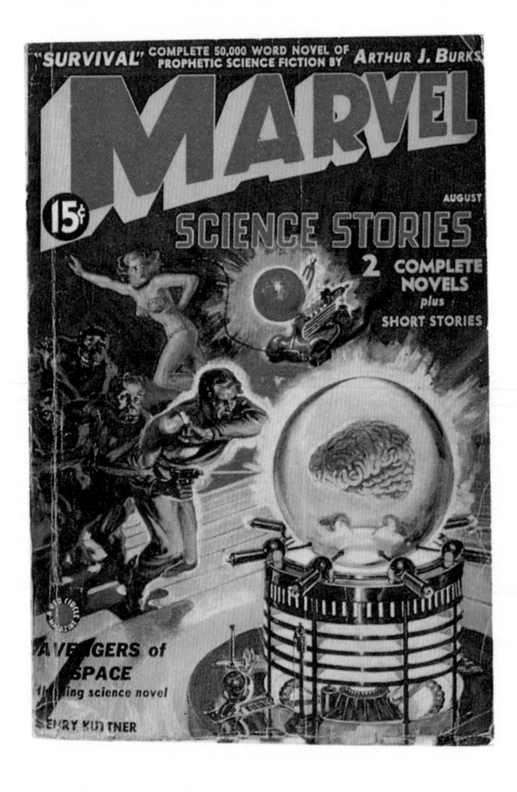

Marvel Science Stories, August 1938, featuring Avengers of Space, first issue. £90

Planet Stories, Winter 1939, Strange Adventures on other Worlds, first issue. £100

(Denis Gifford)

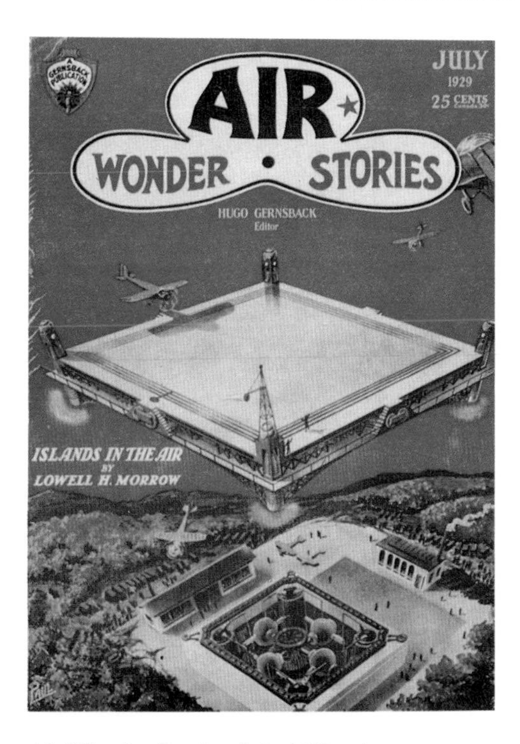

Air Wonder Stories, July 1929 edited by Hugo Gernsback, first issue. £85

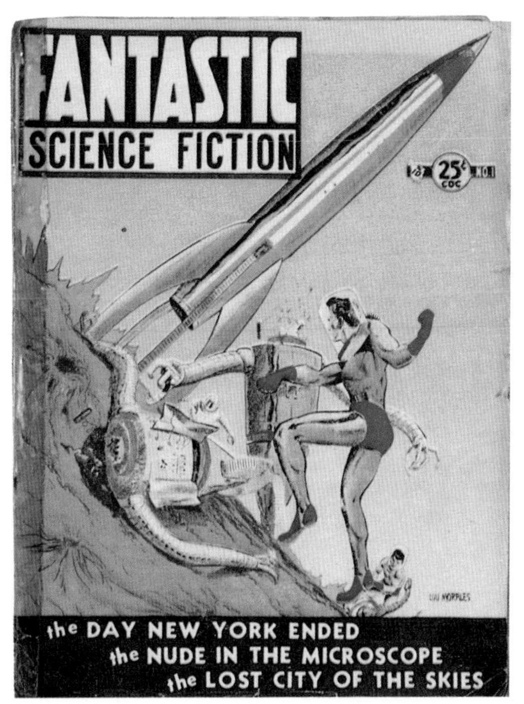

Fantastic Science Fiction, August 1952 featuring The Day New York Ended, first issue. £25

Startling Stories featuring The Black Flame by Stanley G. Weinbaum, January 1939, first issue. £50

Captain Future, Wizard of Science, Winter 1940, first issue. £100

(Denis Gifford)

Children With Flower Baskets, 4in. high. £8

Cherub on a Cloud. £3

Girl in Pink, 5in. high. £5

Rose in Hand, 7in. high. £5

The Lucky Clown, 12in. high. £15

'U' was an Usher, 'V' was a Veteran, 'W' was a Watchman, 'X' was Expensive. £8

Agnes Wickfield and Uriah Heep. £8

H.M.G.M. The Queen in 1897, 10in. high. £10

Old Mr Turveydrop and Peepy and Guppy. £8

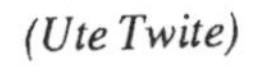

(Ute Twite)

1930's Boy with Flowers, 3in. high. £1

Winged Cherub, 4in. wide. £6

Love Birds, 3in. high. £1

'O' was an Organman, 'P' was a Parson, 6in. high. £8

Victoria Cross Gallery, Sergeant H. Ramage. £8

Red Roses, 3½in. high. £5

Father Christmas with Presents. £5

Kitten in a Floral Basket, 9in. high. £10

(Ute Twite)

Mr Serjeant Buzfuz, Mrs Bardell and Master Tommy Bardell. £8

Robin by her nest with four eggs. £4

Fruit picking, two Victorian girls picking peaches, 7" high. £15

Mother cat and tortoiseshell kitten with red bow. £5

Resting but Watchful, recumbent terrier. £3

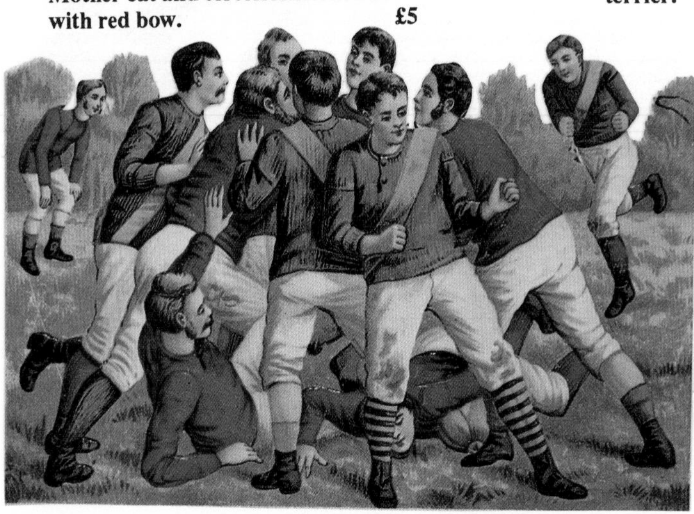

Rough and tumble on the playing fields, 7" wide. £10

Christmas 'angel' in button boots, 5½" high. £4

(Ute Twite)

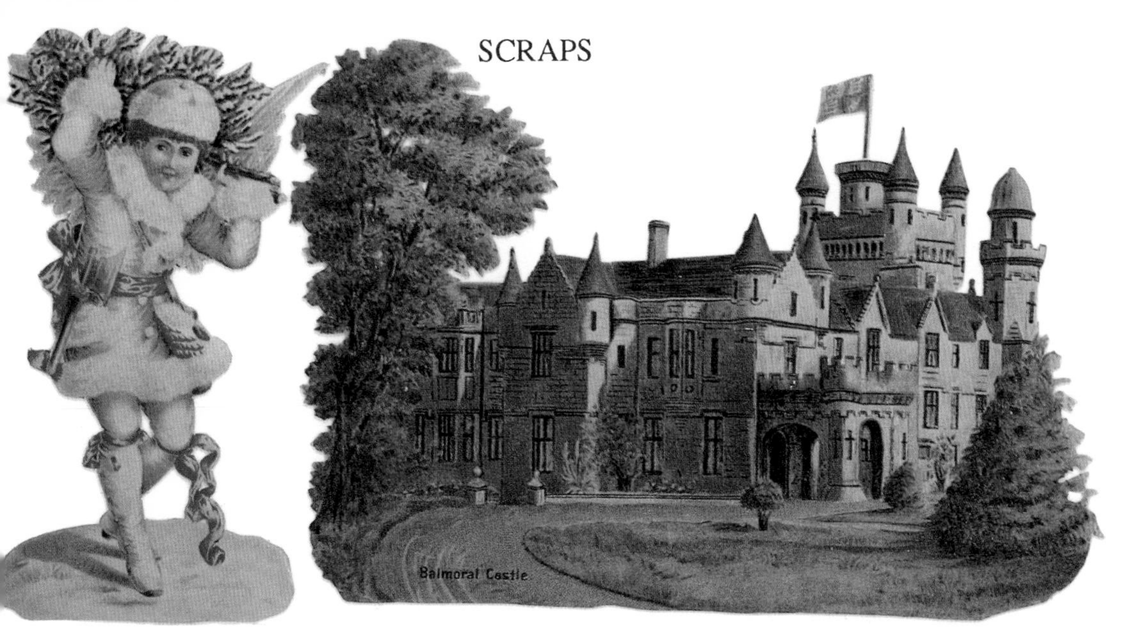

Bringing home the Christmas tree, $5^1/_2$" high. £4

Balmoral Castle – the Royal Family in Residence, 7" wide. £8

Presents for all – Santa Claus distributing presents to dancing children, $12^1/_2$" high. £30

His Majesty King Edward VII in full military uniform, $12^1/_2$" high. £20

(Ute Twite)

Magic Moments by Hal David and Burt Bacharach, 1957. £5

Belgravia Valse by Dan Godfrey. £10

The Loveliest Night of the Year by Paul Francis Webster, 1951. £4

Forty-Seven Ginger Headed Sailors by Leslie Sarony, 1928. £2

You Can't do That There 'Ere by Jack Rolls and Raymond Wallace, 1935. £6

South Pacific Song Album by Rogers and Hammerstein, 1949. £4

Wings Over the Navy by Johnny Mercer and Harry Warden, 1938. £7

Veni-Vidi-Vici by Paul Francis Webster and Jerry Livingston, 1954. £5

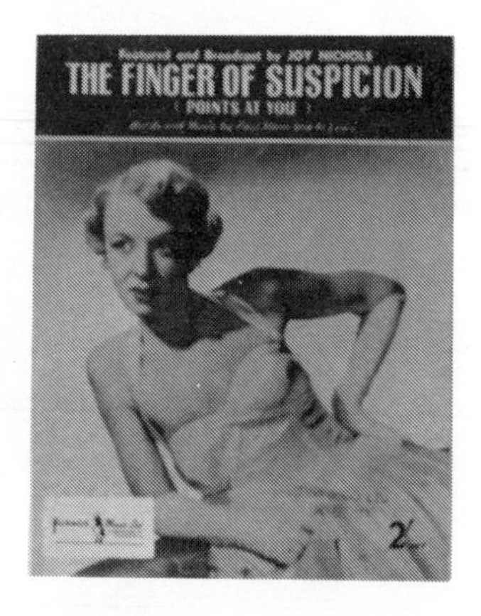

The Finger of Suspicion by Paul Mann and Al Lewis, 1954. £4

(Yesterdays Paper)

White Christmas by Irving Berlin, 1942. £1

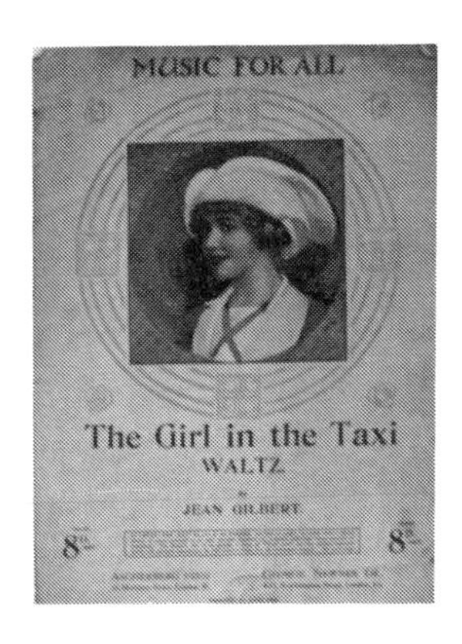

The Girl in the Taxi Waltz by Jean Gilbert, 1911. £3

How do you do it? by Mitch Murray, 1962. £7

Two Kinds of Teardrops by Del Shannon and M. McKenzie, 1963. £6

Oh! My Pa-Pa (O Mein Papa) by Paul Burkhard, 1953. £3

The Dancing Years by Ivor Novello, 1939. £6

Green Fields by Terry Gilkyson, Rich Dehr and Frank Miller, 1960. £6

I'm Sending a Letter to Santa Claus by Lanny Rogers and Spencer Williams, 1939. £2

My Heart Cries for You by Carl Sigman and Percy Faith, 1950. £5

(Yesterdays Paper)

Vilikens & his Dinah by Mr F. Robson, 1840. £12

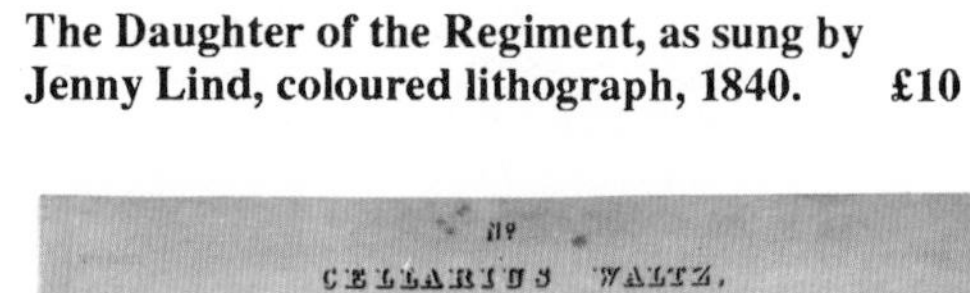

The Daughter of the Regiment, as sung by Jenny Lind, coloured lithograph, 1840. £10

The Jolly Docs Polka, by C. H. R. Marriott, coloured lithograph, 1870. £10

Cellarius Waltz by Charles Coote, 1845. £10

(Spread Eagle Antiques)

The Merry Sherwood Ranger composed by Alexander Lee, 1840. £40

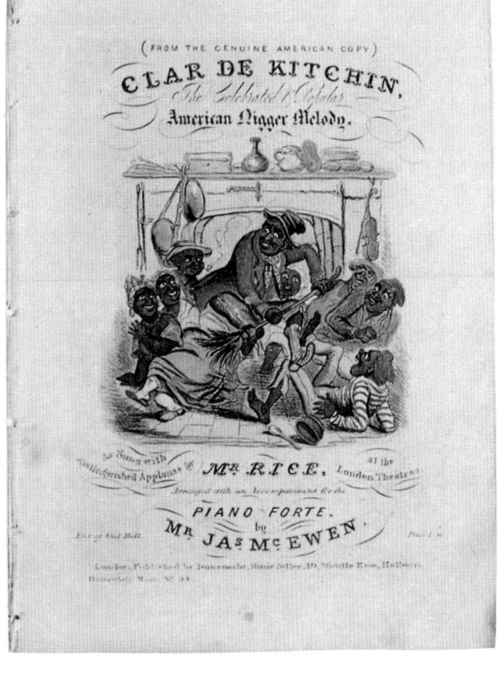

Clar de Kitchin, by Mr Jas. McEwan. £22

I Bought Her a Sealskin Jacket by W. Bint, 1850. £5

The Scientific Simpleton composed by Vincent Davies, 1850. £20

(Spread Eagle Antiques)

Cricket, The Song of the 'Centuries' by J. Harcourt Smith. £12

The Bus Conductor by A. F. Byron. £12

The New Lancers by Charles D'Albert. £8

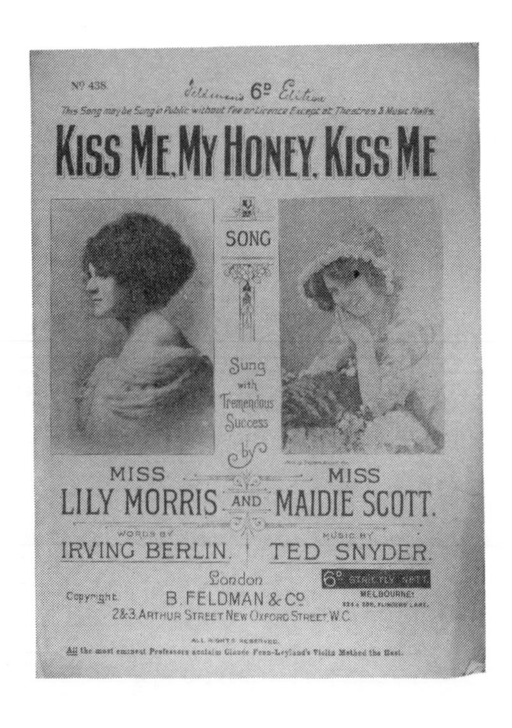

Kiss Me, My Honey, Kiss Me by Irving Berlin. £3

(Yesterdays Paper)

The Gay Photographer by George Grossmith Jun. **£12**

Everybody's Doing It Now! by Irving Berlin. **£3**

Panama, In Sunny Panama by Howard Flynn. **£3**

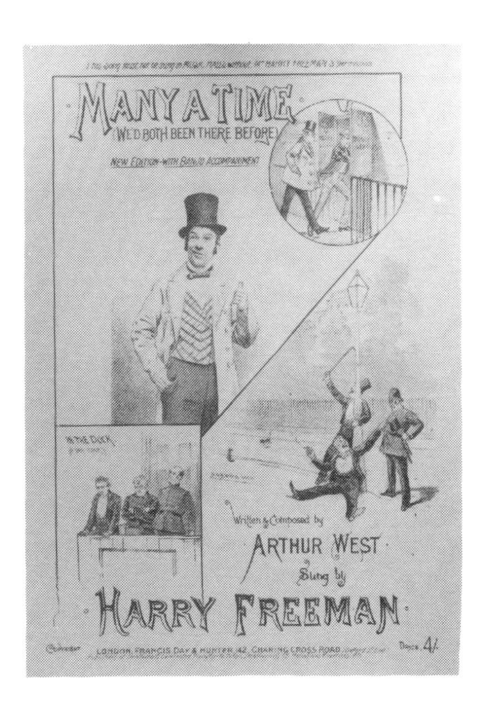

Many A Time by Arthur West. **£10**

(Yesterdays Paper)

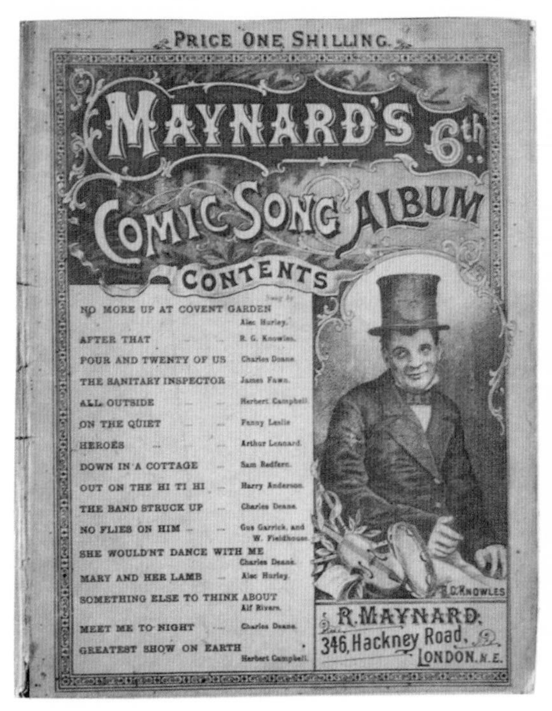

Maynard's 6th Comic Song Album, circa 1850. £8

Dan Tucker & Jim Crackcom, sung by the Ethiopian Serenaders, circa 1830. £14

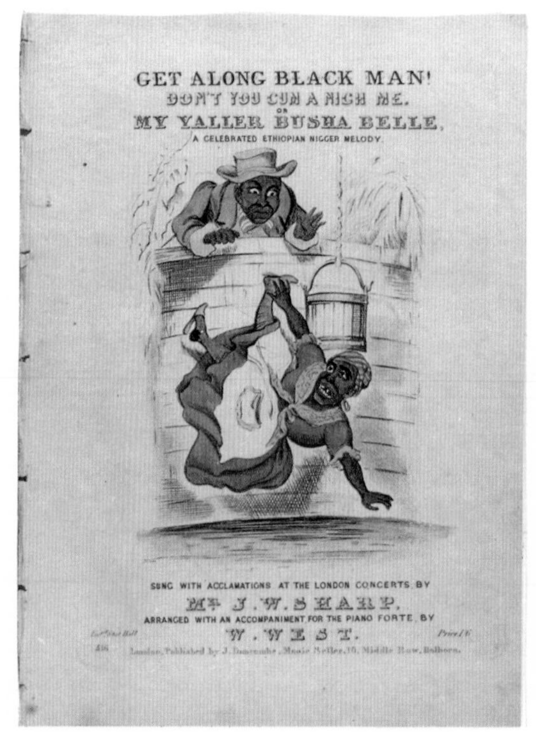

Get Along Black Man! arranged by W. West, circa 1830. £25

The Village Deserted to Follow the Drum, arranged by J. Blewitt, 1830. £10

(Spread Eagle Antiques)

Feldman's First Comic Annual, circa 1850. £8

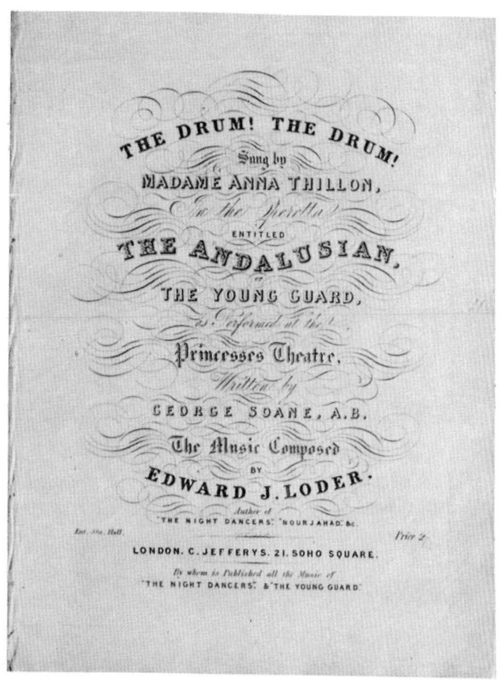

The Drum! The Drum! by Edward J. Loder, circa 1830. £6

'Who's Dat Knockin' at de Door?' arranged and harmonised by Robt. Guylott, circa 1830. £25

News of the World Comic Song Album, circa 1850. £8

(Spread Eagle Antiques)

High Noon by Ned Washington. £2

Buttons And Bows by Livingston and Evans. £2

Ridin' High by Cole Porter. £2

Everybody's Twistin' by Ted Koehler. £2

Jessica by Dusty Negulesco. £2

I Call Your Name by Lennon and McCartney. £3

Tickle Me, Timothy, Do! by Weston and Barnes. £2

Gamblin' Man by Woodie Guthrie and Lonnie Donegan. £3

Singing The Blues by Melvin Endsley. £2

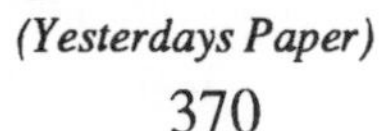
(Yesterdays Paper)

I Took My Harp To A Party by Desmond Carter. £2

I'm Sorry I Didn't Say I'm Sorry by Eddie Pola. £2

It Doesn't Matter Any More by Paul Anka. £4

King Size Twist by Dennis King. £2

Yes, Tonight, Josephine by Winfield Scott and Dorothy Goodman, 1957. £4

I've Got Another Lovin' Mamma by Burke and Herscher. £2

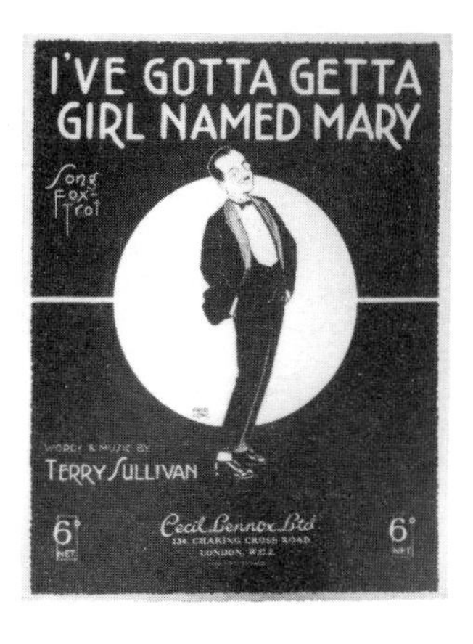

I've Gotta Getta Girl Named Mary by Terry Sullivan. £2

Give Ireland Back To The Irish by Paul McCartney. £2

What's Wrong With Fish by Butler, Tilsley and Evans. £3

(Yesterdays Paper)

Don't do that to the Poor Puss Cat by Leslie Sarony and Frank Eyton, 1928. £12

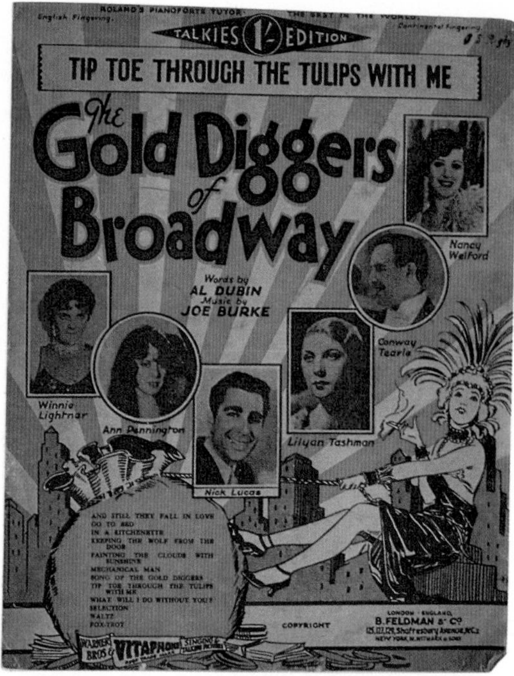

Gold Diggers of Broadway, Tip toe through the tulips with me by A.L. Dubin. £6

Dreaming Eyes Waltz by Thurley Beale, published by W. Paxton & Co. Ltd., London, circa 1904. £8

Imagination Valse, by Gene Williams, published by The Lawrence Wright Music Co., 1920's. £10

(Spread Eagle Antiques)

Je T'aime Moi Non Plus, Love at first sight, published by Shapiro, Bernstein & Co. Ltd., 1969. £4

Dream Daddy played by Jack Hylton's Band, 1923. £5

Bees Worth Hiving, a political comic designed as a music cover. £22

Mme. Vestris' 'Buy a Broom', the Bavarian Girl's song, 1830. £14

(Spread Eagle Antiques)

Have You Seen Your Mother, Baby, Standing In The Shadow by Jagger and Richard. £3

I Can't Give You Anything But Love by Dorothy Fields. £2

Cumberland Gap by Lonnie Donegan. £3

Young Love by Carole Joyner and Ric Cartey. £2

She's A Great, Great Girl by Harry Woods. £2

Peggy Sue by Terry Allison and Norman Petty. £4

Wake Up, Little Susie by Boudleaux Bryant and Felice Bryant. £2

Sitting On The Cold Wet Grass by Weston and Lee. £2

Friends And Neighbours by Scott and Lockyer. £2

(Yesterdays Paper)

When A Lady Meets A Gentleman Down South by Dave Oppenheim. £2

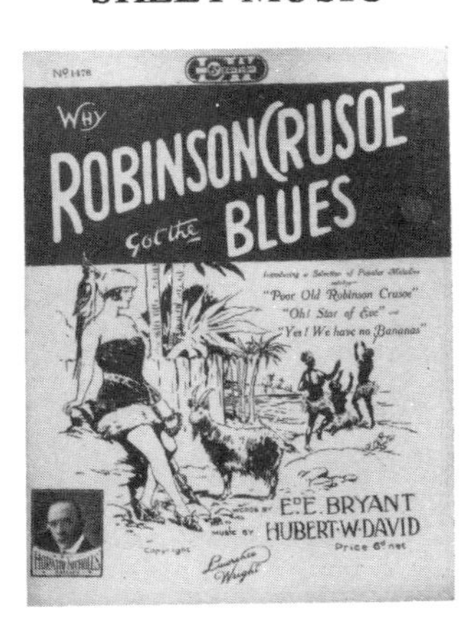

Why Robinson Crusoe Got The Blues by Ed Bryant. £2

Moonshine Is Better Than Sunshine by Theo Norman. £2

She's A Good Good Girl! by Billy Milton. £2

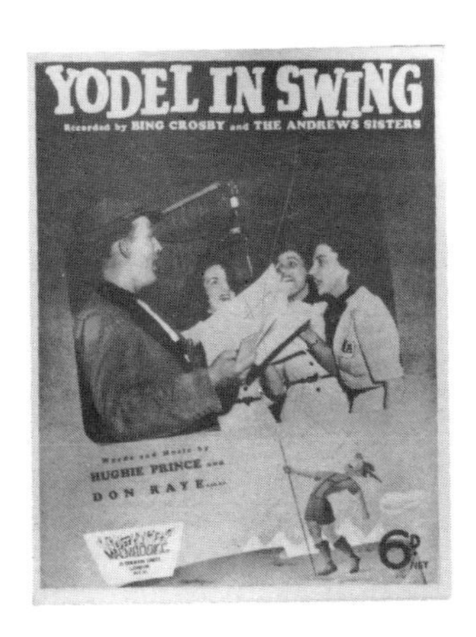

Yodel In Swing by Hughie Prince and Don Raye. £2

When The Waltz Was Through by Archie Gottler. £2

Felix Kept On Walking by Ed. E. Bryant. £8

Oh! How She Touches Me by Flynn and Butler. £2

(Yesterdays Paper)

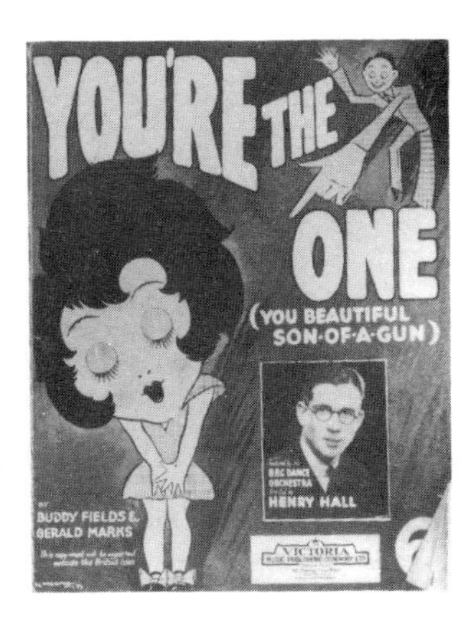

You're The One by Buddy Fields and Gerald Marks. £2

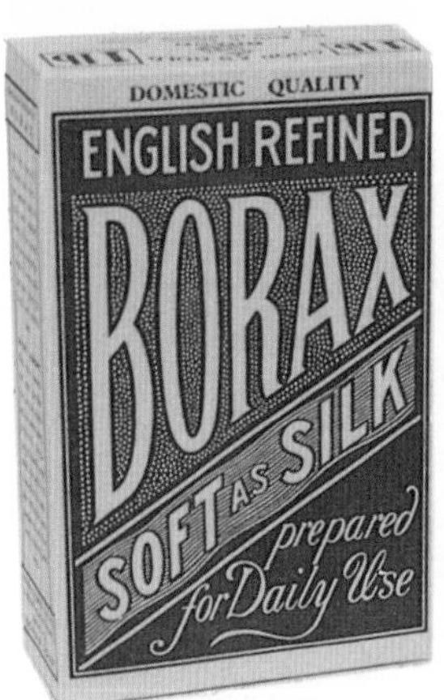

English Refined Borax, Domestic quality, 1920's. £6

Compo The Safe Washer. £12

Chipso Soap Flakes, fine for fine things, 1920. £7

Surf, Lathers like Magic, 1953. £10

Rub-No-More, The Cleanser and Washing Powder, American. £20

S.C.W.S. Sprinkle. £10

Persil, Washes Whiter, Yes it does!, 1950. £7

Diesel, Zelfwerkend Wasmiddel, Holland 1949. £6

New Glee, For Everything You Wash, 1949. £9

(Colin & Janet Davis)

Brownie Washing Powder, 1932. £15

The Wonder Worker Ipso Washes by Itself, 1920's. £7

Blancoline, Dutch packet, 1940's. £6

Perfumed Soap Flakes by Gerards of Nottingham. £18

Rain Drops, Softens, Cleans, Blues, 1940's American. £7

A.1. Soap Powder, Wartime pack. £15

Daz, It's New, Blue, Boils Whitest of All, 1955. £10

Waeslandia, Zeeppoeder, Holland 1949. £6

Bluinite, Yogi Bear pack, 1962. £25

(Colin & Janet Davis)

Fels-Naptha Soap Chips 1930's American packet. £10

The Scotsman Soap Powder. £8

Brobat Suds, All Purpose Washer, Wartime pack. £10

Rinso Washes Whiter than New. £4

Ino Green Soap, 1954. £4

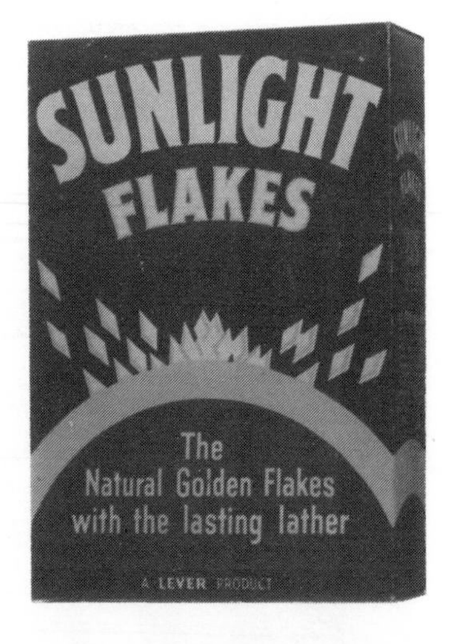

Lavro The Easy Washing Powder, Works by Itself. £4

Greesoff by Homepacs Ltd., Cleans everything in the kitchen, 7" high. £4

Mam'sel for Washing Woollens, 1949. £12

Sunlight Flakes, The Natural Golden Flakes with the lasting lather, 1940. £18

(Colin & Janet Davis)

Kudos Pure Soap Flakes, 1939. £10

Lux Wartime emergency pack. £12

Gossages Dry Soap. £16

Ripley's Oval Blue counter box with contents. £15

Mother Shipton Soap, No Boiling. £3

Frisky Soap Powder. £14

Lady's Maid, Gives Silky Lather for a Wash, 1943. £8

Wulcot Soap Flakes, for everything washable, 1930's. £15

(Colin & Janet Davis)

Smith's Soda, Triple Strength. £9

Dry Soap Powder, Wartime Economy Pack. £18

Tide, Gets clothes cleanest, 1954. £7

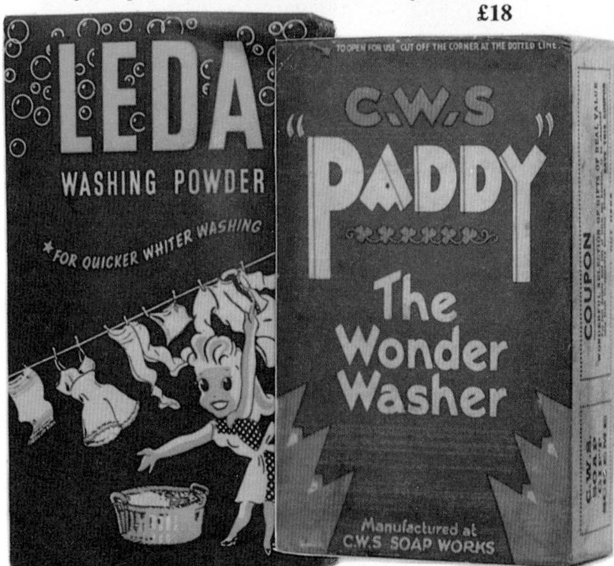

Leda Washing Powder, 1943. £8

C.W.S. Paddy, The Wonder Washer. £9

Puro Soap Powder. £15

Fun-To-Wash, Washing Powder, American packet. £20

Everest Soap Flakes, 1930's. £18

Oxygen Palm Oil Soap Powder. £9

(Colin & Janet Davis)

S.C.W.S. Soap Flakes. £10

Satin Foam, containing three sample packs, 1960's. £14

English Refined Borax, 1920's. £6

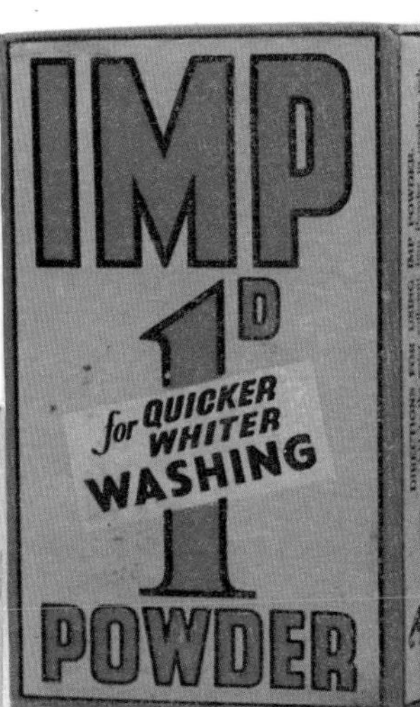

Imp Powder for quicker, whiter, washing. £12

Clozone, specially prepared for washing machines. £9

Twink, Made by the makers of Lux, 1920's. £14

Babee Diaper wash, American packet. £6

Blue Omo with exclusive W.M.7, 1965. £10

(Colin & Janet Davis)

A Delicious Sparkling Non Alcoholic Beverage, Lime Crush, 1930s. £4

Super Cherry Ciderette, 1950s. £2

Doubleday & Co., Diss, High Class Sparkling Raspberryade, 1930s. £3

Lime Squash, 1930s. £1

A Pleasant Tonic Beverage, Iron Brew, 1910s. £5

Lem-Ora Two in One, Contains Fresh Fruit Juice of Lemons and Oranges, 1930s. £1

North & Co. Oxford, American Cream Soda, 1930s. £4

Bowen's Cherry Cider, Morriston Aberdare This Label is Issued Solely by J.S. Bowen & Son Ltd., 1940s. £2

Apricot, George Sahely, Basseterre, St Kitts, 1910s. £5

(Michael Jones)

Soda Water Manufactured by James Dunbar, Albion Road, Edinburgh 1890s. £7

The Super Aerated Water Co. Neath, Dry Lemonade, 1950s. £2

Lemonade, Prepared by James Carmichael, Edinburgh, 1890s. £7

Lemon Squash, 1930's. £1

Sparkling Thirst Relieving Lime Juice and Soda, The Latest Summer Drink, David Nicoll, Dundee, 1920s. £4

Orange Squash, 1930s. £1

Tower Table Waters, Leeds & Dewsbury, Invigorating Sarsaparilla, 1940s. £2

Orange Champagne, 1940s. £2

The Super Aerated Water Co., Neath, Orange Crush, 1950s. £2

(Michael Jones)

Borax Starch Glaze, 1880. £22

Glossie, The Wonder Starch. £4

Pure Gloss Starch, Grace Darling Starch Co. £18

Colman's Cream Starch. £12

Colman's No. 1 Rice Starch. £6

Parsons Fletcher Indian Starch counter box. £15

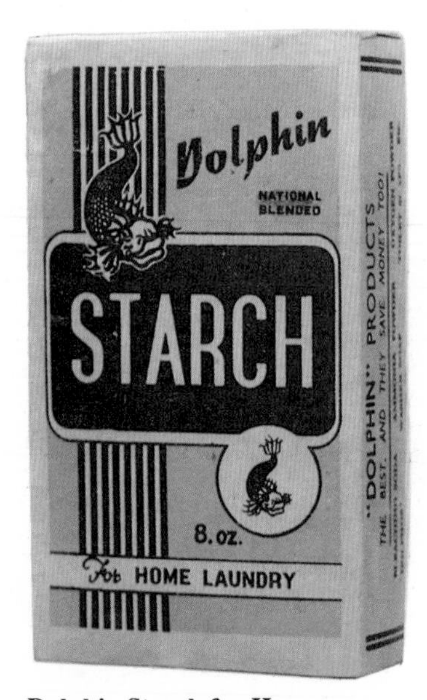

Dolphin Starch for Home Laundry, Wartime pack. £12

Dip, the long life starcher, 1950's. £4

Pure Rice Johnson's Starch. £18

(Colin & Janet Davis)

T. R. Williams – Two young men with a woman plucking game, 1850s, stereoscopic daguerreotype, hand tinted, printed paper label on reverse. (Christie's S. Ken) £4,400

Anon, Nude, 1850s, stereoscopic daguerreotype, lightly hand-**tinted and with gilt highlights, paper-taped with label numbered *No. 14/209* on verso.** (Christie's) **£4,070**

H. Negretti & Zambra, Crystal Palace, one of four stereoscopic daguerreotypes with photographer's printed paper pictorial advertising label, 1850's. (Christie's) £462

A carpenter in his workshop, 1850s, a fine stereoscopic daguerreotype, hand tinted, oval surrounds, passe-partout. (Christie's S. Ken) £2,420

Anon, Reclining nude (inspired by Ingres), 1850s, stereoscopic daguerreotype, hand-tinted, gilt highlights, paper-taped. (Christie's) **£8,800**

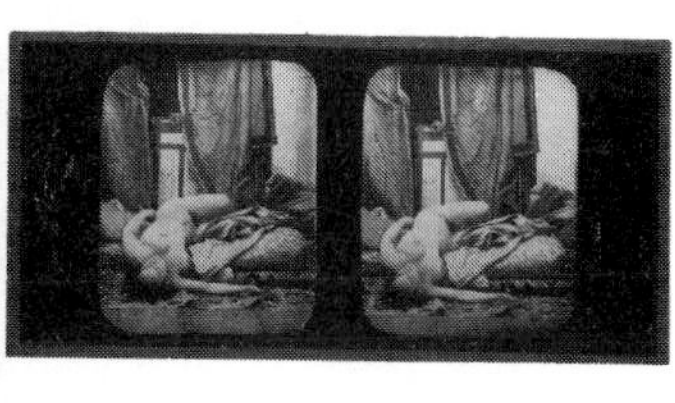

Anon, Reclining nude with a man in the background, 1850s, stereoscopic daguerreotype, hand-tinted, paper-taped. (Christie's) **£10,450**

T. R. Williams, Still life of vegetables and game, stereoscopic daguerreotype, 1850's. (Christie's) £605

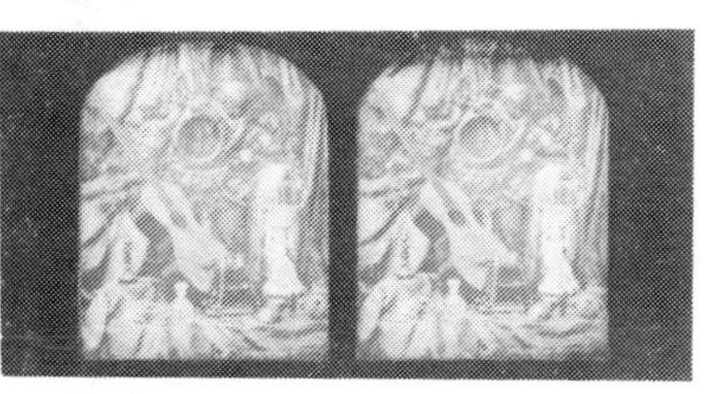

T. R. Williams – Still-life including Brewster stereoscope and studio reflection, mid 1850's. (Christie's) £660

Anon, The basket maker, stereoscopic daguerreotype, black glass surround, 1850's. (Christie's) £308

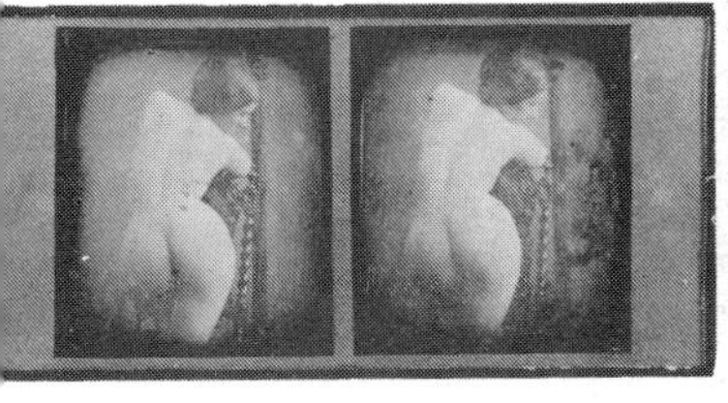

Anon, Standing nude leaning on a chair, 1850s, stereoscopic daguerreotype, hand-tinted, paper-taped. (Christie's) **£1,980**

Anon, reclining nude reading a book, 1850s, stereoscopic daguerreotype, hand-tinted, paper-taped. (Christie's) **£4,620**

Anon, Reclining nude with bird in her hand, 1850s, stereoscopic daguerreotype, hand-tinted, paper-taped. (Christie's) **£2,200**

THE
BRITISH WORKER
OFFICIAL STRIKE NEWS BULLETIN
Published by The General Council of the Trades Union Congress

WORKERS CALM AND STEADY

BLACKLEGS FAIL

LABOUR'S REPLY TO THE PREMIER

General Council's Conditions for Reopening Discussions

"UNFETTERED ATMOSPHERE"

HOW THE "B.W." CAME OUT

AMAZING SCENES

OUR REPLY TO "JIX"

'The British Worker', published by The General Council of the Trade Union Congress, Price One Penny, May 6th, 1926. £5

STRIKE EMERGENCY EDITION
DAILY GRAPHIC
SATURDAY, MAY 8, 1926. ONE PENNY
THE SPIRIT OF GOOD WILL.

'Daily Graphic', Strike Emergency Edition, One Penny, Saturday May 8th, 1926. £5

Daily Express
LONDON, THURSDAY, MAY 6, 1926. ONE PENNY.

COOL COMMON SENSE

FIGURING OUT THE CONSEQUENCES

A Steadfast Nation

AMERICA on the CRISIS

Our Capacity for Emerging Safely

THE LION AT BAY

THIRD DAY OF THE GREAT STRIKE

The Nation faces Crisis calmly

NO SERIOUS DISTURBANCES.

WHOLE COUNTRY CALM

PICKETS FINED AT WEST HAM

ELECTRICIANS ON STRIKE

MORE TRAINS TO-DAY

OMNIBUS ATTACKS

STOCK EXCHANGE

A STRANGE SIGHT

CHESTER RACING

'Daily Express', One Penny, Thursday, May 6th, 1926. £5

Daily News
AND
The Star

GENERAL STRIKE CALLED OFF.

DRAMATIC PEACE VISIT TO PREMIER.

Truce in Disastrous Industrial War.

MINERS' EXECUTIVE DECISION.

T.U.C. Basis for Renewal of Coal Negotiations.

MINERS DEFIANT

THE NEXT STEP

'Daily News & The Star', One Penny, May 13th, 1926. £5

(Yesterdays Paper)

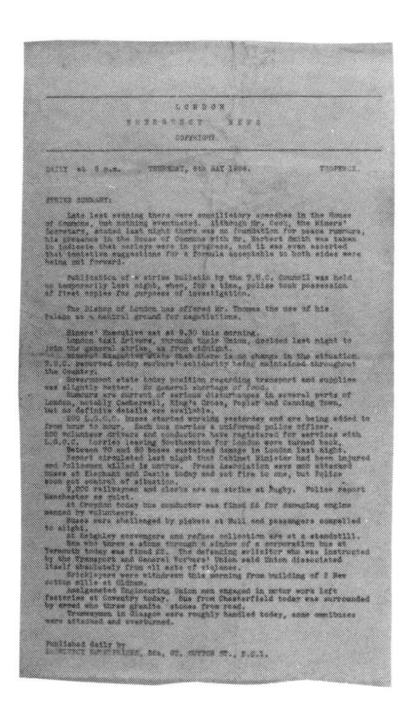

LONDON
EMERGENCY NEWS
COPYRIGHT.

DAILY at 5 p.m. THURSDAY, 6th MAY 1926. TWOPENCE.

STRIKE SUMMARY:

Late last evening there were conciliatory speeches in the House of Commons, but nothing eventuated. Although Mr. Cook, the Miners' Secretary, stated last night there was no foundation for peace rumours, his presence in the House of Commons with Mr. Herbert Smith was taken to indicate that parleys were in progress, and it was even asserted that tentative suggestions for a formula acceptable to both sides were being put forward.

Publication of a strike bulletin by the T.U.C. Council was held up temporarily last night, when, for a time, police took possession of first copies for purposes of investigation.

The Bishop of London has offered Mr. Thomas the use of his Palace as a neutral ground for negotiations.

Miners' Executive met at 9.30 this morning.

London taxi drivers, through their Union, decided last night to join the general strike, as from midnight.

Miners' Executive state that there is no change in the situation. T.U.C. reported today workers' solidarity being maintained throughout the Country.

Government state today position regarding transport and supplies was slightly better. No general shortage of food.

Rumours are current of serious disturbances in several parts of London, notably Camberwell, King's Cross, Poplar and Canning Town, but no definite details are available.

[illegible] L.G.O.C. buses started working yesterday and are being added to from hour to hour. Each bus carries a uniformed police officer. [illegible] volunteer drivers and conductors have registered for services with L.G.O.C. Lorries leaving Southampton for London were turned back.

Between 70 and 80 buses sustained damage in London last night.

Report circulated last night that Cabinet Minister had been injured and Policemen killed is untrue. Press Association says mob attacked buses at Elephant and Castle today and set fire to one, but Police soon got control of situation.

[illegible] railwaymen and clerks are on strike at Rugby. Police report Manchester as quiet.

At Croydon today bus conductor was fined £5 for damaging engine manned by volunteers.

Buses were challenged by pickets at Hull and passengers compelled to alight.

At Keighley scavengers and refuse collection are at a standstill.

Man who threw a stone through a window of a corporation bus at Yarmouth today was fined £2. The defending solicitor who was instructed by the Transport and General Workers' Union said Union dissociated itself absolutely from all acts of violence.

Bricklayers were withdrawn this morning from building of 2 new cotton mills at Oldham.

Amalgamated Engineering Union men engaged in motor work left factories at Coventry today. Bus from Chesterfield today was surrounded by crowd who threw granite stones from road.

Tramwaymen in Glasgow were roughly handled today, some omnibuses were attacked and overturned.

Published daily by
[illegible], E.C.1.

London Emergency News (Strike newspaper) May 6, 1926. £4

PLEASE PASS ON THIS COPY OR DISPLAY IT

The British Gazette

GENERAL STRIKE OFF

The Morning Post.
ON FRIDAY, MAY 14,
THE MORNING POST
will
RESUME PUBLICATION.
Price ONE Penny

'The British Gazette', Published by His Majesty's Stationery Office, One Penny, Thursday, May 13th, 1926. £5

PLEASE PASS ON THIS COPY OR DISPLAY IT

The British Gazette

Published by His Majesty's Stationery Office.

No. 6. LONDON, TUESDAY, MAY 11, 1926. ONE PENNY.

SUPPLIES IMPROVING EVERYWHERE.

MOST SUCCESSFUL DAY SINCE THE STRIKE BEGAN.

STILL MORE TRAINS.

Record Recruiting Of "Specials" In London.

"British Gazette" Passes The Million Mark.

OFFICIAL COMMUNIQUE.

WHITEHALL, May 10.

The situation in all parts of the country is well maintained.

"DIRECT ACTION."

Sir H. Slesser's Significant Opinion.

A Socialist Admission.

THE FIASCO AT OSTEND.

Story of Miners' Failure.

OVER THE POLE.

TO ALL WORKERS IN ALL TRADES.

LINER SAILINGS UNAFFECTED.

30 Vessels Discharging at Liverpool.

SOUTHAMPTON DOCKS NORMAL.

FOODSTUFFS AT SOUTHAMPTON.

THE TRUTH of the COAL NEGOTIATIONS

Where the Responsibility Rests

CONSTITUTIONAL GOVERNMENT CHALLENGED BY TRADE UNION EXECUTIVE

By Sir DOUGLAS McGAREL HOGG, K.C., M.P.
The Attorney-General

The British Gazette (Strike newspaper) May 11, 1926. £8

(Yesterdays Paper)

Virginia, Liam Devlin, 1955. £8

The Lone Ranger, Como Confectionery Co. 1963. £20

Wagon Train, Sweet Matches, Clevedon Confectionery, 1962. £2

Coronation Series (pictures on reverse), Sweetule Products 1953, set of 12. £40 set

Mickey Mouse, Barratt & Co. 1935. £30

Snow White, Barratt & Co., 1930's. £20

Cheftain, Boys Scout's Cigarettes, 1958. £7

Thunderbirds Candy Cigarettes, Barratt & Co. 1966. £15

Star Trek, Primrose Confectionery, 1971. £5

(Mike Johnson)

Red & White, Kane Products, 1955. £5

Sheriff's Special, Lynton Chocolate Co. £2

Hawkeye, Gaylon Products, 1960. £4

Campaign Chocolate Cigarettes, J. S. Fry & Sons, 6 in set. £35 each

Silver Sword, Dickson Orde, 1959. £15

Strand, Sweetule Products. £5

Navy Cut, Kane Products, 1958. £5

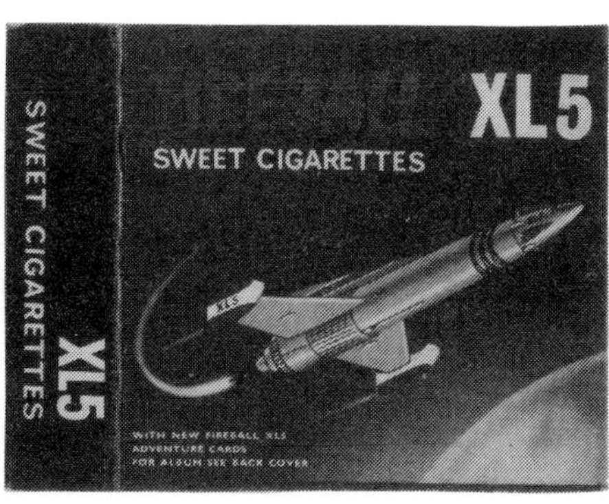

Fireball XL5, Como Confectionery Co. 1965. £15

Rin-Tin-Tin-Cadet Sweets, 1960. £8

(Mike Johnson)

Buccaneer, Cadet Sweets, 1957. £8

Star Time, Kane Products 1960. £15

The World of Ships (ships printed on reverse), Sweetule Products, set of 24. £75 set

Leader, J. Bellamy & Sons, 1908. £2

Hi-Blo Bubble Gum Cigarettes, Barratt & Co. 1970's. £4

Wyatt Earp, Como Confectionery Co., 1962. £8

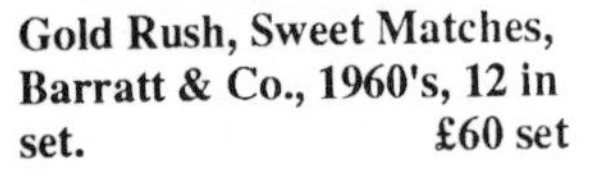

Gold Rush, Sweet Matches, Barratt & Co., 1960's, 12 in set. £60 set

Wagon Train, Barratt & Co. 1962. £15

Olympic Achievement, Comet Sweets 1956, set of 22. £30 set

(Mike Johnson)

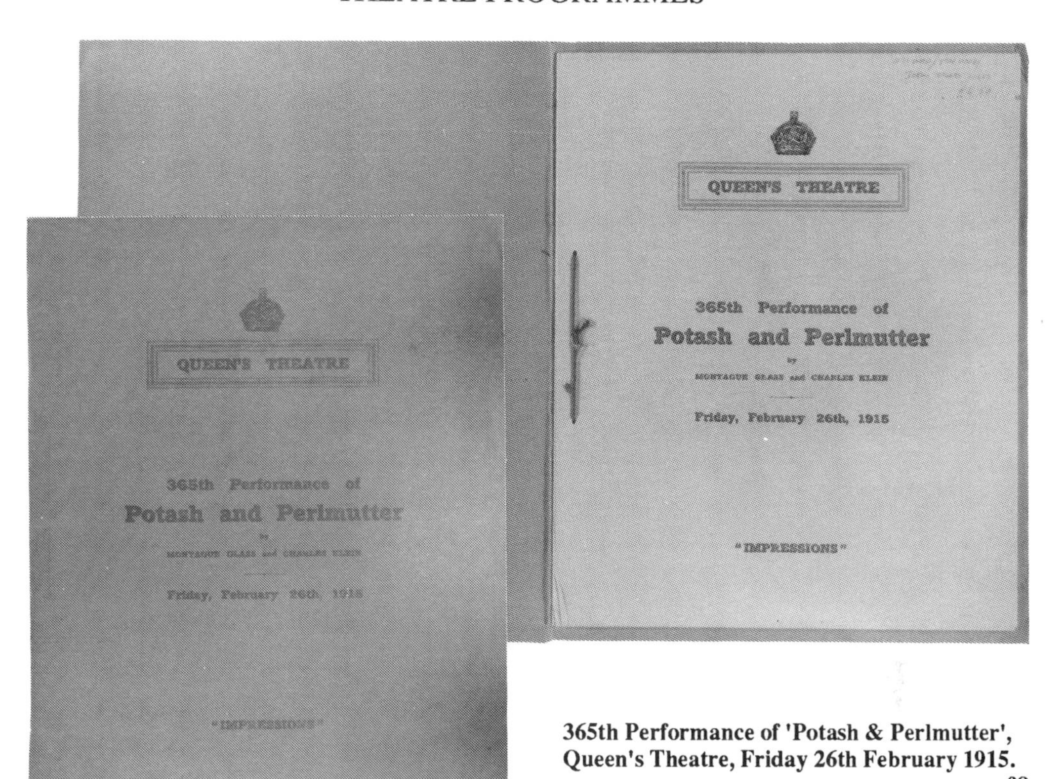

365th Performance of 'Potash & Perlmutter', Queen's Theatre, Friday 26th February 1915.
£8

250th Performance of 'Lady Frederick' at the Criterion Theatre, 3rd June 1908. £10

(Yesterdays Paper)

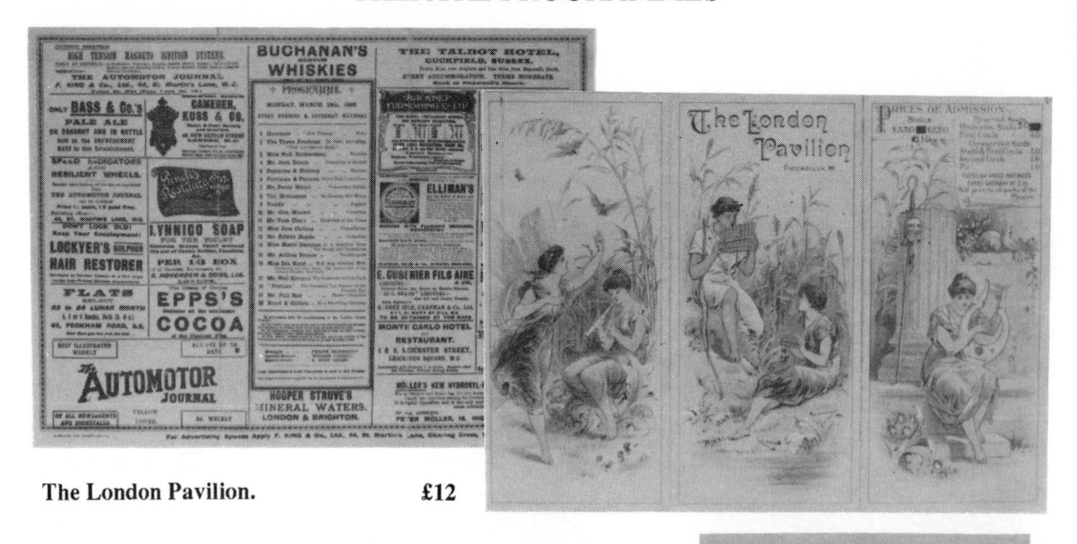

The London Pavilion. **£12**

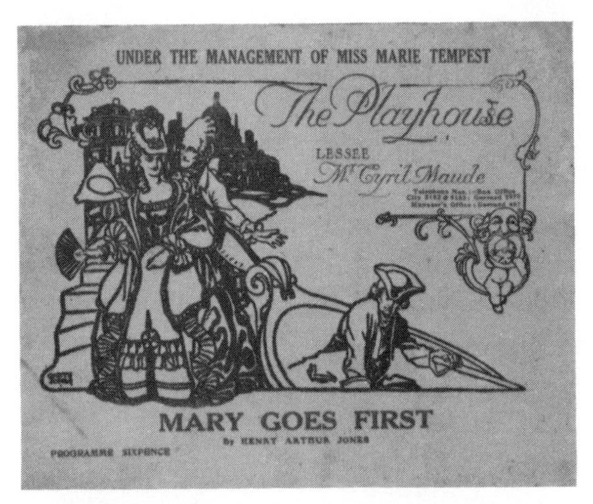

Playhouse Programme 'Mary goes First'. £10

London Pavilion revue programme 'Fun of the Fayre'.
£8

The Oxford Programme. **£15**

The London Pavilion, Piccadilly W. **£15**

(Spread Eagle Antiques)

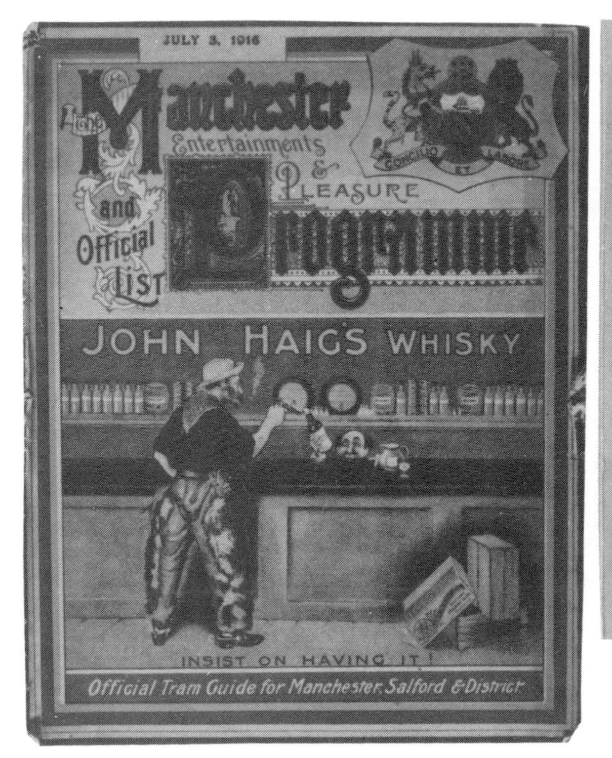

Manchester Entertainments Programme, July 3, 1916. £18

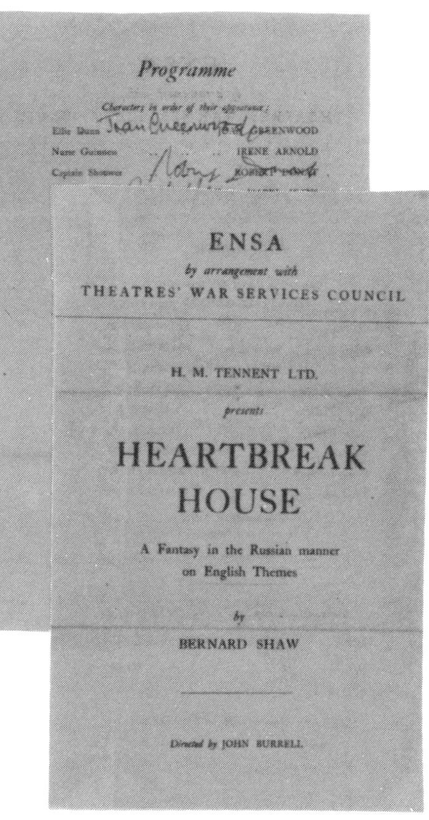

Signed ENSA programme for Heartbreak House. £5

The Oxford Programme, January 18th 1909. £15

(Spread Eagle Antiques)

Souvenir 'A White Man' Lyric Theatre, 1908. £12

The Palladium Programme, Monday, May 4th, 1931. £12

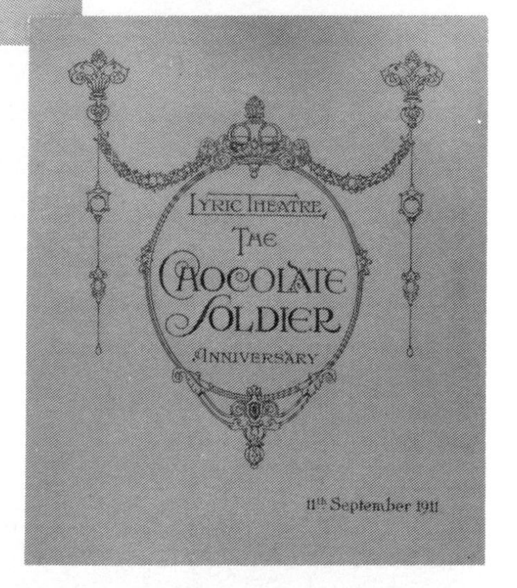

'The Chocolate Soldier', Anniversary, 11th September 1911, Lyric Theatre. £8

'Parts I Have Played' by Mr Lewis Waller 1883–1909. £10

Souvenir Album 'Ben Hur', 1900. £8

(Yesterdays Paper)

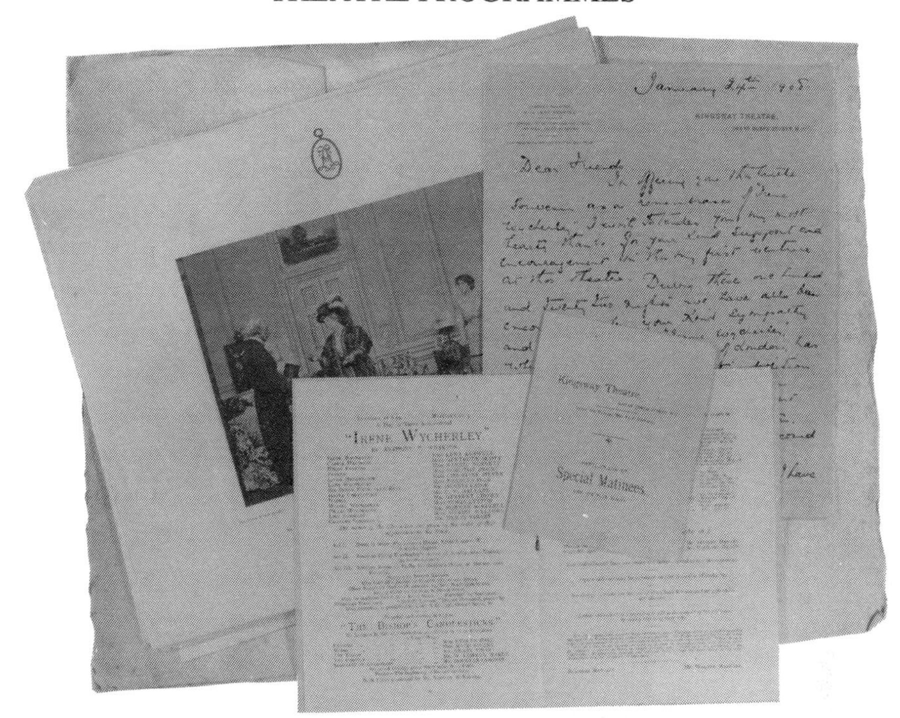

Souvenir of 'Irene Wycherley' with Lena Ashwell, January 24th, 1908. £10

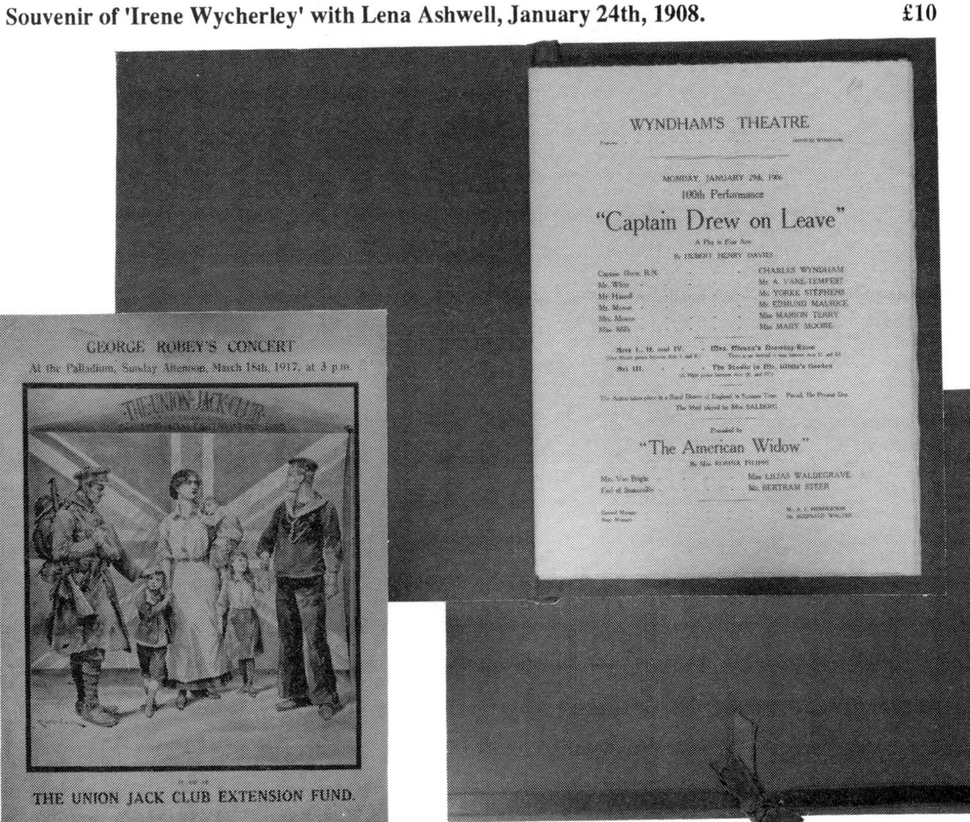

WYNDHAM'S THEATRE

MONDAY, JANUARY 29th, 1906

100th Performance

"Captain Drew on Leave"

Captain Drew, R.N.	CHARLES WYNDHAM
	Mr. A. VANE-TEMPEST
	Mr. YORKE STEPHENS
	Mr. EDMUND MAURICE
	Miss MARION TERRY
	Miss MARY MOORE

"The American Widow"

	Miss LILIAS WALDEGRAVE
	Mr. BERTRAM STEER

George Robey's Concert at the Palladium, March 18th 1917. £8

100th Performance of 'Captain Drew on Leave', January 29th 1906. £8

(Yesterdays Paper)

Strand Theatre '1066 and All That', 1935. £2

His Majesty's Theatre, 'Nero', Souvenir Programme, 9th March 1906, 50th Performance. £12

The Mermaid Theatre, 'Hadrian VII', 1968. £3

The National Theatre, 'The Importance of Being Earnest', 1982. £2

Victoria Palace, Jack Hylton's 'Crazy Gang' Review, 1959. £4

Palace Theatre, Anna Neagle in 'The Glorious Days', 28th February, 1953. £2

Savoy Theatre, 'Whose Life is it Anyway?' Tom Conti, December 1978. £2

Her Majesty's Theatre, Proprietor and Manager, Mr Herbert Beerbohm Tree, '12th Night' Souvenir Programme, 9th April 1901. £15

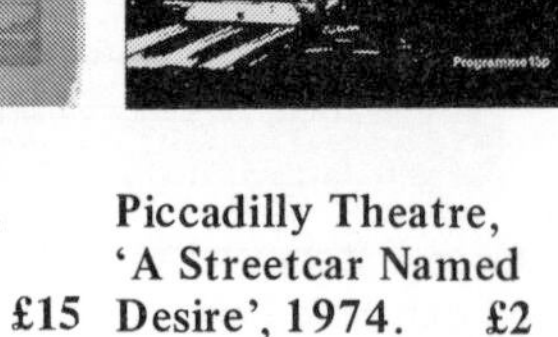

Piccadilly Theatre, 'A Streetcar Named Desire', 1974. £2

(Yesterdays Paper)

Richmond Theatre, 'Before the Party', February 11th, 1980. £2

The Lanchester Marionette Theatre directed by Waldo and Muriel Lanchester. £8

'Gone with the Wind', Palace Theatre, Shaftsbury Avenue, London. £3

Bostock and Wombwell's Royal Menagerie, originally established in 1805. £20

Talk of the Town Theatre Restaurant Souvenir Brochure. £5

Vic Oliver in Idiot's Delight, Birmingham Theatre Royal. £3

Jazz Shows Ltd., present Mr Acker Bilk. £4

'Cavalcade' Programme, Theatre Royal, Birmingham, 1933. £3

(Yesterdays Paper)

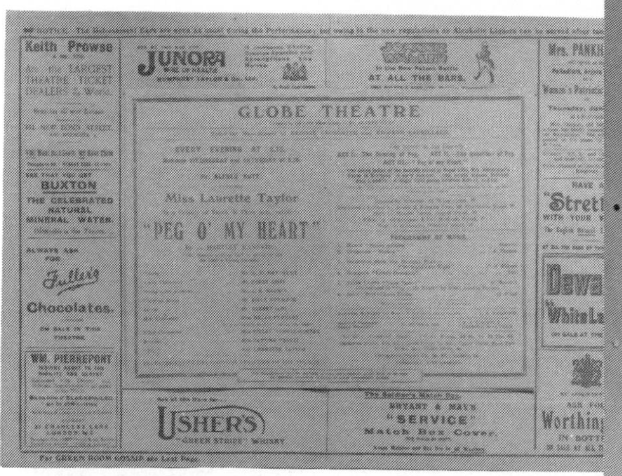

'Peg O' My Heart' at the Globe Theatre, May 31st 1915. £5

Souvenir 'The Merry Widow', First Anniversary, June 8th, 1907, Daly's Theatre. £15

Souvenir of the Opening of The Playhouse, 28th January 1907. £15

'When Knights Were Bold', 1st Anniversary, 29th January 1908, Wyndham's Theatre. £10

(Yesterdays Paper)

Titanic Leaving Southampton, glossy monochrome postcard, published by Nautical Photo Agency, N.W.7. (Onslow's) £140

A contemporary account written by Mrs F. Angle of the disaster dated 15 October 1913, on two sheets. (Onslow's) £600

White Star Royal Mail Steamer Titanic, artist drawn, pre-sinking colour postcard, postmarked 1st August 1912, State Series, Liverpool. (Onslow's) £140

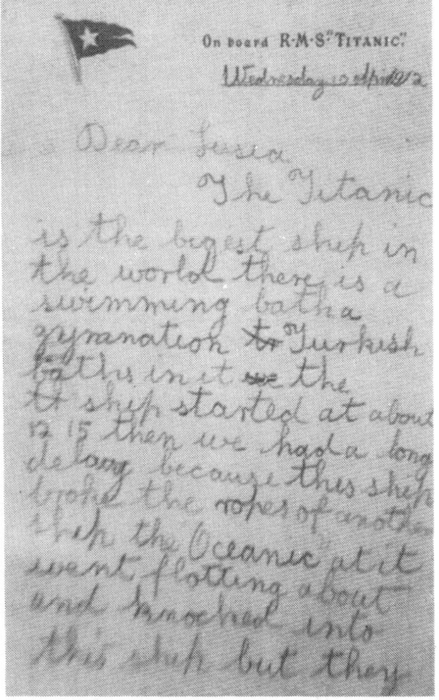

On board R.M.S. "Titanic."
Wednesday 10 April 1912

Dear Jessie
The Titanic is the bigest ship in the world there is a swimming bath a gymnastion or Turkish baths in it the ship started at about 12 15 then we had a long delay because this ship broke the ropes of another ship the Oceanic at it went flotting about and knocked into this ship but they

Letter written on R.M.S. Titanic notepaper by Eileen Lenox Conyngham on April 10th 1912. (Phillips) £1,600

In Memoriam, Hereos All, Titanic April 14th 1912, postcard. £35

'The Iceberg', a contemporary bromide photograph with ink inscription, 'Iceberg taken by Capt. Wood S.S. Etonian 12 April 1912 in 41° 56N 49° 51W S.S. Titanic Struck 14 April and sank in three hours', 200 x 255mm. (Onslow's) £230

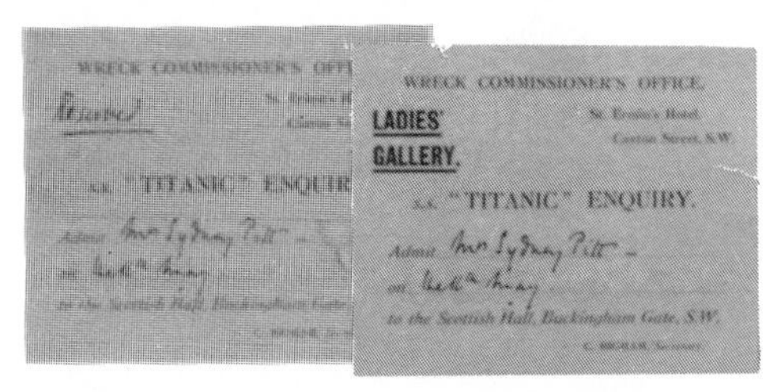

WRECK COMMISSIONER'S OFFICE.
St. Ermin's Hotel,
Caxton Street, S.W.

LADIES' GALLERY.

S.S. "TITANIC" ENQUIRY.

Admit Mrs Sydney Pitt —

to the Scottish Hall, Buckingham Gate, S.W.

SS Titanic Enquiry, two admission tickets issued by the Wreck Commissioners Office, to the Ladies Gallery admitting a Mrs Sidney Pitt.
(Onslow's) £150

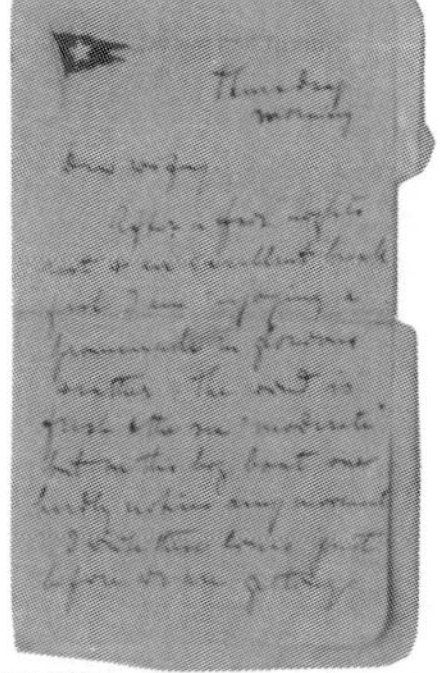

On Board RMS Titanic, an autographed letter on official lettercard together with envelope with embossed company burgee signed Adolphe. (Onslow's) £550

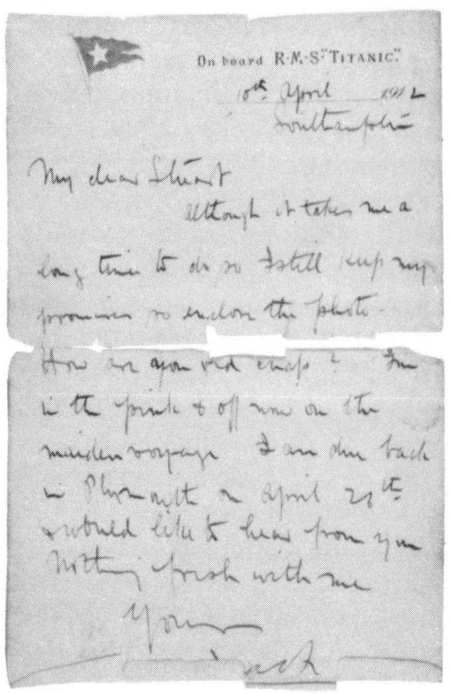

On board R.M.S. "TITANIC."
10th April 1912
Southampton

My dear Stuart
Although it takes me a long time to do so I still keep my promise to enclose the photo.
How are you and chaps? I'm in the pink & off now on the maiden voyage. I am due back in Plymouth on April 29th & would like to hear from you. Nothing fresh with me.
Yours
Jack

On board R.M.S. Titanic, an autographed letter on official writing paper with embossed company burgee, signed Jack 10th April 1912, Southampton. £1,700

The new White Star liner 'Titanic', artist drawn pre sinking photographic postcard, Real Photos Series. (Onslow's) £1,600

No. 657
WHITE STAR LINE.
R.M.S. "TITANIC."
This ticket entitles bearer to use of Turkish or Electric Bath on one occasion.
Paid 4/- or 1 Dollar.

White Star Line RMS Titanic Turkish bath ticket No. 657, 5cm x 8cm, together with letter of provenance.
(Onslow's) £900

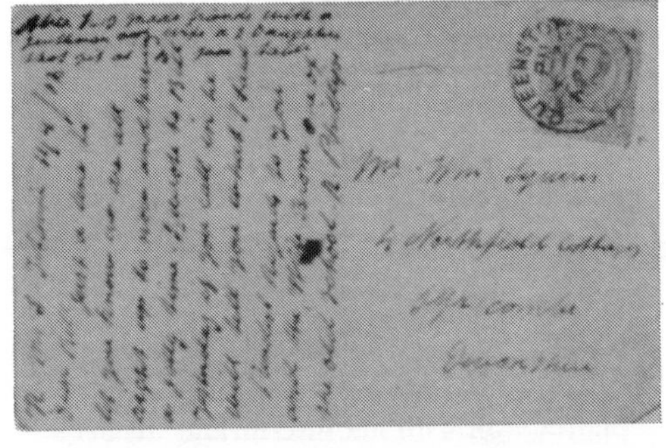

White Star Line Triple-Screw R.M.S. Olympic and Titanic 45,000 tons each, The Largest Steamers in the World, a colour postcard from R. Phillips to Mr. Wm. Squires, 4 Northfield Cottages, Ilfracombe, Devonshire, postmarked Queenstown 5.45pm 11 April.
(Onslow's) £2,000

A contemporary watercolour drawing of R.M.S. Titanic Leaving Southampton April 12th 1912 Sunk April 15th 1912, signed J. Nicholson, in oval satin mount, 13 x 24cm. (Onslow's) £120

Launch of White Star Royal Mail Triple-Screw Steamer Titanic at Belfast, Wednesday, 31 May 1911, at 12.15pm, a printed card admission ticket in two portions, each numbered 1246, overall size 84 x 136mm. (Onslow's) £1,100

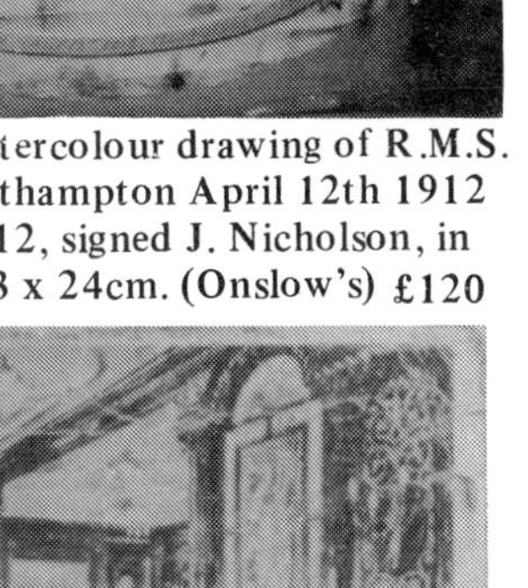

White Star Line Olympic and Titanic Smoke Room, a monochrome postcard to Master Tom Richmond, 14 Lennox Road, Crookston, Paisley, Lothian, postmarked Queenstown 3,45pm 11 April. (Onslow's) £1,500

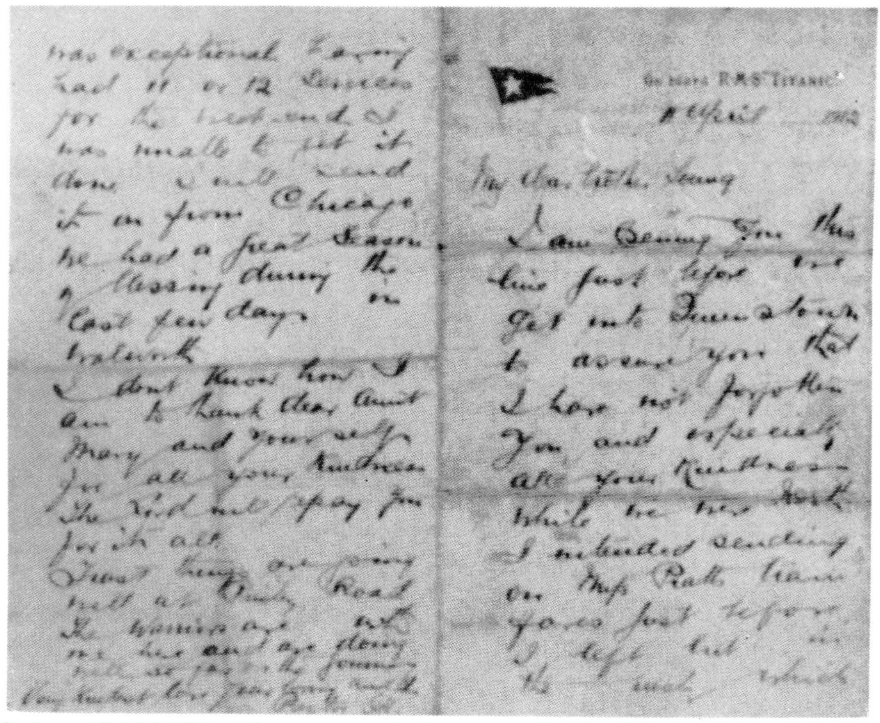

On board R.M.S. 'Titanic', an autographed letter on official writing paper signed by Pastor John Harper, 11th April 1912. (Onslow's) £3,800

B.D.V. War Leaders, General Cadorna. £7

B.D.V. Victoria Cross Heroes, Lieut. General Sir Douglas Haig, K.C.B. £8

B.D.V. Celebrities, King of Roumania. £5

Kensitas Flowers by J. Wix & Sons, 1934. £1

B.D.V. Cigarettes, Regimental Colours, 14th The Kings Hussars. £4

War Leaders, B.D.V. Lord Kitchener. £6

B.D.V. Celebrities, Princess Mary. £12

B.D.V. British Admirals, Admiral Sir John R. Jellicoe, 1916. £6

B.D.V. Celebrities, David Lloyd George. £10

B.D.V. War Leaders and Celebrities, the New Coalition Cabinet, Mr Balfour, Admiralty. £6

Old Masters Set 5, Auguste Strobel. £3

B.D.V. Old Masters, The Blue Boy, cabinet size. £20

B.D.V. Regimental Colours, Prince of Wales, North Staffordshire. £5

B.D.V. Old Masters, Bacchante, cabinet size. £20

Great War Leaders and Warships, B.D.V., Rear Admiral Bernard Currey. £6

Flags series B.D.V., the Allied Flags. £8

B.D.V. Great Leaders and Warships, Admiral Sir George Neville. £6

Madame Tussaud's Guide. £5

Waddington's Guide to 'Kirkstall Abbey'. £3

Castleton, Abel Heywood & Sons Guide Book. £2

Burrow's Guide to Bedford, Elstow and Olney. £2

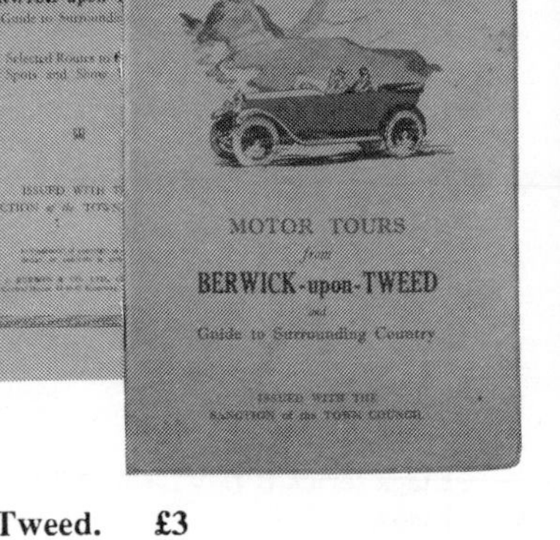

Motor Tours from Berwick upon Tweed. £3

The Homeland Handbooks, Boston, 1916. £2

(Yesterdays Paper)

Canterbury, 'A Description of its Fabric', 1917. £2

Old North London, The Hackney Gazette, 1928. £5

General country motor bus routes, 1926. £4

Ordance Survey 'One-inch' Map, Dorking & Leith Hill. £10

London Transport tram map. £5

The Silver Jubilee Tattoo, 1935, Aldershot. £4

London Zoo Guide, 1966. £1

(Yesterdays Paper)

Bacon's Large Scale Plan of Brighton, 1896. £8

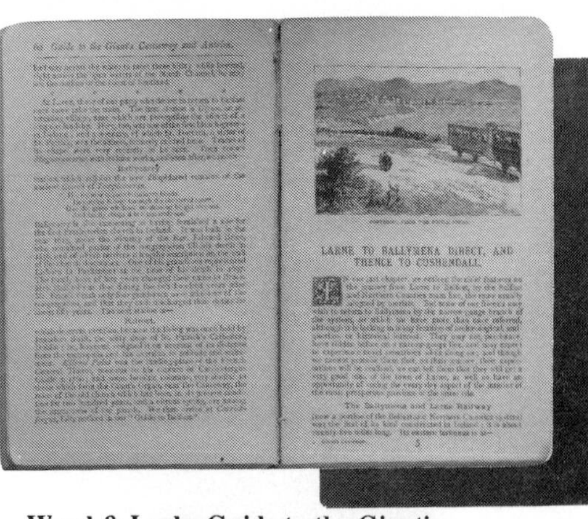

Ward & Locks Guide to the Giant's Causeway, 1893. £8

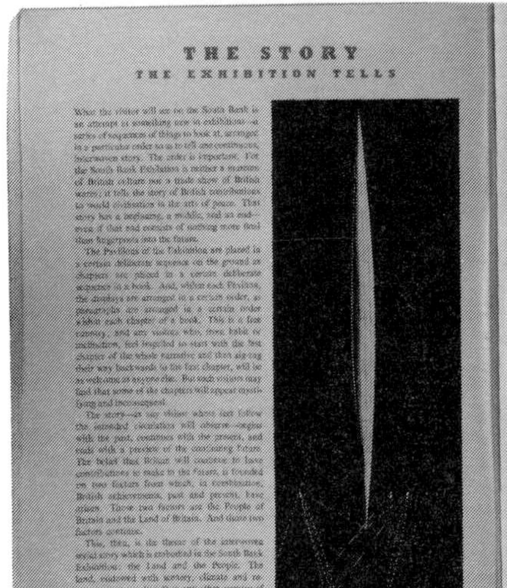

Festival of Britain Guide Book, 1951. £10

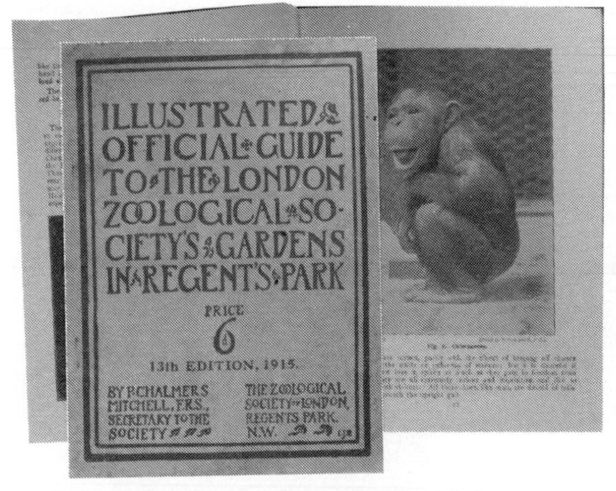

Guide to The London Zoological Society's Gardens, 1915. £6

The Handy Guide Series 'Weardale', 1920. £2

(Yesterdays Paper)

'A good angels visit, Scovill's Sarsaparilla and Stillingia or Blood and Liver Syrup.' £8

Clark's Mile-End spool cotton trade card. £5

Kendall Mfg. Co., French Laundry, 'To protect yourself from the evil effect of using soap made from impure materials', Providence, R.I. £5

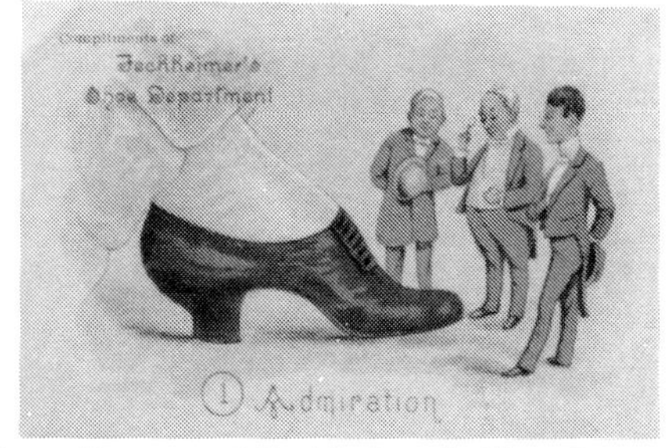

'Compliments of Fechheimer's Shoe Department, 102 W. Fifth Street. Admiration'. £7

Hagan's Magnolia Balm, 'For beautifying the complexion', presented by J. W. Robinson, Druggist and Chemist, Southbridge, Mass. £5

'Now dollies, if you be good we'll have Bromangelon for dessert. Nothing but the addition of hot water required'. £4

Prize Lincoln Buck Wilton, 'Compliments of the Domestic Sewing Machine Co. £8

J. & P. Coats' Thread, 'I say Sissy! the umbrella that boy has got was certainly not sewed with Coats coloured thread'. £7

Hires' Rootbeer, 'An uninvited guest', the Charles E. Hires Co., 11-119 Arch Street, Philadelphia. £5

Brown's Iron Bitters, 'A certain cure for diseases. Beware of imitations'. £3

'A flat Dutch cabbage', E. F. Harmeyer, Walnut Street, Cincinnati, Ohio, Agricultural Implements. £4

'Perfumed with Austen's Forest Flower Cologne', W. J. Austen & Co., Oswego, N.Y. £4

Sailing ship trade card for Vouwie Bros, 'Forest City Baking Powder, absolutely pure'. £12

'Agers Dry Hop Yeast is the best in use', Dole & Merrill Mfrs., Boston, New York. £3

Hoyt's German Cologne, 'Fragrant and lasting', E. W. Hoyt, Lowell, Mass. £5

'The White is the Sewing Machine of the Day', by C.H. Burdick, Boxo, Brookfield, New York. £10

'Balls Health Preserving Corset is the best in the world', Walter H. Tarr, Cincinnati, Ohio. £4

Presented by Household Sewing Machine Co., Providence, R.I., T. S. Arnold, Agent. £8

'King of the Blood', D. Ransom, Son & Co., Proprietors, Buffalo, New York, 'Read the testimonials'. £4

Willimantic Six Cord Thread, 'The best, so good, so smooth, so strong, so free'. £5

Lautz Bros. & Co., Master Soap, Buffalo, New York. £4

The Allenburys' Clock, 'This clock can be used to inform the mother as to the hour for giving baby his next bottle.' £12

'For Tomato Catsup, E. F. Harmeyer, 227 Walnut Street, Cincinnati, Ohio, Agricultural Implements'. £3

Beatty's Organs, Beatty's Piano s , Washington, New Jersey, 'The largest piano and organ establishment on the globe'. £5

'Use Tarrant's Seltzer Aperient, to regulate the stomach, the liver, the bowels'. £4

Warren & Wing, New England Agents, Tremont Street, Boston, Household Sewing Machine Co. £8

Austen's Forest Flower Cologne, 'The most fashionable and lasting perfume of the day'. £5

Clark's spool cotton, Hard to Beat, trade card. £5

'Dran Pa oo ought to put on one of Carters Backache Plasters', Carter Medicine Co., New York. £3

J. G. White, 'Harness, Trunks and Bags, Carriage Trimming', Sign Big Trunk, Cooperstown. £5

A large scrap type trade card by Hoeninghausen's Central Tea Store, Detroit, Michigan. £8

'Dr White's Cough Drops are the best, they are in truth a veritable delicacy'. £6

Industrial Insurance, Metropolitan Life Insurance Co., Central Block, Lewiston, Me. £5

Horsfords Acid Phosphate, 'For mental and physical exhaustion, Dyspepsia'. £5

John English & Co. 'Imperial diamond drilled eyed needles', patent Great Britain, 1863. £5

Lister 'Horse Clipping Machines', July 1st, 1951. **£2**

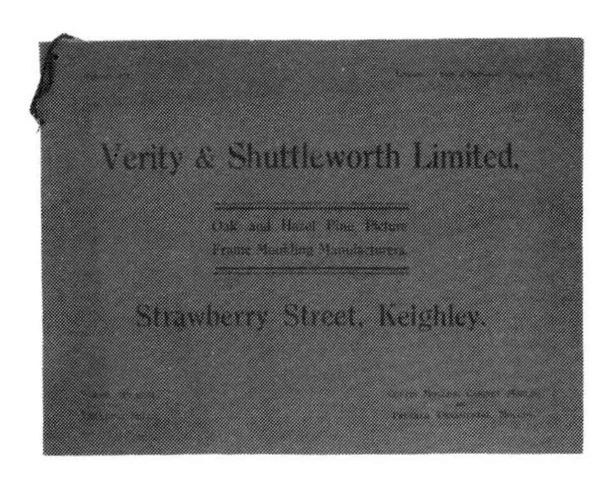

Verity & Shuttleworth Ltd., Keighley, Picture Frame Manufacturers. **£4**

R. A. Harding, Manufacturer of Invalid Carriages and Motors. **£12**

The 1956 Gadgets Annual compiled by V. M. Lawrence-Swan. **£30**

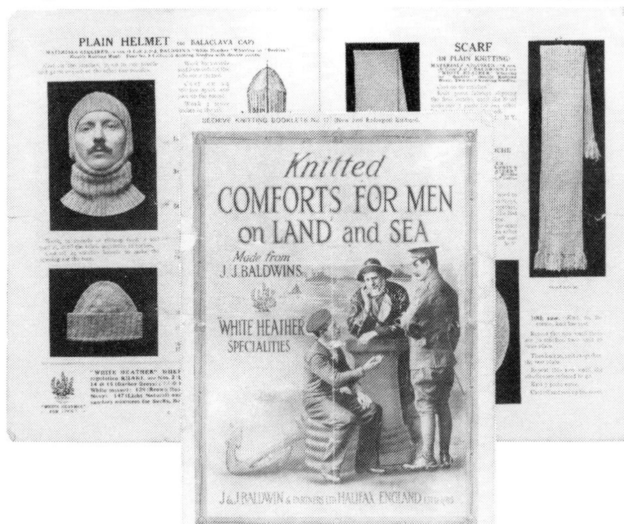

Knitted Comforts for Men on Land and Sea, by J. & J. Baldwin, Halifax. **£8**

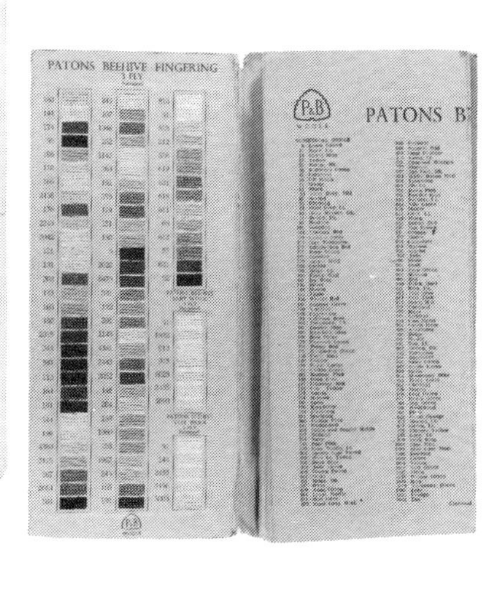

Paton's Beehive Fingering wool samples. **£7**

(Yesterdays Paper)

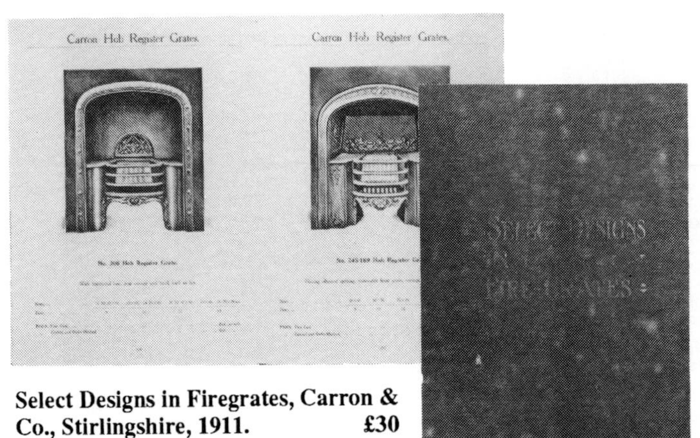

Select Designs in Firegrates, Carron & Co., Stirlingshire, 1911. £30

Wells Gardener, Darton & Co., 'Popular Books', 1904. £2

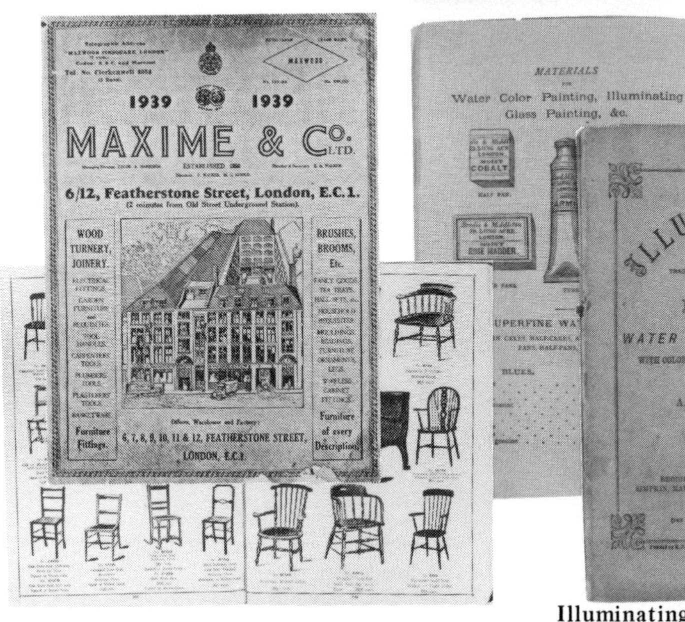

Maxime & Co., London, 1939. £20

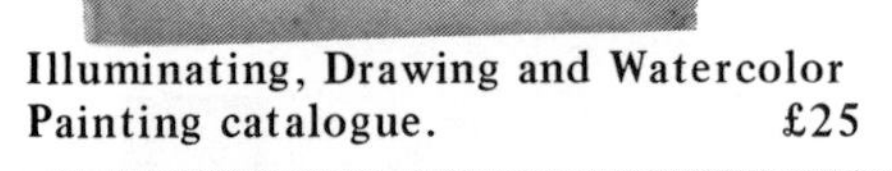

Illuminating, Drawing and Watercolor Painting catalogue. £25

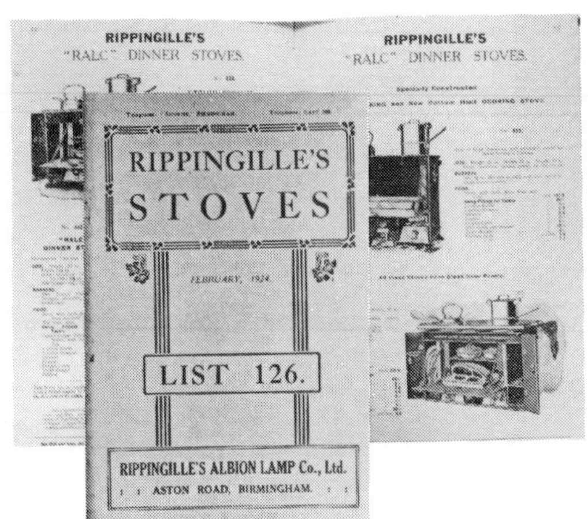

Rippingille's Stoves, Birmingham, 1924. £10

Cutler Desks, Plimpton & Co., Liverpool, 1903. £15

(Yesterdays Paper)

'Rustless Iron', The Rustless Iron Company, Keighley. £1

Paget's for Winter Sports, 1933–34 Season. £3

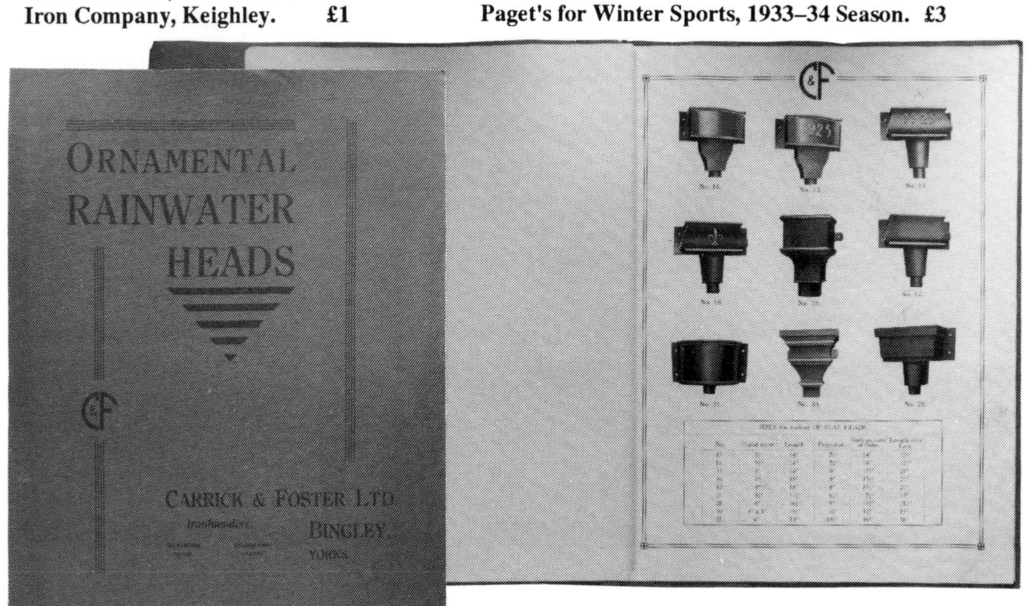

Carrick & Foster Ltd., Bingley. Rainwater Heads. £4

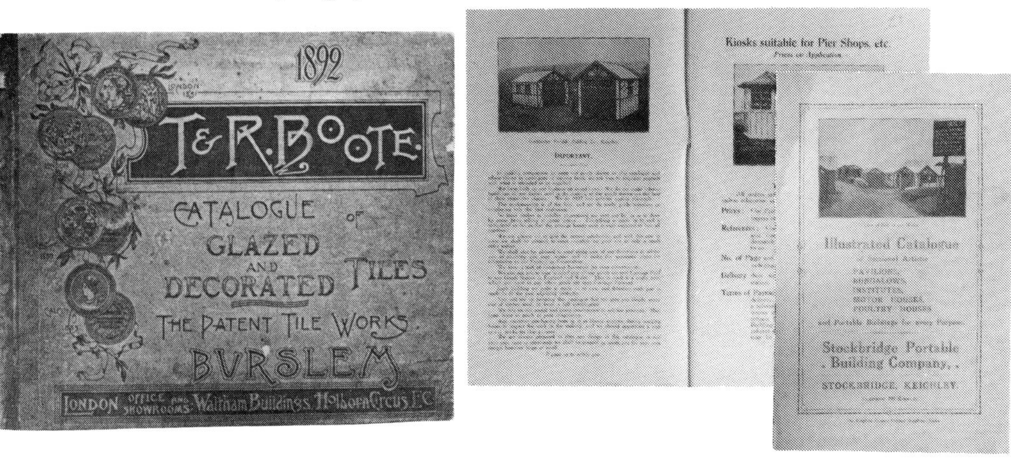

T. & R. Boote, Burslem, 1892. £75

Stockbridge Portable Building Co., Keighley. £5

(Yesterdays Paper)

The Home Book by Olive E. Innes. £2

Eastman Kodak 'How to Make Good Pictures'. £3

Chipperfield's Circus Programme 1963. £2

Elizabeth Ann's Book For Women, A Findon Publication. £1

Brushes, Hamilton & Co., Decorators and Grainers brushes, 1904. £5

The Guinea Gold Booklet compiled by the Cartophilic Society. £30

(Yesterdays Paper)

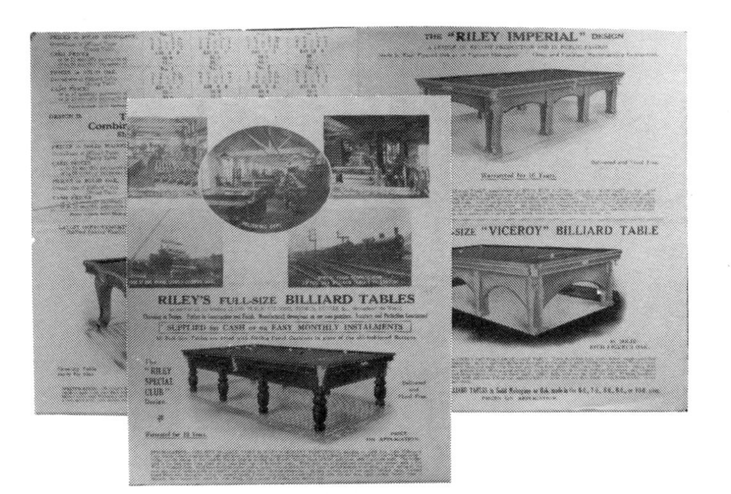

E.J. Riley Ltd., Billiard Tables, Accrington. £8

W. & R. Chambers Ltd. 'Xmas List'. £2

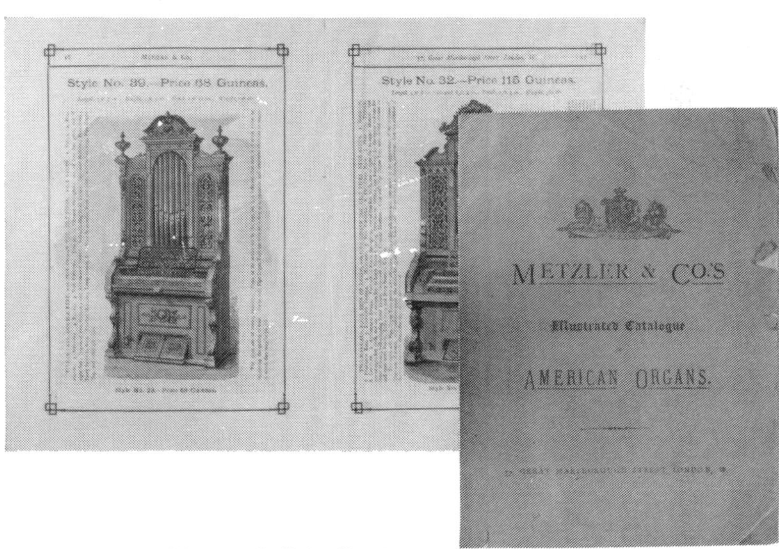

Plasmon Foods, Statements by the Lancet. 50p

Metzler & Co's. Catalogue of American Organs. £18

John Brinsmead & Sons, Pianoforte Manufacturers, 1868. £20

(Yesterdays Paper)

Fairy Dyes for Home Dyeing. 50p

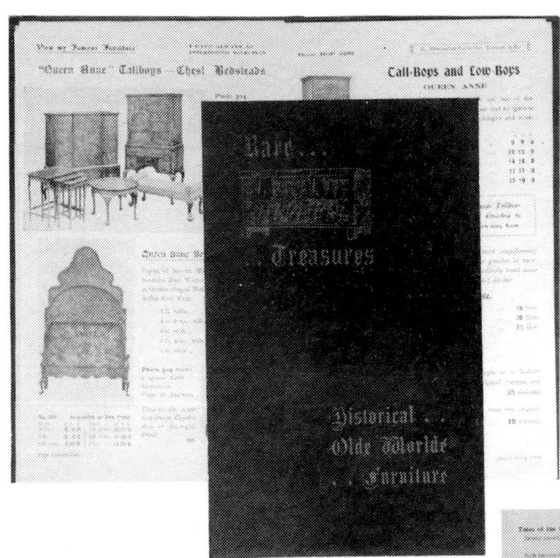

Olde Worlde Workshops of Adam B. Smith. £6

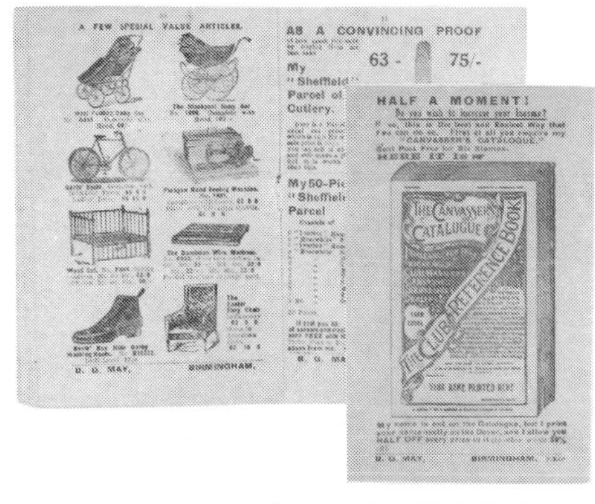

The Canvasser's Catalogue, the Club Reference Book. £8

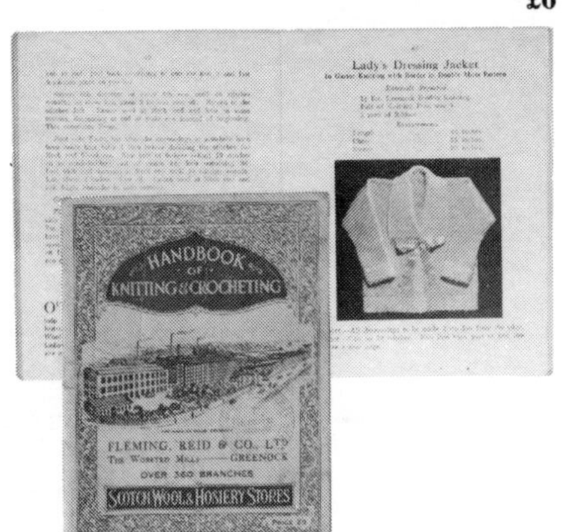

Handbook of Knitting and Crocheting, Scotch Wool & Hosiery Stores. £5

Books for Presents and Prizes by Wells, Gardner Darton & Co. Ltd. £10

Robinson of Rochdale, Centenary Brochure 1938. £5

(Yesterdays Paper)

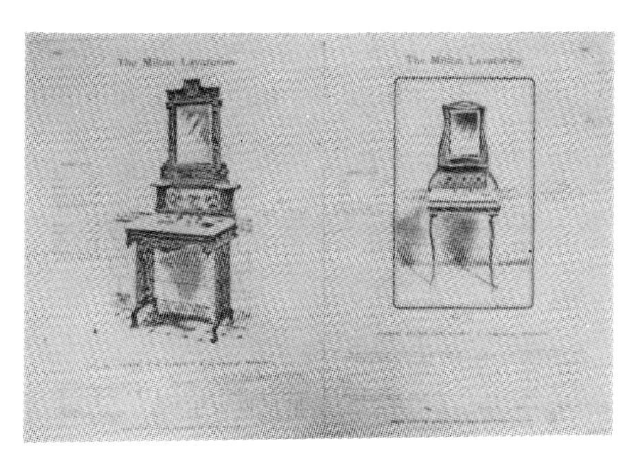

Baths & Lavatories catalogue of McDowell, Steven & Co., circa 1910. **£25**

Keighley Corporation, Water Supply 1923. £3

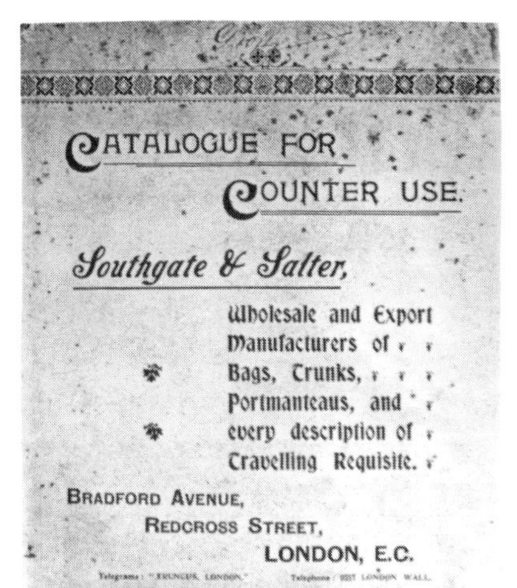

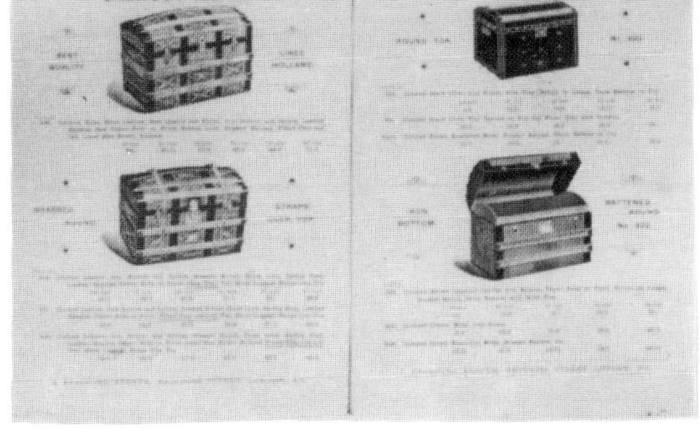

Luggage catalogue from Southgate & Salter, Redcross Street, London, circa 1910. **£15**

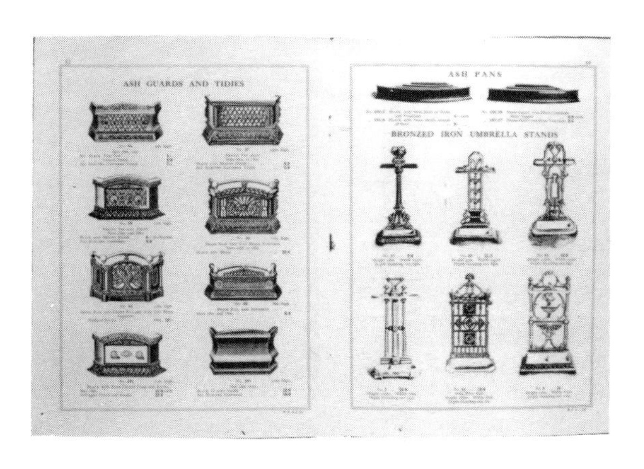

Hearth Furniture from Benjamin Parkes & Sons, Dudley, circa 1930. **£15**

(Yesterdays Paper)

Ellis Silas, 'Orient Line To Australia', double royal.
(Onslow's) £490

'Edgware by Tram', double crown, 1929.
(Onslow's) £75

L. C. Mitchell, 'Mount Cook New Zealand', double royal.
(Onslow's) £230

L.N.E.R. Camping Coaches In England and Scotland, poster, published by L.N.E.R., 1939.
(Onslow's) £80

'The Golfing Girl Well Out On The True Line', by The Caledonian Railway,
102 x 76cm. (Onslow's) £3,400

'Dunbar, First Class Golf', designed by Alfred Lambart.
(Onslow's) £370

Aberdeen & Commonwealth Line to Australia, by P.H. Yorke, double royal.
(Onslow's) £80

For Real Comfort, New Statendam, Holland-America Line, by Adolphe Mouron Cassandre, lithograph in colours, 1928, 1050 x 806mm.
(Christie's) £1,000

Rio de Janeiro by Royal Mail to South America, by K. Shoesmith. (Onslow's) £240

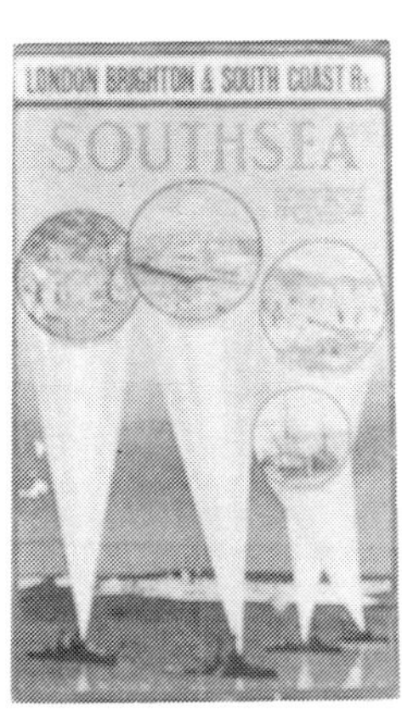

Guy Lipscombe, 'LBSCR Southsea', double royal. (Onslow's) £520

Jack Roussau, 'Chemins de Fer de L'Etat de Brighton Paris A Londres' (Thames punting), double royal on linen. (Onslow's) £150

Roger Soubie, 'Vichy', 106 x 76cm. (Onslow's) £840

Cunard Line 'Quickest Route New York to London and the Continent via Fishguard', by Odin Rosenvinge. (Onslow's) £1,000

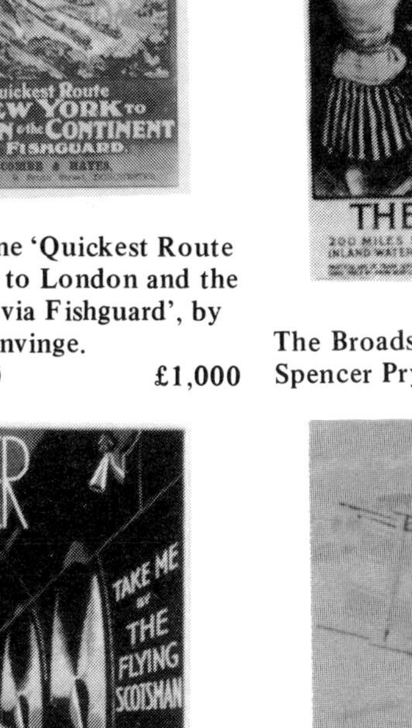

The Broads, poster by Gerald Spencer Pryse. (Onslow's) £170

'Express Ease, The Harrogate Pullman', published by L.N.E.R., designed by George Harrison. (Onslow's) £500

'Take Me by The Flying Scotsman', designed by A. R. Thomson. (Onslow's) £1,300

'East Coast Types No. 5 The Deck-Chair Man'. (Onslow's) £130

Montague B. Black, 'White Star Line Europe To America' (Olympic), double royal. (Onslow's) £700

'The Continent, Via Harwich', by Higgins. (Onslows) £500

The Broads, poster by Gerald Spencer Pryse. (Onslow's) £170

Hunstanton, poster by Higgins. (Onslow's) £70

Plant Your Works On The L.N.E.R., poster by Andrew Johnson. (Onslow's) £55

Tours in Connemara Galway Achill and The West of Ireland, poster by Fhugo D'Alesi, 127 x 92cm. (Onslow's) £110

The Broads, poster by Gerald Spencer Pryse. (Onslow's) £200

Tynemouth, poster by Alfred Lambart. (Onslow's) £340

Discretion in Mixing Cocktails and Serving Crusted Port, published by L.N.E.R. (Onslow's) £360

'The Continent Via Harwich', designed by Higgins. (Onslow's) £400

SALTBURN BY THE SEA

Saltburn By The Sea, poster by H. G. Gawthorn. (Onslow's) £160

In Winter to Vienna, published by Waldheim-Eberle, double royal. (Onslow's) £60

L.N.E.R. Camping Coaches In England and Scotland, poster, published by L.N.E.R., 1939. (Onslow's) £80

Skegness Is So Bracing, poster by John Hassall. (Onslow's) £350

The Royal Route Via Sandringham To Broadland, poster, published by Midland & Gt. Northern Joint Railways. (Onslow's) £290

Continent via Harwich, poster by Tom Purvis. (Onslow's) £250

Hunstanton, poster by Wilton Williams. (Onslow's) £230

"Queen of Scots" All Pullman, poster by Fred Taylor. (Onslow's) £620

Belgium, Harwich, Zeebrugge, by Higgins. (Onslow's) £195

'London's Country No 3 Cow Keepers In Hertfordshire, by E A Cox, published by General, double royal.
(Onslow's) £65

Aberdeen & Commonwealth Line England to Australia, by Longmate, double royal.
(Onslow's) £55

'Hereford', by Claude Buckle, published by LMS, double royal.
(Onslow's) £170

'Spend Your Summer Holidays At Blackpool In June' published by LMS, double royal.
(Onslow's) £110

'GNR Holiday Excursions Every Dog Has His Day by GNR Lets Haste Away', by Lionel Edwards, published by GNR, quad royal.
(Onslow's) £360

'Holiday Handbook 1939 by LNER', by Michael, double royal.
(Onslow's) £120

L'Oiseau Bleu, by Adolphe Mouron Cassandre, lithograph in colours, 1929, on wove paper, 996 x 616mm.
(Christie's) £780

Nord Express, by Adolphe Mouron Cassandre, lithograph in colours, 1927, on wove paper, 1048 x 752mm.
(Christie's) £1,300

Brien, 'Silloth on the Solway Finest Seaside Golf', published by LNER, double royal.
(Onslow's) £740

'Remember East Anglia Orfordness Sentinels of Britains Beauty', by Frank H Mason, published by LNER, double royal on linen.
(Onslow's) £120

'Cunard USA and Canada (Aquitania)', by Odin Rosenvinge, double royal.
(Onslow's) £340

'Come and Explore', by S R Badwin, published by British Travel & Holidays Assoc, double crown on linen.
(Onslow's) £220

Aberdeen & Commonwealth Line to Australia, by P.H. Yorke, double royal.
(Onslow's) £80

Austin Cooper, Cruden Bay By East Coast Route, quad royal, 40 x 50in.
(Onslow's) £660

'Silloth On The Solway Finest Seaside Golf', by Brien, published by LNER, double royal.
(Onslow's) £650

John Vickery, 'Tasmania Australia', double royal.
(Onslow's) £300

Etoile Du Nord, by Adolphe Mouron Cassandre, lithograph in colours, on wove paper, 1048 x 752mm.
(Christie's) £850

'The Flying Scotsman's Cocktail Bar', published by L.N.E.R., designed by Maurice Beck.
(Onslow's) £1,300

'Holland American Line Southampton to New York' (Statendam), by G. H. Davis. (Onslow's) £580

'Cunard Europe America' (Aquitania), by Odin Rosenvinge, with loss to right margin. (Onslow's) £420

'United States Lines to America Safety Courtesy Comfort and Speed'. (Onslow's) £100

'Cunard Europe America' (Berengaria), by Odin Rosenvinge. (Onslow's) £850

S. R. Badmin, 'Come and Explore Britain', published by The Travel Association, double crown on linen. (Onslow's) £300

'Cunard Line to All Parts of the World' (Lusitania). (Onslow's) £720

'Cunard Line to All Parts of the World' (Mauretania). (Onslow's) £1,250

'Cunard USA and Canada', by Frank H. Mason. (Onslow's) £2,500

E. McKnight Kauffer, 'Spring', published by LT, double royal, 1938. (Onslow's) £170

'Cunard Line to New York', by Charles Pears, loss to right margin. (Onslow's) £540

Air Atlas, Casablanca, lithograph poster in colours, 1950, printed by Hubert Baille & Cie, Paris, backed on linen, 39 x 24½ in. (Christie's) £154

'Cunard The Connecting Link Europe America'. (Onslow's) £770

'Cunard USA—Canada', extensive loss to right side. (Onslow's) £120

'Cunard Line A Cunarder In Fishguard Harbour Quickest Route New York to London', by Odin Rosenvinge. (Onslow's) £440

'Grand Trunk Railway System to Canada'. (Onslow's) £200

'Cunard Line Europe—America', by Kenneth D. Shoesmith. (Onslow's) £2,800

'White Star Line Canada's Call to Women'. (Onslow's) £250

'Cunard Europe—America', by W. S. Bylitipolis. (Onslow's) £700

My Darling Still, Rememberest The Gladsome Time. £10

Long Have Loved Thee Truly. £8

My Comfort and My Joy £5

Members of the Building Society. £10

'Faith, Hope and Charity', four in set, sometimes three in set. G. B. & Co. Series, embossed chromo litho with gold leaf applique. £5 each

Max Ettinger Series No. V125, 'Asylum for Lunatics'. £8

'My Love to You', Royal Series by Max Ettinger Series No. V86, printed in Germany. £6

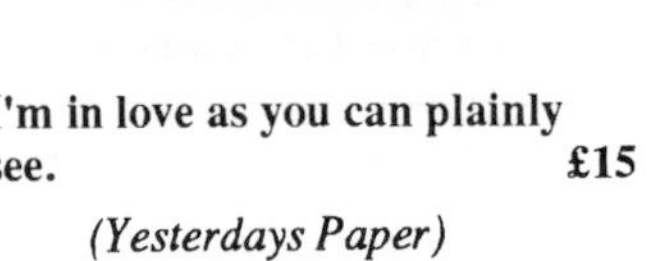

I'm in love as you can plainly see. £15

Dove, heart and flowers, 'To My Valentine', Max Ettinger Series No. V75. £6

(Yesterdays Paper)

A Valentine For Someone Often In My Thoughts. £2

Early Victorian Valentine in the form of a banknote. £20

To My Valentine, Raphael Tuck & Sons, 1930's. £4

Valentine Greetings, 'Though Walls Should Part Us', 1921. £10

I Love But Thee. £10

Forget Me Not For I'll Remember Thee. £10

My Heart Will Ever Be Thine, Forget Me Not. £10

'Maiden thy little heart to let'. £15

To Arms, to Arms, ye British Brave. £25

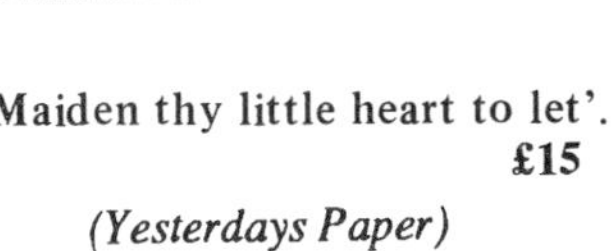

(Yesterdays Paper)

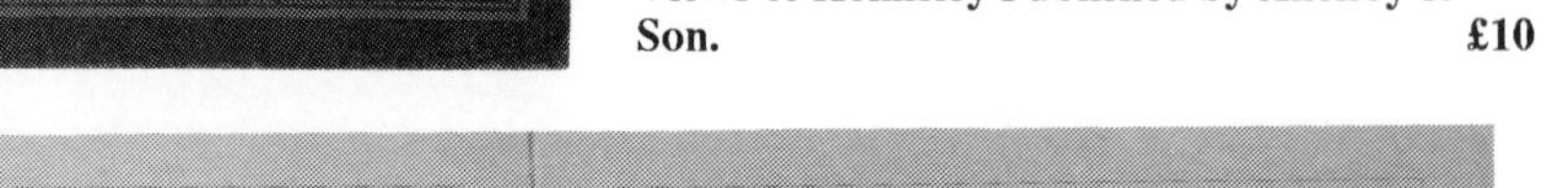

Views of Helmsley Published by Allenby & Son. **£10**

Views of Gourock District Published by William Sutherland. £10

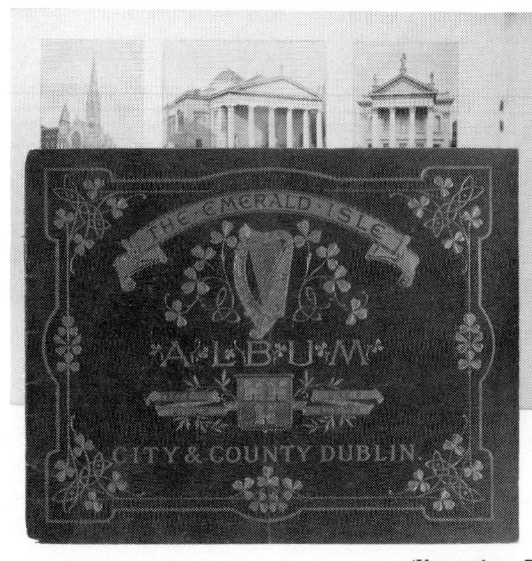

The Emerald Isle Album, City and Country Dublin. £12

(Yesterdays Paper)

The Emerald Isle Album, West of Ireland. £10

Waldsanatorium Arosa, Switzerland, 1920. £8

Marshall's Royal Album of Windsor Views. £12

(Yesterdays Paper)

'Save Serbia our Ally', published by the Serbian Relief Committee of America, by Theophile Steinlen, 36 x 24in. (Onslow's) £75

'Polish Army in France', by W. T. Benda, on linen, 36 x 27in. (Onslow's) £110

'Your King and Country Need You', by Lawson Wood, No.17. (Onslow's) £70

'The Veteran's Farewell, Enlist Now', by Frank Dadd, sepia. (Onslow's) £110

'Follow Me, Your Country Needs You', by E. V. Kealey, No.11. (Onslow's) £85

'Blue Cross Fund, Help the Wounded Horses at the War', by A.J.M., on linen. (Onslow's) £55

'Are You In This', by Lord Baden Powell, No. 112. (Onslow's) £130

'Be Ready! Join Now', No.81 on linen, 38 x 25in. (Onslow's) £70

'National Service, Women's Land Army', by H.G. Gawthorn. (Onslow's) £100

'Hitler Will Send No Warning – So Always Carry Your Gas Mask' by Fougasse, double crown.
(Onslow's) £35

'Keep Mum She's Not So Dumb! Careless Talk Cost Lives', 39 x 26cm.
(Onslow's) £85

'Subscribe to the 5½% Loan', depicting a worker turning shells on a lathe, Russian.
(Onslow's) £110

'War, To Arms Citizens of the Empire', published by the Underground, on linen, colour lithograph. (Onslow's) £250

'Britishers You're Needed, Come Across Now', by Lloyd Myers, on linen, 41 x 28in.
(Onslow's) £150

'National Service, Women Clerks Wanted At Once', by Savile Lumley. (Onslow's)
£170

'See the World and Get Paid For Doing It', by Alfred Leete.
(Onslow's) £110

'Who's Absent, Is It You?' by V. Soutril, No.125, on linen.
(Onslow's) £58

'Everyone Should Do His Bit, Enlist Now', by Baron Low, No.121. (Onslow's) £100

Halt the Hun, Buy U.S. Government Bonds, double crown.
(Onslow's) £40

U.S.A. Bonds, Third Liberty Loan Campaign, Boy Scouts of America, double crown.
(Onslow's) £130

Teufel Hunden, German nickname for U.S. Marines, double crown. (Onslow's)
£24

'Keep A Pig Save Waste and Make Food' by Fougasse, double crown.
(Onslow's) £85

Ministry of War Transport Road Safety campaign series issued by Tillings Association, 36 x 23cm., one of seven.
(Onslow's) £95

'Telling a Friend May Mean Telling the Enemy', 39 x 26cm.
(Onslow's) £5

Strictly Between These Four Walls Careless Talk Costs Lives, poster by Fougasse.
(Onslow's) £85

Come Into The Ranks and Fight For Your King and Country, poster by W. H. Caffyn, double royal.
(Onslow's) £30

Holidays By The Sea Take Care of Minefields, poster by Chan, double crown; and one other.
(Onslow's)
Two £45

Take The Road To Victory Join The W.A.A.F., poster by Foss, double crown.
(Onslow's) £35

Everyone Should Do His Bit Enlist Now, poster by Baron Low, double crown,
(Onslow's) £110

Every Woman Not Doing Vital Work is Needed Now, poster by Winslade, double crown.
(Onslow's) £60

'Care of Arms is Care of Life Mud Snow Ice in your rifle muzzle cause burst barrel', 38 x 25cm. (Onslow's) £30

'Mary Had An Air Force Lad Who Talked To Her of OP's', by Quier, published by Counter Intelligence ASC–USSTAF, 32 x 46cm.
(Onslow's) £90

John Gilroy, 'We Want Your Kitchen Waste', double crown.
(Onslow's) £170

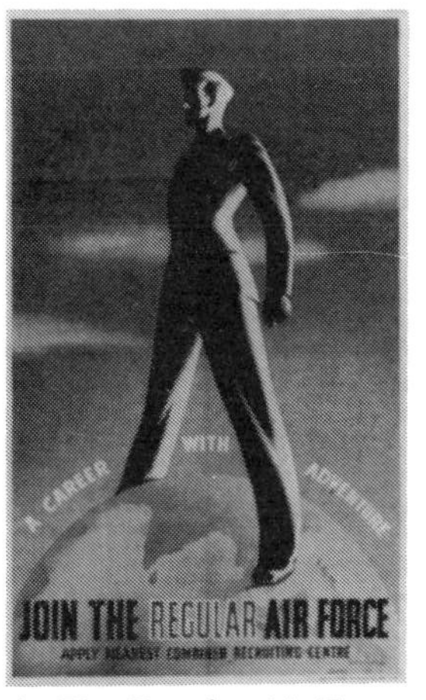

Join The Regular Air Force A Career With Adventure, poster by Winslade, double royal.
(Onslow's) £65

Daddy, What Did You Do In The Great War?, poster by Savile Lumley, double crown.
(Onslow's) £310

'Zec, Women of Britain Come Into the Factories', double crown. (Onslow's) £300

'The Pilot's Home Because Nobody Talked!', 39 x 26cm.
(Onslow's) £120

'She Knows What You Want But She Wants What You Know', original artwork, watercolour, 51 x 37cm.
(Onslow's) £170

'Danger Don't Touch', by Abram Games, double royal.
(Onslow's) £170

Chatham and the Medway at Sheerness Navy Week in aid of Naval Charities.
(Onslow's) £260

Marc Stone, 'The Downfall of the Dictators is Assured', double crown.
(Onslow's) £70

The Remaking of Belgium by Frank Brangwyn, 102 x 76cm.
(Onslow's) £100

'An Appeal To You', 98 x 63cm.
(Onslow's) £45

A U.S. Army Recruiting poster, American Lithograph Co. N.Y. 1909, image 35½ x 24¾in. £70

'Don't Forget That Walls Have Ears!' by Fougasse.
(Onslow's) £350

'Join The Women's Land Army', by Gates Willson, double crown.
(Onslow's) £130

'Talk Less You Never Know', original artwork by Noke, signed, gouache, 57 x 44cm.
(Onslow's) £170

'Careless Talk May Cost His Life Don't Talk About Aerodromes or Aircraft Factories', 50 x 34cm.
(Onslow's) £210

'Keep It Dark Careless Talk Costs Lives' by Maurice Bennett, 38 x 25cm.
(Onslow's) £35

Abram Games: 'Join the ATS', signed by the artist and model and dated *1941*, double crown, together with a scrap book of photocopies and cuttings concerning the famous poster.
(Onslow's) £3,000

'Carry On Canal Workers You're Doing A Fine Job', by Reginald Mount, double crown.
(Onslow's) £60

H. M. Bateman, 'Coughs and Sneezes Spread Diseases', canteen, double crown.
(Onslow's) £480

Coughs and Sneezes Series, 'Man In Underground Railway Carriage', by H M Bateman, double royal.
(Onslow's) £95

E. Kealey, 'Women of Britain Say Go!' double crown. (Onslow's)
£240

Harrison's Young Ladies' Journal, Oct. 12, 1912. £5

Vogue's 26th Knitting Book. £2

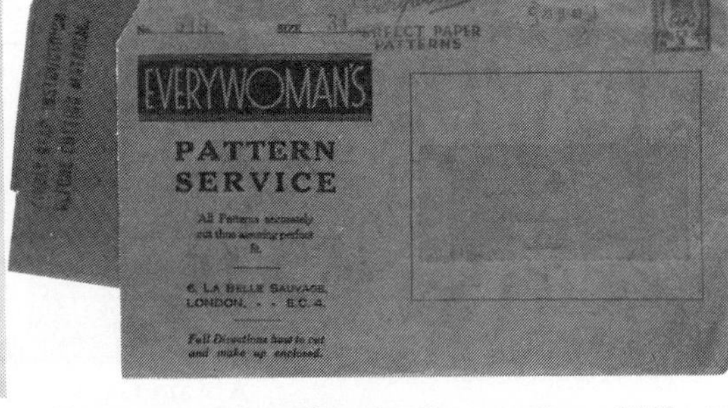

Everywoman's mail order dress pattern, 1940. £4

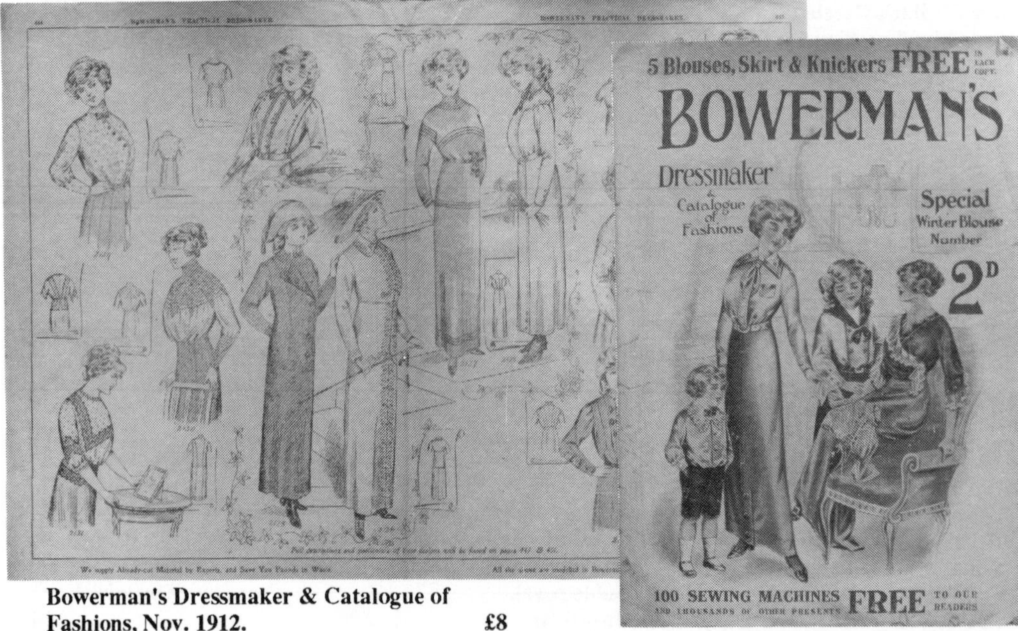

Bowerman's Dressmaker & Catalogue of Fashions, Nov. 1912. £8

(Yesterdays Paper)

Weldon's Home Dressmaking, Summer Dress Issue, 1908. £6

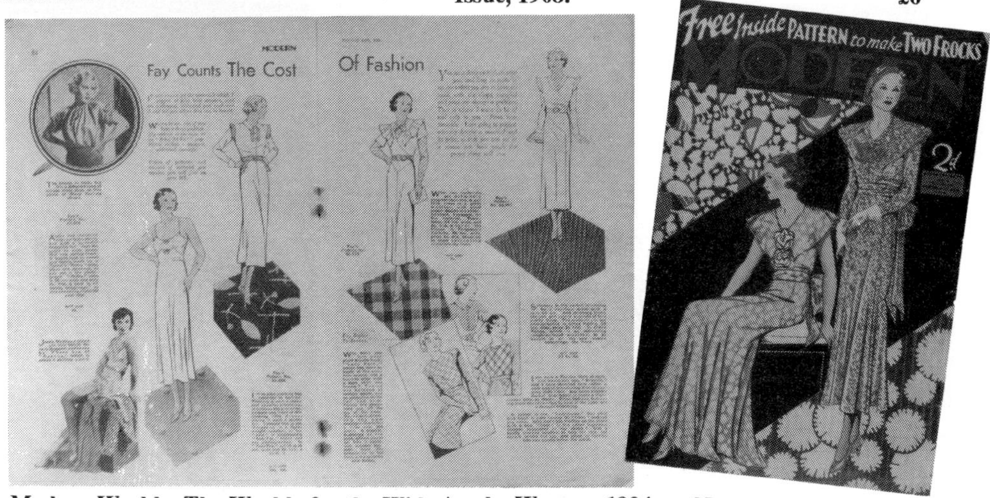

Modern Weekly, The Weekly for the Wide Awake Women, 1934. £5

Leach's Children's Dressmaker, August 1911. £6

(Yesterdays Paper)

Good Housekeeping, April 1923, Jessie Wilcox Smith Cover. £3

Woman's Magazine, February 1951. £1

Woman's Journal, December 1956. £1

Housewife, March 1965. £1

Woman and Home, October 1960. £1

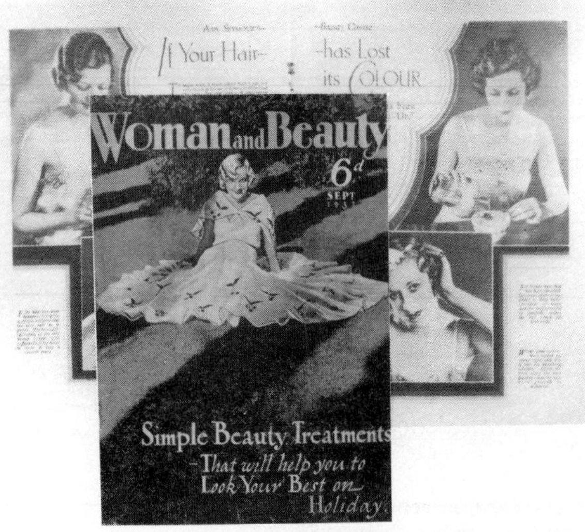

Woman, December 1952. £1

Woman and Beauty, September 1932. £3

(Yesterdays Paper)

My Home, December 1959. £1

Smart Novels, Long Complete Love Story, February 1966. £1

The Lady's World, January 1925. £3

Home Notes, For Every Woman in the Family, Nov. 1952. £1

Mother, The Home Magazine, August 1938. £1

The Queen, International Fashion Number, Sept. 1956. £2

Vogue, June 1947, London Season Issue. £8

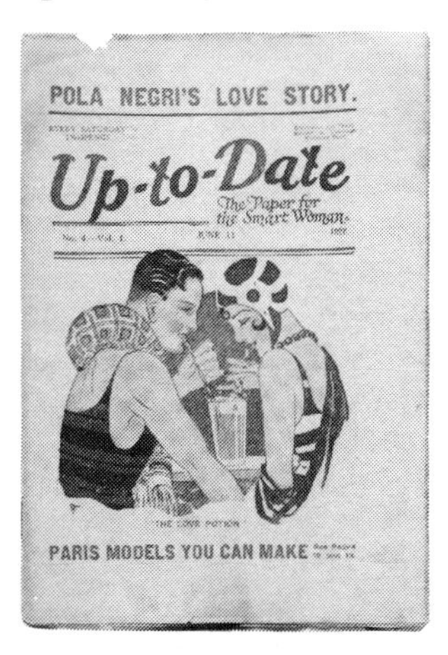

Up-to-Date, June 11th, 1927, 'The paper for the smart woman'. £6

(Yesterdays Paper)

My Home, New Designs Inside, April 1937. £3

Woman's Magazine, February 1937. £3

Good Needlework Magazine, January 1931. £3

Bestway Carnival Costumes, 1930's. £8

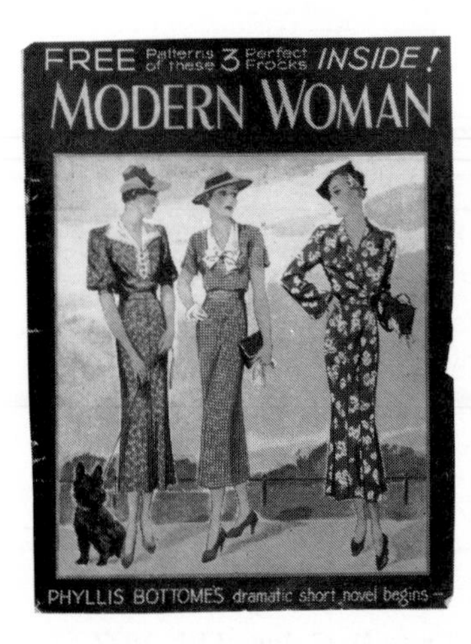

Modern Woman, June 1936. £3

Everywoman, October 1957. £1

Elle, Winter Collection, Sept. 1957. £4

(Yesterdays Paper)

Wife and Home, October 1954. £1

Vogue, January 1944, 50 Years of Vogue. £8

Woman's Friend, Christmas Issue 1936. £1

Woman's Own, No. 1, February 27th 1937. £15

Woman and Home, Sept. 1950. £1

Vogue, May 1946, Cover by Eric. £8

Woman's Pictorial, October 1932. £3

(Yesterdays Paper)

Weldon's Children's Fashions, July 1917. £8

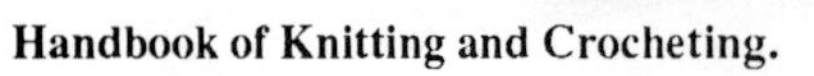

Handbook of Knitting and Crocheting. £5

The Crochet Book by Simpkin Marshall & Co., 1850. £5

The Needlewoman, July 1929. £6

(Yesterdays Paper)

INDEX

INDEX

INDEX